TUNNELLING '88

Papers presented at the fifth international symposium, 'Tunnelling '88', organized by the Institution of Mining and Metallurgy, with the cooperation of the British Tunnelling Society, the Institution of Mining Engineers and the Transport and Road Research Laboratory, Department of Transport, and held in London, England, from 18 to 21 April, 1988

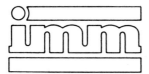

The Institution of
Mining and Metallurgy

Published at the office of
The Institution of Mining and Metallurgy
44 Portland Place London W1 England
© The Institution of Mining and Metallurgy 1988

ISSN 0143-3911   ISBN 1 870706 01 3

Printed in England by Stephen Austin/Hertford

Foreword

Fifteen years ago the proposal to hold an international symposium in Britain was mooted and an Organizing Committee under the Chairmanship of the late Professor Robert Pryor brought the proposal to fruition with the first symposium in 1976. At that time the Channel Tunnel project had just been shelved, but the Organizing Committee, with considerable foresight, decided to proceed with the symposium, which has subsequently become recognized as the premier international triennial event in the field of tunnelling technology. We are proud to follow this tradition with 'Tunnelling '88'.

The organization of 'Tunnelling '88' has involved members of the Institution of Mining and Metallurgy, the Institution of Mining Engineers, the British Tunnelling Society and the Transport and Road Research Laboratory, Department of Transport, H.M. Government, the Secretariat of the Institution of Mining and Metallurgy playing a pivotal role. One of the major successes of this series of symposia is the way in which the various disciplines have combined over the past twelve years. Civil construction practices have increasingly found a place in the mining industry; 'roadheading' machines developed for the mining industry are in regular use by civil engineering contractors. More recently, the tragically dramatic effects of methane have been brought to the attention of the tunnelling industry and the techniques developed for coal mining can assist in the elimination of these hazards. This cross-fertilization of ideas has become a feature of these symposia and we eagerly look forward to the synergistic effect of 'Tunnelling '88' on design and working practices.

Tunnelling is currently a booming industry. The Channel Tunnel is now under way; tunnels are proving more economic alternatives than bridges in many situations; public utility applications are increasing; the mining industry has to provide longer tunnels for high-speed, high-capacity transport as working places move progressively farther from shaft bottom; underground storage is looking economic; and nuclear waste disposal presents a challenge. Tunnelling has never been so vibrant or exciting as it is today. Those engaged in the business of tunnelling can look forward to tomorrow with confidence and expectation of further technical challenge.

The symposium will again start with the Sir Julius Wernher Memorial Lecture,* entitled 'When an invention is something new: from practice to theory in tunnelling', which is to be delivered by Dr. Ing. Gerhard Sauer (Austria). The final summing up will be in the capable hands of Dr. Myles O'Reilly.

The Organizing Committee did sterling work to ensure the success of the symposium, for which I record my grateful thanks. Special thanks are due to the three sub-committee chairmen, Geoff Pearse, Tom King and Ian Elliott. The Organizing Committee wishes to record its gratitude to all the authors who submitted papers, whether published or not. Inevitably, some papers cannot be published because of space reasons and a need to maintain a balance of content. The Organizing Committee hopes that unsuccessful authors will not be discouraged by these unfortunate omissions and will continue to submit their work for publication. Thanks are due to all those companies which are participating in the associated exhibition and those organizations which have kindly offered hospitality to both the British and European post-conference tours. Without the efforts of the Secretariat of the Institution of Mining and Metallurgy, 'Tunnelling '88' could not have taken place. The Organizing Committee recognizes a debt of gratitude to them for their excellent work.

Finally, we hope this volume of proceedings will be of a standard equal to and complement those of the previous symposia, taking its place on the bookshelves of the international tunnelling industry.

Professor Tom Atkinson
Chairman, Organizing Committee

February 1988

---

*To be published in *Trans. Instn Min. Metall. (Sect. A: Min. industry)*, **97**, April 1988.

Organizing Committee

Professor T. Atkinson (Chairman) (United Kingdom)
G.E. Pearse (Chairman, Papers Sub-Committee) (United Kingdom)
I.H. Elliott (Chairman, Tours Sub-Committee) (United Kingdom)
T.I. King (Chairman, Exhibition Sub-Committee) (United Kingdom)
L. Aerts (Belgium)
S. Babendererde (Federal Republic of Germany)
J.V. Bartlett (United Kingdom)
N.S.M. Berry (United Kingdom)
O.M. Bevan (United Kingdom)
S. Bjørgum (Norway)
Professor R. Ciccu (Italy)
E.L. Dempster (United Kingdom)
D.R. Donaldson (United Kingdom)
Professor I. Duddeck (Federal Republic of Germany)
Professor I. Farmer (U.S.A.)
Dr. G. Fukuchi (Japan)
J. Hainey (Canada)

H. Hamrin (Sweden)
A. Hill (United Kingdom)
Dr. S. Johansson (Finland)
R. Kersten (South Africa)
M.C. Knights (United Kingdom)
Professor Liu Boashen (China)
A. Neyland (Australia)
Dr. M.P. O'Reilly (United Kingdom)
Professor T.D. O'Rourke (U.S.A.)
J.H.L. Palmer (Canada)
M. Panet (France)
Dr. P.H. Phillips (United Kingdom)
Dr. B. Pigorini (Italy)
A.G. Provost (U.S.A.)
J.F. Raffoux (France)
R.J. Robbins (U.S.A.)
Dr. G. Sauer (Austria)
V.W. Shtenko (Canada)
K.B. Smale-Adams (United Kingdom)
H.O. Smith (United Kingdom)
Professor O. Stephansson (Sweden)
Dr. J. Temporal (United Kingdom)
F. Von Mandach (Switzerland)

Contents

Foreword   *Page* **v**

Organizing Committee   **vi**

Madrid underground station renewal at Puerta del Sol
A. BELTRAN AND J. BUSTINDUY   **1**

Tunnel boring at Vinstra power plant, Norway—excavation of the 17-km long headrace tunnel by use of tunnel-boring machines
A. BORG   **9**

Excavation of the inclined haulageway in the Sulcis coalfield, Sardinia
A. BORTOLUSSI, R. CICCU, P.P. MANCA, G. MASSACCI, L. OTTELLI AND S. PEDDIS   **25**

Review of ground treatment carried out for tunnels of the Singapore Mass Rapid Transit System
S. BUTTLING AND J.N. SHIRLAW   **39**

Supplementary site investigations for the Channel Tunnel, 1986–87—an overview
G. CRIGHTON, P. MARGRON, W.J. RANKIN AND B. SECHET   **55**

Application of NATM at Barrow-upon-Soar gypsum mine to construct two surface drifts
W.G. DEACON AND J.F. HUGHES   **69**

Practical results from reduced-scale testing of pick cutting heads for tunnelling applications
E.P. DELIAC AND Ph.R. CORDELIER   **79**

Summit tunnel—post fire remedial works
S.D. DUNCAN AND W. WILSON   **87**

Methane hazards in tunnelling operations
J.S. EDWARDS, B.N. WHITTAKER AND S. DURUCAN   **97**

Construction of a difficult tunnel in a developing country
M. ERDEMGIL AND Y. ZAIM   **111**

Great Belt railway tunnel project, Denmark
T. ERIKSEN, R.N. CRAIG, K.H. OSTENFELD AND O. BOJESEN   **121**

Diaphragm wall techniques for the Channel Tunnel shaft-sinking on the French side
G. EVERS AND C. HOVART   **135**

Some experiences of rapid excavation in Lubuge hydroelectric power tunnel, China
GUO ZONGYAN AND WAN SHENGPEI   **143**

The Aalesund Fjord tunnels
B. KIELLAND   **149**

Tunnelling investigation in a highly complex marine-volcanic sequence, Honolulu, Hawaii, U.S.A.
J.K.P. KWONG, J.W. MAHAR AND E.J. CORDING   **159**

Excavation and support of the CERN point 4 experimental zone
C. LAUGHTON   **175**

Underground civil works in Texas
B. KENT MERRITT AND R.M. VALENTINE   **183**

The Los Angeles Metro Rail Project— planning and design of tunnels in gassy ground
K.N. MURTHY   **195**

Longer rounds to improve tunnelling and development work
B. NIKLASSON, R. HOLMBERG, K. OLSSON AND S. SCHÖRLING   **213**

Borehole radar applied to site investigations prior to tunnelling
O. OLSSON, S. CARLSTEN, L. FALK, B. NIVA AND E. SANDBERG   **223**

Evaluating and predicting ground settlements caused by tunnelling in London Clay
M.P. O'REILLY   **231**

A1(M) Hatfield tunnel
M.J. PALMER AND J.F.L. LOWNDES   **243**

Computer-aided drilling for tunnelling accuracy and economy
T. PUHAKKA   **257**

The Dosco CTM5 tunnelling machine
G. RICHARDSON AND M.J. GOLLICK   **265**

Development of roadheading equipment for tunnelling by NATM
A. SANDTNER AND K.H. GEHRING   **275**

Slurry shield tunnelling for Mexico City
J.M. SCHMITTER, M.V. LOPEZ PORTILLO AND
J.C. OROZCO   289

Ground movements and settlements
caused by tunnelling for the Singapore
Mass Rapid Transit System
J.N. SHIRLAW AND S. DORAN   295

Use of finite-element modelling to assess
factors affecting circular tunnel ring
performance *in situ*
B.G.D. SMART AND P.W.H. OLDEN   315

Use of tunnel deformation monitoring for
excavation control in weak bedded rock—
Isangoyana Rail tunnel, Zululand
C.R. SPEERS AND J.C. SHARP   323

Use of underground mining and
tunnelling techniques for *in-situ* oil
recovery
H.G. STEPHENSON AND R.W. LUHNING   333

Problems associated with tunnelling
operations in the construction of the
Warsaw underground
J. SZYNDLER, J. MATEJA AND K. RUŁKA   347

Comparison of calculated and measured
displacements on cut-and-cover tunnels
A. TISA AND K. KOVARI   357

Application of recently developed
grouting procedures for tunnelling in the
Milan urban area
R. TORNAGHI, B. BOSCO AND B. DE PAOLI   363

General philosophy of pipe jacking and
caisson sinking lubrication
J. WASHBOURNE   377

The A55 North Wales Trunk Road
Penmaenbach Tunnel: use of NONEL
blasting techniques
R. WATTS   389

Undersea cable tunnel between
Singapore Mainland and Pulau Seraya—
design and construction by the immersed
tube method
C.R. WEEKS AND N.S. RASMUSSEN   401

The Pre-metro link to the left bank of the
River Scheldt by means of a bentonite
shield
A. WITTEMANS AND E. HEMERYCKX   415

Railroad tunnel modification and
rehabilitation in North America
D.C. WYLLIE   427

Madrid underground station renewal at Puerta del Sol

A. Beltrán Ing.
J. Bustinduy Ing., M.Sc., M.I.T.
Cia. Metropolitano de Madrid, Madrid, Spain

SYNOPSIS
Besides being the most representative square in Madrid, by historical and symbolic reasons, la Puerta del Sol is the most important interchange station of the Metro network, where the three oldest lines (n. 1,2 and 3) cross each other.

They were built respectively in 1919, 1924 and 1936, and access and interchange facilities have been continuously added, one at a time, in order to provide capacity to cope with an increasing demand that lasted for more than 50 years. Last big improvement, including extension of line no.1 station from 60 to 90 mts. occurred in the late sixties.

The result was an incredible labyrinth were passengers became disoriented, passenger walking distances increased and access and interchange times elapsed. Station condition was also very poor.

Taking advantage of the city hall action to be developed on the surface, Madrid Metro considered Sol station renewal, with the following objectives:
- Spatial identification of paths, reduction of walking distances and connection times.
- Underground areas to be considered as urban space.
- Increased passenger comfort (waterproofing, air conditioning, old time aesthetics, etc.)

Different alternatives were studied to fulfill these objectives, which are shortly presented in the paper.

Important restraints were imposed by the need of construction works not to interfer with operation of the three metro lines, passenger connections between them (Sol is the single station at which they intersect), passenger access to the station (13 million passenger a year), and keeping traffic on the surface running.

The alternative adopted consisted in the excavation of a central trapezium around 1000 m^2 surface surrounded by the three lines, 7 meters high, at different levels, at which the three ticketing halls are also connected.

Cut and cover technique was used, with special structures provided to

counterbalance lateral forces in brick vaults caused by emptying of the central area. Remaining areas of the old station were either waterproofed and decorated when they were to be kept in service, or closed for company use where it was not the case.

Works began in September 1985, and ended December 20, 1986, being therefore performed in 15 months.

The paper describes both design and construction alternatives, solutions adopted and results.

GENERAL REMARKS
The Sol underground station is located under the Puerta del Sol Piazza, an important square in Madrid's old city area. The square is named after the engraving of a sun that was located in one of the arches that enclosed the fortress built in that area when it was the main entrance to the city. After the gateway was demolished, the "sun" theme

Fig.1 Scheme of Metro network.

continued in the area and the square has been named Puerta del Sol ever since.

Since the XVII th century, Puerta del Sol has witnessed the main events in the town, such as gas lighting, the first tramways, the first automobiles, war events (as 2nd May 1808, inmortalised by Goya) and, second to none, the first Metro line, opened in 1919. The underground network of Madrid consists of ten lines, with a total length of 112 kms and 154 stations. Sol station remains the busiest station of the system, with more than 370,000 passengers a day either entering, transfering or passing through the station. The station is served by three lines, numbers 1, 2, and 3 respectively. The general scheme of the Madrid underground network is presented in Fig. 1

CONSTRUCTION BACKGROUND
Construction of line number 1 started in 1917 and was completed in two years. Fig. 2 shows the general arrangement of the station in 1919. This scheme was operated until 1925 when line number 2, with its tunnel crossing over line 1 was built and ticket hall and accesses were enlarged to deal with increasing and expected passenger traffic. Fig. 3 depicts an artist's impression of the station in that time with lines 1 and 2 operating. The drawing is dated 1924 and it is, therefore, a design scheme, because operation of line 2 started in October, 1925.

At that time, elevators were provided to traverse the level difference between the street and the platforms of line 1, which is approximately 15 meters. The main hall was designed by Antonio Palacios, a well known architect of the Otto Wagner school and author of such important buildings as those

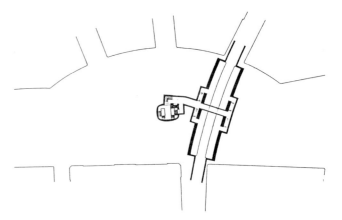

Fig.2   The station in 1919.

surrounding the Cibeles square in Madrid. Tile decoration was used extensively depicting the coats of arms of the Spanish provinces, as well as Sevillian ceramics, reflecting copper and gold, mixed with coloured marble. On the keystones over the principal doorways the emblems of the Province and City of Madrid stand out.

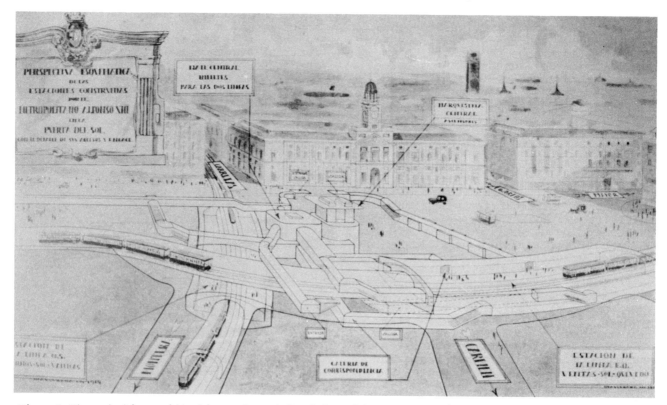

Fig. 3 The station with lines 1 and 2. Schematic perspective.

The construction of line number 3 was closely followed by the construction of a new ticketing hall in the west area of the square, to cope with increasing passenger volumes. Line 3 started operation in August 1936, shortly after the Spanish Civil War was initiated. Operation with this arrangement continued until the late 60's when new additions were needed specifically to accommodate transfer passengers, as a result of line extensions in the network. At that time stations of line number 1 were enlarged from 60 to 90 meters, in order to accomodate six car trains, instead of the 4 car trains that were used up to then.

In the particular case of Sol station, the enlargement of line number 1 station was made up to 120 meters length because of the assymetrical distribution of platforms imposed by existing buildings. To cope with transfer passengers, a new by-pass corridor was built connecting lines 1 and 3 to the main accesses and ticketing halls of the station. The profile of this by-pass corridor is accommodated to the constraints imposed by the existing constructions as well as to the need for keeping the station in operation at the time of construction (Fig.4).The result of all these successive enlargements was an incredible labyrinth where passengers became disoriented and

walking distances, access and transfer times all increased. The general condition of the station was also poor.

In 1984, The City Hall of Madrid decided to renovate the surface of the square, as a part of a programme of urban renewal in the center of Madrid. The opportunity to perform a renewal of the metro complex of stations underneath the square, with an open air construction method was not to be missed.

DESIGN CRITERIA AND ALTERNATIVES
The Plan area was, at the underground level, completely occupied by the subway corridors and tunnels. The overall requirement of all the various different alternatives was to make a large under-ground volume that would accommodate both passenger traffic with minimal distances and clear orientation and underground urban services.

All alternatives should cope with severe basic constraints, the most important being:
a) location of the three underground lines, as well as keeping trains in operation in all of them during the construction period.
b) lack of space between line number 2 and the surface.
c) need for transfer between the different subway lines, during the construction

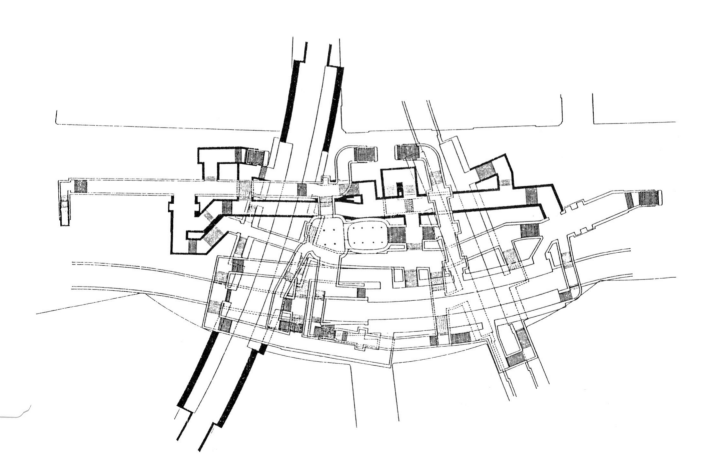

Fig. 4 Corridor connecting lines 1 and 3 enlargement of line 1

period (lines 1,2, and 3 intersect each other only at Sol station).

d) need for access during the construction period for the three lines, Sol station being the most important station of the network.

e) surface occupation during the construction period, and diversion of vehicle traffic and pedestrian traffic.

f) subordination in the final appearance to the aesthetic concept decided for the surface renewal of the square.

g) presence of different utility ducts and tunnels in the area, besides those related to the subway operation.

First alternative

The first alternative considered was based on a large pedestrian use of the subsurface of the square, by the subway passengers as well as for public areas related to an idea of intensive vehicular use on the surface that was abandoned later by the City Hall planners.

The excavation was to be about 25 meters deep, which allowed the three subway lines to cross it encircling both lines and platforms in glass tunnels, the subway being a "show" taking place in a huge underground urban volume in the busiest part of town. Fig.5 presents an artist's impression of this alternative. The surface would have covered the entire square area with eventual underground extensions connecting with the large department stores located nearby.

Second alternative

This embraced a more intensive pedestrian use of the surface that would not need such a gigantic underground development, the idea being to enhance the importance of the surface keeping underground use strictly for subway passengers. It consisted of the creation of a large underground volume, this time located at the level of line 2 crossing over lines 1 and 3 and reserved for transit passengers.

In order to optimize passenger movements, as well as space identification with the general configuration of the Piazza, both tracks of line 2 were isolated, as shown in Fig. 6, the lenticular space between providing room enough for the platforms, the general

transfer movements to line 2 and the station accesses and ticketing halls.

The alternative solution at the level below the previous one, in order to provide transfer between lines 1 and 3 included a corridor with visual connections with both lines as well as with the general volume at the level of line 2. At this level room was provided for general station services and staff rooms. Orientation was provided by the fact that the station was aligned along a single axis coincident with the axis of the square, with accesses located at both ends. Visual integration with the surface level was solved by two fountains, which were part both of the surface and the underground levels, light coming through them into the underground area.

The construction interfered with the vault of line 2, which would have had to be demolished, as well as the adjacent line 2 tunnel sections, in order to provide room for the line track separation. Reconstruction of some of line's 1 and 3 vaults were needed for the transfer passenger corridor construction. As a result of the cost increases derived from these modifications as well as others generated by the need to keep operation of the three lines during the construction period, this alternative, although debated for a long time, was finally rejected by financial reasons.

Third alternative

The basic layout of the three lines offered a clear possibility of action in the central trapezium, approximately 1000 m², defined by the vaults of the three lines. The excavation of this volume provides a central space with great accessibility to the three lines, and associated advantages as far as orientation, walking distances, and disruption of the "underground labyrinth feeling" are concerned.

This space can then be treated in consonance with its importance both in the station, in the network and in the city, taking advantage of the existence of a previous "Central Atrium" idea already developed back in 1919, and thus allowing the resuscitation of the station's initial concept that had been spoiled under the successive enlargements of the station. In order to preserve this "Central Atrium" the three ticketing halls were added to the external area, enhancing the relationship with the pedestrian areas on the surface and increasing accessibility to the station.

Comparative cost estimates and construction time favoured the selection of this alternative, which became the final choice.

PROJECT GENERAL DESCRIPTION
Functional layout

Ticketing halls are built in the perimeter of the square at a level scarcely 3 m below surface, with a comfortable access and adjacent to the central space. A bridge connecting the

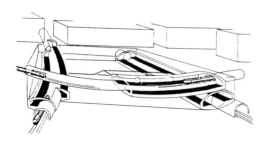

Fig. 5 First solution artistic perpective.

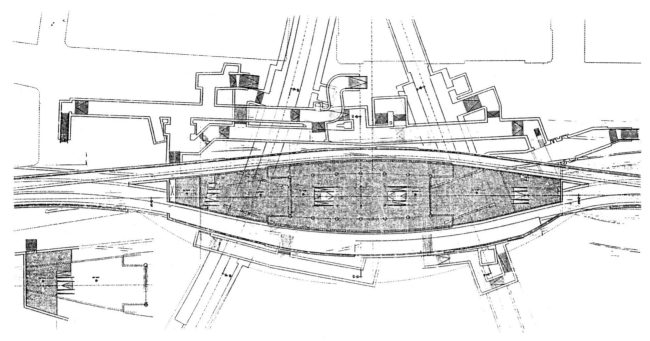

Fig. 6   Second alternative

ticketing halls crosses the central space in a north-south direction and gives access to the escalators and fixed stairs. Passengers descend by them while they get familiarized with the configuration of the station and the location of the three lines.

Upon arrival at floor level, they select the appropriate way to reach their platform. Transfer connections between lines generally are through the central space, enhancing the perception of the station concept, although some direct connections between lines have been conserved as alternative paths. Exits from platforms are also through the central space and ticketing halls and thence to the surface.

Room for commercial concessions has been provided in a veranda overlooking the central space, which is also used as an exit corridor from line 2.

In order to provide a smooth transition to the stations and plarforms not structurally changed, outside the central space, corridors keep their cross-section and finishes are different from those in the central space. Several old corridors that were not needed any more have been reserved for Company use, in a central location as a hub of the network,providing great accessibility to all parts of it (Fig.7).

Structural concept

The stratigraphic column at the station starts with 8 meters where no soil exists, subway and other services tunnels and galleries covering the whole area. From that depth and up to 18 m, sands are prevalent, while plastic clays appear below the sands.

While the three ticketing halls are constructed with conventional reticulated

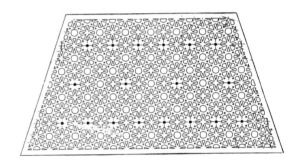

Fig. 7   Slab of the central space

slabs lying on perimetral walls and columns, the central space faces stability problems due to old brick vaults in the subway lines with a span of 14 m, and intermediate construction phases where assymetrical loading (due to excavation constraints) needs special attention.

The four walls of the trapezium, three of them coping with stresses coming from the line's station vaults, have been constructed with reinforced concrete walls, disposing piles in strategic locations, such as intersections of corridors where stresses were particularly important.

The north wall, suffering stresses from line 2, which is located 4 m over the central space floor, was the most delicate case. The brick vault was provisionally reinforced by means of beams located 1 m apart from the interior of the station and three beams disposed along the floor of the central space were transfering horizontal loads to the south wall. The wall was formed by 1050 mm piles adjacent to each other, on top of which the wall itself, 2.5 m high, was built. During first phase of construction this wall was secured by tying it to the first row of columns of the central space.

The columns of the central space are built on top of 1050 and 1500 mm piles, driven through all existing galleries and concreted by pouring into a metallic envelope that ensured no losses at the crossings of the different galleries. Once they reached floor level, HEB-400 profiles were embedded in the piles, and later these were concreted as octogonal columns. The column's capitals are constructed by means of UPN-200 profiles welded with plates 60x1000x12 mm, and spirals made of Ø-10 to connect with the main slab. This large slab, 43x24 m and with a trapezoidal form, is the most prominent part of the station, and was conceived to perpetuate the primitive ceiling of the original station.

Initially the slab was designed to be 30 cm thick and reinforced by tendons in four directions, paired at right angles. In order to achieve a perfect finish it was, in fact, constructed as a flat slab 50 cm thick with precast elements of glass reinforced concrete through a further 30 cm thickness.

Construction phases

As already established, construction phases were determined by the need for operation as well as transfer and access for the three subway lines, maintaining and minimizing undesirable effects on vehicular and pedestrian surface traffic. The most demanding constraint was to establish routes for subway passengers to allow access and transfer connections between lines. Another particular constraint that conditioned the whole construction process was the fact that the existing telephone exchange of the subway system was located in the central space and had to be changed to a new location.

Taking advantage of the existence of multiple connections between the different lines, four construction phases were established, satisfying all traffic, with two ticketing halls continuously in operation and no traffic paths through platforms to cause passenger congestion.

Fixed installations

Taking advantage of the construction of the central space, all station systems have been renewed, particularly the following:

a) Power supply for the three lines, related to a new project for the entire system. Under the station construction, room was provided for transformers (15000/380V).
b) Emergency lighting system.
c) New lighting at stations, platforms and corridors, as well as in the central space.
d) New digital telephone exchange to control the entire subway network.
e) Television and public address systems.
f) Air cooling for station and platforms, connected with extraction of hot air coming from train equipments through ducts under the platforms at the stations.
g) Fire detection network.
h) Waterproofing both of new and old areas. The system in new areas was disposed in the outer part of the structure, simplified by the cut and cover construction method. In old stations, a waterproofing layer was fixed to the vault and later a grid was also fixed and shotcreted to provide a final

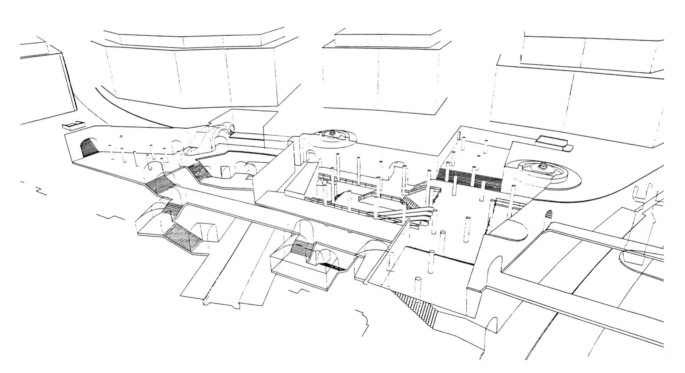

Fig.8   General view of final solution

finish with an accoustic layer and final
painting.

GENERAL DATA
The Plan area of the renewal project was
6500 m^2, 2700 in areas of new construction
and the remaining 3800 m^2 adapted from
existing areas. The central space counts
for 1000 m^2 of new construction.
     The works began in September 1985, and
ended on December 20th 1986, being
therefore performed in 15 months.
     The cost of the underground station
renewal project was 1035 million pesetas
(8´6 million US $), and the total cost
of the project, including the surface
area as well as houses facade renewal,
was 1500 millions pesetas (12´5 millions
US $).

Fig. 9   General view

Tunnel boring at Vinstra power plant, Norway—excavation of the 17-km long headrace tunnel by use of tunnel-boring machines

A. Borg
Selmer-Furuholmen AG, Winterthur, Zurich, Switzerland

ABSTRACT

In summer, 1986 the owner asked for bids for the extension of the existing Vinstra power plant. A major part of this bid was the cross section enlargement of the headrace tunnel. Consequently the power production had to be stopped during the construction period. High risk was connected to the kind and quantity of rock support works required by drill and blast excavation in an old tunnel through partially weak rocks. These led Selmer Furuholmen to the concept of building a parallel tunnel to the existing headrace tunnel excavated by TMBs. This alternative construction solution was finally accepted and chosen by the owner.

INTRODUCTION AND SHORT DESCRIPTION OF THE PROJECT

The Vinstra Hydropower Plant, situated in the Gubdrandsdalen valley in central southern Norway, was built shortly after World War II.

Due to high loss of pressure in the narrow tunnels, and the need for more efficiency, the owner decided on an extension of the power plant combined with replacement and renewal of 40 year old equipment. In 1986 the owner had finished the planning of the plant's extension and contractors were asked for bids. Briefly, the extension work of the power plant consists of:

Lower part:

- extension of the power station by rock excavation, support and concrete works

- excavation of pressure tunnel, cross section = 35 m², L = 3000 m

- excavation of the pressure shaft, cross section = 20 m², L = 500 m

- cross section enlargement of the existing tailrace tunnel from 30 to 52 m², L = 1000 m

Upper part:

- cross section enlargement of the existing headrace tunnel from 32 to 52 m², L = 17000 m

- excavation of pressure tunnel, cross section = 35 m², L = 3000 m

HEADRACE TUNNEL

1. Geology

The headrace tunnel passes through a sedimentary rock formation of Cambrian-Ordovician epoch. The rocks consist mainly of phyllites and shales - more or less metamorphosed - in places with quartz beds and sandstone beds with up to 85% quartz content. These strata are mostly horizontal. Sections with weak rocks and even fault zones are known from the previously existing tunnel. By the TBM-excavation method, the total rock support will be greatly reduced compared to the drill and blast method and may only be required in the above mentioned sections with weak rocks and tectonic deformations. According to experience with similar rocks, the water inflow is also expected to be low (Fig. 1).

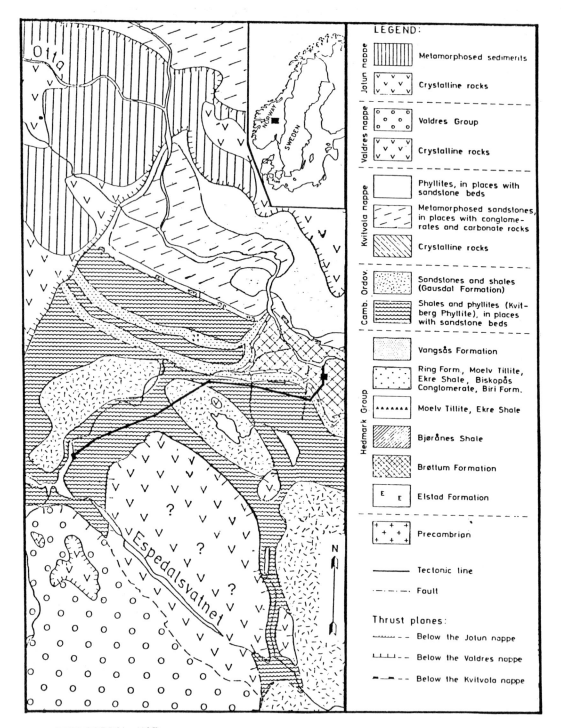

LEGEND:

Jotun nappe
- ||||| Metamorphosed sediments
- v v v Crystalline rocks

Valdres nappe
- o o o Valdres Group
- v v v Crystalline rocks

Kvitvola nappe
- Phyllites, in places with sandstone beds
- Metamorphosed sandstones, in places with conglomerates and carbonate rocks
- Crystalline rocks

Camb. Ordov.
- Sandstones and shales (Gausdal Formation)
- Shales and phyllites (Kvitberg Phyllite), in places with sandstone beds

Hedmark Group
- Vangsås Formation
- Ring Form., Moelv Tillite, Ekre Shale, Biskopås Conglomerate, Biri Form.
- Moelv Tillite, Ekre Shale
- Bjørånes Shale
- Brøttum Formation
- E E Elstad Formation

- + + + Precambrian

- —————— Tectonic line
- —·—·— Fault

Thrust planes:
- Below the Jotun nappe
- Below the Valdres nappe
- Below the Kvitvola nappe

GEOLOGICAL MAP

From J.O. Englund, 1973:

Stratigraphy and Structure of the Ringebu-Vinstra District, Gudbrandsdalen.

Fig. 1

2. Enlargement of existing cross section, excavation by the drill and blast method

The owner's project papers for bids did not include an alternative solution; only an enlargement of the cross section of the existing tunnel from 32 to 52 m² was foreseen. During this work the power production had to be stopped. In order to reduce these losses, the owner asked for the shortest possible construction period, i.e. within 1 or 2 summer seasons. To meet this stipulation it would have been necessary to drive simultaneously from all 5 existing access tunnels with correspondingly high manpower and more equipment. Sections through weak rock would require the erection of rock support. As the tunnel had not been inspected since 1960, high risk was also connected with poor rock conditions and consequently with extensive rock supports.

3. Construction of a parallel tunnel, excavation by use of TBM

3.1 Description of the alternative solution

The previously described problems invited the contractor to look for alternatives and better solutions. The best of these was found in using two fullface boring machines to excavate a 17000m long tunnel parallel to the old tunnel. See plan of power plant and arrangement of TBM, Figs. 2, 3 and 4.

A new 500m long access tunnel had to be excavated by the drill and blast method. From this access one machine bores to the left towards the power station and the other to the right towards the intake. The left branch length to bore is 9970 m and the right branch length is 6900 m. The excavation performance - based on two work shifts per day and 100 shift-hours per week - was estimated at approximately 110 m per week and machine.

The most obvious advantages of this alternative are:

- the stop in power production during the enlargement of the existing tunnel cross section by benching was reduced from a minimum of one season to one month

- the elimination of the high risk connected with poor rock and need for the erection of safe rock supports

The higher price for the TBM alternative was compensated by the value of electrical production during the enlargement as described above. There would not have been any TBM-boring at Vinstra without the availability of two suitable machines with complete back-up equipment. The use of new machinery was not competitive because of both price and delivery time.

The alternative was accepted by the owner and the joint venture, Selmer Furuholmen-Veidekke was awarded the biggest tunnel excavation job by TBM in Norway.

3.2 Tunnelling equipment

a) Tunnel Boring Machines (TBM)

Two Robbins machines were available.

Not only Selmer Furuholmen's extensive experience in tunnel boring, but also the lack of competitive proposals from other manufacturers for this project made it easy to decide in favour of these machines.

The two Robbins machines, mod. 148-212 and 213 were manufactured in 1979/80, and had since then bored 17600 m, respectively 14300 m in Norway and 45000 m in Sweden. Both machines had to be totally overhauled and the diameters enlarged from 4.5 m to 4.75 m.

These extensive revision works were done at Selmer Furuholmen's workshop and at Normas Industrier A.S., both in Trondheim, under the management of MCS of Scandinavia.

For machine dimension, weight, power etc. see overleaf.

b) Back-up system (back-up)

Two complete back-up systems - to follow behind the TBM - were also available. They were originally designed by LEAG and built in Switzerland.

11

TBM SPECIFICATIONS

MACHINE DIAMETER   : 4,75 (NEW CUTTERS)   "

MAIN BEARING TYPE   : TAPERED ROLLER   "

CUTTERS   : TYPE   : ROBBINS DISC   "
                    QUANTITY : 36   35
                    Size   : 15,5 IN. (32)   17 IN (31)
                               12   IN. (4)   15,5 IN (4)

MAXIMUM RECOMMENDED
AVERAGE CUTTER LOAD: 40.000 LB. (18.141 kg)   "

MAXIMUM RECOMMENDED
CUTTERHEAD THRUST : 635 METRIC TONS   "

CUTTERHEAD DRIVE   : TOTAL POWER: 1200 HP (840 kw)   "
                      Motors   : 6--380V, 3-PHASE,
                                 50 Hz, 1500 RPM
                      SIZE   : 200 HK (149,2 kw)
                      CH RPM   : 8.0   "

BORING STROKE   : 72 IN (1,83 M)   "

ELECTRICAL SYSTEM :   "

   INPUT POWER   : 6000, 3-PHASE, 50 Hz
   TRANSFORMERS   : 2 -- 650 kVA EACH
   POWER REQUIREMENT: 700 KW AT 75 % OF FULL LOAD

MACHINE WEIGHT   : APPROXIMATELY 210 METRIC TONS   "

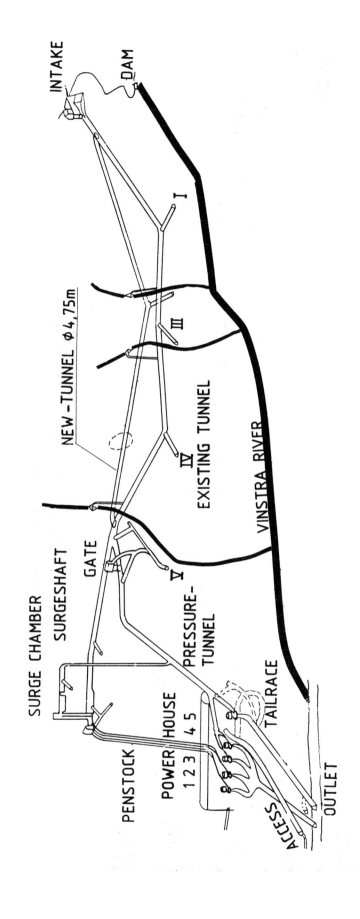

VINSTRA POWERPLANT - CONTRACTORS ALTERNATIVE

Fig. 2

13

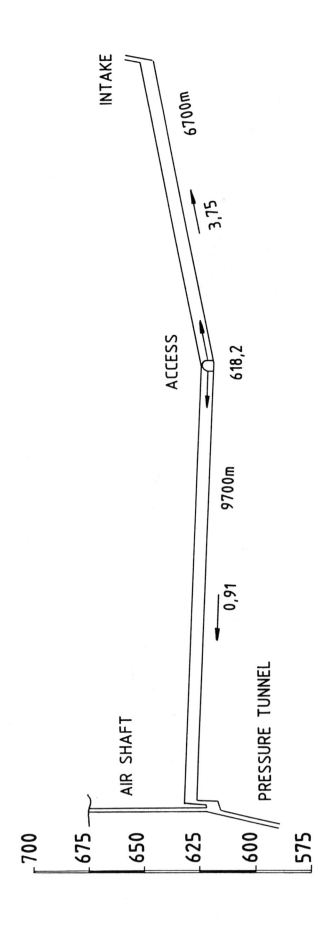

LONGITUDINAL SECTION TBM

Fig. 3

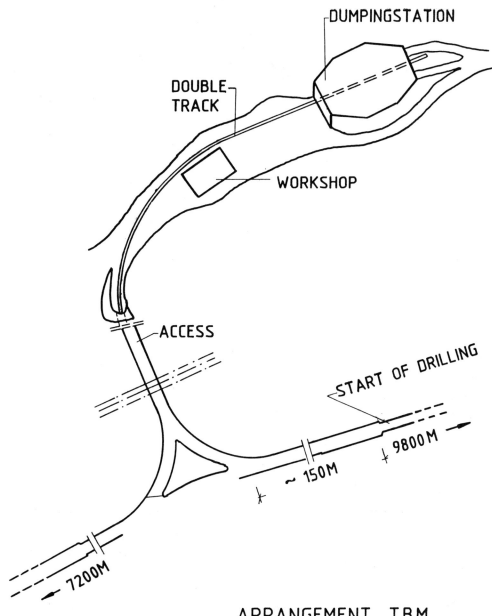

DUMPINGSTATION

DOUBLE TRACK

WORKSHOP

ACCESS

START OF DRILLING

9800M

~ 150M

7200M

ARRANGEMENT TBM

Fig. 4

15

Necessary equipment for the excavation operation such as transformers, electric and hydraulic power units, ventilation and dust scrubber systems, loading conveyors, hoists and even a lunch room are located on the back-up unit.

There is a double rail track giving room for a haulage train with 10 muck-cars on each track.

A short transverse belt conveyer enables cars loading on both sides.

During loading the cars are hooked up to a chain which can pull the cars back and forth.

The back-up is 112 m long, consisting of 16 sections each 6 m long, plus the ramp. The towed back-up rolls on the tunnel rail track. Together with a counterweight - instead of support legs - the back-up has a total weight of approximately 200 tons.

c) Trailing equipment

- Tunnel rail track: tracks complete with steel sleepers, in 10m long sections, are transported on special cars to the front end of the back-up. Here - just behind the TBM and under the bridge conveyor - the track is laid on the tunnel invert with solid wood wedges placed between the sleepers and the rock. The track width is 750 mm.

A California switch will be erected at a station between 3000 to 4000 m - depending on the excavation rate.

Each tunnel heading has its own track line going through the 500m long access tunnel to the dumping station which is outside. The cars are unloaded by tipping to the left or to the right side from the dumping bridge - one separate line for each heading.

- Muck cars: original LEWA-design except for the tipping mechanism which was changed to a hydraulic tipping system. Two tipping cylinders are mounted on each car. These are connected by hoses to the cylinders on the next car, etc. At the dumping station the hose line is hooked up to a stationary hydraulic power unit and the haulage train of 10 cars is unloaded within 2-3 minutes.

Selmer-Furuholmen designed this system in 1976, and since then it has been used with success, i.e. very low repair and maintenance costs with very few breakdowns - if any.

Specifications:
Capacity: 5 m^3
Length: 4600 mm
Width: 1008 mm
Height: 1580 mm
Weight: 3300 kg

- Locomotives: All locomotives at the job site have dieselpowered engines. Most of them are AGEVE locomotives, manufactured by AB Gaevle Vagnverkstad in Sweden.

Specifications:
Length inc. couplers: 3950 mm (156 inches)
Length exc. couplers: 3500 mm (138 inches)
Width: 1300 mm (51 inches)
Height: 1655 mm (65 inches)
Weight: 14000 kg (30860 lbs)
Engine; Deutz: 102 kW (139 hp)
Starting tractive effort: 2180 kp (4800 lbs)
Maximum speed: 23 km/h (15 m.p.h.)

- Ventilation: one ventilator, Korfmann ESN 9, for each tunnel branch at the portal blows the fresh air through a ventilation duct of 1200 mm diameter towards the heading.

With increasing distance to the heading, additional ventilators will be installed.

- Power line in tunnel: power for the TBM is brought from the transformer station outside by a 6.3 KV high voltage cable (3 x 95 # Al + earthing)

- Water supply comes through 4 inch diameter Alvenius pipes

- A telephone line connects the site office with the TBM -operator

16

4. Estimate of the TBM performance

4.1 Drilling Rate Index (DRI)

In hard rock, the excavation performance of the TBM is much more influenced by the geological and rock mass conditions than by the drill and blast method.

Rock properties and factors like strength, content of hard/abrasive minerals (quartz) and weak minerals (mica), stress in the rock mass, and especially the existence of weakness planes given by joints and fissures have been shown to have a considerable influence on the TBM's performance.

The Norwegian Institute of Technology (NTH) in Trondheim has put a tremendous effort into analysing and testing the influence of rock factors on the penetration rate. Different rock specimen tests were carried out in the laboratory, followed up by a comparison of the effective results at the job sites. In this way a prediction model for the penetration was developed step by step - based on the DRI (Drilling Rate Index) - and published in the Project Reports 8-79 and 1-83.

The DRI was originally developed by R. Lien for percussive drilling and later modified by Dr. O.T. Blindheim. The DRI is a combination of two rock tests: the rock brittleness value (S_{20}, a drop testing which includes both the grain size and the grain boundary strength) and the Siever's miniature drill test (SJ, which is an abrasive/hardness test).

An updated Report 1-87 includes a more extensive study of machine and cutter factors that influence the penetration. This was presented by Arne Lislerud in his paper "Hard rock tunnel boring - prognosis and costs" given at the VI Australian Tunnelling Conference in Melbourne, March 1987. Following are shown three of the most significant figures in the NTH Reports. In addition to the contractors' long experience from many kilometers of tunnels bored in various rock formations, these reports have been a big help in predicting the penetration rate - also at the Vinstra Project.

4.2 Estimate of penetration, based on the DRI

Rock type: Phyllite

Tender documents DRI 54-55

Penetration rate

i_b (mm PR)	K_s	$i_n = i_b \cdot K_s$	m/hr
4.4	1.3	5.7	2.73

Operating the TBM at 18 m.tons per cutter, the expected fissure class III and the foliation planes parallel to the tunnel axis, Fig. 2 gives a joint factor for fissures and foliation planes K_s = 1.3.

$$\text{Penetration in m/hr} = i_n \cdot \text{RPM} \cdot \frac{60}{1000}$$
$$= 5.7 \cdot 8 \cdot \frac{60}{1000} = 2.73$$

4.3 Estimate of the weekly advance rate

- Working 2 shifts per day, each 10 hrs long and 5 days/week give 100 working shift hrs/week

- with an utilization factor of 40% over all and a tunnel length of 7000 m, excluding downtime for rock support works, the advance is estimated at

$$100 \text{ shift hrs} \cdot \frac{40}{100} = 40 \text{ machine hrs/week}$$
$$\cdot 2.73 \text{ m/hr}$$
$$= 109 \text{ m/week}$$

5. Achieved TBM performance

It took 7 or 8 weeks to assemble each machine with back-up. Each TBM and back-up has a total weight of 400 m.tons. The first machine for the left heading downstream started production in the 17th week of 1987, followed by the second machine that started boring in week 25 towards the intake.

From the start till week 39 the following performance rates were achieved:

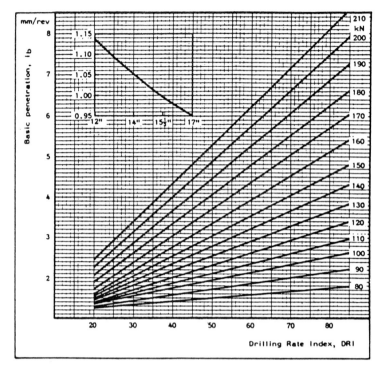

Fig. 5

Basis penetration i_b in mm/rev as a function of the Drilling Rate Index (DRI), thrust per cutter and the cutter diameter.

Net penetration is found by:

$$i = i_b \cdot k_s \qquad (mm/rev)$$

$$i = i \cdot RPM \cdot 60/1000 \quad (m/h)$$

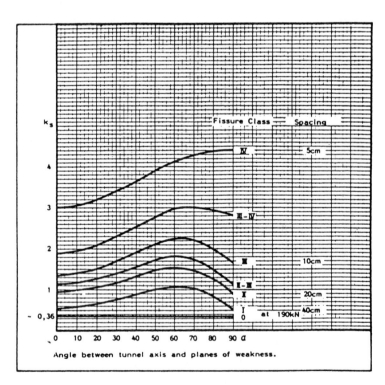

Fig. 6

Joint factor for fissures and foliation planes.

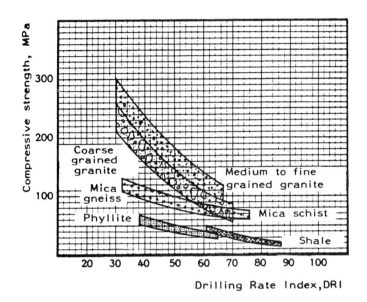

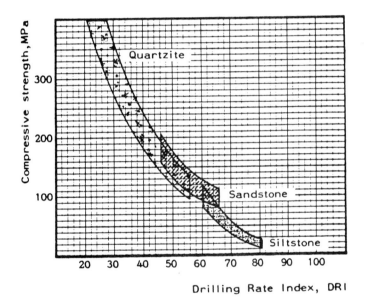

Fig. 7   Relation between Drilling Rate Index
         (DRI) and compressive strength,
         grouped according to rock types.

	Right heading	Left heading
Tot. bored tunnel length in m	2007	2712
Average performance/week	167.0	129.0
Best day	62.2	47.0
Best week	275.0	210.0
Best month	884.0	759.0
Average penetration rate in m per machine hour	3.0	3.1

The weekly performance is also shown in attached Fig. 8, details regarding machine utilization in Fig. 9 and cutter ring wear in Fig. 10.

6. Rock support works

The expectation that the use of the TBM-excavation method would require less rock support was confirmed.

In only two shorter fault zones, so far, was it necessary to support the fractured rock by erecting steel arches, netting and rock bolts. Shotcreting has rarely had to be used up to the present time, and there have been few problems with rock stability.

7. Conclusion

The choice of the TBM alternative over that of drill and blast has prove to be the better solution for both client and contractors.

The tunnel excavation has proceeded at an even higher rate than estimated.

The reasons behind this are the existing rock conditions which are idealfor TBM-boring, the right choice of machinery which was, previous to the onset of the boring, expertly overhauled. Last but not least, the highly qualified and competent staff has done an excellent job. Or briefly, at the Vinstra project the right machines were in the right hands.

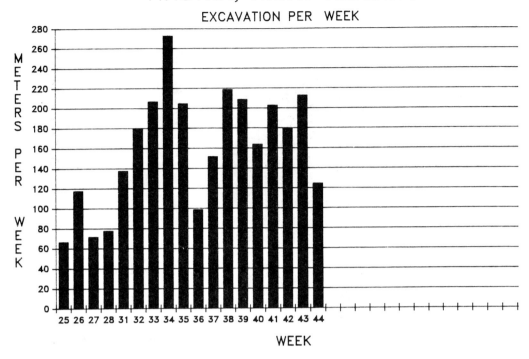

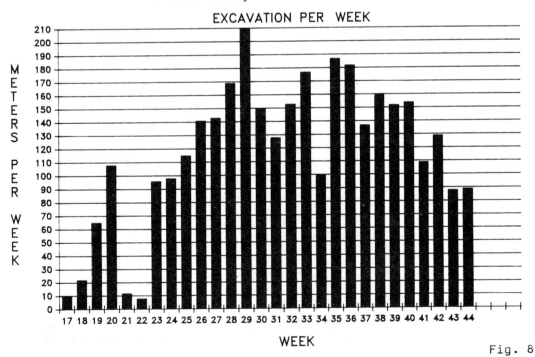

Fig. 8

21

VINSTRA, LEFT HEADING

MACHINE UTILIZATION

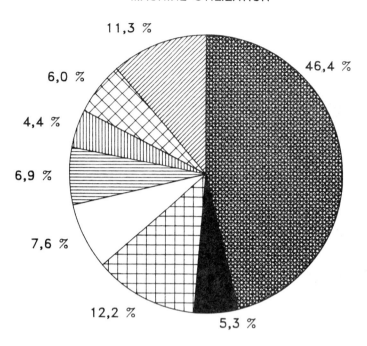

11,3 %

6,0 %

4,4 %

6,9 %

7,6 %

12,2 %

5,3 %

46,4 %

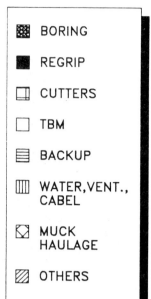

- ▨ BORING
- ■ REGRIP
- ▥ CUTTERS
- ☐ TBM
- ▤ BACKUP
- ▥ WATER,VENT., CABEL
- ◪ MUCK HAULAGE
- ▨ OTHERS

VINSTRA, RIGHT HEADING

MACHINE UTILIZATION

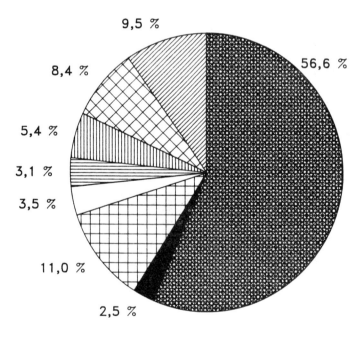

9,5 %

8,4 %

5,4 %

3,1 %

3,5 %

11,0 %

2,5 %

56,6 %

- ▨ BORING
- ■ REGRIP
- ▥ CUTTERS
- ☐ TBM
- ▤ BACKUP
- ▥ WATER,VENT., CABEL
- ◪ MUCK HAULAGE
- ▨ OTHERS

Fig. 9

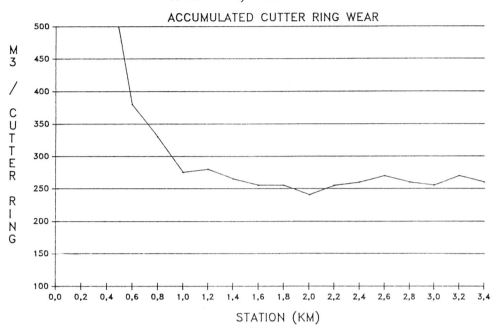

VINSTRA, LEFT HEADING
ACCUMULATED CUTTER RING WEAR

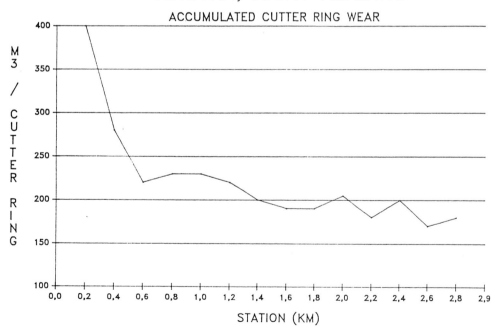

VINSTRA, RIGHT HEADING
ACCUMULATED CUTTER RING WEAR

Fig. 10

23

Excavation of the inclined haulageway in the Sulcis coalfield, Sardinia

A. Bortolussi Dr.Eng.
Mining and Processing Research Centre, CNR, Cagliari, Italy
R. Ciccu Dr.Eng.
University of Cagliari, Cagliari, Italy
P. P. Manca Dr.Eng.
University of Cagliari, Cagliari, Italy
G. Massacci Dr.Eng.
Department of Mining and Minerals Engineering, University of Cagliari, Cagliari, Italy
L. Ottelli Dr.
Carbosulcis S.p.A., Italy
S. Peddis Dr.Eng.
Carbosulcis S.p.A., Italy

SYNOPSIS

After a 10-year stand-by period, a new project has recently been implemented for resuming production at the Seruci - Nuraxi Figus underground coal mines in the Sulcis district (south west Sardinia). About 3.3 million tonnes of run-of-mine will be produced yearly by simultaneously running five longwall stopes. The raw coal will be hoisted through an inclined haulageway provided with conveyor belt, having a net cross section of 28 m^2 over a total length of 3,300 m. The paper first discusses the criteria underlying the selection of both the intake site and tunnel tracking in relation to the general lay-out of underground workings and location of outside installations. The choice of excavation methods was strongly dependent upon the knowledge of geomechanical features of the rocks to be crossed. To this end, a drilling campaign was carried out involving all the overlying geologic formations down to the level of the productive seams, some 400 m below the surface; recovered cores were investigated in order to classify the rocks according to their self supporting characteristics and amenability to excavation. After yard set-up and area preparation, drifting works have recently been started. The results of the excavation study for the first 500 m section are reported, where actual data are compared with the corresponding design parameters. Two different excavation methods have been adopted, depending on rock characteristics. Wherever more resistant and abrasive rocks are encountered, drilling and blasting methods are applied, whereas in the case of weaker or weathered rocks roadheader excavation is instead used. The paper illustrates in detail the equipment employed and discusses the problems encountered together with the technical solutions adopted to overcome them. Moreover, the relevant productivity data are reported in the framework of the overall organization of the working cycle.

Mining and beneficiation in the Sulcis coalfield dates back to more than 130 years ago when the first concessions were granted for the exploitation of outcropping parts of the seams. A peak yearly production of more than 1 Mt of washed coal was reached just before the second world war under the constraint of autarchy, inasmuch as it was the only important domestic resource available. Working force was well above 20,000 men. After the war the production declined somewhat to 700,000 tonnes per year and gradually dwindled finally until the shut down of the mines in 1972.

Following the energy crisis a Commission was appointed by the ministry of Industry for the purpose of verifying the existence of the technical and economic conditions for reopening the mines.

In the light of the positive conclusions reached by said Commission, the Carbosulcis was established, a State-owned Company entrusted with the task of carrying out the feasibility study and eventually starting a new industrial activity.

The study, completed in 1984, put into evidence the presence of economic losses. However considerations of strategic nature and a favourable costs - benefits balance finally led the Italian Parliament to pass a law whereby 250,000 MLit (about 170 million US$) were destined to technical investments in addition to the amount for covering the discounted economic losses during the 25 years period of expected activity.

PROJECT OUTLINE

The main underground structure of the new mine will consist of a network of galleries, over a total length of about 18 km, connecting the two formerly distinct mines of Seruci and Nuraxi Figus, each provided with twin shafts.

Ventilation, carriage traffic, personnel transit, coal haulage and services supply will be ensured through that system.

Five 800 x 200 m^2 panels mined with a retreat longwall method will allow an average yearly production of 3.3 Mt of raw coal as the standard basis. The run-of-mine will be hoisted via a 14 % inclined haulageway sunk from the surface down to a depth of about 400 m, which should reach the concession area at a roughly baricentric position. The run-of-mine will be beneficiated in a processing plant to be built near the incline intake giving 1.7 Mt per year of clean coal suitable for combustion in the nearby power stations. About 2,500 workers will be employed altogether.

In planning the new mine, coal hoisting represented a major aspect. For economic reasons the incline was finally preferred to the twin shaft solution previously adopted whose capacity could no longer accomodate the larger production rate scheduled by the project.

GENERAL FEATURES OF THE INCLINE

The run-of-mine coal will be hoisted by means of a 1,200 mm wide conveyor belt to be placed at one side of the tunnel, leaving enough room for light vehicle traffic. The tunnel will also serve as the main air inlet for underground ventilation.

The incline, with a finished cross area of 28 m^2, starting from a net excavation area of 40 - 42 m^2, consists of three sections of alternating direction over a total length of about 3,300 m. Overall horizontal clearance on the road plane will be 6.75 m to be maintained over a wall height of 1.5 m. Vault profile is semicircular with a 3.4 m radius.

The general lay out of the basin showing the tunnel location is sketched in Figure 1.

The surface intake site was selected within the

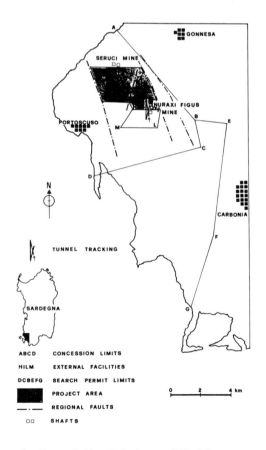

Fig. 1 Map of the Sulcis coalfield.

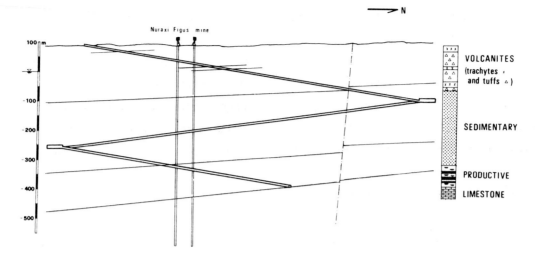

Fig. 2 Simplified N-S geologic section of the Sulcis coalfield showing the tunnel direction. The stratigraphic column is referred to the intercept points of the rock formations with the tunnel.

restrictions imposed by the position of the external facilities and by the need to limit the impact on the environment and the neighbouring residential areas.

The choice of the underground layout was dictated by the long term optimization of the haulage problem taking into account the mining constraints: its position close to the southern border of the project area is almost baricentric with respect to the whole concession area which extends southwards beyond that border.

The tunnel is intended to serve also as the access way for the development of new zones. As regards the near future, northern parts of the concessions incorporated in the production plan, which are limited by some regional faults as well as by the presence of worked out stopes, can be reached by prolonging the first northbound section.

The direction of each tunnel section was mainly dictated by the geotechnical features of the rock formations overlying the productive seams and in particular by the need to avoid weak zones, whose crossing would have involved more burdensome excavation and support problems.

The first section, 1,190 m long strikes northwards with a pitch of 14%; it crosses a

sequence of volcanic rocks of post Eocene age consisting of trachytes and tuffs. The second, 1,270 m long with an almost opposite direction will be driven through predominantly sedimentary formations consisting of sandstones, siltstones and conglomerates. The third, 820 m long and again striking North, will cross a sedimentary sequence including marls, limestone, mudstones and carbonaceous materials as well as the top part of the seams.

At each junction the tunnel is enlarged in order to allow the necessary room for conveyor belt motors and tensioning devices. The finished volume of these connecting caverns with horizontal floor will be roughly 7,000 m^3. A geologic profile on a vertical plane along the axes of the planned tunnel sections is sketched in Figure 2.

The portal, designed in such a way as to protect the intake from water inflows, consists of a 70 m long artificial gallery. The tunnel vault and walls will be lined with concrete placed between the shotcreted walls and the slip forms; the surface will be smoothed in order to minimize friction air-pressure drop. The support system consists of steel frames and electro-welded net inside the shotcrete as described later in more

27

detail; roof bolting is added where required.

If weak rocks are crossed, the tunnel section is completed by an invert.

The tunnel roadway, designed to withstand the load of heavier vehicles, will be concrete lined with nonskid features. Three major enlargements 25 m long and 3.5 m wide in the middle of each section and a number of smaller 'monkey headings' at intervals throughout the tunnel will be dug. Water drainage devices are also envisaged in the project.

In the neighbourhood of the underground outlet, four large 10 m diameter cylindrical coal bunkers with a total storage capacity of 4,000 m^3 will be excavated in a suitable position above the tunnel floor so as to allow conveyor belt feeding. Walls will be lined with wear and shock resistant concrete.

Two opposite ramps and a connecting horizontal drift will reach the top head of the storage bunkers. A secondary ventilation gallery, 160 m long with a cross section of about 30 m^2 will by-pass the storage system. A properly designed 130 m long junction with the same features as the tunnel itself completes the works.

The tunnel project was commissioned to Snam-progetti, a sister Company of Carbosulcis within the ENI Group (the Government controlled Italian Board for Energy), which was also entrusted with managing the excavation contract.

PRELIMINARY SITE INVESTIGATION

In order to predict the expected cost and set down the tunnel excavation plan, a ground investigation programme was executed. This enabled Carbosulcis and Snamprogetti to provide the tenderers with all useful information required for the technical and financial success of the tunnelling contract.

The geological situation is characterized by a set of NW-SE faults dipping SW about 4 km apart, crossed by some perpendicular faults dipping

North, leaving a rectangular area of about 48 km^2 in which major disturbances are absent.

About 50 boreholes have been drilled up to now throughout the basin, 20 in recent years. The cores of the latter, recovered over the full hole length, have been the object of accurate studies aimed at identifying the geotechnical properties of the rocks involved in the tunnel drivage.

During the drilling campaign the percentage of solid core recovered was systematically recorded together with some relevant features of the operation such as penetration rate, tool wear and water circulation losses. Field observations concerning the mineral-petrographic characteristics of the various geological formations crossed by the hole were also taken.

Based upon these indications, three main groups of rocks were identified:

- volcanites, outcropping over almost the entire area of the basin and consisting of trachytes interbedded with tuffs. Their thickness varies from 100 to 150 m near the centre of the field and tends to increase in the southern portion;

- sedimentary rocks, locally known as 'Cixerri formation', consisting of conglomerates, sandstones and marly to silt clays, often intermingled. Their overall thickness can be roughly estimated at around 250 m;

- 'productive' formations, including more or less carbonaceous clays, marls, limestones and a number of coal seams of varying thickness. They are found at depths between 200 and 400 m below surface and tend to sink seawards dipping along a SW direction.

Selected samples of recovered cores were tested at the rock mechanics Lab of the University of Cagliari, Department of Mining and Minerals Engineering.[1]

For each kind of rock encountered, the following mechanical properties have been measured:

- uniaxial compressive strength;

- tensile strength;
- elastic longitudinal modulus;
- Poisson coefficient.

In addition the intrinsic curves for some lithotypes have been obtained through triaxial tests.[2]

Fracture characteristics have been also evaluated by studying:

- the average fracture spacing which enabled the rock quality index RQD to be determined;
- the conditions of fracture surfaces allowing to estimate roughness profiles and to define the nature and thickness of filling materials;
- fracture pattern restricted to sub-vertical and sub-horizontal groups only, as it was practically impossible to correctly orient the cores.

Measurements of mechanical properties and fracture assessment have been carried out according to the procedures suggested by ISRM, the International Society of Rock Mechanics.[3] Tests have been repeated for each lithotype showing constant features. Fewer points were necessary for the volcanic series which is rather more homogeneous than the sedimentary formations.

The results of in situ investigation and laboratory testing enabled the classification of the various lithofacies according to the

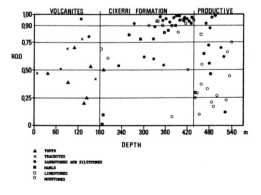

Fig. 3 Sulcis coalfield. Borehole 1/78. Diagram of RQD values for the various lithofacies as a function of hole depth.

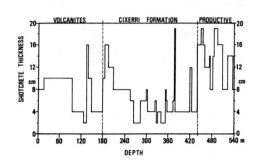

Fig. 4 Sulcis coalfield. Calculated shotcrete thickness according to Wickam's criterion for the various rock formations crossed by the 1/78 borehole at increasing depths.

different classification systems proposed in the literature.[1]

As far as Deere's criterion is concerned, higher and less dispersed RQD values around an average of 0.90 have been found for the 'Cixerri formation' whereas for the other two groups points are almost uniformly scattered around a lower mean value. This means that the latter have extremely variable fracturation features. RQD values are reported in the diagram of Figure 3.

Louis classification, based upon the measurement of uniaxial compressive strength compared to the maximum compressive stress on the tunnel contour, suggested that rocks to be traversed might inherently be capable of self-supporting; therefore the real static situation encountered underground and, correspondingly, the suitable wall support to be installed would predominantly be influenced by fracture conditions.

Rock classification after Wickham's criterion allowed to obtain a clearer idea of the kind and size of support demanded based upon RSR index values.

For instance, the calculated shotcrete thickness related to the various lithotypes crossed by the boreholes at increasing depths is shown in Figure 4.

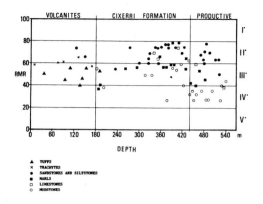

Fig. 5 Sulcis coalfield. Borehole 1/78. Diagram of RMR values after Bieniawski's rock classification criterion.

Finally, rocks have been classified according to Bieniawski's RMR criterion which is believed to be the most appropriate in tunnelling design.

RMR values at the various hole depths are reported in Figure 5. Most points fall into classes II and III, whereas only some clayey lithofacies of the 'productive' group fall into class IV. Bieniawski rock rating data enabled to calculate the permissible unsupported tunnel span and the corresponding self-supporting time.

Results are shown for each group of rocks in Figure 6. It can be observed that the situation varies widely, especially as far as sedimentary formations are concerned.

CONTRACT PROBLEMS

Well aware that the tunnel to be excavated would have required sound experience not yet available within the newly established Company, Carbosulcis decided to assign this task to a contractor of

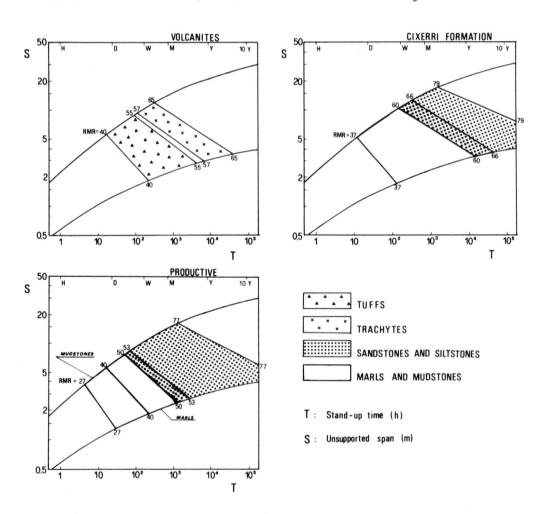

Fig. 6 Unsupported tunnel span and self-supporting time for the various rock formations, calculated on the basis of RMR values.

major importance. This decision could offer the additional advantage of accelerating the completion of the underground structure, thus substantially reducing the overall time required for accomplishing the project.

The work was put on to tender around mid-1986. Potential applicants were supplied with any useful information concerning the results of site investigation in order to evaluate better the problems involved and work out their internal cost budget on a more realistic basis. The final choice out of about 10 tenderers fell on TURNU SpA of Milan on the grounds that its offer was less costly and envisaged a shorter completion time. Detailed engineering and in particular concrete structural design including material testing was also contracted out.

The contract was articulated according to the current customary practice of correlating pricing figures to the relevant geologic features. It was agreed to distinguish three classes of rocks and correspondingly three different price levels:

- competent rocks with fair self-supporting properties, slightly fractured and weakly weathered, generally stable, possibly subjected to block fall or localized caving only, corresponding to class II of Bieniawski's rating and including most trachytes and part of sedimentary formations such as sandstones and siltstones (rock type A);

- moderately fractured and weathered rocks, often heterogeneous, rather unstable when exposed to air or water, with poor strength character-istics if not properly protected with provisional support, falling into RMR class III and including most tuffs, conglomerates and marls (rock type B);

- heavily jointed or little cohesive rocks, strongly weathered and susceptible to easy deterioration when exposed, often presenting a markedly plastic behaviour, belonging to class IV of Bieniawski RMR criterion and con-

sisting mainly of clayey materials (rock type C).

Rock type A is expected to be encountered over a total tunnel length of about 750 m; type B over about 1500 m; type C over the remaining 1100 m. The following kinds of roof support are provided for by the contract:

- Provisional support:

shotcrete 10 cm thick as the immediate measure for rock types B and C as well as for jointed zones of rock type A;

- Ultimate support characterized by:

electro-welded net for all rock types;

resin-anchored 24 mm bolts, 2.5 m long, distributed as needed for rock type A, placed according to a 2 m square grid for rock type B and to a 2 x 1.5 m grid for rock type C;

segmented NP 140 steel frames spaced 4 m, 2 m and 1 m for rock types A, B and C, respecti-vely;

a second shotcrete layer of decreasing thick-ness according to rock rating; an invert for rock types B and C.

Investigations carried out throughout the tunnel area enabled a reliable prediction of support requirements. However, the task of provisionally assessing both blasting results and cutting machine performance on the basis of rock rating indexes was rather more onerous.

As regards blasting, the major economic aspects were tool wear and explosive consumption. Bit wear could be roughly predicted on the basis of free silica content, taking into account that bit wear index is related to the drilling rate index of rocks.

Explosive consumption was calculated using the available literature data: the expected specific charge for the different rocks with normal fracturation patterns was estimated as a function of tunnel cross-sectional area and blasthole diameter. A specific charge of 1.5 kg of gelatine explosive per bank cubic metre was deemed necessary in trachytes, sandstones and limestones where drivage by drilling and blasting seemed preferable.[4]

Obviously in softer or weathered rocks, mechanical cutting looked more promising. It is a widely accepted fact that roadheader performance strongly depends upon local fracture conditions, penetration rates increasing significantly when fracture spacing falls below about 0.3 m. However this advantage is often deceptive, inasmuch as intensively fractured rocks involve more burdensome and time consuming support problems thus slowing down the effective drivage progress.

Although hardness tests and mineralogical analysis were of some help, the most reliable prediction of roadheader cutting rates and tool wear could have been obtained through specifically designed laboratory cutting tests on relatively large samples of rock; unfortunately core sizes were too small for this purpose. Therefore, the only available data of some relevance was the uniaxial compressive strength to which machine performance can be correlated to a certain extent using published diagrams or equations.[5,6,7]

Apart from excavation, debris mucking and hoisting also called for particular attention owing to the economic relevance of the operation. It was retained that hoisting by trucks could be economically feasible up to a chainage of 300 - 400 m; beyond that, shifting to conveyor belt was deemed necessary, haulage distances being too long for a discontinuous system.

Finally, underground water conditions was considered to be a factor of primary importance especially for roadheader excavation, owing to the larger proportion of fines produced by mechanical cutting.

Available data and past experience acquired in shaft sinking and borehole drilling suggested that no major water inflows were to be expected; however water percolation through heavily jointed or faulted zones was likely to occur with variable and hard to predict rates.

TECHNICAL ASPECTS OF TUNNEL EXCAVATION

Yard installation

Shortly after the official appointment as tunnel contractor, TURNU started the installation of external facilities in the second half of 1986. Yard set up included maintenance shop, cement mixing plant, fan station, management offices and the general services as well as the roadway system and the dumping site.

Part of the external facilities are shown by the photograph of Figure 7.

Excavation work began in January 1987.

Fig. 7 Sulcis coalfield. Nuraxi Figus incline. Partial view of the external facilities for tunnel excavation.

Portal and intake section

On account of the flat countryside, portal design provided for the digging of a trench down to a burden thickness of about 6 m above the tunnel vault level in order to meet the necessary stability conditions. A maximum wall depth of about 11 m was thereby attained, corresponding to the beginning of underground excavation. A 45° side slope has been maintained except for the lower 5 m, dug with vertical walls.

Trench excavation was carried out by bench blasting with a parallel hole pattern. Conventional quarry equipment consisting of a wagon drill, a wheel loader and dumpers was used. Slurry 'Tutagex' explosive was loaded into 51 mm diameter vertical blastholes, 5 to 6 m long, with an average consumption of 1.95 kg per cubic metre of solid rock.

An artificial gallery with a rectangular cross section, roofed with a continuous concrete slab on pretensioned beams cast across supporting walls was housed in the trench; the roof was then covered, except for the first 25 m, with dumped natural soil over a waterproofing layer.

Tunnel excavation by drilling and blasting

The first tunnel segment, about 120 m long, has been driven by drilling and blasting into slightly weathered and moderately jointed trachytes having a variable compressive strength up to 100 MPa.

A double V-cut was finally adopted after a preliminary blasting study aimed at improving explosive efficiency whilst minimizing over-excavation effects. However, unwanted blast-induced block falling occurred locally notwithstanding the precautions taken, especially in jointed zones.

The blast pattern consisted of 90 drillholes, 3.2 m long on average, in planes parallel to the tunnel floor and progressively converging toward the central symmetry line. The explosive load was about 240 kg per blast of 'Tutagex' slurry and decoupled 'Profil X' cartridges were used for smooth blasting at tunnel contour. Blasts were fired by means of 5 subsequent numbers of HI caps with 250 ms delay. Blasthole pattern and initiation sequence are shown in Figure 8.

An advance rate of 3.0 m per round was finally achieved as the result of improved design.

A twin-boom Atlas Copco H 175 jumbo attended by

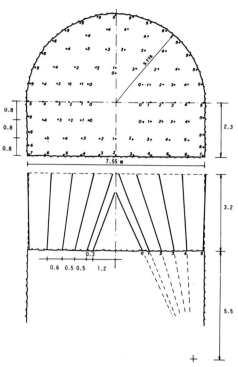

Fig. 8 Sulcis coalfield. Nuraxi Figus incline. Blasthole pattern and initiation sequence adopted in tunnel drivage through trachytes.

three workers and equipped with hydraulic drifters was used for drilling 53 mm blastholes. Two shifts per day were devoted to drilling and blasting and the third to debris hoisting and auxiliary operations.

Twenty working days have been required for driving the tunnel through 115 m of trachytes obtaining an average penetration rate of 5.75 m per day, corresponding to slightly less than one full round per shift.

Joint-isolated hanging blocks on the tunnel vault have been supported by resin-anchored bolts; shotcrete and ribs have been applied according to contract.

Except for some blast firing troubles encountered in the first rounds, no major problems arose.

Roadheader excavation

At chainage 115, tuffs began to emerge at the tunnel floor gradually replacing trachytes over the full face within about 30 m. Shifting to mechanized excavation soon became necessary in

33

order to exploit the amenability of tuffs to cutting methods.

A Westfalia Lunen WAV 178 roadheader capable of excavating strata with up to 120 MPa compressive strength was therefore introduced; its main features are as below:

- service weight: 73 tonnes;
- overall length: 15.7 m;
- width of loading apron: 4.2 m;
- overall height: 3.34 m;
- maximum cutting width: 8.86 m (.64 m at the crown and 6.41 m when undercutting);
- maximum undercut depth: 0.9 m;
- diameter of cutting heads: 1.1 m;
- ground pressure: 160 kPa;
- total installed power: 437 kW, 300 of which are at the twin cutting heads fitted with round shank bits;
- rated output: 20 to 100 m^3/h;

The geotechnical characteristics of the tuffs were extremely variable from 0.1 to 27 MPa compressive strength according to weathering; workability was always adequate provided that rock was dry; otherwise the cutting heads were easily covered by a layer of sticky material which resulted in a deterioration of bit penetration and shearing efficiency.

The size of excavation cuttings was rather fine and almost evenly distributed; even in jointed zones, where the rock tended to break into lumps, complete disaggregation was achieved after heap loosening and pushing back to assist loading. Average bit replacement rate was around 0.8 per metre of tunnel length.

Tuffs have been found down to chainage 425; then trachytes again emerged as expected. The major problems in this 300 m section were created by the presence of water pouring through opened joints communicating with perched groundwater bodies. Four distinct streams have been intercepted giving a total flow rate of 5 l/s. Any attempt at fracture sealing being impractical,

the problem of limiting water accumulation near the tunnel face was coped with by resorting to collecting devices. Upward holes were drilled deep into the rock so as to facilitate drainage by means of rubber hoses discharging into sumps; uncaptured water was channeled by shallow gutters dug across the floor. Despite these precautions, drenching could not be avoided with adverse effects on cutting machine performance and haulage rate.

In fact, the roadheader tended to sink into the weakened muddy floor so a type of movable wood crosstie platform had to be placed under the crawlers in order to ensure more favourable conditions for adequate machine performance.

The problems of loading consisted in a more difficult penetration by the front apron into the wet, sticky heap and a highly irregular material flow along the flight conveyors.

Excavation into the tuffs required 65 working days with an average effective penetration rate of 5 m/d on a three shifts per day basis, even slower than that obtained with the much tougher trachytes. This unsatisfactory result was due to the very slow advance in the wet rock which turned out to be about half the rate achieved in suitably dry conditions. Actually, in this latter case pure excavation rate was about 1 m/h, i.e. more than 40 m^3/h, not much less than the maximum nominal capacity.

As mentioned above, trachytes were again encountered from chainage 425 onwards and are expected to be found until chainage 480. The contractor had to decide whether changing to drilling and blasting was more convenient instead of risking the roadheader under the new conditions which appeared to exceed the rock strength limit suggested by the machine manufacturer.

Actually the strength has been found to be considerably higher than in the case of outcropping and thus more weathered trachytes.

However, it was decided to continue with the

roadheader on account of the joint pattern which was believed to favour rock fragmentation into coarse cuttings according to the mechanism of fracture propagation under the impact action of revolving cutter picks. The decision was motivated by the relatively short distance to overcome under these very critical conditions.

As expected, tool wear was quite high, about 15 times higher than in the case of tuffs: although being shorter and tougher, the bits tended to break under impact on the rock with uneven wearing; on average, 15 to 20 bits had to be replaced per metre of tunnel length.

On the other hand acceptable advance rates, around 6 m per working day on a three shift basis have been obtained.

The debris material, although of a relatively coarse size, was amenable to hoisting by conveyor belt. Only a few boulders, up to 0.5 m in size, required a secondary fragmentation at the face.

The excavation into both soft and tough rocks put into evidence the presence of some drawbacks connected with the characteristics of the roadheader. In fact the machine so far used proved to be too heavy and scarcely flexible at the different operational conditions. A new machine of smaller size and better manoeuvrability is being considered for driving the tunnel into the sedimentary formations where rocks of widely varying properties are expected to be encountered.

Temporary and final support

As mentioned above, the kind of support to be used was specified in the contract documents.

The only variations with respect to design figures concerned the shotcrete thickness which in certain places was considerably higher than estimated owing to unwanted blast-induced over-excavation in heavily jointed trachytes. On the other hand some tunnel sections did not need temporary support.

The guidelines for tunnelling operations followed in the Nuraxi Figus incline excavation are those suggested by the New Austrian Tunnelling Method (NATM), according to which rock formations are integrated into an overall ringlike support structure completed with an invert. The basic condition is that appropriate support must be applied well in time, thus keeping stress and deformation within acceptable limits.

In weathered or fractured tuffs, the unsupported tunnel length was never left larger than 10 m and the maximum time span was about 48 hours. Under these conditions, rock stability was acceptable, in agreement with forecasts based upon RMR rating. Dry and competent tuffs were capable of self-supporting for a much longer time so that immediate shotcreting could eventually be avoided over about 80 m out of 325.

Shotcrete is usually being applied at an average rate of around 3 m^3/h, much lower than the peak capacity of the shotcreting machine, owing to clearance restrictions. It takes roughly 4 h per day to cover the new surface produced. Current gunite consumption for immediate temporary support is 1.7 m^3 per coated metre of tunnel

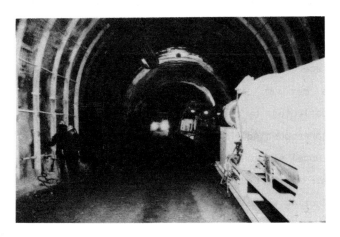

Fig. 9 Sulcis coalfield. Nuraxi Figus incline. View of the tunnel showing the roadheader working at the face, the secondary ventilation assembly, the 1,800 mm main ventilation ducting and the shotcreted steel frames.

length.

Bolting requires about 10 min per piece, including drilling. The operation requires three men.

Ribs are assembled at the tunnel floor and set in place with the help of a wheel-loader. Placing each rib requires 5 men and takes about 1.5 hours, including connections to the adjacent structure.

A picture of the tunnel being excavated with the roadheader, showing the features of the installed support is reported in Figure 9.

Ventilation

A relatively low quantity of dust is generally produced during roadheader excavation of the naturally moist or wet volcanites. Therefore the problem of removing the dust in suspension from the face is easily overcome without the necessity to use high ventilation rates. However dust increases when dry rocks are dug so that secondary ventilation is helpful for both improving the roadheader operator visibility and assuring a healthy working environment; to this end a movable axial fan assembly provided with dust collection system is activated.

Two main pressure fans in parallel powered with 150 kW motors, located at the surface, ensure a forced ventilation rate of about 30 m^3/s at the face. Actually the fans are capable of supplying a maximum rate of 40 m^3/s: the excess is deflected by means of an adjustable vane device. Correspondingly the mean air velocity across the tunnel section is slightly lower than 1 m/s.

Air is forced through a 1.8 m diameter flexible ducting whose outlet is maintained some 30 - 40 m from the face.

Mucking and haulage

In the first tunnel section driven by drill and blast the debris was mucked and hoisted to the dump site using a discontinuous system of 20 t payload Perlini T 20 dumpers and a CAT 966 wheel-loader which was preferable to a conveyor belt owing to the size of blasted material which included frequent boulders.

During tunnel driving into wet tuffs, haulage by dumpers was soon hampered by poorer road conditions as well as by the fact that rated bucket volume could not be fully exploited if material flow-back during tunnel climbing were to be minimized. Consequently machine utilization dropped to unacceptably low levels.

Transport inefficiency accelerated the shifting from dumpers to the conveyor belt, which was installed at one side on a relatively light steel frame in order to facilitate the necessary displacements for both maintenance and tunnel support installation.

CONCLUSIONS

After 7 months of underground excavation about 500 m of tunnel have been dug. During this period a variety of rock conditions have been encountered, ranging from tough competent trachytes to easily caving wet tuffs. Despite this, geologic predictions turned out to be quite accurate: each lithofacies has been intercepted at the predicted depth and the fracturation pattern was in good agreement with expectations.

The validity of the preliminary rock classification carried out on borehole cores has been substantially confirmed in the field except for few localized instances characterized by intense weathering especially when corresponding to water percolation through closely spaced joints.

Technical results so far obtained and the corresponding tunnelling costs are not fully acceptable, particularly as far as advance rate is concerned, owing to the fact that average productivity figures still suffer from the incidence of initial phases when both machinery setting and organization of the working cycle were not yet optimized.

As time elapsed excavation results gradually

improved thanks to a better understanding of rock characteristics and to a deeper insight into the problems involved, which allowed the identification of the most suitable technical solutions under the varying work conditions.

This fact leads the authors to believe that the time lost in the early phases can be recuperated before the scheduled completion period, thus increasing confidence in the technical and financial success of the tunnelling contract.

REFERENCES

1 - Manca P.P. and Massacci G. La classificazione geomeccanica delle rocce ed i problemi di sostegno delle opere minerarie sotterranee. Determinazioni sperimentali, analisi critiche e previsioni di comportamento per opere nelle rocce di copertura del bacino carbonifero del Sulcis. Resoconti Associazione Mineraria Sarda, anno LXXXVI, n. 2, 1981, 131-157.

2 - Manca P.P. and Massacci G. Osservazioni sull'impiego di dati desunti da prove di laboratorio nella progettazione dell opere di sostegno delle gallerie. Resoconti Associazione Mineraria Sarda, anno XC, n. 2, 1984, 5-24.

3 - ISRM Suggested methods: Rock characterization testing and monitoring. Pergamon Press (1981).

4 - Tamrock Handbook of underground drilling. Tampere, Finland, 1986.

5 - Mc Feat-Smith I. and Tarkoy P.J. Site investigation for machine tunnelling contracts. Tunnels and Tunnelling, march 1980, 36-80.

6 - Aleman V.P. A strata strength index for boom type roadheaders. Tunnels and Tunnelling, march 1981, 52-55.

7 - Aleman V.P. Prediction of cutting rates for boom type roadheaders. Tunnels and Tunnelling, January 1983, 23-25.

Review of ground treatment carried out for tunnels of the Singapore Mass Rapid Transit System

S. Buttling Ph.D., B.Sc.(Eng.), A.C.G.I., C.Eng., M.I.C.E., M.S.I. Arb.
Scott Wilson Kirkpatrick & Partners (Hong Kong), Hong Kong (formerly Mass Rapid Transit Corporation, Singapore)
J. N. Shirlaw B.Sc., C.Eng., M.I.C.E., M.H.K.I.E., F.G.S.
Mass Rapid Transit Corporation, Singapore

SYNOPSIS

The building of the Singapore Mass Rapid Transit Railway, which began in 1983, has been carried out in four phases : I, IA, 2A and 2B. It was originally planned to build these phases in sequence, but several accelerations in the planned programme have resulted in all four being under construction simultaneously. At the time of writing the 41 stations of the four phases are at various stages of construction, with the Phase 1 stations being prepared for opening within three months and the Phase 2A/B stations more than 50% structurally complete. An additional phase, 2C, with one station is now being planned bringing the total number of stations to 42.

Fifteen of the stations are underground and thirteen of them are linked by bored tunnels, as shown in Figure 1. Between these underground stations are 10 route kilometres of bored tunnel. This length of route required about 22 linear kilometres of bored tunnelling, typically twin running tunnels of between 5.2 and 5.4m internal diameter.

About 6 kilometres, or 25%, of the bored tunnelling was through the soft clays and sands of the Kallang Formation. The recent clay deposits, laid down in marine or estuarine conditions, are typically normally consolidated to lightly overconsolidated with shear strengths varying from under 10kPa near the ground surface to 70kPa at 40m depth. Greater detail on the origins and engineering properties of the clays are given in Tan and Lee[1]; Tan[2]; and Buttling, James and Shirlaw[3]. Interbedded with the soft clays are stiffer clays and sand lenses of fluvial origin.

As described in Shirlaw and Doran[4], many of the individual tunnel drives encountered quite variable ground conditions, from sandstones with an unconfined compressive strength of 150MPa to clays with an undrained shear strength of only 40kPa or loose sands. Most of the tunelling was therefore carried out using open-face Greathead type shields, with the addition of compressed air

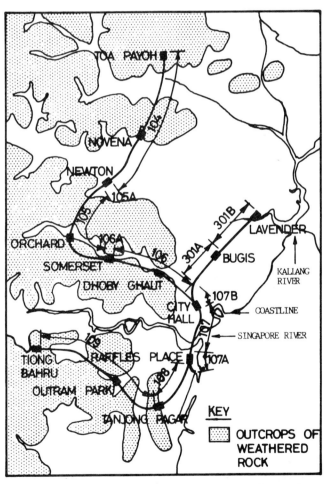

Figure 1 A map of the bored tunnel sections of the Singapore MRT.

in unstable ground. As the water table was typically 1 to 2m below ground level, all the soft clays and sands of the Kallang formation were potentially unstable. In addition to compressed air, use was made of jet-grouting, chemical grouting and lime treatment to improve the characteristics of the ground. Since each of these methods of ground improvement had quite distinct uses, specific applications will be described in detail below under the three broad categories. Chemical grouting will be further sub-divided between long gel time and short gel time grouting.

JET GROUTING

The jet grouting method uses very high pressure (20 to 30MPa) jets of cement grout to break up, mix with, or replace the ground. The aim is to form columns of pure grout, or of a grout-ground mixture, which are significantly stronger than the untreated ground. The technique deliberately breaks up the ground, unlike more traditional grouting methods which ideally try to permeate the soil without disturbing it. Consequently, jet grouting is applicable in virtually all soil types, from soft clays and silts to coarse sands and fine gravels.

In Singapore, where the normally consolidated soft clays of marine and estuarine origin pose many of the most interesting geotechnical problems, the use of jet grouting provided obvious benefits. It was used on most of the major tunnelling contracts for the MRT, as shown in Table 1 of Shirlaw and Doran. Jet-grouting tends to be used as a single generic term, although it covers a suite of methods. The Japanese originators use a variety of names such as CCP, JSG, CJG, JG and SSS-man to categorise the various methods (Miki[5]). On the MRT it was found more convenient to separate the methods mainly by the number of coaxial tubes used for grouting.

In single tube grouting only a jet of cement grout is used. The radius of action of the jet is limited, and the resulting pile is normally about 0.5m in diameter.

In double tube grouting the jet of cement grout is sheathed in compressed air, greatly improving its penetrating power (Shibazaki and Ohta[6]).

In triple tube grouting three coaxial tubes carry cement grout, air and water. There appear to be two fundamental philosophies in triple tube grouting. One is to use high pressure water to precut the ground, and to use low pressure grout to fill the resulting void. The second is to use low pressure water to do some precutting, although the main cutting is done by the high pressure grout. In this latter method the main purpose of the water is to dilute the sludge flowing back up the annulus.

All three basic methods, and both forms of triple tube grouting were used on the MRT. Some examples of their application are given below, separated according to the MRT contracts on which they were used.

C108 - Grouting for building protection

The largest single section of jet grouting on the MRT, possibly the largest single application of jet grouting ever carried out anywhere, was along Robinson Road in the centre of the Singapore Central Business District. Because of the presence of a large number of multi-storey buildings on either side of the tunnels, it was decided to form a 1.5m jet grouted annulus around the tunnels, as shown in Figure 2. The tunnels would be driven within the annulus using open face shields with compressed air. The lengths of tunnel treated were 560m (eastbound) and 400m (westbound). To achieve the 1.5m annulus around the tunnels over the required length involved the formation of a total of 4700 individual piles, on a 1.3m grid (Berry et al[7]).

Two different specialist sub-contractors undertook the work, each using both double and triple tube methods. Both high and low water pressure systems were used on C108, as shown in Figure 3.

Because Robinson Road is a very busy road, within which only limited possession was available, the restricted works area and the need to collect jet-grouting spoil meant that most of the grouting had to be done from inclined holes (Fig. 4). The contractors advised that triple tube methods were inadvisable at inclinations to the vertical over 10°, due to a lack of robustness in the rods and problems in coupling extensions. As the work proceeded it became apparent that large surface movements were occurring. The

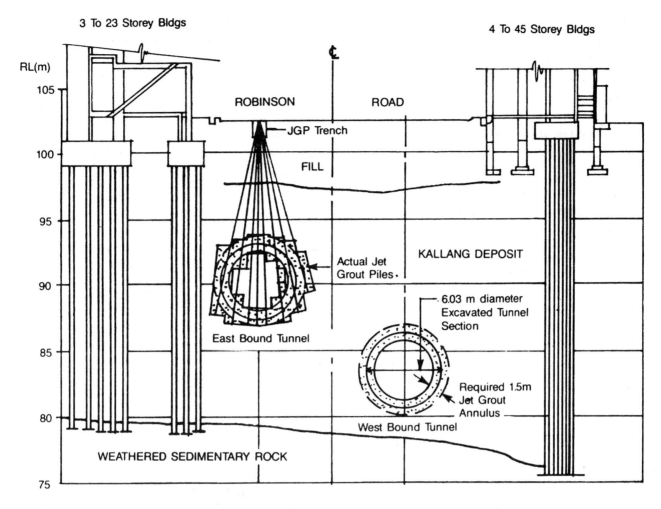

Figure 2 A cross-section showing the jet-grouting along Robinson Road on C108.

maximum heave recorded was 550mm. The heave caused over £300,000 worth of damage to utilities alone. In addition, there was damage to road pavements, footpaths and non-structural building fascias, although no adverse effect was recorded on building structures.

Because of the concern about surface heave, trials were carried out to study how sensitive

SANSHIN L&M	SANSHIN L&M	BACHY SOLETANCHE
(Double Tube) Rods ⌀ 73 Grout (hp) or water (precutting) Air Jetting facility Drill Bit ⌀ 150-300	(Triple Tube) Cutting wings ⌀ 150 Water (lp) Grout (hp) Air Rods ⌀ 73 Jetting facility Drill Bit ⌀ 150-300	(a) Double Tube (b) Triple Tube Rods ⌀ 90 Grout (hp) Grout (hp) Water (hp) Air Air Jetting facility Drill Bit φ 150-300

Typical pile diameter 0.8-2m
Speed: 5-10rpm, 11-22min/m
 	
          Pressure   Flow
Grout 20Mpa   60 l/min
Air   .6-.7Mpa   1-3 m³/min
Grout mix w/c = 1
	Typical Pile diameter 0.8-2m
	Speed: 5-10rpm, 11-16min/M
	
	          Pressure Flow
	Grout 20Mpa 60 l/min
	Water 1-2Mpa 30-40 l/min
	Air .6-.7Mpa 1-3 m³/min
	Grout mix w/c = 1
		Typical pile diameter 1.5-2m
		Speed: 5-10rpm. 20-25min/m
		
		          Pressure Flow
		Grout (a) 20Mpa 70 l/min
		       (b) .5-2Mpa 70 l/min
		Water (b) 20-30Mpa 65 l/min
		Grout mix w/c = 1

Figure 3 Nozzle arrangements and pressures used on C108.

the heave was to a variety of factors. These factors included:-

a) Hole diameter

b) Drill bit configuration

c) Use of double or triple tubes

d) Rates of monitor withdrawal and rotation

e) Inclination angles of the holes

f) Sequence and spacing of each hole

g) Relief holes

h) Sludge flow and density monitoring

i) Stage treatment of each hole

j) Precutting with a water jet prior to jet grouting

k) Pretreatment of surface fill layer

l) Use of casings

m) Modifications to the mix design

From the trials it was concluded that the most important factor in controlling heave was to ensure that the sludge could flow freely up to the surface without the hole choking off. A blocked annulus would quickly lead to cavity expansion in the soft clays under the high grout pressures used. The triple-tube method was clearly superior to the double-tube in this respect, as the water-jet helped cut and dilute the clay, making a less viscous and more uniform slurry. Figure 4 compares the heave recorded over near-vertical triple-tube jet grouting and angled double-tube grouting. Irrespective of the method, a careful watch had to be kept on the volume of sludge returning up the hole. Any signs of a reduction in flow required quick action.

Because of the nature of the work at C108, with the need to grout inclined holes due to the restricted available work space, only limited use could be made of the information gained from the trials.

The C108 tunnels, with compressed air for additional support, were driven through the treated soft clays with few problems. The rate of advance was significantly better on these

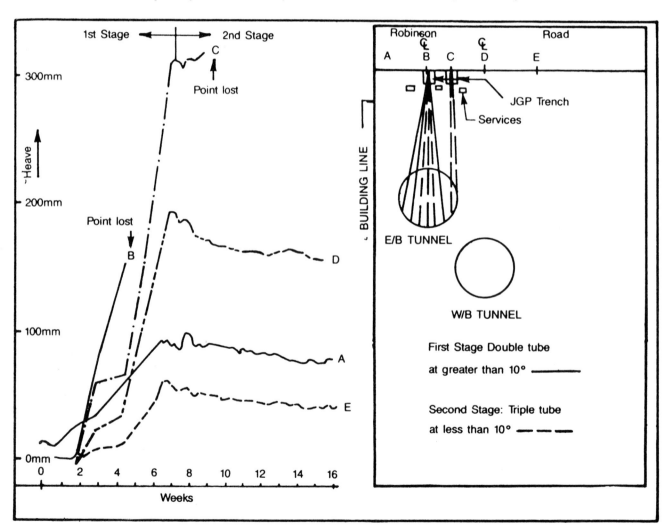

Figure 4   Results of heave trials with double and triple tube monitors.

tunnels compared with tunnels through untreated marine clay. The grouted columns broke up into a granular material which was easy to handle and assisted in the mucking of the very sticky untreated clay. The settlement over the tunnels, at 30 to 60mm, was generally somewhat less than the 30 to 120mm measured over untreated tunnels in marine clay. Two adverse aspects were the heat generated by the grouting and the release of ammonia from the face. Ground temperatures of 45°C were measured, compared with normal values of about 30°C. The cooling system had to be upgraded to provide a reasonable working environment in the tunnel. The grouting, and particularly the high pH of the cement grout, was thought to convert ammonium salts present in the marine clay into ammonia gas in aqueous solution. When in contact with the air, upon excavation of the tunnel, the ammonia gas in solution was released as free ammonia (G.C.G.[8]). The ammonia required a further upgrading of the tunnel ventilation system.

On C108, although the jet-grouting itself should have been sufficient to stabilize the ground, the tunnels were driven with compressed air, for two reasons:-

a) The very sensitive nature of the area, right in the heart of the commercial and banking centre of Singapore, meant that all risks had to be eliminated. The compressed air was used in part to guard against any unexpected gaps in the treatment, since full annular jet grouting had not been used on this scale before and neither its successfulness nor the effects of any deficiencies, were predictable.

b) At the junction of Robinson Road and various intersecting streets, the concentration of utilities was so high that treatment had to be discontinued for as much as 10m. These major untreated gaps could not have been safely tunnelled without the compressed air.

C106 - Treatment to allow free air tunnelling

On Contract 106, between Dhoby Ghaut and City Hall Stations, the ground investigation showed that the tunnels would encounter two large valleys of soft soils in drives that were mainly in stiff, competent strata. The area was much

less sensitive than the Robinson Road area, with playing fields and open, grassed areas over the tunnels. On this contract it was therefore acceptable to drive the tunnels in free air after treating the soils in the valleys using jet grouting. The treatment of the first of these valleys, some 90m long, has been described by Tornaghi and Cippo[9].

A second valley was treated in a similar fashion. The two tunnels were at different levels through this second valley, so that while treatment for the S/B tunnel was only 86m long and from axis up, the treatment for the N/B tunnel was 161m long, and in places the full section of the tunnel had to be treated. Fig. 5 shows a section through the N/B treatment.

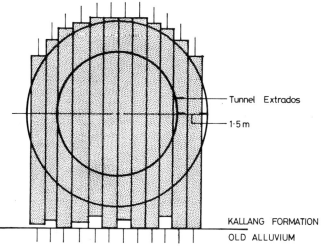

Figure 5   Section showing treatment through soft valley on C106.

Grouting in both areas was carried out using a single tube system, mainly with vertical holes. At the first valley, as reported by Tornaghi and Cippo, there was no significant change in ground surface level. However the treatment coincided with excavation of the nearby Dhoby Ghaut Station. Settlement related to station construction was of the order of 300 to 400mm, and it seems that the treatment did cause heave, but that this was controlled to compensate the settlement resulting from the station excavation. At the second valley there was generally little need to control heave, as a playing field was over much of the treated area. Ground heave of up to 1600mm was recorded. Where the treatment was under a road, heave was controlled to a large extent by altering the sequence of working. Heave of up to 230mm was, however, still recorded on the road kerb, and a small section of cariageway showed signs of distress. Nevertheless, the contractor on this section did appear to achieve a degree of control over the heave by varying the rate of withdrawal and the grouting pressure, and without the sophisticated triple-tube method found necessary on C108. The S/B tunnel was driven first, using a Grosvenor shield. In the first treated valley a discontinuity in the treatment resulted in an inflow of soft organic clays into the tunnel and a cavity at the surface. The discontinuity appeared to be related to the problem of achieving uniform treatment under utilities which prevented drilling at a certain location. Although angled holes were drilled to compensate, the resulting treatment was not as consistent as that produced by vertical drilling.

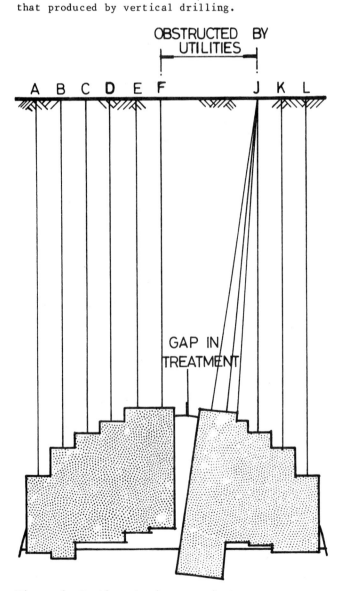

Figure 6   Section showing gaps in treatment on C106.

The N/B tunnel was driven with a similar Grosvenor shield, but with the addition of hydraulically controlled breasting plates capable of providing full support to the face above axis level. One aspect of particular concern was the existence of gaps in the treatment, as shown in Fig. 6, again caused by the presence of utilities disrupting the ideal drilling pattern. Two such gaps were known to exist, one estimated at 0.5m wide, and the other 1m wide. These gaps were overcome by :-

a) Stopping the drive short of the gaps, drilling ahead and injection grouting using cement grout.

b) Driving through the gaps with the breasting plates to control the ground.

The 0.5m gap caused no problems, primarily because the clay was much stiffer than normal marine clay. This was thought to be due to the effects of heat and chemical interaction with the adjacent jet grouted columns, causing a significant increase in shear strength of the clay. Similar effects were not noted at the first valley, but this was probably due to the organic nature of the clay. It is known that lime or cement stabilization are much less effective in organic than in inorganic clays (Broms [10]). The one metre gap was noticeably softer, showing that the indirect effects of the jet-grouting had only a limited radius. However, with the use of the breasting plates no adverse problems were encountered even in the second gap.

C301 - Treatment in localised areas

The use of jet-grouting for such extensive treatment was not repeated on the project. Other phase 1 contracts involving tunnelling in soft marine clay were in much less built-up areas, and for the later Phase 2A tunnelling EPBS machines were employed (Elias & Mizuno [11]). Jet grouting was still widely used, but for much smaller sections. Typical applications included :-

a) Treatment of a few metres for breakouts from shafts and for connection at station end walls.

b) Treatment of sumps and cross-passages, so that these could be formed in free-air.

c) Treatment of gaps left in a diaphragm wall due to the presence of utilities (for

cut-and-cover tunnel construction on C301B).
d) Treatment to ease the passage of earth
   pressure balance shields under piled bridge
   abutments.

All of these applications were used on C301, and
some of them will now be described in greater
detail to demonstrate the application of some of
the lessons learned from the earlier treatment.

Treatment under the Victoria Bridge
The drives from Lavender to Bugis Stations were
carried out using earth pressure balance shields,
as described in Elias and Mizuno. About 50m from
the shaft at the west end of Lavender Station the
shields had to pass under the Sungei Kallang
drainage canal, and the Victoria Bridge over the
canal. The bridge, built in 1914, had abutments
founded on bakau piles. These timber piles,
still commonly used in Singapore and Malaysia,
are typically 50mm -75mm in diameter and are
driven in one or more 2.4m lengths, in large
numbers at close centres.

During the assessment of the use of earth
pressure balance shields on this contract,
concern was expressed at the ability of the
shields to cope with a dense mass of small
diameter timber piles. There was some evidence
from Japan that using carefully controlled
advance, so that the timber was cut rather than
displaced by the shield, the problem could be
overcome. However, as an additional measure it
was proposed to form a jet-grouted wall on either
side of the lines of bakau piles. This was

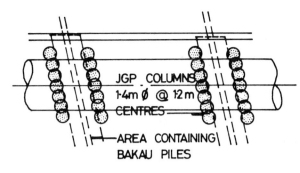

PLAN

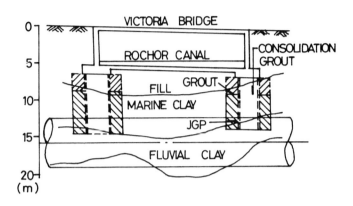

SECTION

Figure 7 Plan and section of jet-grouting under
Victoria Bridge on C301.

designed to fix the bakau piles in position and
make it easier for the EPB machines to cut
through them (Fig. 7).

The bridge had a single, fairly flat, arch and
heave on the scale of that in Robinson Road would
have been unacceptable. Very careful
consideration was therefore given as to how to

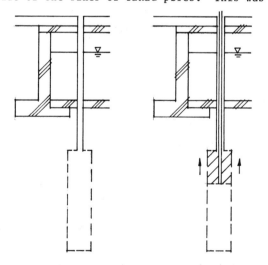

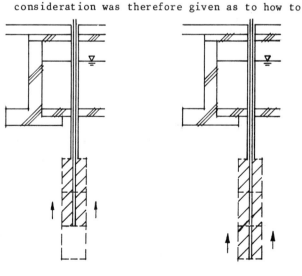

PRELIMINARY – CASE TO TOP
            TREATMENT ZONE

STAGE 1 – DRILL 2m BELOW
          CASING & JET
          GROUT

STAGE 2 – DRILL 4m BELOW
          CASING & JET
          GROUT

STAGE 3 – DRILL 6m BELOW
          CASING & JET
          GROUT

Figure 8 Jet-grouting in downward stages, as used under Victoria Bridge.

avoid any chance of movement. It was proposed by the contractor to carry out the treatment using triple tube methods, with the treatment carried out in downward stages (Fig. 8).

In this way the length of the unsupported borehole was kept at a maximum of 2m, minimising the chance of necking of the annulus around the rods.

In practice this method of treatment proved extremely effective in preventing heave, in fact, a very small settlement was recorded on the bridge abutments.

Cross-passage treatment

A cross-passage had to be provided between the eastbound and westbound tunnels as shown in Fig. 9. Borehole information suggested that it

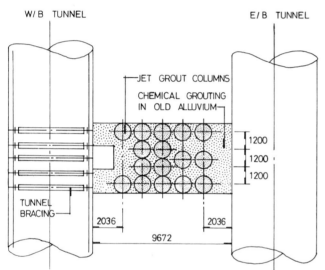

Figure 9   Plan showing the grouting for the C301 cross-passage.

had to be formed in stiff fluvial clays of the Kallang Formation and in the weakly cemented sands of the Old Alluvium. These materials, both dense and of relatively low permeability, were not ideal for treatment by either jet grouting or injection grouting. It was therefore decided to drive the tunnels and then inspect the materials in situ to judge whether the cross-passage could be driven safely in free air. When the segment was taken out it was found that marine clay, with a measured shear strength of 30 to 40kPa, existed below the stiffer fluvial clay. The Old Alluvium, although stable on initial excavation, turned into a slurry overnight, possibly due to the high pore-pressures generated during EPB

tunnelling (Shirlaw & Copsey[12]). Neither material was therefore suitable for free-air tunnelling at a depth of 18m below ground level, and 16.5m below the water table.

The design of the treatment had to take into account two particular considerations. The first was to avoid putting undue pressure on the segmentally lined tunnels. The second was how to treat the Old Alluvium. The SPT 'N' values, typically in the range of 50 to 100, meant that the effective radius of jet-grouting would be severely limited. With a permeability in the range of 10^{-6} to 10^{-9} m/sec only the most open lenses could be treated using chemical grout. A combination treatment was therefore applied, the marine clay being treated by jet grouting, and the Old Alluvium with both jet grouting and a silicate/reagent grout (Fig. 10). To avoid undue pressure on the lining the jet-grout holes were cased to the top of the treated zone. Triple tube grouting was carried out in a single upward stage. Because of the limited thickness of marine clay, this was considered acceptable in this instance. The pattern of the columns was made slightly discontinuous for the side walls.

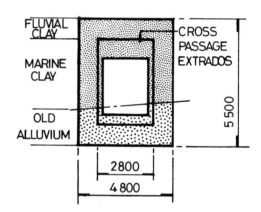

KEY
▓ JET GROUTING
▒ CHEMICAL GROUTING

Figure 10 Section through the grouting carried out for the C301 cross-passage.

The hand-mining of the cross-passage, while it had to be done with extreme care, was successfully completed. The stiff fluvial layer which had been expected in the face, in fact turned out to be in the crown for much of the drive, and greatly assisted in maintaining heading stability.

Treatment for gaps in diaphragm wall
Because of the existence of utilities the
diaphragm walls for the cut-and-cover tunnels
running eastwards from Lavender Station could not
be constructed at certain locations. The
contractor proposed to seal off these gaps with
four lines of jet-grouting, as shown in
Figure 11.

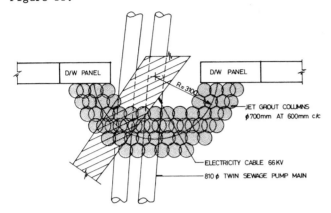

Figure 11 Plan of treatment for gaps in diaphragm
wall, C301.

Since the grouting was taking place below
utilities, particularly high voltage cables, the
ground movements needed to be controlled,
although the situation was less sensitive than
the Victoria Bridge and cross-passage treatments
described above. The particular sub-contractor
proposed for this job did not have triple-tube
monitors immediately available, and instead
proposed to carry out precutting with a
single-tube monitor. The method proposed was to
drill while jetting with water only. This was
designed to precut the soil. After reaching the
design depth the jetting action was changed from
water to cement grout in standard single-tube
monitor operation. Generally this method did
keep ground movements to under 50mm heave, but
localised heaves of up to 200mm were recorded.

Break-out Treatment
A block of treatment was carried out adjacent to
the sheetpiled shafts for the break-out of the
EPB machines, as shown in Fig. 12. Excavation
and strutting had started before the grouting,
but was stopped after excavating 5m. The
grouting, using double tube methods, caused a
100mm inward deflection of the sheet piles and
distress in the struts, before triple tube
methods were adopted.

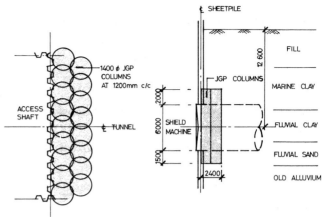

Figure 12 Plan of treatment for breakout from
Lavender Shaft, C301.

Summary of jet-grouting
It was clear from the MRT experience with
jet-grouting that significant ground heaves, or
lateral underground movements, can occur in soft
clays. Methods for overcoming these surface
heave were developed which controlled them to
varying degrees.

CHEMICAL GROUTING
It had been anticipated that jet-grouting would
be the major method of soil treatment on the MRT
due to its applicability to soft clays. However,
it was found on Phase I that jet-grouting could
cause detrimental surface effects, and also that
Singapore marine clay could readily be tunnelled
with little surface settlement using only
compressed air and shields (Shirlaw and Doran[4]).
Therefore the use of jet grouting tended to
become much more localised and selective, as
described above.
While adequate compressed air can provide a
stable face in soft clays, the effect on sands
may not be so beneficial. This depends largely
on the nature of the sand. Well graded sands,
particularly if they have a fines content of over
20%, tend to be less of a problem than uniform,
clean sands. A uniform, clean sand has no
natural cohesion, and when dry will tend to run
back to its angle of repose. When subjected to a
hydraulic gradient the sand will simply flow.
In uniform sands it can be impossible to find a
suitable compressed air pressure to maintain a
stable face. If the compressed air is set to
balance the hydrostatic pressure at the base of

the layer then the top is dried out by the air, and the dry sand runs. If the pressure is set near the top of the layer, then the water flows at the bottom, bringing in the sand with it.

C104 - Treatment of uniform sand

It was found, from experience on MRT contract 104, that once the depth of sand in the face exceeded about 3m, the problems of face stability became sufficiently great to warrant stopping the drive and grouting the sand. The log and grading curve of the sand at a point where the face had to be stopped are shown in Fig. 13, and the air loss at this stage was about $64m^3$/min.

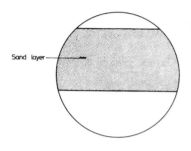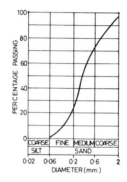

Figure 13 Face log and grading curve at a point on C104 where the drive was stopped and the sand treated.

Grouting on C104 was carried out using two methods. The first involved injection of 7% by volume of LW grout, the second 30% by volume of a silicate reagent grout. The detailed composition of the two grouts is shown in Table 1. Both grouts had short gel times, the LW 45 to 60 seconds, the chemical grout 5 to 20 seconds. The injection principle was the same for the two grouts. Each grout was mixed as two separate solutions, A and B. The two solutions were pumped down coaxial rods, mixing at the base and then being injected into the ground. This use of fast setting grouts, common in Japan, has the advantage of limiting the spread of the grout, particularly in layered soils (Karol[13]). Disadvantages may include a reduction in the ability of the grout to permeate fine sands, because of the high mean viscosity. Another minor disadvantage recorded on C104 was a tendency to produce ground heave. Although not of the same order as the heave over the jet grouting referred to above, an upward movement of

up to 50mm was still recorded. Once the grouting, and localised regrouting in low pressure areas, was complete then the tunnel drive restarted. No problems were experienced in the treated sands, which were fully stabilized by the injection.

LW Grout

	Solution A		Solution B	
Sodium Silicate	250 l	Cement	250kg
Water	250 l	Water	436 l
	-----		----	
Total	500 l		500 l	
	-----		-----	

Chemical Grout

	Solution A		Solution B	
Sodium Silicate	250 l	Chemical Hardener	50kg
Water	250 l	Water	500 l
	-----		----	
Total	500 l		500 l	

TABLE 1 - GROUT COMPOSITIONS USED ON C104

C107A - Chemical injection to allow free air tunnelling

On C107A two 170m long tunnels had to be driven to connect Raffles Place Station with future cut-and-cover tunnels under the Telok Ayer Basin (Shirlaw, Doran and Benjamin[14]). The tunnels were driven using the New Austrian Tunnelling Method from a shaft near the sea towards the station. The majority of both tunnels had a full face of S3, the Singapore 'Boulder Bed'. This material consists of hard sandstone boulders in a very stiff clay matrix, and is suitable for free air tunnelling. However, for the first 60m of the upper, northbound drive, a bed of sand and corals occurred, tapering from axis to crown level (Fig. 14). The coral, in large masses, was highly permeable. A laboratory permeameter test on a sample obtained from a piece of coral

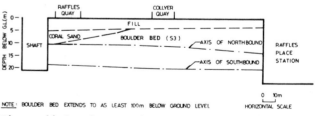

Figure 14 Section showing the coral sand requiring treatment on C107A.

48

recovered from the shaft gave a value of 2×10^{-4} m/sec.

The N/B tunnel had to be driven under Raffles Quay, a major, five-lane road feeding the Central Business District. It was therefore essential to ensure that the coral sand was fully stabilised before starting tunnelling. For such a short stretch of sand the use of compressed air was uneconomical. In any case the high permeability of the deposit would have led to unacceptable air losses unless the ground was pregrouted. It was therefore preferable to grout the coral sand in such a way that it could be tunnelled in free air.

The presence of the large coral 'boulders' was thought to preclude the use of jet grouting. The coral was strong enough to resist erosion by the jets, which could have been reflected. The need to grout up the voids within the coral itself, to prevent excessive water-make and resulting settlement, also precluded the use of the fast-setting chemical grouts of the type used on C104. It was felt that the fast-setting grouts would not achieve significant penetration into the coral. The contractor therefore proposed the use of tubes-a-manchette (Ischy[15]) for the injection of two phases of grout, first a cement-bentonite (C/B) then a silicate reagent. Because of the coarseness of the sand (Fig. 15) and the critical nature of the tunnelling, a high strength silicate/reagent grout with a 40 minute gel time was used. The unconfined compressive strength of the grout when set into a fine sand

was 3MPa. The grout mixes are given in Table 2. Initial design quantities were 10% C/B and 25% chemical grout, although in practice rather less C/B was used, due to pressure refusal, and rather more chemical, during regrouting.

The tubes were drilled in at 1.2m spacings across the tunnel as shown in Fig. 16. Rows of tubes were placed 1.0m apart along the tunnel route, until the required cover of S3 over the crown was achieved. A small settlement was recorded during the drilling, but there was virtually no further ground movement during grouting.

Testing of the efficacy of the grouting was carried out by coring, measurement of in situ permeability and by inspection from the shaft; then the tunnel was driven. The grouted coral sand was found to be generally stable and dry. Some seepage occurred, particularly at the sand/S3 interface, but this was relatively minor. It was noticeable that the resulting grouted mass did not display such high strengths as the laboratory unconfined compressive strength quoted above. Reasons for this difference could include :-

a) The very coarse nature of the sand grouted. This has a significant effect on the UCS of the resulting grout/soil combination (Shirlaw[16]).

b) Dilution of the grout by intermixing with the groundwater at the grout/groundwater interface (Mouxaux[17]).

c) In laboratory samples the sample is usually 'double grouted'.

d) The effect of slow water seepage through the grouted soil mass (Shirlaw[16]).

The grouted sand was stable in the NATM excavation. However, the observation of significant strength reduction confirmed the need to use the high strength silicate grout in this

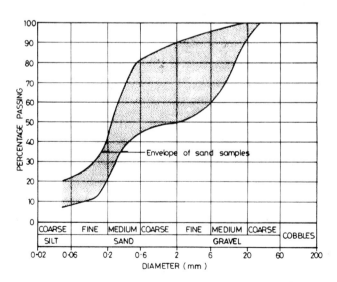

Figure 15 Grading envelope of sand treated on C107A.

Cement Bentonite Grout		Chemical Grout	
Cement	300kg	Sodium Silicate	540 1
Bentonite	54kg	Hardener	63 1
		(Rhone Poulenc	
		D-600-c)	
Water	Balance	Water	397 1
	-------		----
Total	100 1		1000 1
	-----		-----

TABLE 2 - GROUT COMPOSITIONS USED ON C107A

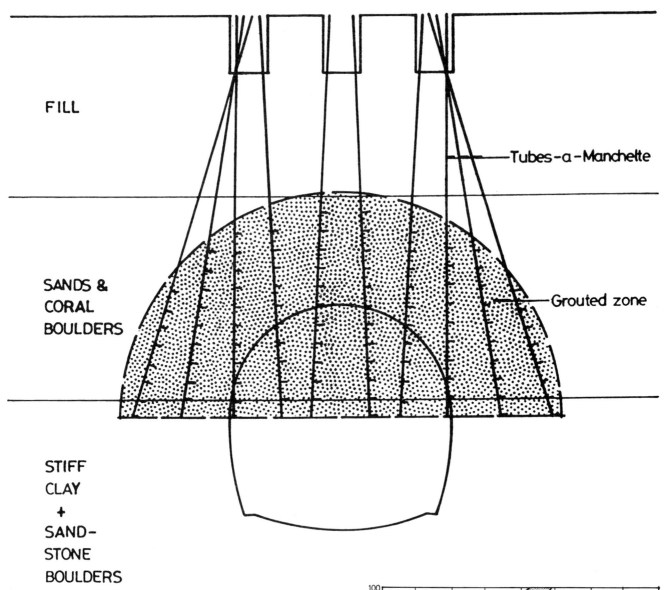

FILL

SANDS &
CORAL
BOULDERS

STIFF
CLAY
+
SAND-
STONE
BOULDERS

Tubes-a-Manchette

Grouted zone

Figure 16 Tube-a-manchette arrangement, C107A.

application, rather than the low viscosity
silicate grouts more commonly applied.

C107 - Chemical grouting for compressed air
       tunnelling through beach sand

On Contract 107, between Raffles Place and City
Hall Stations, the northbound, shield driven
tunnel had to pass through a buried valley
infilled with clays and sands. The predominant
feature of this valley was a thick layer of
poorly graded beach sand (Fig. 17). At one point
there was expected to be virtually a full face of
sand in the shield, which was equipped with
extendable face and hood rams but was without the

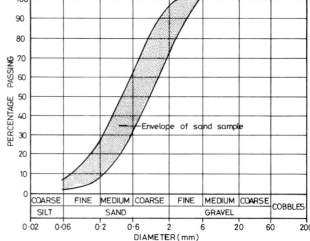

Figure 17 Grading envelope of beach sands treated
on C107.

extendable decking or face grids used on many
other MRT shields (Hulme et al[18]). There was
very little clay cover above the sand, as shown

in Fig. 18, and again air-loss was expected to be a major problem. It was therefore decided to carry out chemical grouting to the sands as shown . In addition the marine clays underlying the beach sand were treated by jet grouting. The method of chemical grouting was almost identical to that used on C104, although for programme reasons the pretreatment with cementitious LW grout was dispensed with. Jet grouting was carried out with double-tube methods. The jet grouting caused a heave of up to 800mm. Virtually no net surface movement was recorded during the chemical grouting.

Tunnelling through the treated zone was not accomplished with the ease of C104 or C107A. The sand was in an upward fining sequence, so that the material on the interface was predominantly a coarse sand with gravel. Despite the use of a compressed air pressure of 0.9bars, there was a considerable inflow of water along the interface. The sand on the interface was very poorly cemented and some material was brought in with the water. As a result of this poor stability the face was kept fully timbered, greatly slowing progress. The relatively finer sand in the crown was, however, much more effectively treated and stable.

Air losses were fairly high, but were at an acceptable level while the tunnel face was under the road surface of Connaught Drive. When the tunnel reached the open area of the Singapore Padang, air losses increased to over $100m^3$/min, and the air pressure could not be maintained, falling to 0.8bars. Despite this reduction in the air pressure the tunnel was driven, with some difficulty, the short remaining distance through the buried valley.

The grouting for the C107 valley was crucial to the successful completion of the tunnel, as without it the face stability and air loss problems would have been unacceptable. However, there was a marked contrast between the effectiveness of the chemical grouting in this case and in the cases previously described. The relatively poor result on C107 was probably due to a lack of pretreatment with cement-based grouts and the use of low viscosity silicate grouts in coarse sand.

KEY

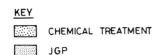

CHEMICAL TREATMENT

JGP

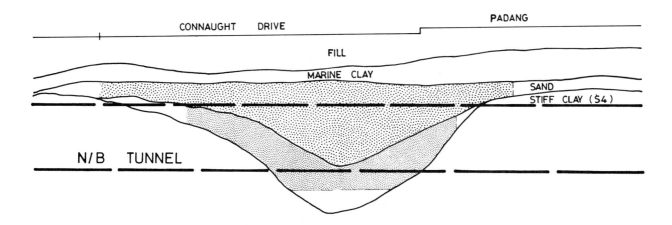

Figure 18 Section showing treatment in buried valley, C107.

Applications of chemical grouting on C301

As mentioned previously, the use of jet grouting on the Phase 2A Contract 301 was relatively limited and selective compared with the often extensive use on Phase 1. The tunnels driven from City Hall to Bugis Station using compressed air included both jet and chemical grouting, with the greater part being chemical grouting. Three major areas of sand were treated, each with a slightly different method. The varieties were :-

a) Tube-a-manchette with cement-bentonite and high strength silicate grout.

b) Co-axial tube with LW and high strength silicate grout.

c) Co-axial tube with LW and low viscosity silicate grout.

The particular choice depended on the relative importance of the location and the type of sand being treated. As all of these sections were successfully tunnelled without problems, it is not proposed to discuss them in detail here. One aspect that was of interest, however, was the ground movements recorded over the treated areas. In cases a) and b) there was minimal ground movement during the grouting, while in c), a ground heave of over 80mm was recorded. The different values recorded can be explained in terms of the soil grouted and the method of grouting. Area b) was similar to the treatment on C107, into a thick layer of beach sand. This sand layer was easy to identify and continued above the grouted zone. At a) and c), however, the treatment was applied to sand layers sandwiched between clay layers. It was difficult to identify the sand layer precisely, and some grouting was probably carried out in the overlying clay. The heave at area c) was almost certainly related to the fracturing and uplift of the soft clay when the chemical grout was forced into it. Because of the very fast gel time of the grout the fracturing resulted in permanent lenses of grout in the clay. The longer gel time grout used in a) did not have the same effect because, once the grouting pressure was removed, the still fluid grout could flow back along the fissure. The overburden pressure could thus close up the facture again, resulting in little or no permanent heave. This type of behaviour has been described previously by Caron[19].

CHEMICO-LIME PILES

Chemico-lime piles are one of two commonly used methods to carry out deep treatment of soft clays using lime. While the Scandinavian method (Broms[10]) relies on a kind of large egg-beater to mix the soil with lime, the Japanese chemico-lime pile method forms columns of a chemically treated lime in the soil. As the lime slakes it expands, and the increased horizontal stress, together with the water absorbing properties of lime, produce an accelerated consolidation. As well as the reduction in water content of the clay, and consequent increase in shear strength, the lime is chemically treated so that the column itself has significant strength.

The tunnels from Lavender to Bugis were driven using Earth Pressure Balance Shield machines from a shaft close to Lavender Station. The sheetpiled shaft was separated from the diaphragm wall of Lavender Station by approximately 7m and in the gap was marine clay with a shear strength of about 20kPa from axis level upwards, with stiffer fluvial clay below (Fig. 19). It was

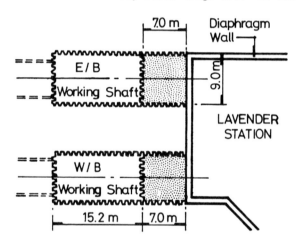

Area treated with chemico line columns @ 1·0m centres

Figure 19 Plan of chemico-lime piling, C301 backshunts.

proposed to tunnel by hand across the gap, producing backshunts for the EPBS drives and it was therefore necessary to stabilize the marine clay. Various methods to do this were considered, but the final choice was largely governed by the need to carry out soil improvement to restrict deflection of the diaphragm walls at Bugis Station during excavation. The method under consideration at Bugis was chemico-lime piling but this technique had only been used once before in Singapore, and it was therefore felt necessary to carry out a trial to determine its effectiveness. Treatment of the clays at the backshunts would both be useful in its own right, to allow them to be mined, and give the opportunity for extensive testing of the method.

The treatment has been described in detail by Kado et al[20], so only a brief summary will be given here. The piles were installed by driving a 0.4m diameter hollow mandrel into the ground. When the mandrel had reached the designated toe level, the chemico-lime was blown from a hopper into the core of the mandrel using compressed air. As the mandrel was then slowly withdrawn, the shoe at the end automatically opened, and the air pressure ensured that the chemico-lime was blown out to form a column in the soil.

For the backshunt treatment the piles were installed at 1.1m centres. Testing both from the surface and from the tunnel showed that the mean shear strength of the marine clay varied from about 60kPa at 100mm from the edge of a column to about 45kPa at the midpoint between columns. The backshunts were driven through the treated marine clay using ribs and laggings for temporary support. No instability problems were noted in the treated marine clay. One noticeable feature was the strength of the chemico-lime piles. A sample taken from the later treatment at Bugis Station was measured to have an unconfined compressive strength of 540kPa.

The piles installed near the sheetpiled cofferdam had been predrilled to prevented putting undue pressure on the walls. The treatment, without predrilling, at Bugis Station resulted in both a heave of the ground surface and a 20mm outward deflection of the diaphragm walls. It is not clear how much of the heave was due to the displacement method of installation and how much to the effects of expansion of the chemico-lime piles.

DISCUSSION

It has not been possible within the limits of this paper to describe fully either all the individual areas of ground treatment on the MRT or to give a complete technical description of the methods used. Within this review particular emphasis has been placed on the reasons for and effect of specific treatment cases, and on the surface movements associated therewith.

The study of settlements over tunnels is a subject of considerable research at the moment. The magnitude of ground movements due to pre-grouting for tunnels is, however, hardly mentioned. Data from the Singapore MRT has shown that ground movements due to grouting were frequently greater than those associated with tunnelling, and could develop very quickly. In an urban environment these effects can be of considerable importance. An understanding of the causes of the movements is therefore equally important in order to be able to minimise them when grouting is essential. It is considered that, after the fairly wide range of experience on the MRT, a basic understanding of the causes of surface movement due to grouting in Singapore soil conditions has been achieved. With this understanding it has been possible to grout successfully in very sensitive locations without unacceptable ground movements.

CONCLUSIONS

In soft clays very large (up to 1.6m) heaves have been recorded when jet grouting has been used. This heave can be controlled, if the appropriate methods are employed. The jet-grouting for the MRT was very successful in allowing safe tunnelling and no injuries were reported as a result of the few incidents of face instability. Apart from the heave, other disadvantages included high temperatures and the generation of ammonia gas.

Chemical grouting was also generally successful. The need to use high strength silicate grouts in coarse sands was confirmed. Chemical grouting using fast setting grouts could produce significant ground heave if the grouting could not be targeted accurately at the sands requiring treatment. Long gel time chemical grouts did not appear to give the same problem. Chemico-lime piles were successfully used to allow the mining of shunts in free air through marine clay.

REFERENCES

1. Tan S B and Lee K W. Engineering geology of the marine member of the Kallang Formation of Singapore. *International Symposium on Soft Clay*, Bangkok, 1977. pp75-88.

2. Tan S L. Geotechnical properties and laboratory testing of soft soils in Singapore. *1st International Geotechnical Seminar: Construction Problems in Soft Soil*, NTI, Singapore, 1983.

3. Buttling S, James J and Shirlaw J N. The shear strength of Singapore Marine Clays. *5th International Geotechnical Seminar: Case Studies in Soft Clay*, NTI, Singapore, 1987.

4. Shirlaw J N and Doran S. Ground Movements and settlements recorded during bored tunnel works on the Singapore MRT system. This conference.

5. Miki G. Soil improvement by jet grouting. *3rd International Geotechnical Seminar: Soil Improvement Methods*, NTI, Singapore, 1985. pp45-55.

6. Shibasaki M and Ohta S. A unique underpinning of soil solidification utilizing super-high pressure liquid jet. *Conference on Grouting in Geotechnical Engineering*, ASCE, New Orleans, 1982. pp680-694.

7. Berry G L, Shirlaw J N, Hayata K and Tan S H. A review of the grouting techniques utilized for bored tunnelling with emphasis on the jet grouting method. *Singapore Mass Rapid Transit Conference*, SMRT/IES, 1987. pp207-214.

8. Geotechnical Consulting Group. Ground Temperature and Ammonia Gas (In Tunnels). *Report for TSMC* reference TSM2-082 and TSM2-083, March 1986.

9. Tornaghi T and Pereli Cippo. A soil improvement by jet grouting for the solution of tunnelling problems. *Tunnelling '85* IMM, Brighton, 1985. pp265-276.

10. Broms B B. Stabilization of soft clay with lime columns. *1st International Geotechnical Seminar: Construction Problems in Soft Soils*, NTI, Singapore, 1983.

11. Elias V and Mizuno. Tunnelling with earth pressure balance shield. *5th International Geotechnical Seminar: Case Studies in Soft Clay*, NTI, Singapore, 1987.

12. Shirlaw J N and Copsey J P. Settlements over tunnels in Singapore marine clay. *5th International Geotechnical Seminar: Case Studies in Soft Clay*, NTI, Singapore, 1987.

13. Karol R H. Chemical grouting technology. *Journal of Soil Mechanics and Foundation Division*, ASCE, Vol. 94, No. SM1, January 1968. pp175-205.

14. Shirlaw J N, Doran S and Benjamin B. A case study of two tunnels driven in the Singapore 'Boulder Bed' and in grouted coral sands. *23rd Annual Conference of Engineering Group of Geological Society*, Nottingham, September 1987.

15. Ischy E and Glossop R. An introduction to alluvial grouting. *Proceedings of the Institution of Civil Engineers*, 21, 1962. pp449-74.

16. Shirlaw J N. The choice of grouts for hand-dug caisson construction. *Hong Kong Engineer*, February 1987. pp11-22.

17. Mouxaux J. Boring device for recording soil data to avoid pollution due to grouting and to predict unfavourable tunnelling conditions. *Conference on Tunnelling under difficult conditions*, Tokyo, 1978. pp257-262.

18. Hulme T W, Nicholls D, Burchell A J and Stewart D F. Tunnel construction for the Singapore MRT. *Singapore Mass Rapid Transit Conference*, SMRT/IES, 1987. pp261-275.

19. Caron C. The state of grouting in the 1980's. *Conference on Grouting in Geotechnical Engineering*, ASCE, New Orleans, 1982. pp346-358.

20. Kado Y, Shirlaw J N, Ishii T and Lim K. Chemico-lime pile soil improvement. *5th International Geotechnical Seminar: Case Studies in Soft Clay*, NTI, Singapore, 1987.

Supplementary site investigations for the Channel Tunnel, 1986–87—an overview

G. Crighton
Transmanche-Link (TML), Sutton, Surrey, United Kingdom
P. Margron
Bureau de Recherches Géologiques et Minières (BRGM), Orleans, France
W. J. Rankin
Mott, Hay & Anderson (MHA), Croydon, Surrey, United Kingdom
B. Sechet
Transmanche-Link (TML), Sutton, Surrey, United Kingdom

1.0   Synopsis

This paper summarises the development of the Cross-Channel Link over the past one hundred years and provides a brief description of the scope and cost of the present twin rail tunnel scheme. The sub-contract arrangements and details of the marine geophysical and borehole surveys are given together with an as indication of costs and ratio of productive to unproductive working in the Channel. The main findings of these marine surveys and their likely influence upon tunnel construction will be discussed.

2.0   Development of the Project

The provision of a fixed link between England and France has received repeated consideration since the mid nineteenth century, but the first major investigation into the practicality of a bored tunnel was carried out in France and England around 1881/82. This included the driving of some 4 kilometres of tunnel by Col. Beaumont, a little over half of this length in England and the remainder in France. The project was briefly resurrected in 1920 and the first serious modern study was carried out in 1958/59 to investigate the feasibility of either a bored tunnel or submerged tube crossing. Subsequent investigations took place in 1964/65 and 1972/74, with the later investigations and trials being solely aimed at providing a bored tunnel, Grange and Muirwood (1970), Muirwood and Caste (1970), Gould, Jackson and Tough (1975). As the 1972/74 investigations were underway preparations were being made for the construction of pilot tunnels, Curtis et al (1976). At Sangatte in France an existing deep shaft was re-established and a number of adits formed and work commenced on construction of a widened access adit (the Descendrie). At Shakespeare Cliff in England there were comparable activities, including the construction of a widened adit and a large marshalling chamber to provide access to the proposed tunnelling horizon and erection of the tunnel boring machine (TBM). The project was cancelled in 1974 at the point where the TBM was in position and ready to drive the service tunnel. Subsequently, during 1975, a trial length including some 250m beneath the sea was driven through a zone of instrumented ground which provided valuable performance data on ground behaviour and development of loads upon linings. During this short length of tunnelling an instantaneous rate of advance of the TBM of 12 metres per hour was achieved and a sustained rate of advance of around 8 metres per hour was demonstrated.

In 1985 the French and British Governments issued an "Invitation to Promoters" for the privately financed construction and operation of a fixed link. A considerable number of entrepreneurial groups were formed and a wide variety of options for the fixed link were put forward including; a large span bridge, an aerial tunnel, a part bridge, part submerged tube scheme and various forms of bored tunnel. A consortium of five British and five French contractors, see Table 1, known as 'The Channel Tunnel Group' (CTG) and France Manche (FM) respectively put forward their submission based on the 1974 twin bored tunnel – rail only scheme in October 1985. This scheme was announced as the preferred scheme by the French and British Governments in early 1986, and the concession was granted in March of the same year. Finally in July of 1987 the last legislative hurdle was overcome when Her Majesty the Queen gave assent to the Channel Tunnel Bill.

Channel Tunnel Group	Trance Manche
Balfour Beatty Construction Ltd	Bouygues SA
Costain Civil Engineers Ltd	Dumez SA
Tarmac Construction Ltd	Société Auxiliaire d'Entreprises SA ·
Taylor Woodrow Construction Ltd	Société Generale d'Entreprises SA
Wimpey Major Projects Ltd	Spie Batignolles SA

TABLE 1.   Contracting Groups

The scheme is to provide two 7.6m,i.d bored railway tunnels together with a central 4.8m,i.d service access tunnel beneath the Channel with terminals sited near the coast in each country. The operators will run a shuttle train service between the Terminal that will carry cars, coaches and commercial vehicles which will be loaded on specially designed roll on–roll off shuttle wagons. In addition the terminals will allow for the through passage of British and Continental main line services linking the capital cities of Europe. The terminal to terminal tunnel transit time is estimated to be 30 mins and the journey time between Paris and London will be 3 hours and hence in competition between centre to centre journey times by air. The overall costs of the scheme are given in Table 2.

£ Billion

Tunnels, lining and structure	1.4
Terminals, cooling, control system	1.2
Shuttles, locomotives	0.2
Corporate or other costs	0.6
Provision for inflation	0.5
Net financing costs	1.0
	£4.9 Billion

TABLE 2   Basic Overall Cost of the Project

Of the total cost of some £5 Billion pounds, the civil construction costs are estimated to be £2.3 Billion and the loans negotiated include a contingency sum of £1 Billion, approximately 20%. An initial three tranches of

equity have been raised including the most recent final tranche comprising some £770 million worth of shares on a public flotation. The successful flotation has secured the necessary bank loans and construction has started. Presently the driving of the service tunnel is underway from the UK coast and preparations are nearing completion for the six marshalling chambers at the bottom of the large shaft at Sangatte ready for commencement of the two service tunnel drives in March this year.

3.0   Organisation

Once approved as being the preferred scheme, CTG and FM were re-organised into two parts one owner/ concessionaire, Eurotunnel; the other constructor, TML. The structure of the organisation is shown in Figure 1. From this it can be seen that TML is split into three parts Translink Construction (TL), TML Engineering and Transmanche Construction (TMC). TML Engineering is an Anglo-French team of engineers responsible for both for co-ordinating the design of the project through their various consultants and their own 'in-house' design units and for ensuring that the construction teams carry out the works according to the various design specifications.

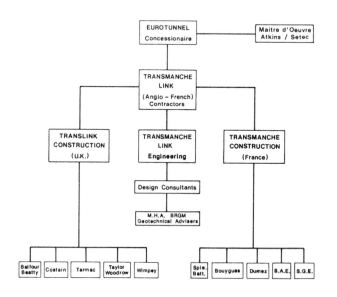

Fig.1 Organisation Chart

Transmanche Link have a target cost contract for the construction of the tunnels and a fixed lump sum contract for the construction of the Terminals. The construction is programmed to be complete by 1992 and following a further twelve month period of installation of electrical and mechanical equipment, trials and commissioning, the system is due to start operating in 1993.

4.0   Geology

The geological formations outcropping on the English and French coasts in the vicinity of the tunnel alignment were proved to be continuous across the Channel more than a century ago. The basic geology on both sides of the Channel comprises generally north-easterly inclined Cretaceous strata, distinguished by the Chalk and underlying Gault Clay which are in fact separated by a thin transition stratum known as the Glauconitic Marl (Tourtia). The proposed tunnel lies entirely within these strata on the northern limb of a large regional anticlinal feature known as the Wealden-Boulonnais dome. On the English side the strata are flat lying with a dip of usually less than 5° but towards the French coast this increases, locally up to 20°, see Figure 2. The stratigraphical sequence on either side of the Channel together with typical values of thickness for the various formation is given in Table 3.

The upper and middle sections of the Chalk comprise the characteristic white chalk whilst the lower section becomes progressively more grey in colour. This reflects an increasing proportion of clay in the Chalk; the Chalk Marl occurs at the base of the Lower Chalk. The combination of chalk and clay results in a material which is relatively strong, stable, generally free from open discontinuities and hence virtually impermeable and

has long been considered an ideal medium for tunnelling. The underlying Gault Clay, whilst also being impermeable, is weaker, exhibits greater plasticity and is likely to exhibit a greater degree of time dependent deformation as a result of stress changes due to tunnelling. The thickness of the Gault Clay decreases markedly between England, where it is around 45m thick, and France where it is commonly 15m thick. The Glauconitic Marl (Tourtia) which separates the above strata is a thin but persistent bed characterised by generally weakly cemented calcareous glauconitic sands. The boundary with the Chalk Marl is gradational and the base of this stratum is occasionally represented by a moderately strong sandstone horizon and there a characteristically abrupt contact with the underlying Gault Clay. These strata have been subjected to flexing and folding with associated faulting and fracturing, although to a lesser extent on the English side of the Channel, as can be seen in Figure 2.

The normal processes of erosion and weathering, especially during sub-aerial periods of exposure during inter glacial periods, have resulted in a degree of weakening of the chalk but generally to a limited depth, and well above the tunnel alignment. One major surface feature of significance, which was identified in mid-Channel in 1964/65 surveys, is a buried infilled valley system termed the Fosse Dangeard which reaches depths of up to 80m below sea bed. The valley system is probably related to some structural geological feature and is believed to have developed as a result of fluvial erosion in Quaternary.

Formation	Typical Thickness (m)		Brief Description
	England	France	
Middle Chalk	80–90	60–70	White marly chalk, some flints in upper part. Hard nodular Melbourn Rock (11m to 15m thick) and Plenus Marls (2m) at base of formation.
Lower Chalk	75	70	Top : Homogeneous yellow white chalk. Middle: Grey Chalk – grey marly chalk. Lower : Chalk Marl – grey chalky marl. Base : Glauconitic Marl – marly sands (2m to 3m).
Gault	45	15	Grey-blue calcareous clay/mudstone.
Lower Greensand	50	15	Alternations of weakly cemented sand and clays.

TABLE 3 Simplified Geological Succession

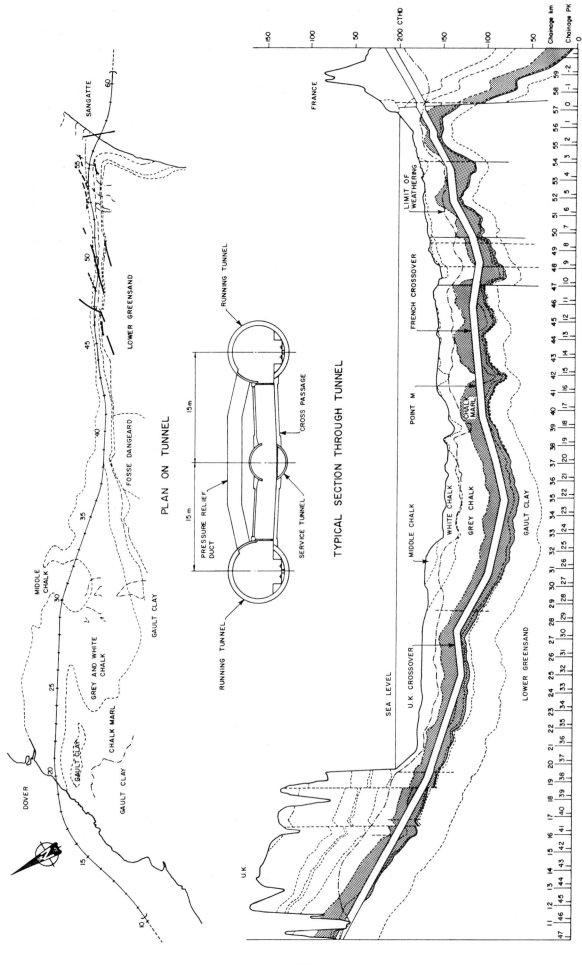

PLAN ON TUNNEL

TYPICAL SECTION THROUGH TUNNEL

Fig. 2 GEOLOGICAL PLAN AND CROSS SECTION

58

As a result of the major investigations in 1964/65 and again in 1972/74 there was a large volume of data already available on the ground conditions beneath the Channel. Changes in standards, improvements in techniques and developments in understanding during the intervening twenty five years have been considerable in the field of geotechnical engineering. Therefore in the process of evaluation of this data a considerable amount of re-working and re-appraisal has been required. In this respect the requirements for further investigations have been structured to complement and improve upon the existing information and density of data, whilst being cognisant of its variable quality. This reappraisal has permitted identification of specific requirements for the 1986/87 surveys.

5.0 Appointment of Technical Advisors

In July 1986 TML began progressively to second personnel from the parent companies, but at this early stage the technical team at TML Engineering proved insufficient to adequately cover the geological surveys needed in advance of the project and external technical advisors were appointed for the ground investigations.

The role of the technical advisors was to assist TML in defining the survey programme, preparing technical specifications, putting out calls for tenders, processing the results, supervising the investigations and issuing summary reports of stratigraphy, permeability, geotechnical properties, tectonics, etc.

For this role TML selected the Mott, Hay and Anderson/Bureau de Recherches Géologiques et Minières group which had the advantage, of being an Anglo-French association that was already well acquainted with the project as BRGM had assisted the France Manche Group and MHA the Channel Tunnel Group in the submissions to their respective governments in 1985.

The MHA Geotechnical Division is part of an independent consultancy that has been closely involved in the 1972/74 investigations and trials and for providing input into the design at that time. In addition it was recognised that MHA would be providing the design for the UK tunnels. BRGM are a semi-public organisation, based in Orleans, France, with a very large worldwide staff, providing comprehensive geological and mining services both to the French Government and international companies. In particular they play a central role in assessing and developing 'state of the art' techniques for acquisition and processing of geological data for the French Government.

6. Aims and Objectives of Marine Surveys

6.1 General

In order to optimise the alignment of the three undersea tunnels with respect to the geological hazards and constraints, the aim of the marine surveys was to be able to predict the geological structures and features, at the scale required for such a civil engineering project. Efforts were concentrated on optimising one of the most significant parameters for the project, the level of the top of the Gault Clay, but without neglecting the requirements to determine the position and extent of faults, the thickness of the Chalk Marl, the permeability of the Chalk Marl and surrounding strata, the extent of penetration of weathering with the Chalk and the location and depths of palaeo-valleys. The intention of the surveys was to take advantage of the substantial improvements, particularly in geophysical profiling and geological interpretation that have occurred since the previous surveys in 1972/73.

6.2 Marine Geophysical Surveys

The main objective of the marine geophysical surveys was to improve, update and supplement the geological and geotechnical information across the Channel particularly in areas where significant changes in alignment from previous schemes were envisaged.

The existing output from 1964/65 and 1972/74 geophysical surveys can only be used as qualitative space-time sections and as it was not previously possible to precisely correlate the various stratigraphic horizons with the 'reflectors' identified in the geophysical survey. The 1986/87 marine surveys were designed so as to permit a quantitative interpretation of the seismic survey data and an assessment of its accuracy.

6.3   Marine Boreholes

The main objectives of the marine boreholes were as follows:

(a)   To investigate directly the ground conditions at discrete points of interest identified as a result of previous studies, the foregoing geophysical survey, or in relation to key features of the scheme.

b)   To improve the knowledge of the permeability of the strata surrounding the tunnels, both in areas of uniform geology and in potentially disturbed ground.

c)   To correlate the borehole lithology with reflectors identified in the geophysical survey by means of modern geophysical well logging techniques.

d)   To determine as accurately as possible the level of the top of the Gault Clay in key areas affecting the selection of route alignment and profile.

e)   To obtain intact core samples for laboratory testing and verification of engineering properties on intact specimens as well as micropalaeontological analysis to provide stratigraphical control.

7.   Sub–Contracts for Marine Investigations

The first task of the technical advisors in 1986 was to assist TML in defining the marine survey programmes, taking into account the existing data. The programme quickly developed towards continuous geophysical cover to be correlated with 12 cored boreholes drilled down to locate the Gault Clay/Lower Greensand interface. The geophysical cover comprised 5 longitudinal profiles covering likely variations in alignments, and transverse profiles spaced at intervals of about 1000m apart on the UK side in the relatively uniform geological conditions reducing to 250m on the French side as the geological complexity increases.

The international call for tenderers for the geophysical survey led to TML selecting the British company WIMPOL LTD, which entered into contract with Translink Joint Venture (TLJV) and completed the geophysical survey in the autumn of 1986 in accordance with the technical specifications drafted by the technical advisors.

Following a similar international call for tenderers for marine boreholes TML selected the French company GEOCEAN, which entered into contract with TLJV for the completion of the first boreholes. After an unsuccessful trial using a drilling vessel equipped with dynamic compensation for rough sea conditions, self-elevating oil exploration platforms were adopted since these are unaffected by bad weather after the rig is secured to the sea bed. In order to reduce the overall completion time, drilling contractor WIMPEY LABORATORIES LTD were appointed to undertake a section of the works, using a platform supplied by LAND and MARINE a subsiduary of Costain and as such part of the main TML group. Specialist well logging and vertical seismic profiling tests within the marine boreholes were entrusted to Schlumberger, CGG and BRGM.

Despite bad weather during the winter period, the 12 deep boreholes were successfully completed in less than 90 days, and both platforms were demobilised at the end of January, 1987.

The laboratory tests on samples taken from the boreholes were entrusted to MECASOL.
The costs of the 1986/87 exploratory surveys for the marine part can be broken down as follows:

–	Geophysical Survey	£ 520,000
–	Offshore Boreholes	£5,750,000
–	Laboratory Tests	£ 100,000
–	Interpretation, Quality Control and Summary Reports	£ 900,000
	Total	£7,270,000

8.   Physical and Operational Constraints

Whilst it is a simple matter to site a borehole or delineate a geophysical survey route on a plan, it is far more difficult to proceed with the site work and navigate a geophysical survey vessel according to a specific route, or to precisely position a drilling rig or vessel in mid-Channel.

For the successful completion of these tasks it is necessary to meet the requirements of both the British and French authorities, seek compromises or arrangements with other sea users e.g. fishermen, and progress the works in adverse weather conditions such as wind, swell, fog and low temperatures. The regulations governing safety of navigation in the Channel are the responsibility of the Department of Transport on the British side and of the Secrétatiat d'Etat à la Mer on the French side. As a result of an international agreement on safety of navigation in the Channel between the United Kingdom and France, the requirements of the maritime authorities are the same on both sides of the Channel, although this does not preclude the need for completing the same procedures and formalities in the French language on one side and in the English on the other. The ´Arrété Préfectoral´ or the ´Consent´ stipulates the rules to be observed in regard to safety of navigation in the Channel.

For geophysical surveys these rules are relatively simple. The geophysical survey vessel must comply with the normal navigation requirements and may only follow a geophysical survey route in the direction of the maritime traffic. This constraint led to considerable additional sailing in order to manoeuvre in and out of the shipping lanes in the required manner.

As regards boreholes, which necessitates maintaining a self-elevating rig or a vessel equipped with dynamic compensation for rough sea conditions in a fixed position during the course of the work, the rules are considerably more stringent. It is necessary for the drilling area to be marked by means of 4 cardinal buoys and the marked area protected by 2 guard vessels having special features (the vessel should be painted red, equipped with radar and have a minimum power rating). It is also stipulated that the drilling vessel or rig may only be situated in an already marked zone. On completion of drilling, it is then necessary to await favourable weather conditions to be able to transfer the buoys first, followed by the drilling rig.

In some cases the wind and swell may facilitate transfer of the drilling rig (moved with the assistance of 3 powerful tugs) but obstruct the transfer of the buoys which is carried out using lighter service craft. Occasionally, where wind and swell may facilitate transfer of the cardinal buoys and drilling rig, fog may reduce visibility to such an extent as to compel the maritime authorities to cancel any movement of drilling

equipment. In addition to the requirements strictly associated with safety of navigation, there are a number of other constraints. For example, the interconnection between the British and French electricity supply grids (IFA 2000) comprises four cables laid on the bed of the Channel. It was necessary to ascertain that the drilling of each borehole was compatible with the submarine cables runs and to obtain approval from both the British authority (CEGB) and the French authority (EDF). A similar procedure was required by the Belgium and Spanish telecommunications authorities due to the presence of a cable link between the two countries. Additionally due to the length of the platform's self elevating legs, up to 100m, their height above sea level considerably exceeds that of the rig during towing or when the water level is low. Therefore it was necessary to adopt appropriate safety measures in conjunction with the French and British navigation authorities to enable aircraft overflying the Channel to obtain advance warning of the presence of these obstacles.

Even after obtaining official clearance in a given area, further local arrangements have to be made with other sea users such as fishermen who considered the survey areas to be potential fishing zones. In these circumstances negotiation for loss of earnings proved necessary.

Weather conditions play a major role in the quality of geophysical measurements and the survey often had to be discontinued for several days to achieve the necessary sea state. For boreholes self-elevating rigs have the advantage of ensuring all-weather operation once the rig is correctly installed and located on the sea bed. Nevertheless moving between boreholes requires relatively calm conditions and on occasions a waiting period of some 5 to 10 days was required before finding a suitable 'weather window' enabling the buoys and rig to be moved.

In the worst case, after days of stormy weather hampering operations the lull in the wind can be accompanied by the return of fog and visibility may become so restricted that the authorities are compelled to ban any movement despite the fact that the rig and guard vessels are equipped with radar. Intense cold periods were also experienced when the drilling fluid had to be mixed with fuel to prevent it freezing within the rods and hoses at the deck level.

Finally, attention should be drawn to the existence in French coastal areas of ancient feudal rules, necessitating a "waiver of flag" for non-French vessels. Although this is often no more than a formality provided no French vessel is available to carry out the work it did not prove possible to achieve permission for a British drilling rig at the end of 1986, largely due to local labour difficulties in the French ports.

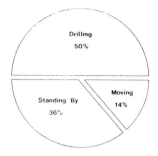

Fig. 3a Time Analysis
Jack-up Rigs

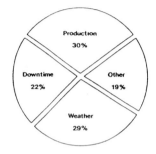

**Fig. 3b Time Analysis
Geophysical Investigation**

Figures 3(a) and 3(b) show details of the breakdown of the marine geophysical and marine borehole site activities into productive and various non-productive elements respectively.

9. Brief Assessment of Main Findings

9.1 Accuracy and Validation

Control of accuracy and validity of interpretation, both with regard to the actual data and the combination thereof and with regard to the interpolation, is necessary requirement for a satisfactory analysis of the data. This was achieved by a systematic analysis of the conditions of acquisition and of the scope of variation of each of the parameters included in the final interpretation, and by the use of geostatistical methods at all stages of interpretation. These methods, which take into account the specific accuracy of each of the data, the distance between data and the variability of each of the different zones of the project, made it possible to quantify the reliance which can be placed on the prediction of level of various geological surfaces.

9.2 Geophysical Results

The main geophysical 'reflectors' have for the first time been objectively identified within the stratigraphic series surrounding the tunnel, this includes the base of the Glauconitic Marl (Tourtia), and the top of the Lower Greensand (Sables Vert). This result, which is essential for correct geological modelling is due to the use of synthetic seismic traces which were established from the sonic and gamma-densimetric logs of the 1986/87 boreholes. The seismic events recorded on the geophysical profiles have been matched with those on the synthetic log and hence the level of individual events can be depth related to the core samples,. The high quality of correlation can be seen in Figure 4.

The appropriate seismic velocities are needed to convert the times at which the previous reflectors were identified into depths below the sea bed. These have been geographically modelled in accordance with the qualitative and quantitative results obtained from the boreholes. This result, which again is essential for detailed modelling, was possible by using multi-channel seismic profiling, which provides an accurate means of analysis of seismic velocities from the data itself. However, it should be noted that there is no continuous reflector associated with the top of the Chalk Marl and no geophysical image of the different limits which can be attributed to the weathering phenomena.

Evaluation of all the data, including the more complex geological conditions occurring on the French side of the Channel, indicates that the level of the base of the Glauconitic Marl over the route corridor can be predicted with a high level of confidence to within about $\pm$ 5 metres. The Chalk Marl has a thickness in the Channel generally not less than 25 metres and the diameter of the running tunnels will be less than 8 metres, the tunnel alignment has been correspondingly positioned some 5 metres above the base of the Chalk Marl wherever possible. The variation of $\pm$ 5m, considered in the context of a water depth of about 45 to 60 metres and a thickness of soil and rock above the proposed tunnel level of a further 45 to 70 metres (amounting to a total depth of 90 to 115 metres), implies that the order of accuracy expected is generally within about $\pm$ 5%.

The survey confirmed the position of the major infilled channel known as the Fosse Dangeard, first described by Destombes, Shephard Thorn and Redding (1975), the centre being some 500m to the south of the alignment and extending to a depth of 80m. However an associated tributary some 12 metres deep and infilled with sediment crosses the alignment in mid-Channel between Pk 18 and 19 (km39 and 38). This feature is located at a point where the Gault Clay is at a relatively high level and thus constitutes a geological 'pinch-point' where it is necessary to optimise the alignment so as to maintain adequate rock cover beneath the buried valley, and minimise penetration of the tunnels into the Gault Clay.

Weathering of chalks outside fault zones or fossil valleys is a progressive phenomenon and the borehole evidence suggests that the majority of the undersea tunnels lie within strata classified as grades I or II, to fresh slightly weathered rock, where this degree of

weathering is unlikely to have caused any significant deterioration of mechanical or hydraulic properties.

9.3   Lithostratigraphic Correlation

(i)   The Base of the Chalk Marl

Of considerable importance to the understanding of the cross-Channel geology and hence the tunnelling conditions has been the identification of two geological horizons which are likely to have engineering significance. Firstly, at the base of the Chalk Marl, on the UK side of the Channel only, there is a layer some 10 to 12 metres thick, of very clayey chalk, Zone 8 of Carter given in Bruckshaw et al (1961). This stratum is of somewhat lower strength and permeability than the upper levels of the Chalk Marl (Zones 9 and 10), which persist across the Channel. Secondly, a zone of

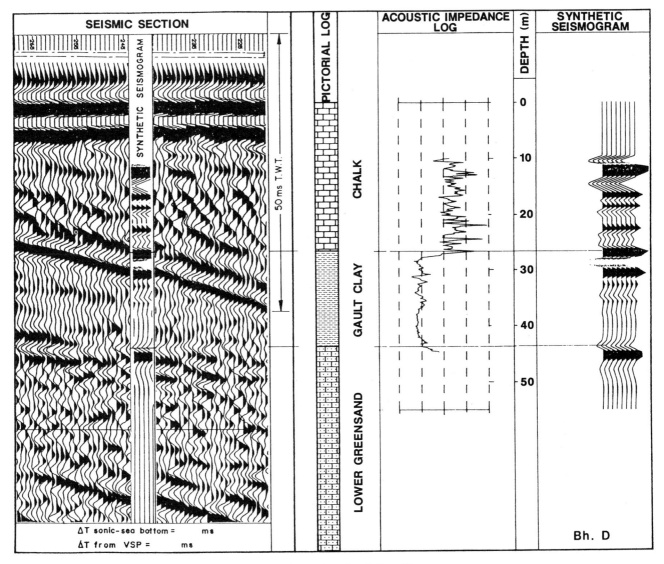

Fig. 4   Geophysical Profiles

63

FOLKESTONE

	Zone	Description	Thickness (Typical)
	9/10	Upper Chalk Marl (UCM)	17 m
Lower Cenomanian 38 m	8	Lower Chalk Marl (LCM)	10 m
	7	Glauconitic Marl (GM)	4 m
	6A		up to 7 m
Albian	5	Gault Clay (GTC)	45 m
Aptian		Lower Greensand	

SANGATTE

	Zone	Description	Thickness (Typical)
	9/10	Upper Chalk Marl "Craie Bleue" (UCM)	27 m
Lower Cenomanian 29 m	7	Tourtia (GM)	2 m
	5	Augiles du Gault(GTC)	15 m
		Aptian	

N.B.   Top of Upper Chalk Marl defined as top of Bed G, defined Robaszynski and Amedro, 1986.

Table 4

Comparison of Geological Succession between UK and France.

calcareous mudstone (Zone 6A) has been encountered and is possibly up to 7 metres thick near the proposed UK crossover location. This zone is of Lower Cenomanian Age and separates the Glauconitic Marl/Tourtia from the true Gault Clay over the UK Section. The basal element of this Zone 6A is glauconite rich and previously may have been confused with the Tourtia or the glauconitic bands in the Gault Clay. These additional geological findings have enabled a more precise framework to be developed and provided an improved basis for correlating geological conditions and observed variations in geotechnical parameters.

(ii)   The Top of the Chalk Marl(Unit G)

The geological structure between the cliffs at Dover and Sangatte has been divided and correlated in detail across the Channel, see Figure 5. A reliable stratigraphic boundary, Unit G, has been identified by Robaszynski and Amedro (1986),on the basis of micropalaeontology and this has been used to define the top of the Chalk Marl. This definition gives a thickness for the tunnelling horizon, Unit G to base of Glauconitic Marl (Tourtia) band, generally between 27m and 34m but thinning locally over the Quenoc's Anticline near the French Coast to approximately 20m, see Table 4. The proposed tunnels have been located within this strata wherever possible.

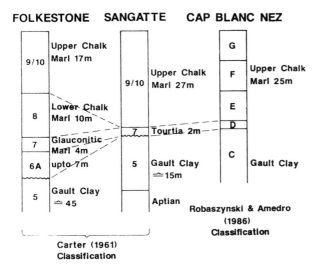

Fig.5 Simplified Cross Channel Stratigraphical Correlation

Unit G, characterised by wide marl interbedding, is both a reliable stratigraphic limit for the Chalk Marl, that avoids past confusions and dissimilarities associated with colour assessment of the chalk, and a geotechnical limit, particularly from the point of view of permeability. The detailed correlations resulted from; observations undertaken onshore in boreholes and the cliff sections; the permeability tests and micropaleontological measurements carried out during previous surveys and in the offshore boreholes, and the detailed statistical analysis of vertical variations in the physical and mechanical features of the chalks and clays.

9.4   Tectonics

The project area is located just outside and to the north of the heavily tectionised zone associated with the complex know as the Midi Fault, and the significant longitudinal fault identified by the geophysical surveys and traversing the project at around PK 7.4 constitutes the northern limit of this complex. This fault appears to be associated with a wide zone of penetrative weathering that may have resulted from horizontal displacements along the fault.

9.5   Geotechnical Results

(i)   Permeability

Unit G has proved a relatively distinct boundary, and the mean permeability of the Tourtia–Unit G interval has been successfully modelled as a result of overall geostatistical synthesis of all the available data from 1883 to 1987. From this modelling it has been concluded that the permeability calculated from the measurements carried out in boreholes are of a similar order to those deduced from dewatering tests in the various existing galleries. In addition, for a given zone, the permeability of the chalks directly above the Tourtia appears to be constant irrespective of depth and is of the order of 1 to 2.10^{-7}m/s up to PK 10 on the French side and 1 to 5.10^{-8}m/s in mid–Channel and on the UK side. The indications are that permeability, on a log scale, increases with decrease in depth to a fairly constant value of 1.10^{-5}m/s at a depth of about 10m below the sea bed, see Figure 6.

(ii)   Engineering Properties

Within the Lower Chalk both the Grey Chalk and the Chalk Marl are characterised by distinctive cyclical

65

bedding comprising clay rich layers grading to limestone bands (sponge beds), and these cycles are typically 0.5 to 2m thick. The harder sponge beds typically make up 10% of the Chalk Marl and result in significant local variations in stiffness and strength and contribute to the overall anisotropy of the Chalk Marl strata, see Figure 7.

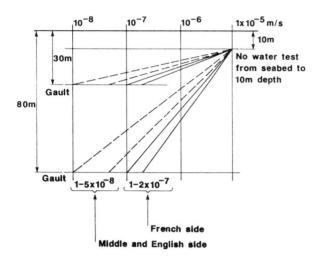

Fig. 6 **Permeability Profile**

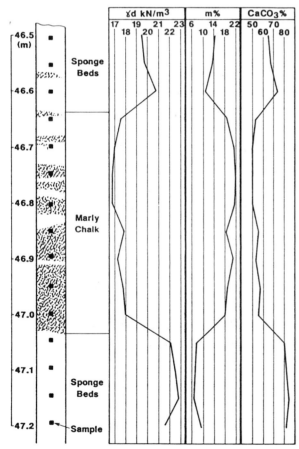

Fig. 7 **Variation in Engineering Properties of Chalk Marl**

The correlation of trends in geotechnical properties with both the lateral variations within the stratigraphical units and vertical variations between strata has provided a rational basis for evaluation of geotechnical parameters, see Figures 8(a) and 8(b). The summaries of recent and previous geotechnical data given from the various borehole comparisons includes the results of laboratory tests of variable quality, but permits the identification of geographical trends and stratigraphical variations. These results have been supplemented by further high quality in-situ dilatometer testing and specialist laboratory testing. These supplementary studies have demonstrated that the stiffness of the Chalk Marl and Gault Clay at small strains is higher than previously considered. The critical importance of high quality laboratory and in-situ testing has been re-emphasised.

The strength and deformation characteristics of the upper layers of the Chalk Marl (Zones 9 and 10) that are continuous across the Channel are similar with a value of unconfined compressive strength of around 10 MPa. It is considered that the previous inclusion of data from Zone 8 gave an erroneous impression of a significant and progressive increase in the mechanical properties of the Chalk Marl from UK to France.

10. Implications for Tunnel Construction

(i) Within the nominal 1 kilometre wide route corridor, the depth of the reference surface of the bottom of the Glauconitic Marl/Tourtia can be predicted with a high degree of confidence to within approximately ± 5 metres.

(ii) The Chalk Marl, in which over 85% of the tunnelling is expected to be located, provides an excellent tunnelling medium and the relevant engineering properties have been verified by field and laboratory testing.

(iii) Whilst geological and operational optimisation of the alignment may necessitate tunnelling outside the favoured Chalk Marl Formation, these should not normally present significant hazard, but may require modifications to the general construction procedures and/or a change of tunnel lining.

(iv) Provision to obtain advance information about adverse ground conditions will be incorporated into the tunnelling process, and contingency arrangements made to ensure that any adverse situations can be controlled and rectified where appropriate.

(v) The geotechnical database established for this study will be extended during the preliminary and permanent construction operations and information on ground conditions systematically gathered, processed and used to re-assess the design assumptions and construction procedures, so that if necessary appropriate modifications can be made. In this context appropriate instrumentation and monitoring will be installed at selected locations.

(vi) The need for site specific information has been recognised at the location of particular structures associated with the tunnels, such as cross-overs and sumps, or particular geological features such as the Fosse Dangeard infilled channel. A further detailed site investigation will be undertaken during 1988 for the cross-overs and the Fosse Dangeard. For structures such as sumps, it is considered that it will be possible to obtain adequate information sufficiently far in advance of their final design from exploratory work and observations initiated from within the service tunnel once this has reached the relevant location.

In summary, the recent geotechnical investigations and studies have not revealed any major adverse feature that had not been previously identified, but the surveys have significantly increased the level of confidence that can be attached to the overall picture of geology that has been obtained.

Fig. 8a

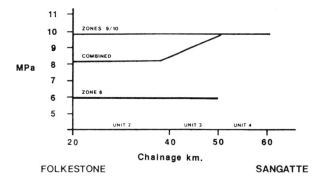

Chalk Marl
UCS Variation across Channel

Fig. 8b

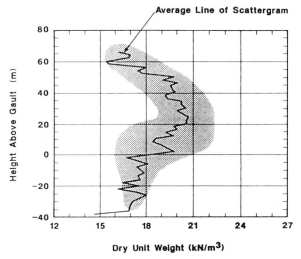

Dry Unit Weight vs. Height Above Gault

Figs. 8a and 8b   Geotechnical Properties

Acknowledgements

The authors express their gratitude to all those who participated in these surveys and they particularly appreciate the high level of Anglo-French co-operation that has been achieved.

67

REFERENCES

(1)   Bruckshaw J.M., Goguel J., Harding H.J.B. and
        Malcor R., (1961).
        The work of the Channel Tunnel Study Group
        1958–1960 Proc.
        Instn Civ. Engs. : Vol. 18 : pp 149–178, see
        Carter's contribution on Micropalaeontology.

(2)   Curtis D.J., Lake L.M., Lawton L.T. and Crook
        D.E. (1976).
        In–situ ground and lining strata for the Channel
        Tunnel Project.   Proc. of Int. Symp. Inst. of
        Mining and Metallurgy.

(3)   Destombes J.P and Shepherd–Thorn E.R., and
        Redding J.H. (1975).
        A buried valley system in the Strait of Dover.
        Phil. Trans. R. Soc. Lond. A. 279, 243–256.

(4)   Gould H.B., Jackson G.O., Tough S.G., (1975)
        The design of the Channel Tunnel
        The Structural Engineer, Journ 1 Struct E. 53
        pp 45–67 Feb, and Dec 1975.

(5)   Grange A., and Muirwood A.M. (1970).
        "The site investigations for a Channel Tunnel
        1964–65"
        Proc. Inst. of Civ. Engineers, Vol. 45 : pp 103–
        123 and disc. in Proc. Inst. of Civ. Engineers pp
        535–539, Dec 1970.

(6)   Muirwood A.M., and Casté G., (1970).
        In–situ testing for the Channel Tunnel
        In–situ investigations for Soils and Rocks.
        Proc. of British Geotech Society Conference
        held in London 13–15 May, 1962. Published 1970
        pp 109–116.

(7)   Robaszynski Fr. and Amedro F. (1986).
        The Cretaceous of the Boulonnais (France) and a
        Comparison with the Cretaceous of Kent (United
        Kingdom). Proc. Geol. Ass. 97(2) pp 171–208.

Application of NATM at Barrow-upon-Soar gypsum mine to construct two surface drifts

W. G. Deacon
British Gypsum, Ltd., Gotham, Nottinghamshire, United Kingdom
J. F. Hughes
Thyssen (G.B.), Ltd., South Kirby, Pontefract, West Yorkshire, United Kingdom

SYNOPSIS

The New Austrian Tunnelling Method (NATM) was adopted for the construction of two drifts through water bearing strata near Barrow-upon-Soar, Leicestershire.

Several methods of construction were considered at the design stage, but the final decision to use the NATM was based on the flexibility of this system to accommodate the variety of ground conditions expected.

Notwithstanding some difficulties, the combination of curtain-wall grouting from surface and NATM has led to the successful completion of the drifts and the establishment of a new underground mine for the production of gypsum.

The gypsum seam lies about 85m below the surface and is overlain by gently dipping strata comprising alluvial and glacial deposits,clays, mudstones and limestones, marl and siltstones. Within this succession lies the fissured Hydraulic Limestone Series which is heavily water bearing and under sub-artesian pressure. The other strata were expected to be impermeable.

The planning, design and execution of the works are described including construction techniques for both primary and secondary linings.

INTRODUCTION

Exploitation of this 35M tonne gypsum reserve is part of a major new investment initiative by BPB Industries plc. In making the decision, British Gypsum first conducted extensive analyses of the competitiveness of indigenous sources of gypsum as compared with imported natural and synthetic gypsums and found that the best business opportunities would be provided by a fully integrated and self-sufficient production facility at Barrow. Successive phases of this project will include construction of a 0.5M tonne per annum bagged plaster plant and a high

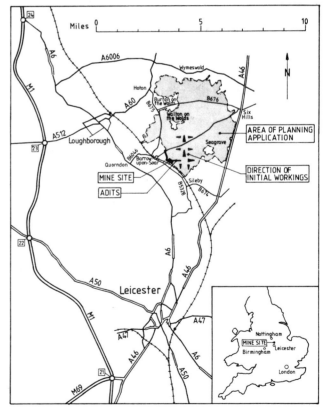

FIG 1. LOCATION PLAN SHOWING EXTENT OF PLANNING APPLICATION AND DIRECTION OF INITIAL WORKINGS.

capacity plasterboard factory.

British Gypsum first invited tenders in 1984 for both two parallel drifts and the combination of one larger drift and a vertical shaft. The contract was to be let on a design and construct basis.

Planning permission for the drivage of two 510m long, 5.5m wide by 3.6m high drifts at 1 in 6 gradient was granted in April 1986 and their completion was planned for the autumn of 1987 in order that British Gypsum could bring the mine into production by 1990. Output is planned to progressively increase from 360 000 to over 1 000 000 tonnes per annum.

At Barrow the gypsum is some 85m below surface and underlies a well known aquifer, the Lower Lias Hydraulic Limestone. This is made up of a number of separate, strong to very strong, limestone beds, each less than half a metre thick, and interbedded with weak silty mudstones over a total thickness of about 6.5m. The limestones are known to have been quarried and mined extensively for use as roofing slates.

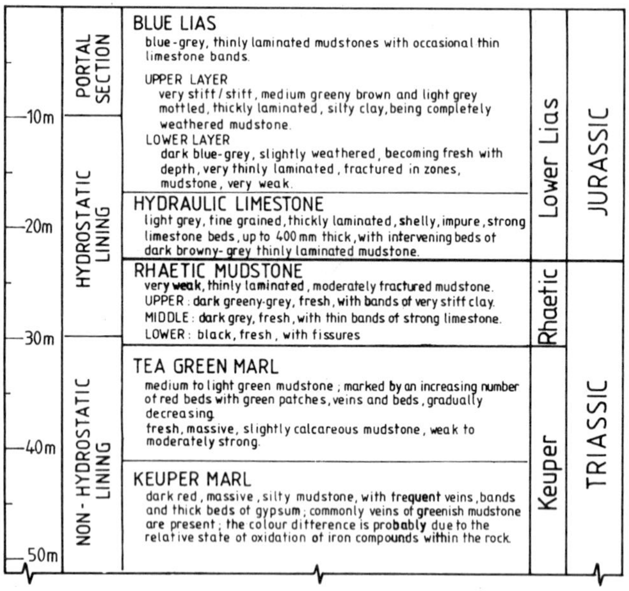

FIG 2. GEOLOGICAL SEQUENCE

Recognising the difficult conditions this geological sequence presented, British Gypsum required the following from the successful tenderer:

i   A guaranteed completion date

ii   Predictable costs with a minimum risk of expenditure overrun.

iii Permanent stability of the lining together with a high degree of water-tightness, specified in the tender as 25 l/min inflow into each drift.

iv   Disturbance and pollution of the local environment and the aquifer to be avoided.

Several methods of excavation and lining were proposed by the various tenderers, mostly based on the use of a shield and precast concrete segments, but initially all tenderers had difficulty in satisfying British Gypsum's water-tightness requirements. Additionally several methods of ground treatment were considered including freezing, dewatering and grouting, the last both by the formation of a grout curtain from surface and by cover drilling from the face.

Thyssen (GB) Ltd, however, eventually the successful tenderer, offered the use of the New Austrian Tunnelling Method in conjunction with a PVC membrane as an alternative to a segmental lining.

Thyssen felt that the alternating nature of the strata (very hard limestones and soft clays) combined with a relatively steep gradient of 1 in 6 and potentially high water inflows, made a large diameter shield drive an unusually daunting proposition. The maintenance of circularity and the back grouting of the segment rings, essential for any degree of watertightness, seemed particularly difficult, making the final inflow requirement unattainable without substantial but unassessable post-lining work. Even with hydrophylic rubber jointing the likelihood of obtaining sufficiently tight, clean joints to contain them seemed small.

Of equal importance was the form of contract. Early commitment to high expenditure in respect

of shield and segments was clearly very risky
to the Contractor in a design and construct
contract,especially if the system turned out to
have been misconceived. Furthermore a shield
and segment offered little operational flexibility, given the varied nature of the strata.

While many tunnels of the required dimensions
and larger had been driven on the Continent utilizing the NATM in similar or in as severe conditions,none had yet been attempted in Britain.
British Gypsum thus made exhaustive enquiries
on the Continent, which culminated in acceptance of the NATM solution offered by Thyssen,
who had by this time formed a joint venture
with their Austrian associate company,
Österreichisches Schacht-Und Tiefbauunternehmen
Ges m.b.H and appointed an experienced NATM
designer, Dr Gerhard Sauer of Salzburg.

Work began on site during July 1986 and was
completed by the end of 1987.

HYDROGEOLOGICAL INVESTIGATIONS

By 1982, British Gypsum had completed geological exploration of the mineral reserves.
During the drilling of the boreholes, the Lower
Lias Hydraulic Limestone Series in particular
was found to be so jointed and water bearing as
to warrant detailed hydrogeological investigation. Further boreholes were therefore
drilled and tested for this and other purposes.

A little water was encountered within the thin
bands of limestone associated with the shallow
Lower Lias Clay but substantial quantities, under sub-artesian pressure, were evident in the
Lower Lias Hydraulic Limestones indicating an
inflow potential during drivage of 50 000
m³/day. The piezometric head recorded in these
boreholes corresponded closely to that encountered in yet further boreholes drilled to
the west to investigate the unexpected and late
discovery of flooded old mine workings within
the Hydraulic Limestones.

Since the disposition of the gypsum reserves

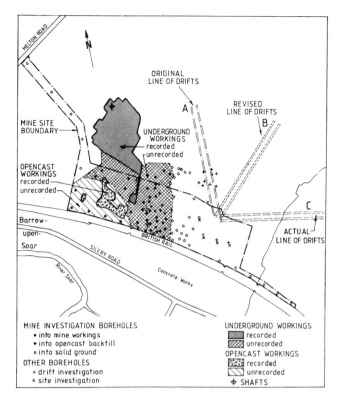

FIG 3. ADJACENT WORKINGS AND THEIR INFLUENCE ON THE LINE OF THE DRIFTS

dictated that access to the mine should ideally
be made by driving almost due northwards (line
A) into the deposit, tenders were invited in
1984 on that basis; either for one large drift
and vertical shaft or two smaller drifts, but
by this time it was becoming increasingly evident that the old flooded workings were in very
close proximity to and up dip from any access
drift so orientated. It also became evident
that, whichever their direction, drifts having
a gradient of 1 in 6 would intersect about 100m
of weak Lias mudstones and about 400m of more
competent limestones and Keuper mudstones and
siltstones. Substantial support and hydrostatic
pressure resistant linings would therefore be
required at least through the Hydraulic Limestone Series.

As a result of the extent of the old mine workings, and other factors, British Gypsum requirements were revised in 1985 to two drifts of the
smaller section and having a northeasterly orientation (line B). This line would have involved the use of land outside the Client's
ownership from which to conduct further explor-

atory drilling to confirm its suitability. As the land proved to be unobtainable, so the line of the drifts was swung clockwise yet again. (line C)

Several frustrating months of 1986 had passed by this time and, in order to complete the drifts by the 1987 deadline, it was essential that further exploratory and hydrogeological work proceeded urgently to establish the viability of the proposed new route and the extent to which ground treatment would be required.

Eighteen (18) new boreholes were drilled. No old workings were encountered and the hydrogeological testing indicated favourable conditions for creating a curtain wall grout box (fully enclosing the drifts where they would intersect the Hydraulic Limestone) utilizing the Rhaetic mud and siltstones below in expectation of their being a natural impermeable "cut-off".

In the meantime, investigations regarding the use of the NATM and finalisation of negotiations had continued and in July 1986 a phased contract was placed with Thyssen-Östu (a) to conduct the necessary exploratory and hydrogeological work and (b) to proceed with the ground treatment and tunnel construction works subject to satisfactory results from the former.

GROUND TREATMENT

155 holes were bored to an average depth of 26m in a rectangular pattern giving 3.5m cover below the drift invert at ch 95m and 5.0m cover above the drift crown at ch 225m. The holes were drilled in four stages, primary holes at 6m spacings, secondary at 3m spacings, tertiary at 1.5m and some quarternary holes between these.

Water acceptance testing was undertaken in all holes at a pressure of 10 bar and grout pumped into those holes taking water. A grouting pressure of 150% hydrostatic was adopted to avoid the possibility of hydrofracturing the

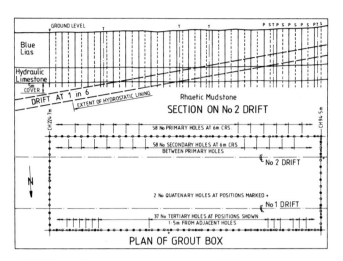

FIG 4. GROUTING FROM SURFACE

strata. A total 78 tons of grout was used.

DESIGN OF THE DRIFTS

The drifts were considered in three sections. Firstly, a portal length of 55m to be built in cut and cover. Secondly, the length through the Lias beds and the Rhaetic mudstones to be constructed with a waterproof lining, at Tender Stage estimated at 172m long. The third length was through the underlying Triassic marls and gypsum beds. Additionally the transitions between one length and the next had to be designed.

Portal

The portal length was constructed in mass concrete, reinforced by pairs of concentric steel arches, each of 100mm RSJ section and mounted on a conventionally reinforced concrete base slab 600m thick. This method was chosen to allow concurrent working through the portal during construction.

Lining through the Lias and Rhaetic Beds

The length through the Lias was designed in three distinct elements. A primary lining to provide support to the strata and protection to the men, both against rockfalls and nuisance water, a waterproof membrane to exclude the water, and a secondary in-situ lining to withstand the consequent hydrostatic pressure.

CHAINAGE (m)	0	100	200	300	400	500
LINING	Portal	Hydrostatic		Non-Hydrostatic		
ROCK CLASSIFICATION		3 4 2 5		1		

ITEM		ROCK CLASSIFICATION				
		1	2	3	4	5
LENGTH OF ROUNDS (m)		2·0 – 3·0	1·5 – 2·0	1·2 – 1·5	0·9 – 1·2	0·5 – 1·0
SHOTCRETE THICKNESS (mm)	to walls and roof	100	150	150 – 200	200	200 – 250
	to invert	—	200	200	200	200
WELDMESH (150×150 3kg/m²)	to walls and roof	1 mat	1 mat	1 mat	1 mat	2 mats
	to invert	—	1 mat	1 mat	2 mats	2 mats
LATTICE GIRDERS		each round	each round	each round	each round	each round
REBAR SPILING (2500 lg, 20 dia)		—	—	if required, sporadic		
ROCKBOLTS (3000 long)		if required, sporadic				

FIG 5. SUPPORT MEASURES

Primary Lining

The primary support was constructed immediately following excavation and in accordance with NATM principles. It comprised a shotcrete lining of varying thickness reinforced by several methods. Additionally, provision was made for the use of other measures when appropriate. Five Rock Classes were delineated by the designer, Dr G Sauer, together with the geological conditions in which each would be applied.

The decisions surrounding their interpretation and application were to be made jointly by Dr Sauer, the Client's Site Representative and the Contractor's Manager. In practice no difficulties were encountered in this process.

The reinforcement mesh used was a 15mm square mesh of 6mm indented high tensile wire, designated SA 188. The lattice girders were each in the form of a three piece arch, constructed with a 30mm bar for the inner section and two 20mm bars against the rock. They were separated by 70mm and known therefore as Type 70/20/30. No longitudinal struts were employed as the mesh and lattice girders were sprayed-in-immediately.

Additional support provisions included radially set rockbolts and rebar dowels for spiling ahead.

A small amount of spiling was carried out in

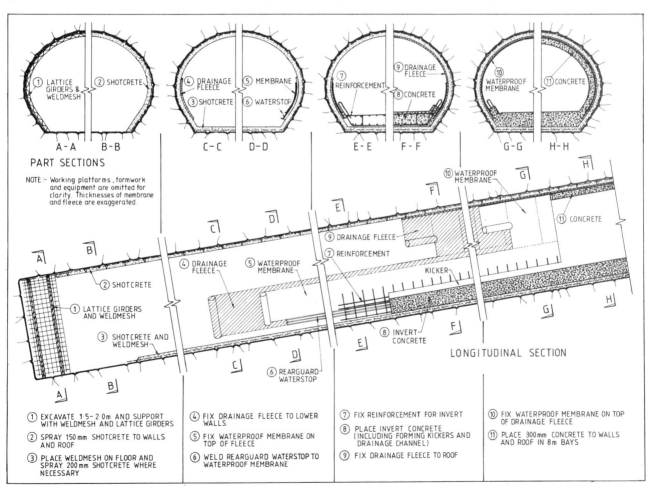

PART SECTIONS

NOTE:- Working platforms, formwork and equipment are omitted for clarity. Thicknesses of membrane and fleece are exaggerated.

① LATTICE GIRDERS & WELDMESH   ② SHOTCRETE   ④ DRAINAGE FLEECE   ⑤ MEMBRANE   ③ SHOTCRETE   ⑥ WATERSTOP   ⑦ REINFORCEMENT   ⑨ DRAINAGE FLEECE   ⑧ CONCRETE   ⑩ WATERPROOF MEMBRANE   ⑪ CONCRETE

LONGITUDINAL SECTION

① EXCAVATE 1·5 – 2·0m AND SUPPORT WITH WELDMESH AND LATTICE GIRDERS
② SPRAY 150mm SHOTCRETE TO WALLS AND ROOF
③ PLACE WELDMESH ON FLOOR AND SPRAY 200mm SHOTCRETE WHERE NECESSARY
④ FIX DRAINAGE FLEECE TO LOWER WALLS
⑤ FIX WATERPROOF MEMBRANE ON TOP OF FLEECE
⑥ WELD REARGUARD WATERSTOP TO WATERPROOF MEMBRANE
⑦ FIX REINFORCEMENT FOR INVERT
⑧ PLACE INVERT CONCRETE (INCLUDING FORMING KICKERS AND DRAINAGE CHANNEL)
⑨ FIX DRAINAGE FLEECE TO ROOF
⑩ FIX WATERPROOF MEMBRANE ON TOP OF DRAINAGE FLEECE
⑪ PLACE 300mm CONCRETE TO WALLS AND ROOF IN 8m BAYS

FIG 6. LINING CONSTRUCTION

the early stages but no rockbolts have been
used in the tunnel for ground support.

As the shotcrete primary lining was not designed to withstand hydrostatic pressure, any water
had to be conducted from behind the shotcrete
into drainage pipes cast into the floor. This
drainage was to continue until the final in-
situ lining, together with the associated seals,
had all been constructed.

Waterproof Membrane

On to the internal surface of the primary
lining was placed a two part membrane. First,
a geotextile was pinned to the shotcrete and
then 1,8m wide strips of PVC sheeting were heat
welded to PVC washers held on the pins securing
the geotextile. The strips were then progressively joined together using an electric welder
incorporating two adjacent rollers to form two
welds separated by a gap of 8mm. Each gap was
then pressurised to test the welds. The PVC
sheeting was 2mm thick to 32m below ground
level and 3mm thick thereafter.

Since the tunnel floor slab was to be relatively thick and by use of water stops and crack
inducers could be made sufficiently watertight
to meet the final water inflow criteria, it was
decided not to continue the membrane under the
invert but to weld it to a longitudinal water
stop keyed into the floor slab.

Secondary Lining

An in-situ concrete lining was constructed by
pumping 35 MPa Class 4 SR concrete behind a
conventional, 8m long, shutter.

Transitions

No particular design detail was required for
the transition section between portal and hydrostatic lining except to take the membrane outside the portal construction.

A seal was required at the bottom of the hydrostatic section to prevent the water migrating

below the waterbearing beds, the first element
of which was a key into sound, homogeneous, dry
marl; this was formed by casting a concrete
crib integral with the secondary in-situ lining
and directly against the strata.

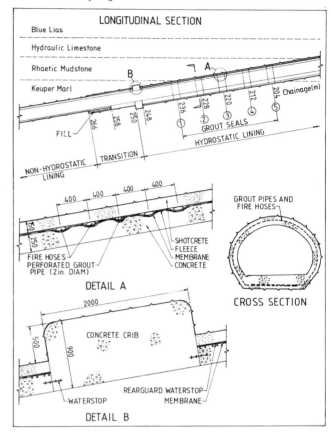

FIG 7. CONSTRUCTION OF SEALS

The second element consisted of five grout seals
above this crib. Each of these seals comprised
five pipes installed circumferentially
around the tunnel and secured to the primary
shotcrete lining outside the waterproofing membrane. The centre pipe of each set was a perforated PVC pipe to conduct the grout. The
outer two pairs were hoses, which, when inflated
with water after the construction of the in-
situ lining, would contain the grout in five
annular rings outside the waterproofing membrane. A further PVC pipe was installed
between each seal to conduct grout between each
annular ring should that prove to be necessary.

The third element was final grouting of all
open drainage channels and pipes, supplemented
if necessary by injecting through holes in the
crib to seal any residual water seepages around
the seal.

CONSTRUCTION

Work commenced on site in July 1986 and was
confined to surface preparation, ground treatment and portal construction until December
1986 when tunnelling began.

Water Control During Excavation

The clays were excavated using a Schaef ITC 112,
a tunnel backactor-cum-chain conveyor loader.
Small 4WD dumpers, suitably converted for
tunnel use, were employed to haul the spoil.
Their size was determined by the need to work
through the portal concreting operation.

Water was first encountered in Drift Nº1, the
northernmost, at ch 120m when the top limestone
bed was encountered. Only a relatively small
amount of water came from the bed itself, but
on breaching it, a considerable flow developed,
quickly washing out the underlying clay bed.
This continued to be the pattern through the
limestones and a routine was established for
controlling the water, firstly by backfilling
any washed out voids with imported, large,
crushed stone and secondly by the establishment
of a drainage system within the temporary shotcrete or concrete floor. This drainage system
consisted of reinforced PVC sheeting laid over
PVC pipes. The shotcrete or concrete was reinforced with one or two mats of mesh. By this
method a firm working floor was established
without pressuring the primary lining.

As progress was made through the limestones, so
the water had to be controlled from the walls
and roof. This was achieved by creating individual drainage points using PVC pipes bonded
into the shotcrete with quick setting mortar.
Where necessary PVC sheeting was also used
behind the mesh reinforcement to divert water.
Shotcrete was applied in the usual way, the
drainage pipes leading water through it directly
into sumps or into the underfloor drainage
system. As well as face sumps, intermediate
sumps and cut off channels were constructed
across the floor. Electric submersible pumps
supplemented by smaller capacity compressed air

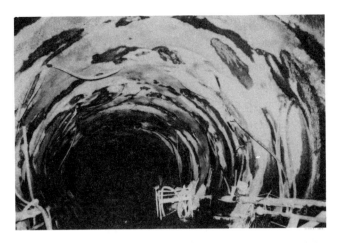

FIG 8. DRAINAGE OF PRIMARY SHOTCRETE LINING

diaphragm pumps were used throughout.

The Lias beds were excavated using the back-
actor fitted with bucket, tooth or hydraulic
breaker. Short lengths of both drifts were
drilled and blasted when necessary. A very
early attempt was made to use a Paurat E134
roadheader in the excavation of Drift Nº2, but
discontinued due to the wet conditions. However the Triassic marl and gypsum beds were all
excavated using this machine in conjunction
with standard belt conveyors, the shotcreting
operation taking place in front of the machine.
The only problems associated with this method
were that shotcreting of the haunch area was
found to be very difficult and the creation of
a temporary floor virtually impossible. Relatively little water was encountered below the
Lias, however, so the need for floor drainage or
support was minimal.

Shotcreting Operations

Sulphate resistant cement was mandatory, so a
series of tests was undertaken to establish a
suitable combination of locally obtainable
cement and accelerator. These were carried out
at the Institute of Construction Materials in
Innsbruck and an allowable accelerator dosage
and strength gain curve for each combination
was obtained. Both liquid and powder accel-
erators were tried, but the tunnel was gauged
to be too small to justify the sophisticated
dosing systems, pipeline or chemical dispensers

needed for the liquid types.

Using an optimum grading curve developed by
Östu, a blend of locally obtained aggregates
was found to conform sufficiently closely.
Stocks of sand and aggregate were stored on
site in covered bins. The batched shotcrete
mix was passed over a coarse static screen
and stored in a hopper from which vibratory
feeders delivered it via small belt conveyors
to the shotcrete machines. These were
Meynadier GM 092 with electric rotary drives
and double height rotors.

Since the drifts are 500m long and effective
use of such machines is impossible further than
250m, the second halves of the drives required
either underground shotcrete stations or service boreholes to connect the shotcrete plant
retained on surface. The latter option was
adopted.

Transport of the shotcrete was via 63mm ID
steel pipe with rubber hoses at bends. As
pipeline erosion and joint leaks cause velocity
drops, quickly giving rise to blockages and
delay, frequent and careful maintenance was
very important.

Monitoring

To confirm the adequacy of the design, monitoring of tunnel convergences and stresses
was undertaken as a routine. Convergence
measurement stations were set up at regular
intervals along each drift.

Each station consisted of four points in the
shotcrete lining. Measurements were taken
between them with a tape extensometer, initially on a daily basis, reducing to a weekly
then monthly interval. The maximum cumulative convergence at any station was 12mm.

Surface settlements of the same order were
observed along the line of the drift, a
large proportion probably being accounted
for by the temporary depression of the water
table.

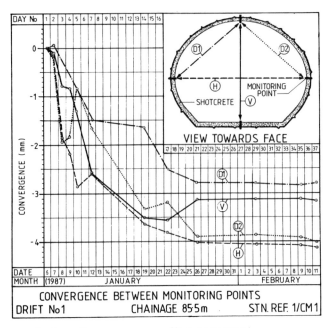

CONVERGENCE BETWEEN MONITORING POINTS
DRIFT No1   CHAINAGE 85·5m   STN. REF. 1/CM1

FIG 9. CONVERGENCE MONITORING

Stresses in both the primary shotcrete
lining and the surrounding rock mass were
measured at two stations only. Glotzl pressure cells were used in pairs at seven positions around the circumference. To date no
significant loads have been observed.

CONCLUSIONS

Over 1000m of tunnel were excavated and lined
through a variety of ground conditions, some
400m being difficult and wet.

Although, at the time of writing, the permanent
lining in N° 2 Drift has not been completed and
neither final water seal has been constructed,
indications are that the water inflow specification (25 litres/sec. per drift) will be achieved without undue difficulty.

The use of conventional tunnelling methods
would almost certainly have been slower, more
difficult and therefore expensive, and less
successful in achieving the objective of a dry
tunnel. Use of the NATM allowed a balance to
be obtained between rate of progress and the
requirement for caution and quality under difficult ground conditions.

The more awkward problems occured as a result
of water from the Hydraulic Limestones wetting

the clays, mudstones and marls but use of the
NATM provided a very flexible and orderly means
of concentrating and controlling water flows,
and to date at least, has justified the decision
to adopt it.

ACKNOWLEDGEMENTS

The Authors wish to thank British Gypsum
Limited and the Contractor, Thyssen-Östu for
their permission to publish this account of the
project.

Practical results from reduced-scale testing of pick cutting heads for tunnelling applications

E. P. Déliac
Ph. R. Cordelier
Mining Technology and Economics Department (TEM), Ecole Nationale Supérieure des Mines de Paris, Paris/Fontainebleau, France

SYNOPSIS

Scale models of actual pick cutting heads were considered as a potentially powerful means of investigation into coal and rock cutting machines at the end of the 70's. A special rig was designed and built by the Paris School of Mines and the French coal research organization in 1980, originally to simulate drum shaped cutting heads. After a first successful step, dealing with the comparison between full and reduced scale heads (scaling ratio 1/6) in the same rock specimens, an analysis of the performances of a continuous miner in a Lorraine iron mine was initiated. The results from the scale model (1/4 scale) confirmed the in situ behaviour of the machine and a set of practical recommendations was derived, to improve the performances by a much as 30 to 40 %.

These initial results led to modifications of the rig in order to accomodate various types of cutting heads, such as those on roadheaders, both in the penetration and shearing modes. The new rig was used to design the prototype of a new machine cutting vertical or sub-vertical shafts, using a set of roadheader type heads. A complete specification was made possible in order to move to the full scale prototype. Eventually, a project aimed at simulating a roadheader cutting head for potential use in a French uranium mine resulted in a preliminary rock cuttability study, followed by the selection of a pick and the decision to test a cutting head at a 1/4 scale.

As a conclusion, the reduced scale approach has proved very successful and it has supplied a valuable "catalogue" of practical results, criteria and recommendations, applicable to pick design, head configuration and machine specifications. The demand is currently increasing to investigate tunnelling by roadheaders in metal mines. It is felt that it could be of interest to both machine (and pick) manufacturers and users (mining or civil engineering companies).

INTRODUCTION

A strong interest has been demonstrated for scale model testing and simulation of heavy and costly processes for years in some engineering fields (such as fluid engineering for the aeronautic industry). Oil producing companies carried out some investigations for drilling tools in the 60's (Raynal, 1960). More recently Roxborough and Eskikaya (1974) established a good basis for understanding the scaling laws when using a plough in an artificial rock, particularly those laws related to the rock properties. Surprisingly enough, in view of these promising results, this early work does not seem to have been followed by in depth investigations until the beginning of this decade (Dubugnon and Janach, 1981, after Dubugnon and Barendsen, 1985; Déliac and Gripp, 1983).

It is the purpose of this presentation to report on work carried out with the assistance of various French mining and civil engineering companies (with particular reference to CERCHAR, the Charbonnages de France research organization), for over five years, dealing with the simulation of pick cutting heads for tunnelling or longwalling purposes. In the first section the experimental rigs and the preliminary investigations, focused on drum cutting, are briefly presented, in order to explain how this work originated. Tests and simulation of roadheader type heads are dealt with in the second section, as well as the the scope for introducing mechanical tunnelling in metal mines.

TESTING DRUM TYPE CUTTING HEADS

The Experimental Rig

A reduced scale rig for testing drum type cutting heads was designed jointly by Cerchar and the Mining Technology and Economics department (TEM) of the Paris School of Mines. This machine was installed at Fontainebleau in 1981. The reduced scale drum was a 1/6 scale near exact replica of drums that used to be fitted on a full scale rig located in the Cerchar laboratory (see figure 1),at Verneuil en Halatte (France). Unlike the way a real shearer works, the rock is in this case fixed on a mobile support moved by a powerful jack as illustrated in figure 2. This figure also shows that the pickholders can move freely along special grooves, in order to simulate a wide range of drum lacings. No clearance ring can be evaluated, as the rock is unconfined on both sides. This rig was fully instrumented and computerized from the start by sensors which record torque, horizontal force (thrust), vertical force, and advance speed. The microcomputer calculates average values for torque and forces over 1800 points for each test (usually lasting sufficiently for 3 or 4 full revolutions). A typical record of forces during a test is illustrated in figure 3.

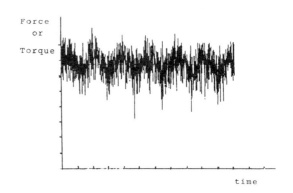

Figure 3 : Record of major forces during a test on the reduced scale rig (after Déliac, 1985)

Figure 1 : View of the full scale rig

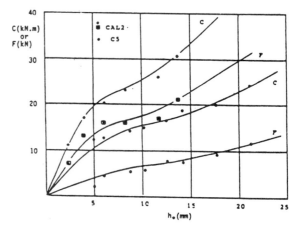

a) full scale results

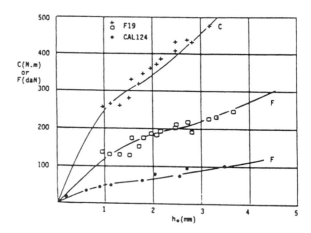

b) reduced scale results

Figure 4 : Experimental drum cutting curves, using radial picks (after Déliac, 1985)

(key : . C and F are respectively the torque and horizontal thrust on the cutting head
. CAL2, C5, F19, CAL124 are identification codes for various rock types, as described in the quoted publication
. ho is the maximum depth of cut per pick per drum revolution)

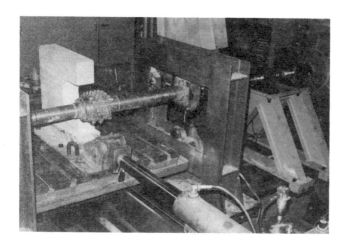

Figure 2 : General view of the reduced scale rig

Preliminary Results

The cutting curves (torque and thrust against advance per pick per revolution) derived from the full scale and the reduced scale experiments are illustrated in figure 4. The vertical force is not shown as it could not be recorded on the full scale rig. The figure shows that the curves confirm the theoretical shape predicted by Lebrun (1978) and further refined by Déliac (1985 and 1986). Furthermore, these curves enabled the calculation of scaling laws. Déliac (1986) established that they could be obtained from standard mathematical laws, together with a correction factor related to the size effect of the rock structure (it is well known that strength parameters of a given rock depend on the size of the sample on which they are measured : the smaller it is, the stronger the rock appears to be).

Testing of an Experimental Continuous Miner

Once the scaling laws were known, it was possible to study actual tunnelling machines, such as continuous miners, for which the influence of the lateral clearance picks is not very important (due to the size of the drum).

A project with the Lorraine iron mines group research organization (SAMIFER) consisted of simulating the drum of an experimental continuous miner, using the reduced scale rig, at a 1/4 scale. The continuous miner was experimental in that it could easily be fitted with three types of drum lacing (Déliac and Léonet, 1984). The scaled drum is illustrated in figure 5a, with the three lacings. In situ tests of the actual machine showed that the sumping phase was critical to compare the performance of the three drums, thus validating the scaled drums cutting rock on half their surface.

Figure 5b illustrates the cutting curves for the thrust force. The laboratory investigation revealed that :

i)   the machine was thrust limited, hence the line shown in figure 5b, corresponding to the scaled available thrust ;

ii) a reduction in rotation speed would result in improved performances, although the advance rate would not increase (because of the wear rate) ;

iii) the optimum pick spacing was obtained with the third lacing ;

iv) should the available thrust be increased by only 10 %, the production rate during the sumping phase would increase by more than 30 %.

The two above mentioned projects clearly demonstrate the interest of reduced scale testing of cutting heads. For this reason it was decided to go ahead with this approach and study more complex problems such as clearance ring (where the gauge picks are located, at the sides of the drum) or roadheader performances. The latter is dealt with in the following section.

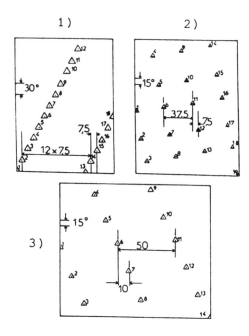

a) the three lacings

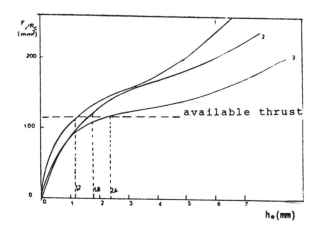

b) the cutting curves
(same key as in fig.4. R_c is the rock unconfined compressive strength)

Figure 5 : Cutting test of the scaled continuous miner half drum (after Déliac and Léonet, 1984)

TESTING ROADHEADERS CUTTING HEADS

Adaptation of the Rig

As explained above, the initial successful results and the limitations of the previous rig led to modifications in order to test various types of cutting heads, such as those on roadheaders, but also drums equipped with clearance rings. The reduced scale head or drum is now set at the end of a rigid shaft so that it is possible to study both the penetration and shearing modes. For this purpose, the rock is fixed on the upper table, rigidly locked with the main lower table (see figure 6). These supports are moved independently by perpendicular jacks. The advance speeds for both jacks can be set from 0.06 to 0.72 m/min according to the characteristics of the hydraulic device.

The scale factor can be adjusted in the range 3 to 6, depending on the full scale head or drum to be tested on the rig. The rock size is approximately 0.5 x 1 x 0.5 m³ (Length–Width–Height). The instrumentation of the rig includes several sensors which measure torque, horizontal (axial and normal to the head axis) and vertical resultant forces on the head, advance speeds in both directions and rotation speed. During each test the information is recorded and processed by a microcomputer to calculate average, minimum and maximum values, and to give a visual display of the data corresponding to each sensor.

The design of the reduced scale heads is quite original because it is possible to change picks lacing along two or three spiral lines with an adjustable geometry (figure 7).

Simulation and Design of the HFC Cutting Heads

The SOLETANCHE group of companies, involved in special civil engineering projects (soil waterproofing for instance) as well as in contracted drilling works for the petroleum industry, decided to investigate the feasibility of a new machine, called HFC, based on the roadheader concept of rock cutting, for sinking vertical shafts (diameter up to 2.4 m). The applications would range from sub-ocean drilling (offshore platform anchoring) to mining purposes. The cutting principle of the machine is illustrated in figure 8.

The project contracted to TEM consisted of

- finding a suitable type of pick
- recommending an "optimal" head design
- deriving an adequate model of the behaviour of the machine

The information provided included overall features (power, weight, geometrical specifications) and assumed that the rock was medium hard (unconfined compressive strength around 40 MPa), for a desired advance rate of 20 m/hr.

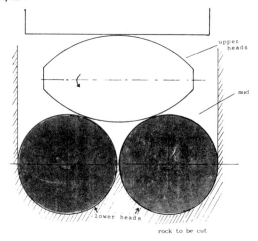

a) vertical section

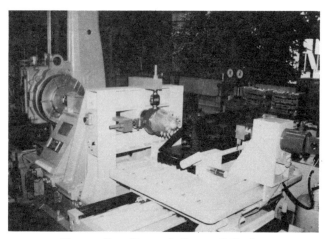

Figure 6 : View of the modified reduced scale rig

Figure 7 : Detailed view of a tested cutting head

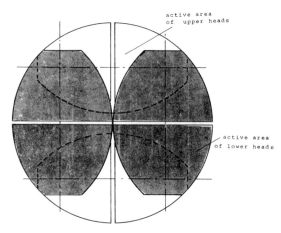

b) horizontal section

Figure 8 : Principle of the HFC cutting assembly

The work was conducted in two separate directions :

- test of a cutting head at a 1/4 scale using the experimental rig
- simulation of the HFC by a micro-computer programme called P.C.HFC

The experimental results showed that a staggered lacing of the picks was preferable and that, in all situations, the desired advance rate would probably not be reached, particularly should significant wear occur (given the machine specifications). It was also concluded that V-shaped chisels or forward attack picks seemed to be suitable, depending on the hardness/ abrasiveness of the rock, although point-attack picks could be used for the nose section of the heads.

The P.C.HFC programme, largely derived from P.C.DRUM, developed by TEM with assistance from CERCHAR, confirmed all experimental results and yielded suggested values for mechanical power, rotation speed, thrust force, etc... necessary to meet the requirements concerning the advance speed. It therefore made it possible to simulate any change in type of pick, head design, rock parameters, etc.

It should be pointed out that this programme is based on an accurate evaluation of the work delivered by each pick individually, averaged over several positions during the head revolution (17 positions of the pick during its contact with the rock), taking into account the relieving or impeding effect of the cut deepening/ interaction cycle for each elementary calculation. A complete run on an IBM PC/AT micro-computer requires approximately one minute.

As an example of the experimental results obtained from the rig, figure 9 shows the variation of the mean torque (C) and penetration force (F) for a two staggered spirals (one pick per line) lacing, as a function of the pick penetration per revolution, for one of the lower heads (contact with the rock on half its surface). The classical shape of the theoretical curves, as predicted by Déliac (1986) can be seen on the figure.

The experimental results did not only lead to eliminate non staggered lacings, but they also showed that a two spirals design was better than a three spirals one. In addition tests were carried to study the nose section of the heads (highly inclined and confined picks, with a low cutting radius) and indicated the large fraction of the total energy required for that part of the cutting assembly.

As far as the scaling laws are concerned, although there was no full scale result available (the protype of the HFC machine is yet to be built), the calculated results for the actual machine, derived from P.C.HFC, seem to confirm the validity of the correction factors depicted by Déliac (1986), based on rock texture. Forces were found to be in an approximate ratio of 12 and the torque scaling

coefficient was evaluated at 45, for theoretical values of respectively 16 and 64 (1/4 scale).

Figure 10 shows an example of a suggested head design as displayed by P.C.HFC for the two spirals (staggered) lacing.

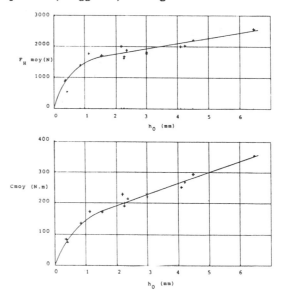

Figure 9 :   Experimental cutting curves at a 1/4 scale for the HFC machine (2-spirals lacing, staggered)

MACHINE : HFC

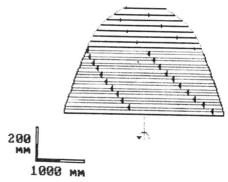

Figure 10 : Display of a head design by P.C.HFC (similar to that yielding the results in fig. 9)

Preliminary Investigations for Mechanical Tunnelling in Metal Mines

In view of these promising results it was thought interesting to look into the feasibility of tunnelling in metal mines using roadheaders, with the machine possibly being completely substituted for the conventional drill and blast method. The TOTAL Compagnie Minière (France) company is mining several uranium orebodies in France and overseas. One of them is particularly rich, worked through an underground method (after the near surface section was exhausted via open pit mining). This mine, called the Bernardan mine (located at Jouac in central France), is contemplating introducing a roadheader to improve the stope productivity and to reduce the number of working areas.

It was therefore decided to look at this project in the following way :

- step 1 :   determine the rock mechanical properties in order to define its cuttability; four major rock types were identified;

- step 2 :   carry out single pick cutting tests in order to confirm rock cuttability and check the behaviour of inclined picks (critical on a roadheader head) (figure 11);

- step 3 :   suggest a roadheader among typical current machines and test the cutting head at a 1/4 scale;

To date, steps 1 and 2 have been completed and the results are described below.

Firstly, the geomechanical tests showed that the rock was not very hard (u.c.s. from 1 to 30 MPa), except for the surrounding granite (u.c.s. above 60 MPa), but very heterogeneous; it could also prove to be abrasive, in spite of a low quartz content, because it tends to become a paste rubbing against the picks (like a clay). Secondly, the pick cutting tests confirmed the low level of forces in rocks belonging to the orebody itself. However, when inclined and due to rock heterogeneity, the picks could encounter high resistance to rock cutting.

Subsequently, an axial type of roadheader (longitudinal head) is felt preferable, rather than a transversal head (rotating perpendicular to the boom); the machine can then penetrate in a soft area and widen the excavation to the desired profile. As an example, figure 12a shows the advance rate calculated by P.C. DRUM during the sweeping phase in the hard ore, using the type of head illustrated in figure 9, whereas a non staggered head design is seen in figure 12b (with a high vibration pattern, illustrated by the difference between maximum and minimum values of the torque).

pick holder   rock sample

Figure 11 :   Cutting test of some Bernardan uranium ore (hematized episyenite)

Available Torque : 20.9 kN.m

Approx. Advance Rate : 71 cm/min

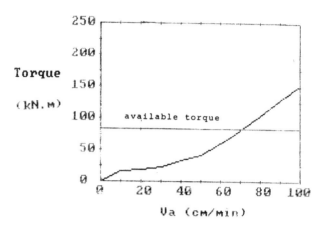

a) staggered lacing (same head as in fig.9)

Available Torque : 20.9 kN.m

Approx. Advance Rate : 14 cm/min

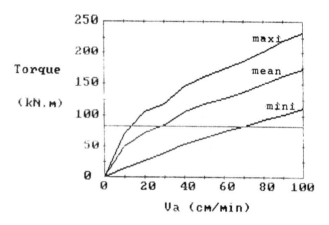

b) non staggered lacing

Figure 12 :   Simulation of hard ore cutting at Jouac with an experimental roadheader head, using P.C.DRUM (torque during the horizontal sweeping phase, as a function of the head advance speed)

Main Criteria for Optimum Head Design or Selection

Figure 13 shows the principle of a typical cutting machine investigation. The central part of the figure is obviously concerned with the correspondence between i) advance rate on one hand and ii) resultant forces on the other hand. This is also the principle of the P.C.DRUM calculation.

As far as head design or selection is concerned, several criteria appear to play a major role :

i) adaptation of the type of head to the local environment : when the rock is homogeneous the choice between a transversal or an axial head is mainly dependent on factors such as manufacturer's availability, desired production rate, past experience, etc...; when it is hetero-geneous, with hard and soft strata, an axial head is often preferable, as it can penetrate into the rock (critical phase of the cutting cycle) in a weak area and thereafter widen the cut by moving laterally in the harder rock; in addition an axial head has the advantage of a simpler transmission of rotation torque through the boom than with a transversal head;

ii) adaptation of the picks to the rock : the cutting tools must be chosen in order to simultaneously comply to good wear resistance and to minimum specific energy (energy per unit volume of excavated rock); a thorough recent work on this topic at TEM is worth being mentioned (Déliac, 1986; Fairhurst, 1987; Sellami, 1987); this choice is generally difficult because of the heterogeneity of the rock; this is probably why the point-attack pick is very frequently used. In agressive grounds however (hard or abrasive), it seems that there is a wide potential for heavy duty forward attack picks; furthermore it may be of interest to use water jets to enhance the cutting action of the picks (e.g. reduce the wear rate and possibly help in debris removal); in that case, an axial head appears more adapted since there are less picks to be assisted, hence a reduced flow at the face and less technological problems to carry the water to the picks; alternatively diamond tipped picks are currently being investigated (Sellami and Déliac, 1987) and could show some encouraging potential in spite of their high cost, particularly when used on sensitive areas of the head, such as the nose section;

iii) lacing of the picks : this bears a strong influence on the vibration pattern of the head, hence on the deterioration rate of the picks; in agressive rocks it is known that staggered lacings behave significantly better than non staggered ones (on this point a comprehensive work has been reported on by the British Coal technical services and confirmed by our reduced scale experiments). In addition the spacing of the picks must be designed so as to optimize the interaction cycle of the cuts during the head revolution, with a minimum number of picks;

iv) rotation speed : two situations can be encountered; the first and most usual one occurs when the machine is thrust limited; the instantaneous production rate then varies in the same direction as the rotation speed; however, if the rock is not very weak, we would not recommend increasing it as it would imply an increased wear rate and the short term

advantage would quickly be offset; the second situation is related to a torque limited machine; a reduction in rotation speed, compatible with the maximum forces bearable by the picks, is then generally of significant benefit to the machine and to the head behaviour. In all cases it is important to determine the limiting factor of the machine in order to assess the likely deterioration pattern of the picks and adapt the head to that problem.

Most of these criteria can be evaluated from a reduced scale experiment, coupled with a computer simulation. Indeed this was done for the HFC project previously described.

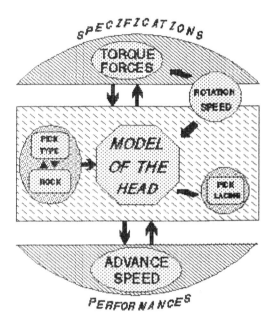

Figure 13 :   Principle of a pick cutting machine evaluation

CONCLUSIONS

Reduced scale testing of cutting heads is a reliable, cheap and fast means of investigation into the cuttability of rocks for tunnelling purposes.

Although more information is needed at this stage, it appears that major improvements in a careful introduction of roadheaders tunnelling to underground workings located in agressive rocks are now possible.

This original approach is made even more powerful when it is coupled with a micro-computer programme like P.C. DRUM, which enables a quick verification of alternative situations before starting a new experiment.

Detailed research is currently focused on the behaviour of inclined picks (used as clearance picks or on the nose section of a roadheader), on a quantitative appraisal of wear and, eventually on a thorough analysis of the high frequency record of data in order to analyse the tool-rock interaction using signal processing techniques).

A major research project has also been initiated with the Mineral Resources Engineering Department of Imperial College / Royal School of Mines, who have a 1 m diameter full face tunnel boring machine, partly funded by the European Community, aimed at studying hard rock cutting.

ACKNOWLEDGEMENTS

The authors wish to express their grateful thanks to the various companies which have been involved in the research presented in this paper. Firstly, CERCHAR and the Charbonnages de France Company provided financial and also invaluable technical assistance concerning the experimental equipment and the fundamental research on rock cutting. Secondly the Lorraine iron Mines are thanked for cooperation on the in situ testing of the experimental continuous miner. Thirdly, the Soletanche Company assisted and funded the work on the HFC machine. Lastly, Total Compagnie Minière France was involved in the uranium mining project and established a strong basis for further cooperation. We are also indebted to the last two companies for allowing us to publish the results quoted above.

REFERENCES

Déliac E.P. and Gripp M.F. (1983) Etude quantitative de l'abattage mécanique par pics à partir d'essais en modèle réduit. Revue de l'Industrie Minérale. Vol. 65. Les Techniques 5-83, May 1983, pp. 275-292.

Déliac E.P. and Léonet O. (1984) Optimisation du matériel pour l'abattage en taille dans les mines de fer lorraines. Revue de l'Industrie Minérale. Vol. 66. July 1984, pp. 331-340.

Déliac E.P. (1985) Recent development in the design and optimization of drum-type cutting machines in France. Proceedings of 7th Rapid Excavation and Tunnelling Conference. 16-20 June 1985, New-York (N.Y., USA). Ed. by C.D. Mann et M.N. Kelley. Soc. Min. Eng. of AIME, New-York (N.Y., USA) pp. 265-283.

Déliac E.P. (1986) Optimisation des machines d'abattage à pics. Doctoral dissertation. Univ. of Paris 6. Ed. by ENSMP/TEM, Paris/Fontainebleau (France). 502 p.

Dubugnon O. and Barendsen P. (1985) Small scale model testing ; a new approach in TBM development. Proceedings 7th Rapid Excavation and Tunnelling Conference. 16-20 June 1985, New-York (N.Y., USA). Ed. by C.D. Mann and M.N. Kelley. Soc. Min. Eng. of AIME, New-York (N.Y., USA) pp. 245-263.

Fairhurst C.E. (1987) Contribution à l'amélioration des outils d'abattage de roches agressives : le pic assisté et le pic vibrant. Doctoral dissertation. ENSMP (Paris School of Mines). Ed. by ENSMP/TEM, Paris/Fontainebleau (France).

Lebrun M. (1978) Etude théorique et expérimentale de l'abattage mécanique; application à la conception de machines d'abattage et de creusement. Doctoral dissertation. ENSMP (Paris School of Mines). Ed. by ENSMP/TEM, Paris/Fontainebleau (France).

Raynal J. (1960) Le problème de la similitude au forage en tricône. Internal report. Ref AD/FO 832 (6th april 1960). Société Nationale des Pétroles d'Aquitaine. Centre de Recherches de Pau (France). 12 p.

Roxborough F.F. and Eskikaya S. (1974) Dimensional considerations in the design of a scale model for coal-face production system research. Int. J. Rock Mech. Min. Sci. Vol. 11, pp. 129-137.

Sellami H. (1987) Le travail du pic usé; application aux machines d'abattage à pics. Doctoral dissertation. ENSMP (Paris School of Mines). Ed. by ENSMP/TEM, Paris/Fontainebleau (France).

Sellami H. and Déliac E.P. (1987) Essais d'abattage mécanique avec pics diamantés. Revue de l'Industrie Minérale - Mines et Carrières - Les Techniques. Vol. 69, pp. 265-273.

Summit tunnel—post fire remedial works

S. D. Duncan B.Sc., C.Eng., M.I.C.E.
British Rail (London Midland Region), Preston, Lancashire, United Kingdom
W. Wilson B.Sc., M.Sc., M.Eng., M.I.C.E., M.I.H.T., F.G.S.
James Williamson & Partners, Glasgow, Scotland, United Kingdom

SYNOPSIS

The paper describes the investigations and consequent remedial measures to the brickwork lining and the surrounding rock of the section of the Summit Tunnel and two of its ventilation shafts which were affected by the spectacular fire in December 1984.

Rock cores and inspection boreholes indicated that damage to the rock due to the 1500°C fire was negligible. At the seat of the fire, parts of the brickwork lining had melted. However, although some layer separation in the brickwork tunnel lining may have been caused by the fire, the brickwork and mortar which remained in place after the fire was remarkably unaffected. At the seat of the fire, some of the inner ring of the brickwork lining had melted but up to 3 rings of the brickwork were shed due to heat induced separation of the rings of brickwork. The brickwork remaining after the fire appeared sound and was covered in a 10 to 15 mm thick glazed layer of vitrification.

The main stability concern was the brickwork in two of the 3.15m diameter ventilation shafts (Nos. 8 and 9) and their intersection with the tunnel. This was stabilised by a 2 x 2m square pattern of 6m long, 38mm diameter dowels installed radial to the tunnel lining, over 7m of the tunnel roof either side of both shafts and the installation over the lower 9m of the shaft of rings of reinforced concrete shear keyseach stressed against the rock by a pair of 450 KN tensioned multi-strand anchors.

The lower reinforced section of both shafts, their intersection with the tunnel and the reinforced section of the tunnel roof were then covered in a 50mm (min) thick layer of steel mesh reinforced sprayed concrete. A 500mm thick mesh reinforced sprayed concrete plug was provided at the base of either shaft which was then filled with polyurethane foam.

INTRODUCTION

On 20 December 1984, a goods train transporting 13 No. 100 ton tankers full of four star petrol from Teesside to Warrington became derailed in the Summit tunnel which lies just south of Todmorden on the cross-Pennine Calder Valley line between Normanton and Manchester. Fig. 1.

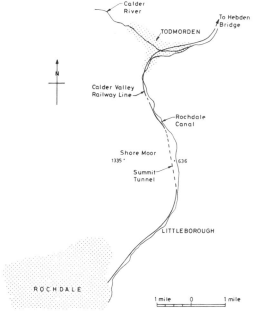

Fig. 1   Location Plan

Whilst travelling at an estimated 40 m.p.h, the fourth wagon apparently became derailed dragging the following wagons after it. Petrol leaked from overturned tankers saturating the rail track ballast and it is believed that sparks from the crash ignited the petrol.

Initially, the fire was limited and the three man crew managed to uncouple the first three wagons and engine and remove them from the tunnel. Approximately three hours after the incident the fire suddenly erupted into a spectacular fireball, possibly due to the ignition of clouds of petrol fumes which may have built up in the roof of the tunnel, leading to a chain reaction of explosions in the other wagons. The resulting inferno raged for 3 days, sending flames leaping high into the air above the two ventilation shafts adjacent to the fire, Fig. 2.

Fig. 2   Flames emerging above ventilation shaft nos. 8 and 9 (Courtesy of the West Yorkshire Fire Brigade)

Tests performed by BR Research Division on samples of material from the site of the fire indicated that temperatures in the tunnel rose to an estimated 1500°C and destroyed the tankers, the rail track and caused extensive damage to the brickwork lining of the tunnel at the seat of the fire.

The derailment occurred at Tablet 106 and the effects of the fire were confined to a length of tunnel within the range Tablet 92 to 118 (1 Tablet = 50 feet). Fig. 3. This paper describes the sequence of exploration activities and consequent remedial works which were carried out to stabilise both the length of tunnel and the two ventilation shafts which were affected by the fire.

TUNNEL CONSTRUCTION

The twin track Summit tunnel was constructed between September 1839 and December 1841. It has a horseshoe profile with a maximum width of approximately 7.2m and a clearance of approximately 6.5m between rail level and the crown. The tunnel is brick lined invert to invert with 6 courses of brickwork.

13 No. 3.15m internal diameter ventilation shafts intersect the centreline of the tunnel. These are lined with approximately 2 courses of brickwork which thickens locally immediately above the tunnel.

GEOLOGY

Summit tunnel lies within the shales and sandstone of the Millstone Grit Series (Upper Carboniferous). Fig.3. Between Tablets 1 and 38, the tunnel lies within the Middle Grit Group. However, between Tablets 38 and 163, which includes the fire damaged zone, the tunnel runs through the Kinderscout Grit Group, within which the strata dips at 8° to 10° to the west and minor, steeply dipping faults cross the tunnel at Tablets 17, 46, 59, 98 and 150.

TUNNEL CONDITION - PRE-FIRE

From May to the beginning of December 1984, a programme of drilling and inspection of the brickwork lining and the immediately surrounding rock was carried out by the Permanent Way Equipment Co. (Permaquip) for British Rail as part of a routine maintenance survey.

The investigation comprised drilling a series of 7 No. 1.5m long, 75 mm diameter open-hole boreholes around the perimeter of the tunnel at cross-sections every 50 or 25 feet along selected portions of the tunnel. Williamson Technical Services Ltd (WTS) acting on behalf of Permaquip, carried out an inspection of these boreholes using a borescope and provided an interpretation of the borehole surveys indicating the condition of the brickwork, its thickness, the presence and width of any voids behind the lining, the condition of the rock behind the lining, seepage and finally an indication of the nature of the loading on the brickwork lining.

canopy for the tunnel rather than a support to the surrounding rock.

B.R.'s detailed tunnel inspection prior to the fire noted that vent shaft Nos. 8 and 9, at tablet 93 and 109 + 10, respectively, were wet, shaft No.9 particularly so, water running down the inside of the brickwork lining. Localised bulging, up to 10 m long, and spalling, typically $1m^2$ of the brickwork tunnel lining was identified between tablets 90 and 113. Bulging of the brickwork is not uncommon in old tunnel linings and such bulging was widespread throughout the entire length of the tunnel.

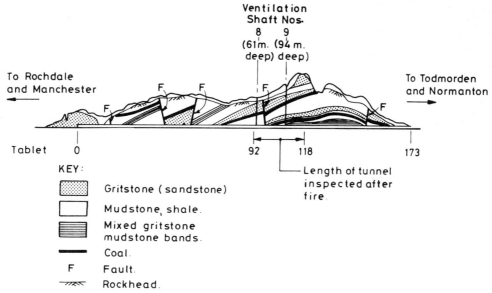

Fig. 3   Geology

It is fortuitous that the tunnel between Tablets 90 and 104.5 which overlaps with the fire affected length of tunnel was included in this survey.

Within this length, the 600 to 700 mm thick brickwork lining was found to be tight. However, some isolated separation of the courses of brickwork and local patches of loose brickwork, up to 300mm deep, were identified.

Generally, the rock was not in contact with the brickwork lining, although the void of 200 to 500 mm width between the brickwork and the rock was loosely filled with rubble. The surrounding rock was generally strong, moderately weathered with some dilation of joints apparent. It was apparent that the brickwork was intended to be a

Bulging is not necessarily indicative of distress, the original construction formwork possibly having been struck before the mortar had gained sufficient strength.

POST-FIRE INVESTIGATIONS

Following the fire, BR commissioned a number of surveys in January 1985 to assess the effect of the fire upon the brickwork tunnel lining, the rock immediately surrounding the tunnel and upon ventilation shaft Nos.8 and 9.

The inspection and testing of the brickwork lining in the tunnel was carried out by BR. Over the 400 m length of tunnel affected by the fire, over 20% of the inner ring of the brickwork lining had spalled and at the centre of the fire up to three courses of brickwork had been lost due to heat, Figs. 4 and 5, sometimes leaving a vitrified surface to the remaining brickwork. Locally, up to three courses of

borescope.

The results showed that where the rock had been exposed directly to the fire, e.g. at the rear of a refuge, the mudstone had been visibly

Fig. 4   Vitrified brickwork slag beneath ventilation shaft no. 9 (Courtesy of the West Yorkshire Fire Brigade)

Fig. 5   Vitrified surface of brickwork tunnel lining (Courtesy of the West Yorkshire Fire Brigade)

brickwork had spalled. At their research laboratories at Derby, BR strength tested bricks taken from the remnant of the brickwork lining at the seat of the fire and compared the results with the strengths obtained from testing similar brick taken from parts of the tunnel remote from the fire. No significant difference was detected. In addition, inspection in the tunnel revealed that the mortar had not been significantly affected by the fire.

A further series of both open hole and cored boreholes was carried out by Permaquip between tablet 92 and 118, spanning the length of tunnel affected by the fire. Williamson Technical Services Ltd specified, supervised, inspected and assessed the results of the core drilling in terms of the effect of the heat of the fire upon the rock immediately surrounding the tunnel. N sized cores approximately 2m long were taken at 50 feet intervals in the crown of the tunnel followed by visual inspection using a

affected by the heat. The surface 3mm of the rock contained patches of brown discolouration and had locally spalled to a depth of around 20mm.

At places where sandstone masonry, probably of local origin, had been used for localised repair work to the brickwork lining, the masonry had reacted to the fire in a similar manner to the adjacent brickwork by spalling in thin slabs parallel to the surface, in this case along weak, micaceous bedding planes. The masonry remaining behind the spalling appeared to be sound.

Visual examination of the rock cores failed to identify any effect upon the rock immediately surrounding the tunnel due to the fire. However, the detailed investigation did reveal that displaced rock appeared to be loading the brickwork lining, with fragmented rock debris at least 1.5m deep locally. Although it could not be proved, it was not considered that the heat had had significant effect on the extent of the rock degradation around the tunnel, the extent and variability of the rock conditions between tablets 92 to 118 after the fire, being similar to those identified before the fire between tablets 7.5 to 17.5, 18.5 to 22.5 and 90 to 104.5.

A video survey was carried out over the entire 61m and 94m height of vent shaft Nos. 8 and 9, respectively, through which the 130m high flames of the fire had leapt. The brickwork lining of both shafts was revealed to be extensively damaged, with severe bulging, spalling, and longitudinal cracking, over the upper 20m of both shafts.

The shafts were wet, shaft 9 in particular being very wet below the upper 20m.

There was little evidence of vitrification of the brickwork in shaft No.8, but the brickwork in shaft No.9 was extensively vitrified, particularly over the lower 65m.

It is not known whether the bulging, cracking and spalling of the shaft brickwork were caused or exacerbated by the fire. However, the brickwork of both shafts was considered to be in a parlous state. The depth of the superficial deposits which surround the upper portion of both shafts appeared to correlate with the extent of the longitudinal fractures and also the emergence of water into the shafts at rockhead.

REMEDIAL MEASURES

It was evident from the post fire surveys that remedial measures to the brickwork linings, were required locally for the tunnel and for ventilation shafts 8 and 9.

The urgency imposed by the closure of the tunnel obliged BR to go out to tender radiply for the remedial works. Following discussions between BR and the successful tenderer, Whitley Moran, BR asked James Williamson and Partners (JWP) to design remedial measures for ventilations shafts 8 and 9 and the areas of tunnel immediately surrounding them.

One of the first actions taken on site was the establishment of distometer arrays on either side of each of the two shafts to monitor any downwards movement of the crown of the tunnel beneath the shaft brickwork. In the event, no downwards movement was recorded.

The remedial measures in BR's tender included the strengthening of the brickwork tunnel lining at the ventilation shaft intersection for a distance of 7.75m on either side of both ventilation shafts. This comprised the installation of arrays of a square 2m by 2m pattern of 6m long, 38mm diameter, resin anchored, galvanised mild steel dowels with face plates and nuts installed radial to the tunnel lining and holding steel mesh to strengthen a 50mm thick sprayed concrete lining. Fig.6.

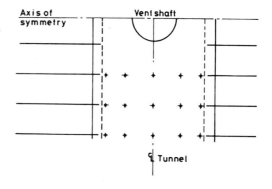

Fig. 6   Layout of dowel reinforcement in tunnel at base of shaft

This is similar to the measures adopted by JWP in 1980 for the strengthening of the brickwork lining of the Falkirk High Tunnel and JWP considered BR's proposed remedial measures for the tunnel to be acceptable.

The brickwork tunnel lining was low pressure grouted to the rock through a pattern of 1m deep boreholes. A thixotropic additive was used to restrict the flow of the grout laterally along the tunnel. The grout holes were then lengthened to 3m or 6m and the rock grouted using low pressures. Following this, dowels were installed through the brickwork and into the rock, and face plates were attached.

As in the remainder of the tunnel affected by the fire, the damaged brickwork was removed prior to the remedial measures. Beyond the shaft intersection zone, the remedial measures to the tunnel brickwork comprised the attachment of steel mesh and the application of sprayed concrete in layers to achieve a thickness equivalent to a five ringed brickwork arch. BR has established from experience that such an arch thickness, with a good profile provides an acceptable lining.

For the ventilation shafts, JWP initially suggested using a pattern of dowels over the entire height of the shaft through rock in order to ensure a continuous shear connection between shaft brick work and

prevented from spalling inwards and would be supported from falling downwards by the installed shear support. The support works to the lower 6.5m and 9m of shaft Nos. 8 and 9 respectively, shown in Fig. 7, were installed from beneath a steel grillage and mesh canopy suspended on chains from the top of either shaft.

Shear support to the shaft lining was provided by a pattern of reinforced concrete shear keys installed through the brickwork and tensioned against the rock. The shear keys were designed to support the entire weight of the brickwork lining of the shaft plus the weight of the proposed foam infilling with a 5% absorption of water. An overall factor of safety of 2.05 was adopted which conservatively assumed that the shaft lining immediately after the fire had a factor of safety of

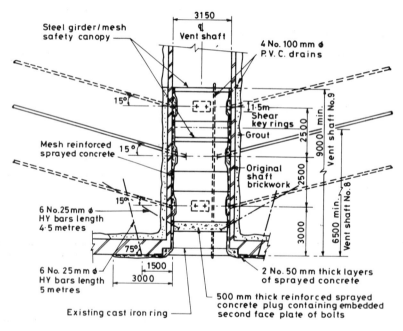

Fig. 7   Shear support at base of shaft

rock. However, the danger to workmen posed by the apparently parlous nature of the shaft brickwork, forced the adoption of concentrated shear support provided over a restricted height at the base of the shafts. BR indicated that they wished to fill both shafts with polyurethane foam and so the existing brickwork lining above the reinforced section of the base would be

1.0.

The shear keys were arranged in rings, 3 in shaft No. 9 and 2 in shaft No. 8, with three shear keys in each ring, 120° apart. Each shear key was supported by a pair of anchors splayed 40° apart and inclined upwards at 15°. Fig. 7 and Fig. 8.

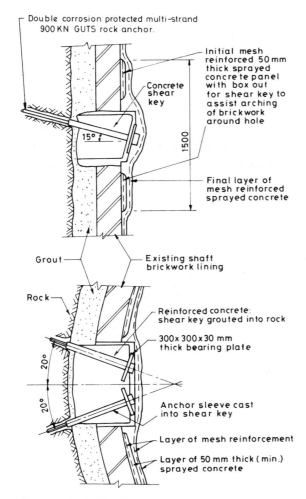

Fig. 8   Detail of anchored shear key

minimum of 50mm of sprayed concrete. The
brickwork in the remainder of the shaft was
then grouted to the rock in small lifts up
to the top of the level of the steel safety
canopy.

With this complete, the first boxout was created,
the reinforced concrete shear key grouted into
position, and the anchor holes drilled through
the sleeves in the shear key and stressed. Once
the three shear keys for each ring were installed
and anchored, the anchors were subjected to lift
off tests and the load in each anchor set to
55% of GUTS. Work then proceeded on the
next ring of shear keys below. On the first
ring in each shaft, the three shear keys were
installed and anchored sequentially in order to
maximise the restraint provided to the brickwork
during the initial stages of the remedial
measures. In subsequent rings, the three shear
keys were installed and anchored in a single
operation.

Three rings were installed in shaft 9 over
the lower 9 m of the shaft and two rings
were installed in shaft 8 over the lower
6.5m of the shaft. Once all rings were
installed, the entire 9 m or 6.5 m of the
shaft was meshed and covered with 50 mm min
thickness of sprayed concrete.

Each of the double corrosion protected
rock anchors consisted of 3 No. 15.2 mm
diameter strand providing 900 kN GUTS. The
bond length of the anchors was assessed from
the results of four, 10m long, N sized cored
exploratory boreholes, inclined at 75° from,
the tunnel roof, aligned parallel to the
tunnel axis and located 2m from the shaft
wall.

The design of the rock anchor required a
bond length of 4m in order to yield
adequate factors of safety under working
and during the proof testing of the anchor
under 70% GUTS. This posed a problem as
the internal diameter of the shaft was
approximately 3.15m.

Prior to the remedial works commencing in
the shaft, the brickwork around the
shaft/tunnel intersection was strengthened
by firstly installing the pattern of 6m
long dowels into the tunnel roof Fig. 6,
and grouting the brickwork to the rock in
the tunnel roof for a distance of 3 m
around the base of the shaft and for 3m up
each shaft. Following this, two rings of
5 m long, 25mm dia high yield steel
dowel with plates were installed at the
intersection around the base of the shaft,
one ring installed almost vertically
inclined from the tunnel roof and the
second ring almost horizontal, installed
into the shaft wall just above the tunnel.
These were used to fix steel mesh around
the intersection, including the original
cast iron beam at the base of each of the
shafts, and the intersection was encased
for 3m around and 3m up the shaft in a

.An articulated bond length was adopted comprising a 2.5m section at the end of the anchor and another 1.5m length of bonded section with a flexible 600mm length of cable between them which was sufficient to allow the articulated bond length to be installed into the anchor hole, Fig. 9. The 2.5m long section of bond length was of sufficient length to allow the entire tensile force in the strand to be transferred into the grout within the corrugated sheathing of the bond length. During installation the flexible length was encased in corrugated plastic sheathing and bonded to the existing bond lengths.

bevelled internal edge, the strand perhaps being caught by the sharp, 90° edge of the tubes during stressing leading to failure. No further losses of strand occurred.

Upon completion of the plug at the base of each shaft, BR filled the shaft with polyurethane foam, a procedure which had already been successfully carried out on the Saltwood Tunnel. Finally a concrete cap was provided at the top of both ventilation shafts.

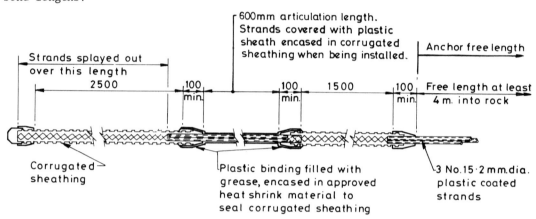

Fig. 9   Anchor bond length

The first anchor pair to be installed was subjected to a full anchorage test in accordance with the method suggested by the ISRM[1].

After the installation of the rings of shear keys, the dowels at the base of the shaft were tensioned to 10 tonnes and extended with extra face plates into the 500mm thick mesh reinforced sprayed concrete plug which was formed at the base of the shaft. Fig. 7 shows the encasement of the cast iron ring in sprayed concrete and the drainage tubes leading water down from the back of the brickwork lining above the fully grouted section and into the tunnel.

In two anchors, one in either shaft, one of the three strands sheared during stressing. After discussion, the tubes attached to the anchor face plates were provided with a

It was in the nature of the works that the cramped and difficult working conditions in the shaft imposed significant constraints upon both the design and construction of the remedial measures. However, the close co-operation between the contractor, Whitley Moran, their sub-contractor Colcrete, and British Rail and their advisors James Williamson & Partners allowed the works to be successfully completed in a short time scale, the works being completed on 19 August 1985, in a period of 4 months. The cost of the remedial measures was of the order of £1 million.

ACKNOWLEDGEMENT

The permission of British Rail to present this paper is gratefully acknowledged.

The work of members of British Rail and James
Williamson and Partners, contributed greatly to
this paper.   In particular, the assistance of
T.P. Davies, Senior Engineering Geologist with
JWP is acknowledged.

Client: British Rail, London
Midland Region
Consulting Engineer: James Williamson &
Partners, Glasgow
Main Contractor:Whitley Moran
Grouting/Anchoring
Sub-Contractor: Colcrete

References

1.   International Society for Rock Mechanics on
      Testing Methods, Suggested Method for Rock
      Anchorage Testing. *International Journal
      of Rock Mechanics and Mining Science*,
      vol. 22, no.2, 1985, p71-83.

Methane hazards in tunnelling operations

J. S. Edwards B.Sc., C.Eng., M.I.Min.E., F.I.M.E.M.M.E.
B. N. Whittaker B.Sc., Ph.D., C.Eng., F.I.Min.E., F.I.M.M., M.A.I.M.E.
S. Durucan B.Sc., M.Sc., Ph.D., C.Eng., M.I.Min.E.
Department of Mining Engineering, University of Nottingham, University Park, Nottingham, United Kingdom

SYNOPSIS

The Abbeystead disaster has raised a number of issues concerning the generation and occurrence of methane, the association of methane with groundwater, and the various methods for the detection of the gas. These matters and their relevance to the tunnelling industry are reviewed and discussed.

INTRODUCTION

The danger arising from the presence of methane in tunnels is highlighted by a number of serious fires and explosions that have occurred despite, in many cases, prior warning of the possible presence of gas coupled with gas testing procedures and special precautions to counter the hazard. Some of the more notable tunnelling incidents include the Furnas hydro-electric scheme (Brazil), Orange Fish (South Africa), Port Huron (Michigan, USA), Chingaza aquaduct (Colombia), Akasombo dam (Ghana), Hongrin (Switzerland), El Colegio (Colombia) and of course, the Abbeystead disaster in the UK. The insidious nature of methane and its widespread occurrence is therefore a cause of great concern to those engaged in tunnelling activities.

Methane is usually associated with underground coal mines but it can occur in significant concentrations in other geological environments. Voitov[1] gives a comprehensive account of methane and other hydrocarbon occurrences throughout the world, with examples from practically every continent. The variety of rocks and minerals with which they are associated is astonishing. Mineral associations include apatite, arsenic, copper, diamond, gold, iron, potash, salt, trona, and uranium and the range of rock types includes limestones, granites, gneisses, mudstone, pegmatites, shales, and quartzite.

The list of examples is by no means exhaustive but serves to demonstrate that methane may be encountered in a wide variety of geological conditions. Voitov concludes that since hydrocarbon gases are present in more than one mine, they must represent a completely regular, and not an accidental phenomenon, which indicates that the presence and probably also the formation of hydrocarbons in the deep lying strata is a widespread process.

THE ORIGINS OF METHANE

Methane is probably the most abundant and widespread of all gaseous fluids in the sedimentary rocks of the Earth and is found in the atmosphere, hydrosphere, and lithosphere. Amongst the principal sources of methane in nature are; marshes and stagnant waters, crude oil reservoirs, natural gas accumulations, coal mines, carbonaceous and bituminous shales, ocean waters, ground waters and some metal mines.

Methane is produced by the decomposition of organic matter in sedimentary deposits. It is generated first by near-surface bacterial decay, then at greater depths by thermochemical degradation, preceding, accompanying, and following the formation of petroleum, coal or disseminated coaly matter, depending on the richness of organic matter in hydrogen.

Source rocks for hydrocarbon fluids consist mainly of organic clays, shales, carbonate muds, and coal seams. These are essentially fine-grained, low porosity and low permeability rocks which are not capable of holding all the gases generated. The transfer of hydrocarbon fluids to reservoir rocks, which usually have relatively high porosities and permeabilities, is termed "migration". The most common reservoir rocks are sandstones and limestones although the occurrence of methane in other geological formations has been reported.

The organic content of sedimentary rocks may vary from a fraction of a percent in some chemically deposited sediments to almost 100 per cent in the case of some coals. It is suggested that the total organic matter in the sedimentary rocks of the world is nearly 4 quadrillion tonnes[2]. Less than one per cent of this total is accounted for by the coal deposits of the world, the greatest proportion lying in muds, shales and silty shales of both marine and nonmarine origin. The ultimate destruction of the organic matter in these sediments therefore constitutes a great potential for widespread methane occurrence in the rocks of the Earth's crust.

The first step in the decomposition of organic matter in shallow water sediments occurs immediately after deposition and is biochemical, involving bacterial reactions. This early stage of bacterial decomposition takes place during the deposition of the first few tens or hundreds of metres of sediments where the effects of temperature and pressure increases are relatively small. Although the limiting depth for the generation of biochemical methane is not exactly agreed upon, biogenic methane can be found at depths of thousands of metres due to subsequent deep burial of originally near-surface generations in younger sediments.

With increasing depth of burial, temperature increases and nonbiogenic thermochemical processes start to become dominant over biochemical methane generation and by the time burial depths of 1000m (60°C) have been attained, thermochemical generation of methane will be dominant. A diagrammatic relation between methane generation and depth of burial (temperature) is shown in Figure 1.

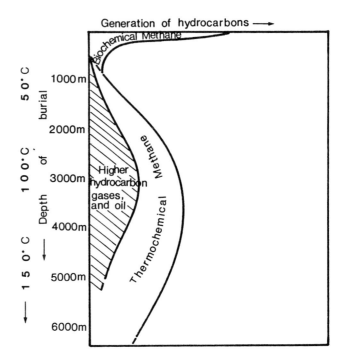

Figure 1 Relation between methane generation and depth of burial. (After Hedberg[2], by courtesy of AAPG).

Coal-related methane

The biological degradation of terrestrial vegetable material in aqueous environments and its subsequent transformation, with time, under the influence of increasing temperature and pressure has produced coals of increasing maturity or "rank". It is estimated[3] that up to 1300m[3] of various gases were generated per tonne of coal produced during the coalification process although only a small proportion of the methane has been retained by the coal seams. Most of the methane has been lost to the atmosphere or dissolved in circulating ground waters and thus removed. Under favourable geological conditions, methane will migrate into high permeability sediments surrounding coal seams, filling the pore spaces or forming accumulations of coal-derived natural gas in traps similar to those in which petroleum-derived gas has accumulated. This type of accumulation is known to contain very small proportions of higher hydrocarbons. Tiratsoo[4] reports that the Upper Carboniferous Measures underlying the U.K. Continental Shelf are thought to be the source of non-associated gas accumulations found in the Southern North Sea Basin. Also, the coal seams of Lancashire, Cumberland and North Wales are thought to be the likely sources of the gas discovered beneath the Northern Irish Sea. It is usual practice in coal mining to assume that the carboniferous strata surrounding coal seams contain between one to ten per cent of the gas content of the nearest coal seam.

Oil-related methane

Natural gas, in which methane is by far the most abundant component (85-98%), is very widely found in close association with crude oil. Therefore, it is often considered to be the gaseous phase of crude oil and shares at least to some degree a common origin.

Oil and associated gases are formed from "kerogen", a disseminated sedimentary organic matter which makes up about 90% of the organic matter in clays and shales. The type and quality of kerogen present in a sediment is one of the principal factors which determines whether liquid oil and "wet" gas or "dry" gas will be formed during the transformation process.

The transformation of kerogens into liquid oils and hydrocarbon gases is a function of increased temperature and the length of time that the heating process has continued. The first stage of alteration takes place during the decomposition of early sediments producing water, carbon dioxide and early diagenic methane. This early stage represents the "immature stage" of gas generation. As the thickness of the sedimentary overburden reaches several thousand metres, the second stage of kerogen transformation begins where liquid petroleum, methane and "wet" gas components are produced. The temperature range of roughly 60°-150°C, where liquid petroleum and C_{2+} hydrocarbons are generated, has been termed the "oil window" which also represents the "mature stage" of gas generation. Below a temperature level of about 150°C, which is equivalent to a burial depth of nearly 5000m only "dry" gas is produced through further decomposition of organic matter and thermal cracking of liquid oil. This stage represents the "overmature stage" of gas generation.

The zones of oil and gas generation and their correlation with the coal-rank scale and various maturation indices are shown in Figure 2.

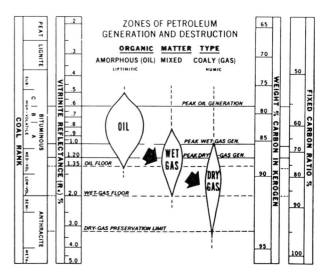

Figure 2   Correlation of coal-rank scale with various maturation indices and zones of petroleum and gas generation. (After Dow[5], by courtesy of AAPG).

Identifying the origins of methane

Identification of the possible origin(s) of any methane encountered in tunnelling may be useful in determining the extent of a problem and in the selection of appropriate control measures.

Carbon has two stable isotopes, ^{12}C and ^{13}C. The variations in carbon isotope ratio ($^{13}C/^{12}C$) of methane are widely used as an indication of the origin and degree of maturity of the gas. Carbon isotope ratios for methane samples are measured in the laboratory using specially designed mass spectrometers. The isotope ratio determined for the unknown sample is then compared with a reference.

The "carbon 13 delta value" for the sample is defined by the equation:

$$\delta^{13}C = [(R_s - R_r) / R_r] \times 1000‰$$

Where R_s and R_r refer to the ratio $^{13}C/^{12}C$ in the sample and reference respectively. The $\delta^{13}C$ value is therefore the deviation from the standard in parts per thousand. It is positive if the sample is enriched in ^{13}C and negative if the sample is depleted in ^{13}C compared to the reference.

Research has shown[6] that methane has the largest $\delta^{13}C$ range of any naturally occurring carbon compound, with a spread of about 80‰ from

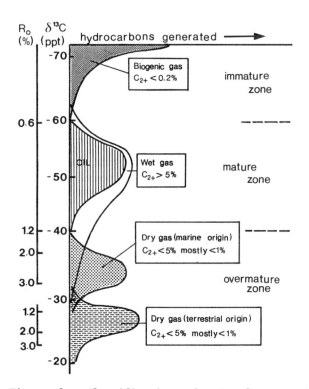

Figure 3 Classification of natural gases by compositional and isotopic variation in different zones of methane generation. (Modified from Schoell[7,8]).

less than -90‰ to about -13‰ . However, it is significant from the isotope measurements that different categories of methane have distinct $\delta^{13}C$ ranges. As shown in Figure 3, ^{13}C concentrations in methane increase continuously from immature to overmature gases. Immature gases generated by bacterial action have $\delta^{13}C$ values in the range -75 to -60‰, whereas mature gases generated in the oil window have $\delta^{13}C$ values of -60 to -40‰ and overmature gases have $\delta^{13}C$ values of between -40 to -25‰. These values are not precisely differentiable; they overlap due to mixing during migration and variations in the organic matter from which the different gases were derived. In general, methane generated from organic material deposited in terrestrial environments have $\delta^{13}C$ values heavier by 10-15% compared with methane from marine deposits. The carbon isotope ratio is not the only indicator of the origins of methane; the ratio of methane to ethane, for example, is also helpful. Biogenic gases contain extremely low concentrations of C_{2+} components. Higher hydrocarbon concentrations are significantly high in gases associated with oil generation and overmature gases contain decreasing amounts of higher hydrocarbons, see Figure 3.

PROPERTIES OF METHANE

Methane is a colourless, odourless gas (though when emitted with impurities such as other hydrocarbons and traces of hydrogen sulphide it may have a characteristic smell) with a density of 0.7168 kg/m^3 giving the gas a specific gravity relative to air of 0.5545.

However, the most important property of methane is that it is flammable and forms explosive mixtures with air. When it burns it combines with the oxygen of the air to form carbon dioxide, water and nitrogen. Prevention of methane explosions during construction and operation of tunnels encountering gassy formations requires a knowledge of the flammability characteristics of methane.

Methane-air mixtures will burn over a wide range of concentrations when subjected to elevated temperatures, however it can only propagate flame freely within a limited range of compositions. A methane flame will propagate from an ignition source at ambient temperatures and pressures only if the surrounding mixture contains betwen 5% and 15% methane. The stoichiometric ratio, where there is just sufficient volume of oxygen in the air to completely burn all the methane in the mixture, is 9.48%. Below the stoichiometric ratio, part of the oxygen remains unburnt and above 9.48% only part of the methane burns and the remainder cools the mixture. In practice the limits of flammability of methane air mixtures are affected by the strength of the ignition source, temperature and pressure of the surroundings.

When a flammable mixture of methane and air is heated to an elevated temperature, an exothermic reaction is initiated that may proceed with sufficient rapidity to ignite the mixture. The time that elapses between the instant the mixture temperature is raised and that in which ignition takes place is called the 'lag on ignition'. In general the time delay depends on the temperature of the heat source; at 650°C the delay is 10 seconds but at 1000°C it falls to 1 second. The performance of 'permitted' explosives results partly from this effect.

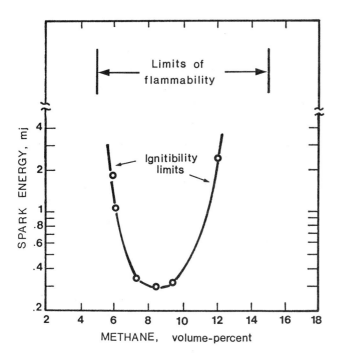

Figure 4 Ignitibility curve and limits of flammability for methane-air mixtures at atmospheric pressure and 25°C. (After Zebetakis[9], by courtesy of the US Bureau of Mines).

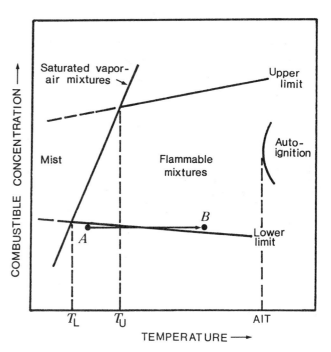

Figure 5 Effect of temperature on limits of flammability of a combustible vapour in air at constant initial pressure. (After Zebetakis[9], by courtesy of the US Bureau of Mines.)

The lowest temperature at which ignition can occur is called the autoignition temperature (AIT), which for methane is 537°C. However, research has shown that this temperature may be considerably higher or lower depending on the type of igniter, the methane content of the air, and the presence of various impurities etc. For ignition to occur, a sufficient volume of mixture must be brought to or above the autoignition temperature for a length of time that allows flame to form and spread. Therefore, in a flowing system, the temperature of the ignition source must be higher than the autoignition temperature of the mixture determined under static conditions. An increase in pressure generally decreases the AIT of methane-air mixtures. For example, the AIT of natural gas in air decreases from 530°C at 1 atm. to 240°C at 610 atm.

Ignition of methane-air mixtures will usually occur by contact with a spark, open flame or a hot surface. Experiments have shown that hot surfaces ignite methane at a temperature much higher than a flame temperature, e.g. the iron gauze of a flame safety lamp needs to be about 1200°C to ignite methane-air mixtures.

In the case of ignition by electric sparks there is a minimum spark energy which is needed to ignite methane-air mixtures. The effect of mixture composition on the spark energy requirements for ignition of methane-air mixtures is illustrated in Figure 4. It is evident that considerably greater spark energies are required to ignite methane-air mixtures at the limits of flammability.

The limits of flammability for methane-air mixtures are dependent on the temperature at constant pressure; as the temperature is increased, the lower limit decreases and the upper limit increases. Thus a nonflammable mixture (A) may become flammable (B) if its temperature is elevated sufficiently, Figure 5 .

The ignition of methane depends on the composition of air with which it is mixed. Either a lowered oxygen content or high inert concentration will make methane ignition more difficult. Figure 6 illustrates the flammability limits of a mixture of methane with air containing various concentrations of oxygen. The minimum oxygen concentration required for flame propagation through a methane-oxygen-nitrogen mixture at 25°C and 1 atmosphere is 12 per cent.

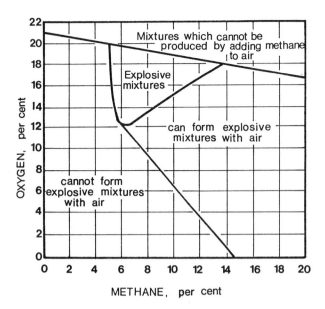

Figure 6 Limits of flammability of mixtures of methane, air and nitrogen.

However, increased pressure lowers the minimum oxygen concentrations required for flame propagation as shown in Figure 7. This factor may be important in compressed-air working.

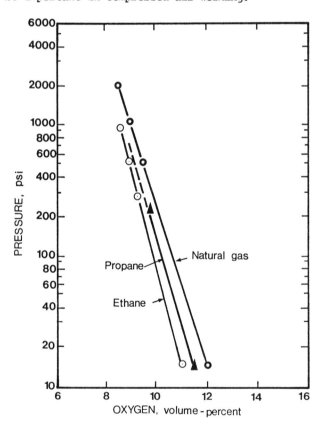

Figure 7 Effect of pressure on minimum oxygen requirements for flame propagation through mixtures of flammable gases with air. (After Zebetakis[9], by courtesy of the US Bureau of Mines.

If the atmosphere contains a mixture of combustible gases, the lower limit of flammability of the combustible mixture will be different from that of methane. The presence of higher hydrocarbons, for which the lower limit of flammability is less than 5 per cent, will reduce the lower limit of flammability for the mixture.

Solubility of methane in water

All gases dissolve in water to a measureable degree. At a given temperature the solubilities of gases which do not react with the solvent to any appreciable extent are directly proportional to the partial pressures of the gases above the solution. This relationship is known as Henry's Law which may be expressed mathematically in the form,

$$P = HX$$

where   P = partial pressure of the solute in
              the gas phase (mm Hg).
        X = mole fraction of the solute in
              the liquid phase.
and   H = Henry's constant (mm Hg/mole).

Henry's Law is exact only in the infinitely diluted state but it is a good approximation in dilute solutions.

When considering the question of dissolved gases in groundwater the relative amounts of solute (the dissolved constituent) and the solvent (the water) are required. This is accomplished by the use of concentration units, the most commonly used being "mg/l" which, for non-saline water is equivalent to 'parts per million' (ppm).If the solubility of a gas is known for one pressure the Henry's Law constant may be calculated and used to calculate the solubility at any other gas pressure.

The solubility of methane in water is dependent upon temperature, pressure and salinity. McAuliffe[10] reports that the solubility of natural gas (predominantly methane) shows a decrease with increasing temperature up to about 80°C and an increase of solubility with temperature above this value. The solubility of methane at 80°C is only 12.64 mg/l compared with the value of 21.47 mg/l at 25°C.

The solubilities of gases show a marked increase with increasing pressure and the solubilities of many gases, including methane, are approximately linear functions of pressure, the deviation being insignificant for the purposes of engineering accuracy. The solubility of methane in water may therefore be predicted[11] over a wide range of pressures from one experimentally determined point and a knowledge of the solubility of the gas at atmospheric pressure serves this purpose. This may be expressed by the relation.

$$V = kp$$

where V, the volume of gas dissolved, is measured at atmospheric temperature and pressure (25°C and 760 mm Hg). If p is the pressure in atmospheres absolute, k becomes equal to the atmospheric solubility (21.47 mg/l/atm.). Table 1. gives some typical values:

Table 1. Effect of pressure on methane solubility

Pressure (atm.)	1	20	40	60	80	100
Solubility (mg/l)	21.47	429	859	1288	1717	2147

Solubilities of gases are normally quoted with respect to distilled or fresh water. In reality however, natural waters containing varying amounts of dissolved salts are the solvent and solubility values should be adjusted accordingly. The effect of increasing salinity is to cause a decrease in solubility; Levorsen[12] states that there is a reduction in solubility of about 5% per 1% increase in weight of dissolved mineral matter when the water is a brine.

Of the three effects, temperature, pressure and salinity, on the solubility of methane in water, the effect of pressure is dominant. When the effects of temperature and pressure are combined, as is the case when the mechanism of gaseous hydrocarbon migration within the earth is being considered, the characteristic graph (Figure 8.), given by McAuliffe[10] is generated: the two opposing influences of temperature and pressure both increasing with depth as a result of the geothermal gradient and hydrostatic head.

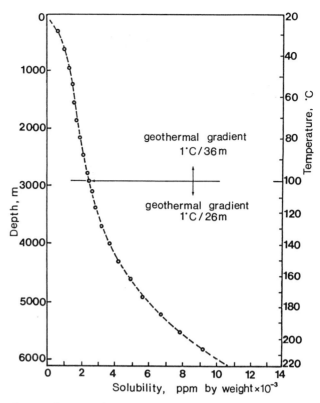

Figure 8 Combined effect of pressure and temperature on the solubility of methane. (After McAuliffe[10], by courtesy of AAPG)

OCCURRENCE OF METHANE IN GROUNDWATER

Most groundwater contains dissolved gases, the most abundant of which are N_2, O_2, CO_2, CH_4, H_2S and N_2O. The first three are derived from the atmosphere whilst the remainder are the product of biogeochemical processes that take place in subsurface zones characterized by extremely low O_2 concentrations - an anaerobic environment.

Methane is a common constituent of groundwater and may be present either as a result of biogenic generation through the decomposition of buried organic matter or, as Tiratsoo[5] considers, may occur in association with natural gas or petroleum accumulations in deep buried strata of organic origin.

Since groundwater is a common problem in tunnelling operations the possibility of methane occurring in association with water should not be overlooked. Examples of occurrences of methane-bearing groundwater and the problems arising therefrom include the Furnas hydro-electric scheme in Brazil[13] where, during closure of the diversion tunnels, methane was encountered which had been released from water leaking into the tunnel from the impounded water behind the dam. The gas thereby contaminated the tunnel atmosphere and an explosion occurred which resulted in the deaths of several men. Large quantities of methane had apparently been generated in the bottom waters of the reservoir where the high pressure had caused a large quantity of methane to become dissolved in the water.

In some South African gold mines methane derived from overlying coal seams is dissolved in groundwater which has percolated downwards into the older gold-bearing rocks and is under considerable pressure in fissures. When a development heading or borehole intersects such a water-bearing fissure the sudden reduction in pressure releases the methane from solution which then enters the workings.

Several instances are recorded of explosions occurring as a result of methane-bearing groundwater being introduced into an enclosure. The most recent example is the Abbeystead disaster in which an explosion in the valve house of the Lune-Wyre water transfer scheme, resulting in the deaths of several visitors to the site, is thought to have been the result of the ignition of a methane-air mixture, the methane having entered the aquaduct in a dissolved state in groundwater leaking into the system.

Buswell and Larson[14] have described the occurrence of methane in water wells in Illinois, U.S.A., which is derived from the decay of organic matter in glacial drift or similar formations. Harder and Holden[15] report that methane occurs in fresh groundwater in California, Illinois, Wisconsin, and Louisiana and conclude that methane in groundwater is more widespread than is known.

In some areas of Hungary the ground water has been described[16] as containing large quantities of gas including methane, nitrogen and carbon dioxide, derived from near-surface and petroleum sources.

A Method for determining the methane content of water.

The most convenient method for determining the methane content of water, which is simple, rapid and very sensitive, is the 'combustible-gas indicator method'. The principle of the technique is based upon the equilibrium which, according to Henry's law, is established between the methane gas in solution and the partial pressure of methane in the gas phase above the solution.

A sample of the water to be tested is added to a container so that the container is between 2/3 and 3/4 full. The container is fitted with a rubber stopper through which pass two tubes extending into the container to different heights above the water surface. The external ends of the tubes are connected, via a stop cock, with flexible tubing. Once the water sample has been added to the container the sample is shaken vigorously for one minute and then allowed to stand for two hours so that equilibrium may be established between the gas in the solution and the gas in the air space above the water. To measure the gas concentration in the air space one of the ends of the tubes is disconnected from the container and fitted to the inlet of the combustible-gas indicator (the old type MSA C4 methanometer with an aspirator bulb is ideal for this purpose). The atmosphere in the container is thus drawn through the indicator and the percentage of methane recorded.

To calculate the methane concentration C in mg/1 in the water sample, use is made of an equation first derived by Rossum et al[17] and subsequently modified by Harder and Holden[15].

$$C = V_f P[\ 0.257(V_g/TV_s)+(890/H)]$$

Where,

V_f = volume fraction of methane in the vapour phase (CH_4%)

P = system pressure (760 mm Hg at sea level).

V_g = volume of the vapour phase (1)

T = system temperature (°K).

V_s = volume of sample (1)

H = Henry's law constant, (mm Hg/ mole fraction).

Safe limits

An important question is the safe limit of methane concentration in water which will ensure safety from explosion at all times. The value may be calculated from the following formula derived by Buswell and Larson[14];

$$\% \text{ CH}_4 \text{ in air at equilibrium} = 3.417 \times 10^2 \text{ Q/P}$$

where,   Q = dissolved methane content of
            water (mg/l)

and   P = absolute pressure in kPa.

Assuming a worst case where an unlimited quantity of water flows through an unventilated air tight chamber at atmospheric pressure an explosive gas mixture of 5% methane would build up if the water contained only 1.5 mg/l. For complete safety the methane concentration would need to be maintained at a much lower level than this and if, for example, the limit of 10% of the LEL is used (0.5% methane) the safe concentration falls to 0.15 mg/l. Larson[18] gives additional data on the problem of methane-bearing water.

The conclusion that can be drawn from the foregoing discussion is that the presence of methane in a dissolved state in groundwater can, given the right set of circumstances, give rise to a serious explosion hazard. Any place where methane-bearing water comes into contact with air is a potential point of danger.

METHANE EMISSION INTO TUNNELS
To understand the various means by which methane can enter tunnels, the theory governing the single- and multi-phase flow of fluids through permeable media must be considered together with strata mechanics and groundwater hydrology.

The laminar flow of fluids through porous permeable media is governed by Darcy's Law. The fluid conductivity (permeability) of a porous rock to a homogenous fluid which saturates it is a property characteristic of the rock itself. If the same rock is saturated with more than one fluid the permeabilities to be associated with each phase (effective permeability) are sensitive functions of their saturations. The effect of saturation on relative permeabilities of two fluids (k_{r1}, k_{r2}) occupying the pores of a porous medium is shown in Figure 9.

Figure 9 shows that simultaneous flow of the two fluids is possible only if saturation in fluid 1 is greater than the irreducible saturation and if saturation in fluid 2 is

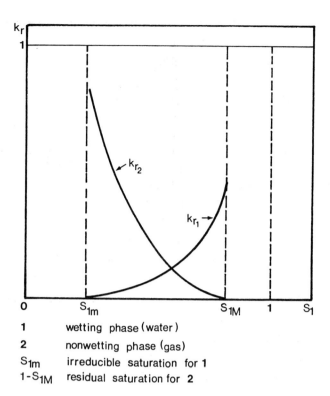

1   wetting phase (water)
2   nonwetting phase (gas)
S_{1m} irreducible saturation for 1
$1-S_{1M}$ residual saturation for 2

Figure 9   Relative permeability curves for water and gas.

greater than the residual saturation. It is also evident that the presence of an irreducible wetting fluid has little effect on the flow of a nonwetting fluid whereas the presence of a residual nonwetting fluid interferes considerably with the flow of a wetting fluid.

The effect of tunnelling on methane flow
The release of methane from reservoir rocks and its subsequent migration towards underground openings is dependent upon the permeability of the rock mass and the pressure gradient. Prior to tunnelling the rock mass, and therefore the gases stored in it, are in a state of equilibrium. As tunnelling proceeds, this equilibrium is disturbed and flowpaths, through which methane and/or groundwater could migrate, are created. The processes which may contribute to the changes in permeability of the rock mass adjacent to the walls of a tunnel include stress redistribution due to extraction, blast induced damage and weathering or interaction between the rock and groundwater.

When a tunnel is excavated, the redistribution of the stresses in the rock mass immediately surrounding the excavation results in

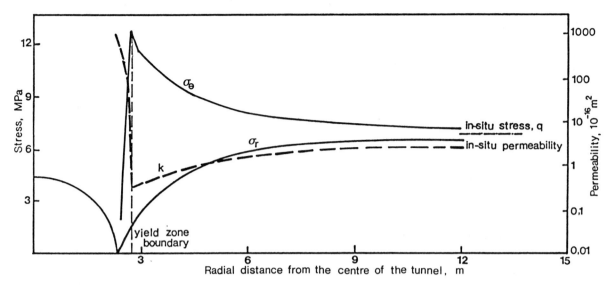

Figure 10 Theoretical stress distribution around a 300 m. deep circular tunnel in mudstone.

the formation of a zone of fractured rock which is referred to as the "yield zone". The fracturing and dilation of the rock mass within the yield zone thus induces a high permeability zone surrounding the excavation. The shape and the extent of the yield zone is dependent upon the lithologic nature and mechanical properties of the rock mass.

Figure 10 shows a theoretical stress distribution at 300m depth along a radius from the centre of a 2.50m radius tunnel in mudstone. The position of the yield zone and the effect of changing stresses on the permeability of the rock mass are also included. The extent of the yield zone around tunnels can be predicted using post-failure strength characteristics of the rocks concerned. Figure 11 summarises the predicted values for the extent of the yield zone around circular tunnels in different rocks for varying depths of cover. It is clear from Figure 11 that, if a tunnel is being driven through gassy rocks, the presence of a high permeability yield zone around the tunnel will constitute a steady source of methane emission as the tunnel advances.

Relatively strong rocks at shallow depths behave elastically where the deformations are theoretically reversible and there is no failure of the rock due to stress redistribution. Under these circumstances, the major disturbance in terms of rock failure and fracture propagation will be due to blasting. The extent of blast damage is more or less independent of tunnel

size. However, it is greatly influenced by the blasting technique. The extent of blast damaged zones reported in literature[19] vary between 0.3 m and 1.5 m. depending on the explosive charge densities and the rock conditions. It is widely agreed that the blast damage can be limited to within 0.3 m. of the opening if controlled blasting techniques with low perimeter charge weights are practised.

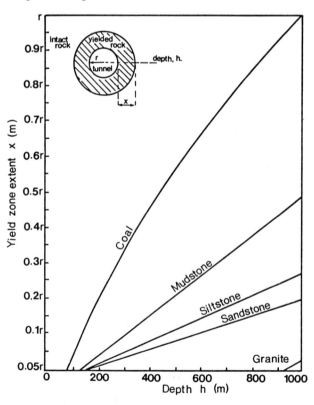

Figure 11 Extent of the yield zone around circular tunnels as a function of tunnel radius and depth of cover.

The permeability of concrete for methane has been reported as $3.1 \times 10^{-16}m^2$ and it decreases further (by two orders of magnitude) if the concrete is wet[20]. When a tunnel is lined, the permeability of the fractured rock in the yield zone will be at least two orders of magnitude higher than the permeability of the lining. A concrete lining thus forms a low permeability barrier which will cause the yield zone to act as a reservoir if it is not well grouted. Methane will tend to accumulate and migrate behind the lining and may enter the tunnel through fractures in the lining or due to a pressure drop in the tunnel.

A tunnel below the water table will act as a sink and lower the water table. Groundwater often contains methane in solution, which may be released due to a pressure drop as water enters a tunnel. Also, the lowering of the water table may reduce the water saturation of the strata to a level below the critical value for methane flow and initiate methane migration towards the tunnel from a nearby gas reservoir.

Various possible means by which methane may migrate towards a tunnel, in the form of dissolved gas, single-phase methane, and multi-phase methane and water, must be understood and taken into consideration during the design, construction and operation of tunnels in gassy environments.

GAS TESTING AND ENVIRONMENTAL MONITORING

Gassy-v-Non gassy conditions

The implications as far as the mining and tunnelling professions are concerned, of the widespread occurrence of methane, is that the classification of any kind of underground excavation as gassy or non-gassy must be made on a rational basis.

The Mine Safety and Health Administration (MSHA) of the U.S Department of Labor classifies U.S metal and non-metal mines as either gassy or non-gassy based on the following criteria set forth in the Code of Federal Regulations, 30 CFR 57.21-1;

(a) The State in which the mine is located classifies the mine as gassy; or

(b) Flammable gas emanating from the orebody or the strata surrounding the orebody has been

ignited in the mine; or

(c) A concentration of 0.25% or more, by air analysis, of flammable gas, emanating only from the orebody or the strata surrounding the orebody, has been detected not less than "12 inches" from the back, face, or ribs in any open workings; or

(d) The mine is connected to a gassy mine.

As a result of the high number of accidental methane gas ignitions in metal and non-metal mines, the USBM recently carried out a study[21] of the incidence of such ignitions in order to provide a simple guideline which would allow mine personnel to evaluate the methane hazard in a given mine. Air samples were collected from 53 metal and non-metal mines and analysed for the presence of methane. 43 of the 44 mines classified as non-gassy had return air concentrations less than 100 ppm and 7 of the 9 gassy mines had return air concentrations greater than 100 ppm.

On the basis of these findings it was suggested that 100 ppm could be used as a simple guideline for determining if a potential methane hazard existed. Subsequent to the publication of their report an explosion occurred at one of the mines and several mines were reclassified. As a result it is now suggested by MHSA that the guideline be set at 70 ppm.

The implication as far as tunnelling is concerned is that the traditional means of testing for gas, whilst perfectly adequate for routine serveillance of the working environment, may not be suitable for determining if methane is entering the tunnel under normal conditions of ventilation. In these circumstances recourse must be made to the taking of gas samples for laboratory analysis or use must be made of instruments capable of responding to methane concentrations in the ppm range. It is preferable to assume that an underground space is gassy until proved otherwise, rather than the reverse which is to consider the environment to be unsafe only when this is demonstrated by incident.

Gas testing and environmental monitoring systems

Since methane has been shown to be a commonly encountered gas it is a sensible precaution to assume that the gas may be encountered in any underground construction. Site investigation should reveal the potential for hydrocarbons to be present within a given geological setting but confirmation of their presence or otherwise can only be determined by testing.

As has already been shown the evidence from metal mining operations is that the 'non-gassy/gassy' threshold may be very low, and certainly well below the limit of detection of the common types of methanometer. For this purpose therefore air samples should be taken for analysis by a laboratory for the presence of methane, possibly down to a few ppm . Such a system of sampling should be initiated at the earliest stage in a tunnel project and continued for as long as tunnelling and construction operations are being carried out.

Whenever methane is proved to be, or suspected of being, present in a tunnel a system of monitoring will need to be established. The term 'gas monitoring' implies continuous and regular testing of the atmosphere, i.e a systematic approach, in contrast to an intermittent series of checks which is the characteristic of 'gas detection'.

Monitoring should be carried out using suitable instruments by trained personnel who are familiar with the instruments and aware of their range of application and limitations. Instruments should be regularly tested for accuracy and recalibrated at regular intervals by an approved authority; an inaccurate instrument can be more of a danger than an instrument that does not work at all. Records of such tests should be kept.

Many types of methanometer are available for use in tunnelling environments and, in common with all scientific instruments, have limitations on their performance. Most methanometers are affected by the presence of inflammable gases other than methane such as ethane, propane, hydrogen and carbon monoxide all of which change the performance of the instrument. In most cases the error is on the safe side but not in all; carbon monoxide, for example, produces a reduced response in the catalytic-oxidation type of detector. Instruments may also be affected by oxygen deficiency, poisoning by vapours such as silicones, phosphate esters, and fluorocarbons and in some cases by varying angles of inclination of the instrument. Optical interferometer types of detectors are also sensitive to gases other than methane. A hydrogen-air mixture results in a negative gas concentration reading and in a 1% hydrogen plus 1% methane-air mixture the two gases produce a net zero response.

In any system of methane monitoring the concept of methane quantity as opposed to methane concentration should be adopted. Although methane concentration is of immediate importance for monitoring current environmental conditions the quantity of methane present in the air is important in relation to source emission rates and the effect on conditions if ventilation quantities change. Any increase in methane concentration should always be checked to determine if the increase represents a change in emission rate.

Most countries have regulations for mining/tunnelling activities which incorporate 'action levels' relating to general body methane concentration values. Typically these action levels are between 1% and 2% and will involve withdrawal of men, the cutting off of electrical power in certain areas and so on. It is tempting to regard such action levels as incorporating a factor of safety but this concept is very misleading and should be discouraged. The importance of these values lies in the recognition that methane invariably enters a mine or tunnel in the pure state, i.e. 100% methane, and that this condition prevails irrespective of the degree of ventilation. In the process of being diluted from its pure state to that of the general body value the methane concentration must pass through the explosive range at some point in the system and the purpose of ventilation is to dilute the gas through the dangerous range as quickly as possible. The 1% and 2% action levels reflect the fact that at these general body concentrations there may be a considerable quantity of gas within the explosive range and that it is a wise precaution to remove both men and possible sources of ignition.

The tunnelling and civil engineering industry in general has a wide range of environmental monitoring equipment from which to select the most suitable instruments for a given set of circumstances. A comprehensive review[22] of available instruments is given in CIRIA Report 80. In addition to the usual types of gas-detection instruments, systems that have been developed in the coal, gas and oil producing industries for emergency shut-down procedures are also available. These systems will continuously monitor the environment and cut off electrical power (other than that required for safety, such as fans) when the methane concentration exceeds predetermined values. Such systems will be extremely useful in the tunnelling industry particularly when the question of flame-proof equipment is under consideration.

CONCLUSIONS

The general conclusions that may be drawn from this review are:

1. The occurrence of methane is widespread and may be encountered in a wide variety of geological conditions.

2. The gassy/non-gassy threshold is low and accurate measurements of methane concentration in the atmosphere are required for the assessment of risk.

3. High standards of environmental monitoring are essential for the maintenance of safe conditions. Equipment should be suitable for the job, and regularly serviced and calibrated.

4. In the case of the occurrence of methane dissolved in groundwater, the extent of the problem needs to be established and the mechanism of its formation understood.

References

1. Voitov, G.I., Gas emanation in ore mines. In: Air Pollution in mines, theory hazards and control. Ed. Lidin, G.D. Moscow: Academy of Sciences of the U.S.S.R., Mining Institute, 1962. Jerusalem: Israel Program of Scientific Translations, 1966, pp.142-161.

2. Hedberg, H.D., Methane generation and petroleum migration. In: Problems of petroleum migration. Eds. Roberts, W.H. and Cordell, R.J. The American Association of Petroleum Geologists, Studies in Geology No. 10, 1980, pp.179-206.

3. Patching, T.H., The retention and release of gas in coal- A review. Canadian Mining and Metallurgy Bulletin, November 1970, pp.1302-1308.

4. Tiratsoo, E.N., Natural Gas. 3rd ed., Beaconsfield, England: Scientific Press Ltd., 1979, 360p.

5. Dow, W.G., Petroleum source beds on continental slopes and rises. The American Association of Petroleum Geologists Bulletin, Vol.62, No.9, September 1978, pp.1584-1606.

6. Fuex, A.N., The use of stable carbon isotopes in hydrocarbon exploration. Journal of Geochemical Exploration, Vol.7, 1977, pp.155-188.

7. Schoell, M., The hydrogen and carbon isotopic composition of methane from natural gases of various origins. Geochimica et Cosmica Acta, Vol.44, 1980, pp.649-661.

8. Schoell, M. Genetic characterization of natural gases. The American Association of Petroleum Geologists Bulletin, Vol.67, No.12, December 1983, pp.2225-2238.

9. Zebetakis, M.G., Flammability characteristics of combustible gases and vapors. U.S. Bureau of Mines, Bulletin No.627, 1965, 121p.

10. McAuliffe, C.D., Oil and gas migration: Chemical and physical constraints. In: Problems of petroleum migration. Eds. Roberts, W.H., and Cordell, R.J. The American Association of Petroleum Geologists, Studies in Geology No.10, 1980, pp.89-107.

11. Frolich, Per K., Tauch, E.J., Hogan, J.J., and Peer, A.A., Solubilities of gases in liquids at high pressure. Vol. 23,5.,1931, pp.548-550

12. Levorsen, A.I., Geology of petroleum. 2nd Ed. Freeman, San Francisco. 1967. pp.211-214.

13. Lyra, F.H., and MacGregor, W., Furnas hydroelectric scheme, Brazil: Closure of diversion tunnels. Proceedings, Institution of Civil Engineers (London), vol.36, pp.21-46.

14. Buswell, A.M., and Larson, T.E., Methane in ground waters. Journal of American Water Works Association, Vol.29, No.12, 1937, pp.1978-1982.

15. Harder, A.H., and Holden, W.R., Measurement of gas in groundwater. Water Resources Research, Vol.I, 1965, pp.75-82.

16. Belteky, L., and Korim, K., Problems related to the use of gaseous waters from artesian wells in Hungary. Vizugi Kozlemenyek, Part I, 1974.

17. Rossum, J.R., Villarruz, P.A., and Wade Jr., J.A., A new method for determining methane in water. Journal of American Water Works Association, Vol.42, No.4, 1950, pp.413-415.

18. Larson, T.E., Properties and determination of methane in groundwaters. <u>Journal of American Water Works Association</u>, Vol.30, No.11, 1938, pp.1828-1835.

19. Kelsall, P.C., Case, J.B., and Chabannes, C.R., Evaluation of excavation-induced changes in rock permeability. <u>International Journal of Rock Mechanics and Mining Sciences</u>, Vol.21, No.3, 1984, pp.123-135.

20. Chen, L.C., and Katz, D.L., Diffusion of methane through concrete. <u>American Concrete Institute Journal</u>, December 1978, pp.673-679.

21. Thimons, E.D., Vinson, R.P., and Kissell, F.N., <u>Forecasting methane hazards in metal and nonmetal mines</u>. U.S. Bureau of Mines RI8392, 1979, 9p.

22. CIRIA, <u>A review of instruments for gas and dust monitoring underground</u>. Construction Industry Research & Information Association, Report 80, London, 1978, 58p.

Construction of a difficult tunnel in a developing country

Mete Erdemgil Prof.Dr.
Yalçın Zaim M.S.
Kiska Construction Corporation, Ankara, Turkey

SYNOPSIS

Similar to any project, tunnelling projects also require the solution of technical, administrative and financial related problems. The 16-km long Kınık Tunnel was planned towards the end of sixties by the Turkish State Water Works Authority (DSİ) as an element of the Water Supply Scheme for the city Ankara. Subsequently the contract was awarded to Ankara based Kiska Construction Corporation in the early seventies.

The national State Water Works authority carried out the pre-planning and design of the tunnel and issued it to various foreign companies since the technology for such a construction was lacking in the country. Later on, not only foreign technology but also foreign finance sourcing was found to be necessary for the execution of the tunnel project.

The excavation of the 16-km long tunnel, under very difficult subsoil conditions, was completed at the end of 1986, in a time of more than 10 years after the construction began. The final linings, contact and consolidation injections were finished few months after the completion of excavation.

During the construction period of more than 10 years, many foreign and a very few local companies made studies, prepared reports and got involved in the construction. On the one hand the contracting company, carrying the financial and contractual risk, tried to bring together the different interests of consulting and equipment marketing foreign companies whereas the local authority, on the other hand gaining experience during construction and trying to manage the work strove to reach applicable decisions on the construction works.

Most of the delay was due to collapse of the tunnel face, being subject to a pore pressure of 20 bars. But the disagreement on the contract text and its application, which occurred due to insufficient investigation of the underground before the contract was awarded causing many project revisions, was another reason.

As a result, the construction of an unusually complicated tunnel in a developing country contains a package of problems which do not exist in the similar projects to be executed in developed countries, at least not to the same extreme extent as technical, administrative and financial problems. In this paper these difficulties are discussed pointing out some specific problems and their solutions.

1.0 Ankara Water Supply Project and the Kınık Tunnel

The supply of drinking and industrial water for the capital city of Turkey, Ankara, required intensive efforts in regard to the planning and the construction. The results of planning studies yield the following:

Year	Population	Water demand (10^6) m3/yr)	Available Water Supply (10^6 m3/yr)
1980	1,878,000	165	128.5
1985	2,251,533	227	128.5
1990	2,422,000	270	358.5
1995	2,687,000	319	358.5
2000	2,981,000	377	Under Planning
2005	3,298,000	443	" "
2010	3,650,000	521	" "

Table 1. The population and water demand of the city of Ankara.

As it is clear from Table 1, the available water resources are deficient in the years between 1980 and 1990, and the gap between demand and available supply increases towards the end of 1980's. The jump of supply from 128,5 to 358,5 x 10^6 m3/yr is planned to be realized from Çamlıdere - Bayındır Dam. As it may be seen from Fig 1., Kınık Tunnel with its 15.5 km length (finished diameter, ID=3400 mm represents a major structure in the project.

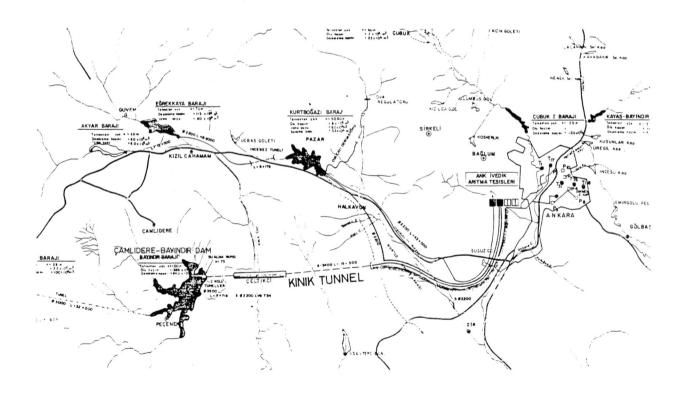

There are two other tunnels just after the Çamlıdere - Bayındır Dam, Tunnels Number 1 and Number 2, with a total length of 7.718 km altogether. In the year 1986 although the rest of project construction between the dam and the Water Purification Plant, close to Ankara, was completed, the excavation of Kınık Tunnel was still in progress with failures occuring at the faces and water inflows about 200 lts/sec. There was no evidence to show as to when and if ever it was going to be completed. But the city of Ankara was experiencing a severe shortage of water. This focused the public attention and the social pressure of the citizens of Ankara politically, with impatient articles in the local press.

2.0 Some Major Characteristics of the Kınık Tunnel

The Kınık Tunnel is composed of a Main Tunnel, two approach tunnels, two shafts and a cut and cover section. Their major characteristics are given in Table 2.

Length of main Tunnel	: 15 824 m
Slope of main Tunnel	: From Km 7+229, 13 towards upstream 0.00015 towards downstream 0.00013
Excavation diameter of main tunnel	: 4.60 m
Internal diameter of main tunnel concrete lining	: 3.40 m
Thickness of concrete lining of main tunnel	: 0.60 m
Maintunnel section	: Horse shoe
Location of balance shaft	: Km 4+457
Height of balance shaft	: 180.06 m
Excavation diameter of balance shaft	: 9.50 m
Clear diameter of balance shaft	: 8.00 m
Evci shaft location	: km 6+704
" " height	: 152.52 m
" " excavation diameter	: 7.20 m
" " final diameter	: 6.00 m
Grout-Approach tunnel no.2 (Y-2) location	: Km 9+060
" " " length	: 1997.64 m
" " " slope	: 0.13
" " " excavation diameter	: 3.20 m
Grout-Approach tunnel no.3 location	: Km 12+656
" " " length	: 1340,25 m
" " " slope	: 0.13
" " " excavation diameter	: 3.20 m
Length of cut and cover section	: 538.35 m
Internal diameter of cut and cover section	: 3.40 m
Shape of cut and cover section	: Circular

Table 2 : Some major Characteristics of the Kınık Tunnel

Fig 2 shows the "As - Built" plan of Kınık
Tunnel.

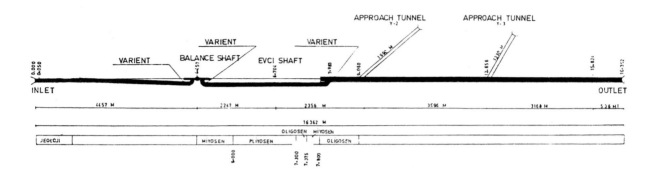

Tunnel with completed lining

approach tunnels	3320 m
shafts	180 m + 152 m = 332 m
main tunnel	15824 m
total tunnels and shafts	19476 m

Figs 3 and 4 show the typical cross-sections
of the Tunnel in relatively stable and in poor
ground.

3.0 Contractual Chronology of The Kınık Tunnel

Table 3 presents a quick overview on the
chronology of the Kınık Tunnel Construction.

Fig 4

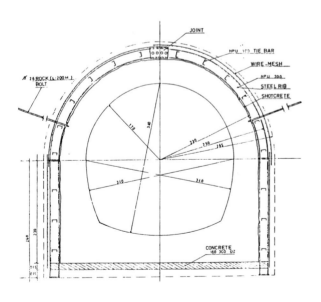

Fig 3

Table 3- Some Chronological Data of the Kınık Tunnel Construction

	Total amount of work (m)	Starting date	Completed date
Inlet - Balance shaft			
Excavation + Trimming	4457	28.10.1974	28.07.1985
Concrete	4457	15.01.1986	30.01.1987
Grouting	4457	30.05.1985	31.05.1987
Balance shaft - Evci shaft			
Excavation + Trimming	2247	10.01.1979	24.11.1986
Concrete	2247	15.02.1987	26.07.1987
Grouting	2247	30.04.1987	18.09.1987
Evci shaft - Approach 2			
Excavation + Trimming	2356	01.02.1978	05.10.1986
Concrete	2356	10.01.1987	15.07.1987
Grouting	2356	15.03.1987	18.09.1987
Approach 2 - Approach 3			
Excavation + Trimming	3596	26.12.1976	13.04.1982
Concrete	3596	01.01.1983	06.01.1985
Grouting	3596	10.01.1985	15.04.1986
Approach 3 - Exit			
Excavation + Trimming	3168	28.10.1974	11.08.1979
Concrete	3168	01.04.1980	10.06.1982
Grouting	3168	01.01.1984	29.11.1985

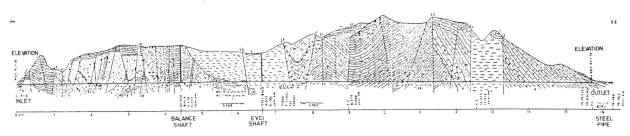

Fig 5

QUARTERNERE

PLIOCEN

MIOCENE

BEFORE MIOCENE

OLIGOCENE

EOCENE

BEFORE EOCENE

JURA

PALEOZOK

An inspection of Table 3 points out the 13 years which elapsed between October 1974 and October 1987 during the construction of the tunnel. During these 13 years the Kınık Tunnel was opened to tender twice, first in 1974 and second in 1980. Five years after the begining of construction in 1979 the client State Hydraulic Works Authority of Turkey and the local construction company agreed to stop the work, since the project was halted both technically and economically. In 1980 the uncompleted project was opened to tender several times, but with no bidder coming forward. Finally bids were obtained and the previous contracting company was the low bidder among the few and the construction began once more. But neither the contractor nor the client knew at that time when and if ever the Kınık tunnel would be completed.

For some two to three years during the 13 years of construction period, the works were stopped completely. This was due to several reasons such as lack of finance to make the payments, lack of approval or decision on a drawing submitted to the client for construction purposes or, a technical deficiency or difficulty such as a collapse followed by a mud flow into the tunnel, when nobody knows what action to take.

4.0   Available Underground Data Prior to the Construction

Perhaps typical for a developing country, only 16 bore holes were opened to find out the underground conditions on the 18 km long tunnel with its approaches. The 16 boreholes, approximately one for each Km were found to be very far from giving accurate information or even an indication on the underground formations to be tunnelled through. Fig 5 shows the geological formations encountered during the construction of the tunnel and numerous bore holes opened for the investigation. It is obvious that the very many faults, formations bearing water at high pressures more than 15 bars, contact zones of soft and weathered granular or rock formations could not have been detected unless intensive underground investigation programs had been applied.

4.1   Major Collapses

The direction and the slope of the governing fault zones in the tunnelling route is N 60 70 E/62 NW. A heavy collapse, at the face towards the exit of the balance shaft took place at Km 4+732. The zone compressed by the intersection of various faults was softened by water at high pressures causing the collapse of the face. The tunnel route was changed afterwards for further construction.

Another major collapse was at Km 7+833, due to a fault zone in the direction N 58 E/50. The flow of water at a rate of 15 lt/sec mobilized the existing plastic clay, causing a collapse of 1500 m3 of soil. In this case the tunnelling route was shifted 50 m. westwards.

The exposure of water at 100 lt/sec caused another collapse at Km 5+340, due to a fault in the direction and slope of N 65 E/60 NW. This collapse climbing to a height of 7-8 m. above the tunnel, was overcome by a by-pass tunnel.

In summary, the Kınık Tunnel excavation was made in poor ground below 50-170 m ground water level. Aquifiers containing water at high pressures caused often major problems especially in the compressed clayey zones. Continuous water pumping during the tunnel excavation was about 400-600 lt/sec as an average. Even single points with water inrush of 200 to 400 lt/sec were also encountered.

5.0   Some Problems Encountered in the Tunnel Construction

5.1   The First Soft Ground Tunnel
Kınık Tunnel was the first soft ground tunnel-

ling project in Turkey when the construction began in 1974. Its length of about 16 Km was also an unusual length as a water supply tunnel in Turkey. The only tunnelling practice to that time was in the rock tunnelling, with mostly drill and blast techniques being used as in some railway tunnels in the east of Turkey. The tunnel workers available in the country had no experience either with water or with unstable ground. The First attempts made by the contractor to employ these workers in the Kınık Tunnel was unsuccesful. The solution to this problem was the employment of coal miners who have been working for many decades, as from father to the son, in northern Turkey, along the Black Sea coast. Coal miners were succesfully used in Kınık Tunnel.

5.2   Lack of experience

The client, the State Hydraulic Works Authority, was also the consultant. The Authority made decisions not only in administrative matters, but also in the technical field. The drawings project and technical proposals prepared by the contractor were being submitted to the Authority for approval. But lack of previous experience on the part of both the Authority and the contractor made the decisions and the approvals a hard task. Long periods of time had to be spent in making decisions keeping the construction waiting. The construction proceeded at a very slow rate and created in turn economical and financial problems.

At the stages where local technical know-how was insufficient to solve the existing problems, foreign experts and companies were called in both by the client and the contractor. The different companies invited, developed solutions to the technical problems of the tunnel, but also created their own commercial problems. The solution proposed by the experts of a machine manufacturing company was the use of heavy machinery in the tunnel. But the solutions of

foreign design or consultant companies were not much different in direction. On the other hand heavy machinery was creating a serious problem for the client and for the contractor since the operators for sophisticated tunnelling equipment were not available in the country. And also the spare parts were difficult to supply in time due to lack of foreign currency at that time and the related custom formalities.

It is worth noting here, that the report prepared by a well known foreign consultant company gives the date of completion of the tunnel construction in the year 1989, with the use of two tunnelling shields. The construction was completed in 1987 with no shield. This shows that solutions of tunnelling problems are not always universal, and local factors play also an important role.

5.3   The Miracle with the Ventilation Holes

As the distance of the tunnel faces proceeded several kilometers away from the shafts entrance or access tunnels, the ventilation became a problem. Sufficient air could not be supplied to the faces. The solution was the vertical holes drilled at a diameter of 14 inches from the surface to the tunnel. Through these holes, at several locations fresh air was supplied.

5.3.1   Concrete Pouring Through Ventilation Holes

The 14-inch ventilation holes were then used for concrete pouring. As the diameter of the tunnel was not large enough to mix and transport the concrete long distances, concrete was prepared at the surface, brought down to the tunnel through the ventilation holes and by concrete pumps in the tunnel horizontally to the form. With one pump a distance of 300 m horizontal transport of concrete in pipes was achieved. For further distances two pumps were connected in series and transport for a distance of 600 m was possible in one direction.

Considering both directions a ventilation hole was used to transport the concrete for a distance of 1200 m.

5.3.2 High Tension Energy Supply Through Ventilation Holes

Supply of electrical energy into the tunnel was necessary for the lights and for the pumps, electro-motors etc. Supply of energy along the tunnel caused loss of voltage after several kilometers, due to the resistance of transmission lines. The resistance of the transmission lines could have been reduced if larger diameter cables had been used. But this would have been extremely expensive. The transmission of electrical energy with high tension cables in the tunnels was considered to be very dangerous.

The solution was again the ventilation holes. The transport of the energy to the ventilation hole at the surface was done by high tension cable. By means of a transformer the high tension was converted to city voltage and then transmitted into the tunnel through the holes.

5.4 Use of Agricultural Tractors for Muck Disposal

The excavation diameter of the main Tunnel was 4.60 m and that of the access tunnels were 3.20 m. Since the main tunnel was not always available for muck transport and the distances through main tunnel were very long access tunnels had to be used for muck disposal. But they are temporary structures and their bottom is loose and wet in most cases. The use of normal transport machinery was not possible as the diameter was small and the slope was steep 12 %. Instead Agricultural tractors were used. Since they were designed to work in field conditions, the water at the bottom was not a problem. With their dump wagon that they pull, they could manage a muck capacity of 5 t. in each case. The agricultural tractors available in large

amounts in the country were used to transport the muck of almost all 16 Km of the Kınık Tunnel. During this construction 65 tractors were used.

6.0 Contractual and Financial Problems

6.1 Main Tunnel was planned without access tunnels

The lack of experience was also a handicap in the preparation of tender documents. As such a long tunnel had not been constructed before in Turkey the importance of length was not recognized. In the planning of the tunnel there were no access tunnels planned. But access tunnels were necessary for the construction of such a long tunnel. If the contractor chose to excavate the access tunnels he was confronted with a situation of no payment since they do not exist on the tender drawings. If he does not construct any access tunnels than the excavation of the main tunnel is practically impossible.

After long discussions, meetings and negotiations it was decided to revise the original designs and add the access tunnels to the project documents.

6.2 Increase in the Quantity of temporary Supports

Before construction the tunnel was expected to be excavated in rather stable ground. But as a precaution 10% of the tunnel was planned to be supported. As constructed the supported section of the tunnel was 90% of the total length.

The gap between the actual underground conditions and the design assumptions caused the delay of payments and further requirements for the approval of new designs consuming long periods of time.

6.3 Shaft Excavation Without the Consent of the Client

Due to the long distances between the tunnel faces and the entrances and access tunnels another shaft, namely Evci Shaft had to be excavated for material and air supply into the tunnel and muck disposal from the tunnel. But this was again not included in the original designs and the client did not want to pay for it.

The compromise solution of the contractor was to construct the shaft with no payment by the client. But afterwards the tunnel excavation should be paid with high unit price as if the much was being transported all through the main tunnel, since Evci Shaft was unpaid and officially unknown by the client.

The 152 m deep, 6.0 m final diameter Evci Shaft was completed on the risk of the contractor. Ground water had to be pumped after 30 m depth from the surface. The construction took a time of 6 months.

7.0 Conclusion

The construction of a difficult tunnel under the conditions of a developing country involves the special problems of that country. They are not universal problems and their solutions are in conformity with the conditions of that country.

The difficulties encountered in the construction of tunnels under these conditions force the engineers to think out new ideas and new solutions some of which have been presented in this paper.

REFERENCES

1. Kınık Tunnel Project, Ankara/Turkey A preplanning Study of the Construction Work by Widmark and Platzer International AB Solna Sweden, Feb. 1974

2. Water Supply Project of Ankara, Report on Kınık Tunnel, Binnie and Partners London and Gizbili Eng. Comp. Feb. 1983.

3. Kınık Tunnel, State Hydraulic Works Authority, 5. Div. Ankara, 1987

Great Belt railway tunnel project, Denmark

T. Eriksen
Ministry of Public Works, Copenhagen, Denmark
R. N. Craig B.Sc., C.Eng., M.I.C.E.
Sir William Halcrow & Partners, Ltd., London, United Kingdom
K. H. Ostenfeld M.Sc., M.A.S.C.E.
COWIconsult, Consulting Engineers and Planners AS, Virum, Denmark
O. Bojesen, M.Sc., C.E., M.ing.F.
Christiani Nielsen A/S, Copenhagen, Denmark

SYNOPSIS

The Great Belt between Zealand and Funen is approximately 18km wide between Korsør and Nyborg. Many schemes have been proposed over the last 100 years to form a fixed link across the Great Belt. In 1987 the Danish Parliament passed a Bill for the construction of a two staged scheme for a railway link to be opened in 1993 and a road link two to four years later. The railway crossing is planned to be either an immersed tunnel or a bored tunnel under the Eastern Channel with a combined bridge over the Western Channel. In the middle of the Great Belt is the Island of Sprogø. The Western Channel has a moderate depth of 20 - 30m and a combined multispan bridge is planned for the railway and the road. The Eastern Channel has a maximum depth of more than 70m. The railway crossing will be in tunnel and the road crossing either by bridge or an immersed tunnel. This paper discusses the conceptual designs for the proposed railway tunnel scheme.

Three schemes have been considered:-

- Concrete Immersed Tunnel

- Steel and Concrete Immersed Tunnel

- Bored Tunnel

The paper discusses the geology under the Eastern Channel of the Great Belt and describes the three schemes. The immersed tunnels are proposed to be 5.5km in length and the units would be sunk at greater depths and in more exposed conditions than for previous projects. The bored tunnel of 7.5km to 8km in length would be constructed at depths up to 75m in Glacial Deposits with boulders and through Marl, partly fissured. The open approaches would be on reclaimed land adjacent to the Island of Sprogø and either on reclaimed land adjacent to Zealand or on Zealand and would have permanent drainage systems to lower the water table.

INTRODUCTION

The Great Belt between Zealand and Funen is approximately 18km wide at the narrowest point between Korsør and Nyborg. In the middle of the Great Belt is the Island of Sprogø. The channel to the West of the Island of Sprogø is relatively shallow at 20 to 30m in depth. The Eastern Channel is, however, the main deep shipping lane into the Baltic Sea and has a depth of up to 70m in the vicinity of the crossing (See Fig. 1).

Many schemes have been proposed over the last century for a fixed link across the Great Belt for both a road and a railway. In 1968 and 1972 studies for various forms of fixed link were carried out including those for a combined bridge over the Western Channel and either a combined bridge or immersed tube for

121

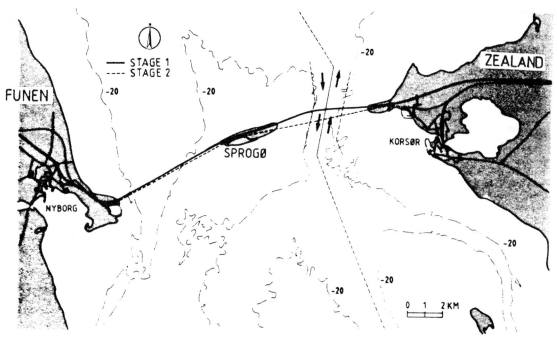

FIG 1   GREAT BELT CROSSING

the Eastern Channel crossing. In 1973 a Bill was passed for a combined road and rail bridge crossing. However the works were delayed on account of the oil crisis. Further studies were carried out in 1973 to 1976 to update the previous studies of a car train tunnel project as well as a combined bridge project over the Western and Eastern channel. A special organisation was formed in 1977 by the Government to promote the combined rail and road bridge proposal. The design of the link which was carried out by the Storebaelt Gruppen was at an advanced stage when the scheme was cancelled in 1978.

The results of reassessment studies were published in 1982. Based on new traffic forecasts modified schemes were proposed for crossings with a four lane motorway with emergency lanes and twin railway tracks. The motorway and the railway could either be made as separate constructions or as a combined construction. The original design was developed for a six-lane motorway with emergency lanes and twin railway tracks.

Following a Parliamentary debate in 1983 more detailed technical studies were initiated for a variety of technical options. The results

of these formed part of a comprehensive feasibility study published in 1985. A political agreement between the Government and the major opposition party was reached in the Summer of 1986. It was agreed to start the construction of a rail-only crossing preparing for a four lane motorway to follow two to four years after the completion of the railway stage. The necessary legislation for doing so was passed in Spring 1987.

In the Summer and Autumn of 1986 conceptual designs were carried out for the railway crossing of the Eastern Channel with either an immersed tunnel in concrete or steel and concrete or a bored tunnel. This paper covers the conceptual designs for the three schemes and details of the methods of construction and the structures proposed.

GEOLOGY AND HYDROGEOLOGY

The sequence of the strata in the Eastern Channel of the Great Belt in the vicinity of the crossing of the tunnel alignment is as follows:-

- Quaternary   Post glacial
                Glacial;   Clay
                Tills, Sand Tills
                and Melt Water
                Deposits

- Tertiary   Middle Paleocene
                Marl; Clays,
                Calcareous Marls
                and Limestones
                Lower Paleocene
                Limestone
                (Danian);   muddy
                and sandy
                Limestone   with
                flints

Several site investigations have been carried out since the mid 1960's along the bridge alignment and in 1983 and 1986 along the bored tunnel alignment. These site investigations have included a large number of boreholes and vibrocores and many kilometres of seismic surveys. These investigations and those in 1987 will form the basis for a three dimensional EDP model of the geology of the area.

The Glacial Deposits consist of four types:-

- a dark grey Clay Till with minor intervals of Sand Till and Melt Water Deposits - the Great Belt Till

- a lighter grey Clay Till with some Sand Till and Melt Water Deposits

- a brownish grey Till with a higher Calcium Carbonate ($CaCO_3$) content

- Melt Water Deposits and Tills of varying composition

The first Till covers the majority of the Deposits on the Western side of the deep Channel, while all four Deposits are present on the Eastern side of the deep Channel. The permeability of the Deposits is in the range of 0.04 to 5.0 x 10^{-6} m/s with values as low as 10^{-11} m/s in the Clay Till.

Rounded or subrounded boulders and cobbles, mainly of granite composition, occur sporadically within the Clay Tills. Studies have been carried out, and are continuing, on the size and frequency of these boulders. Present estimates of the size and number of boulders suggests that for the construction of the bored tunnel scheme, where up to 800,000 cubic metres of material would be excavated, several thousand boulders of under 600mm would be encountered in the face and that the larger boulders would reduce in number to a handful of a size between 2000mm and 3000mm. For the immersed tube scheme there would be approximately 3.5 million cubic metres of dredging with a corresponding increase in the number and size of boulders. In addition there would be compensation dredging for whichever scheme is chosen to compensate for the projects obstructions/resistance to the flow of water through the Great Belt and to maintain the existing water flow.

The Middle Paleocene Marl is subdivided lithologically into Clay, Clay Marl, Marl, Calcareous Marl and Limestone on the basis of the relative Calcium Carbonate content. This content has allowed a subdivision of the sequence into three layers. The Paleocene Marl has zones of closely spaced fissuring and alternating zones of highly fractured and less fractured rock. The Paleocene Marl has a horizontal permeability generally of 1 to 10 x 10^{-6} m/s with values locally up to 4 x 10^{-4} m/s.

The Lower Paleocene Limestone, called the Danian comprises muddy and sandy limestones with layers of flints. The percentage of flints in the boreholes varied from 5 to

15%. On the present alignment the immersed tubes and the bored tunnel would not encounter the Danian.

IMMERSED TUNNELS

General

Similar horizontal and vertical alignments were chosen for the concrete and the steel and concrete immersed tunnels. The horizontal alignment is just to the North of the bridge alignment. A northerly alignment was chosen as the depth of the deep channel, of more than 70m, reduced to the North.

In choosing the vertical alignment, consideration was given to:-

    .   the maximum or economical depth of water for the open cut section at the two portals

    .   the optimum height for an embankment on the sea bed of the deep channel on which to place the immersed tunnel section in order to reduce the overall length and cost of the immersed tunnel without affecting the water exchange through the Great Belt

    .   the maximum gradient of 1.7% specified by the Danish State Railways, however minimising lengths with the maximum gradient are to be limited

    .   minimise the depth of dredging for the trench for the immersed tunnel and therefore the backfill

    .   provide the necessary cover over the tunnel to allow for the compensation dredging adjacent to the two portals.

The final horizontal and vertical alignments are shown on Fig. 2. The vertical alignment has been designed to give a minimum water depth above the tunnel and the protection fill of 40m. The maximum gradients have been used of 1.7% either side of a 25000m vertical curve. On the East side the gradient reduces to 1.2% at approximately the quarter point. On the West side a shallow gradient of 0.5% has been provided at the quarter point at the location for the compensation dredging with a 1.2% gradient to the portal.

For the proposed vertical and horizontal alignments, a length for the immersed tunnel of 5.3km and approximately 100m of cast insitu tunnel at each portal have been assumed to give an overall length of 5.5km. The total volume of trench excavation would be 3.4 million m^3, sand fill 1.3 million m^3 and stone fill approximately 0.4 million m^3.

The immersed tunnel units would be 140 to 150m in length giving a total of 35 to 38 units between the portals. The units at depths of less than 22m would be covered by a 2m thick layer of boulders to protect the top of the units from anchors or ship impact. Although immersed tunnel units hitherto have not been placed in similar depths of water and exposed surface conditions, well known technology would be applicable, provided that sufficiently heavy equipment is used.

The immersed tunnel structure would carry twin railway tracks in separate tunnels divided by a central wall. Cross passages would be provided in the central wall at 70 to 75m centres. The track would be supported on concrete sleepers in a reinforced concrete slab supported on a rubber mat. Services would be provided for emergency ventilation, drainage, lighting, fire fighting with monitoring of air pollution, temperature and air speed together with a drainage system to cater for cleaning water, fire fighting water or spillage from the trains.

124

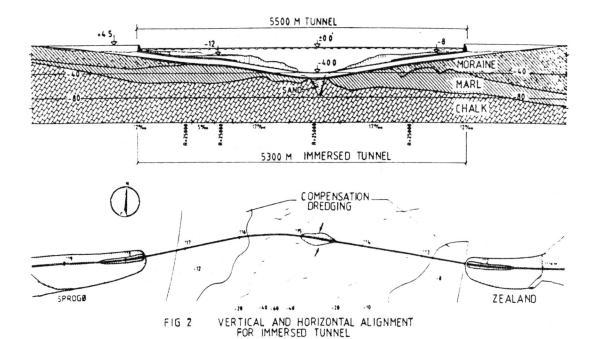

FIG 2   VERTICAL AND HORIZONTAL ALIGNMENT
FOR IMMERSED TUNNEL

Concrete Immersed Tunnel

The proposal for the concrete immersed tunnel consists of 36 units, each of 148m in length. Each unit would be divided into monolithic sections made of watertight reinforced concrete, approximately 25m long and connected at expansion joints allowing small angular changes and small longitudinal movements. The combined units would be bolted together during towing to their location. Fig. 3 shows a section of the concrete immersed tube.

The reinforced concrete box units would have a 6mm thick steel membrane on the outside of the walls and base slab for additional waterproofing and a bitumen membrane on the outside of the roofslab. The bitumen membrane would be protected from damage from anchors with a 200mm layer of reinforced concrete. The expansion joints would have double gaskets to ensure watertightness. The main quantities for the concrete immersed tunnel are given in Table 1.

In the preliminary designs it has been assumed that the concrete units would be cast in four specially built dry docks, excavated to a depth of 10m and adjacent to an excavated trench on the water side with a depth exceeding 10m. If possible the dry dock would be at a convenient location adjacent to the alignment to reduce the towing distance, but the location could be at any suitable place adjacent to deep water.

The tunnel units would be cast in 12.5m sections with a vertical central construction joint. Following the casting of the units, temporary water ballasting tanks and pipes would be placed in the units and temporary bulkheads at the ends. When all four units have been completed the dock would be flooded and the units would be floated with a free board of 100 to 200mm.

Fig. 4 shows the proposed details of the joint between the concrete units. A rubber gasket alongside the outer rim of the chamber between the bulkheads of the units to be joined, would be firmly compressed by the large water pressure when the chamber is emptied of the enclosed water. The steel membranes of the two units can then be welded together in the dry inside the chamber, finally securing the watertightness of the joint. The bulkheads would then be removed. Reinforcement would be fixed in the joint using the couples and the joint cast. Permanent concrete ballast would then be placed within the units.

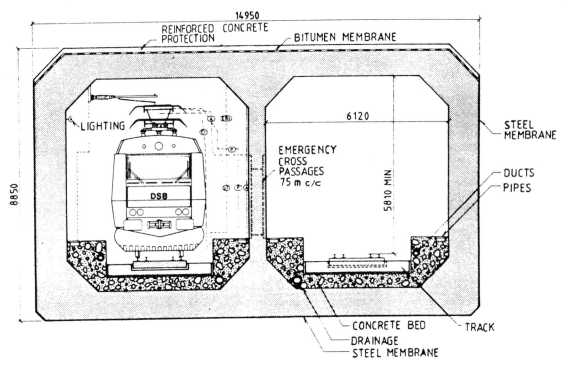

FIG 3   CONCRETE IMMERSED TUNNEL SECTION

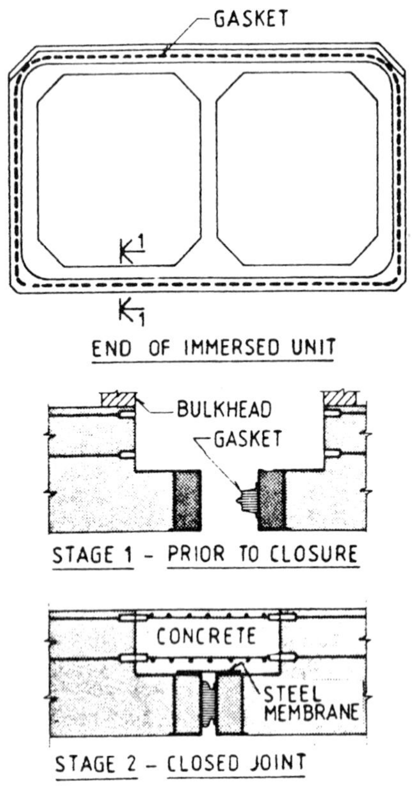

GASKET

END OF IMMERSED UNIT

BULKHEAD
GASKET

STAGE 1 - PRIOR TO CLOSURE

CONCRETE

STEEL
MEMBRANE

STAGE 2 - CLOSED JOINT

FIG 4   CONCRETE IMMERSED TUNNEL — JOINT DETAIL

Steel and Concrete Immersed Tunnel

The steel and concrete immersed tunnel proposed consists of 37 units each 144m long. The exterior of the units would be a continuous fully welded steel tube with no expansion joints. The length of the units could be varied to suit existing shipyard facilities.

The steel and concrete box structure is shown in Fig. 5 and would consist of a steel tube braced by a twin-celled reinforced concrete box. The steel tube would form the watertight structure while the internal reinforced concrete box would not have to be watertight or resistant to saltwater. Above the steel shell would be a 1m high ballast box, which would be filled with stones or aggregate during the immersion. In the final position the ballast would act as a load distributing and energy absorbing protection layer against the impact of ships and anchors. An inner steel membrane would be provided inside the concrete. The steel shell would be protected from corrosion by

126

means of a cathodic protection system. The main quantities for the steel and concrete immersed tunnel are given in Table 1.

After fabrication of the steel tube and its longitudinal central bracing in a shipyard it would be provided with a temporary bulkhead, launched and towed to a quay where the internal reinforced concrete would be cast.

Fig. 6 shows the joint between the adjacent steel and concrete units. The pressure on the bulkhead of the unit would compress the seals in the joint. The adjacent units would then be welded together creating structural continuity and a watertight joint. The inner steel tubes would be welded together and concrete cast in the void between the steel tubes.

BORED TUNNEL

Alignment

In 1983 when the bored railway tunnel alignment was considered two boreholes were drilled to check the geology for alignments 1 or 2km to the North of the bridge alignment. In 1986 a more detailed site investigation was carried out. The approximate horizontal alignment was chosen based on three main criteria:-

.   the landing point at Korsør just to the North of the bridge alignment

TABLE 1

PRINCIPAL QUANTITIES FOR IMMERSED TUNNELS

	Concrete Tunnel	Steel/Concrete Tunnels
Structural Concrete (m^3)	255,000	240,000
Concrete Protection (m^3)	15,000	–
Ballast Concrete (m^3) or Ballast Box	44,000	63,000
Reinforcement (tonne)	22,000	8,000
Structural Steel or Steel Membrane (tonne)	7,500	31,000
Bitumen Membrane (m^2)	85,000	–

Well proven different methods of immersion, joining and foundation of the completed tunnel units are applicable for both the concrete and the steel and concrete schemes.

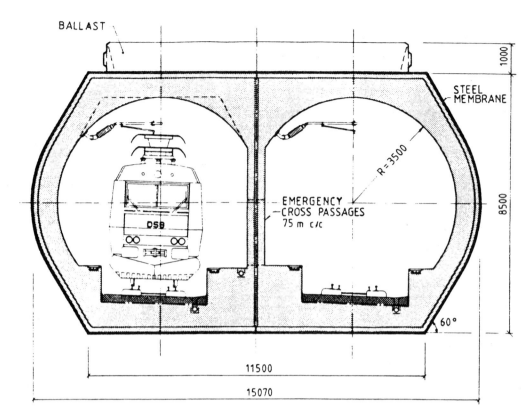

BALLAST

STEEL MEMBRANE

EMERGENCY CROSS PASSAGES 75 m c/c

DSB

R = 3500

1000

8500

60°

11500

15070

FIG 5   STEEL AND CONCRETE IMMERSED TUNNEL SECTION

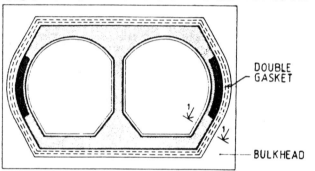

DOUBLE GASKET

BULKHEAD

END OF IMMERSED UNIT

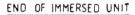

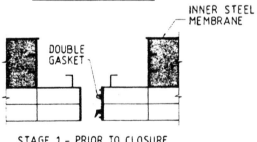

INNER STEEL MEMBRANE

DOUBLE GASKET

STAGE 1 - PRIOR TO CLOSURE

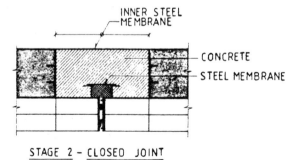

INNER STEEL MEMBRANE

CONCRETE

STEEL MEMBRANE

STAGE 2 - CLOSED JOINT

FIG 6   STEEL AND CONCRETE IMMERSED TUNNEL — JOINT DETAIL

128

- the connection to the open cut, embankment and bridge alignment to the North of the Island of Sprogø
- a saddle in the deep channel about 200m wide where the Paleocene Marl comes to within 2m of the sea bed

The final vertical alignment has not yet been fixed and would depend upon the detailed site investigation at present in progress. The criteria to be used in the selection include:-

- the maximum gradient of 1.7% for a maximum length of 3km or 1.5% for the whole length of the inclines
- an Eastern portal on the mainland of Zealand with a cover of 4 to 6m
- a Western portal off the Island of Sprogø with a maximum depth to invert of approximately 18m below sea level
- a minimum cover below the deep channel at the Nadir of 10m of Paleocene Marl

Several alignments were considered giving lengths of bored tunnel of 7.5 to 8.0km. The maximum depth of the tunnel would be 70 to 75m below sea level.

The bored tunnel would have an internal diameter of the order of 7.2m. Cross passages would be provided at 250 to 500m centres and the two tunnels would be approximately 22m apart. Fig. 7 shows the approximate vertical and horizontal alignment for the bored tunnel scheme.

Method of Construction

The ground conditions have been described earlier in the paper. The main concerns for a bored tunnel are:-

Glacial Deposits

- the presence of boulders in large numbers and of sizes up to approximately 3000mm
- the pockets of Melt Water Deposits with high water pressures and unstable conditions
- permeabilities of 10^{-3} to 10^{-6} m/s in the Melt Water Deposits and 10^{-8} m/s in the moraine clay

Paleocene Marl

- fissures and a zone near the base of the Marl containing silica with vertical fissures
- permeabilities of 10^{-5} m/s with local values in the more fractured siliceous zones of 10^{-4} m/s, with inflow of ground water for a 10m unlined tunnel in the worst conditions of the order of 500m^3/hour.

When choosing a method of construction consideration must be given to the difficulty in predicting the location of the unstable Melt Water Deposits. Probing ahead would locate most of the lenses but some lenses may not be picked up by the probing. Experience in the grouting of the Melt Water Deposits shows that it is difficult to stabilise the layers by injections.

The conclusion in the preliminary design stage was that a tunnel boring machine with hydraulic pressures at the face would be necessary to deal with the water and unstable ground conditions. This type of machine, however, would have difficulties in dealing with boulders. Small boulders have been dealt with by full face slurry type machines

129

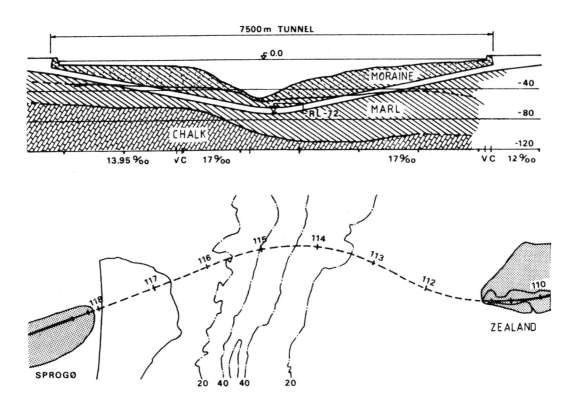

FIG 7   VERTICAL AND HORIZONTAL ALIGNMENT FOR BORED TUNNEL

but a special design would be necessary for the conditions in the Great Belt. Detailed designs would be considered in the pre-contract stage of the project. In this later stage the possibility of using an open face and grouting is being reconsidered together with ground support of arches, rockbolts and shotcrete.

The full face machine must be designed for water pressures up to 70 to 75m of water and particular attention would need to be paid to the seals between the tail of the shield and the outside of the precast concrete lining.

Tunnel and Internal Works

Fig. 8 shows the cross section of the tunnel with an internal diameter of 7.2m and an external diameter of 7.9m. Initial calculations for the tunnel lining suggest that a thickness of 300mm would be necessary for the permanent ground and water loadings. The tunnel would be at depths up to 70 to 75 metres and in a saline ground water environment. To ensure the watertightness of

the lining, gaskets would be provided and consideration would be given to second and third levels of waterproofing.

Inside the tunnel the railway track would consist of sleepers and a reinforced concrete slab resting on a rubber mat. Precast walkways would be provided. Services similar to those for the immersed tunnels would be installed for monitoring and maintenance and a drainage system provided for seepage water, maintenance and emergency water and for accidental spillage from trains.

Openings at 250 to 500m centres would be provided in the running tunnels using specially designed segments at the location of the cross passages. The design would allow the segments within the opening to be removed without temporary support for the tunnel lining. The cross passages would be lined in 4.5m internal diameter segment. The excavation for the cross passages and the forming of the junction lengths would be carried out by hand. Probing ahead and grouting would be carried out to reduce the ingress of water (Fig. 9).

130

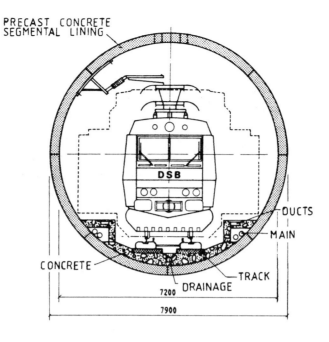

FIG 8   BORED TUNNEL SECTION

The main quantities for the bored tunnel
scheme are:-

Excavation (m^3)	500,000
Structural Concrete (m^3)	160,000
Reinforcement (tonnes)	15,000

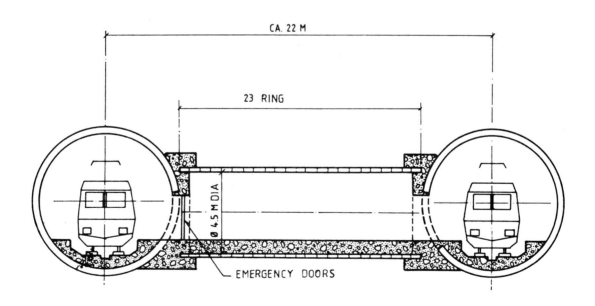

FIG 9   BORED TUNNEL CROSS PASSAGES

COMPENSATION DREDGING

The political agreement on the Great Belt link included an assurance that the two staged scheme would be carried out without affecting the environment and without any changes of the water flow into and out of the Baltic Sea. It is proposed to achieve this by shortening the bridge embankments and by dredging certain areas and reefs to compensate for the increased resistance to the flow caused by the bridge, piers and ramps and by the immersed tunnel section in the deep channel.

Initial calculations show that this compensation dredging in the first stage of the project for the railway tunnel under the Eastern Channel and the bridge over the Western Channel may be in the range of 7 to 14 million cubic metres for the different schemes. This dredging would be staged to suit the construction of the railway and road schemes. Fig. 10 shows the dredging zones.

RAMPS FOR RAILWAY TUNNEL

On the Zealand side of the deep channel the ramp for the immersed tunnel would extend some 1.3km into the Great Belt. The Eastern ramp for the bored tunnel would be on Zealand. Both schemes would require reclaimed land on the Eastern side of the Island of Sprogø. The ramps for the immersed tunnel schemes on the Zealand side and the ramps on the Island of Sprogø side for the immersed as well as the bored tunnel schemes have been widened to be able to include the bridge embankments or immersed tunnel ramps for the second stage road crossing. The reclaimed land would be protected by embankments of boulders and stones with a crown level of 4.5m. The area between the embankments would be filled to a level of 2.5m. Fig. 11 shows plans of the ramps on or close to Zealand.

The ramps for the immersed tunnel and the bored tunnel would be formed as open, drained ramps and would be kept free of water by locally lowering the water table by means of permanent drainage wells alongside the railway. Additional safety at critical points would be obtained by sheet pile cut offs. The material required for the ramps, based on the schemes considered in the studies are in Table 2.

TABLE 2

QUANTITIES FOR RAMPS

Material	Immersed Tunnel	Bored Tunnel
Stone (m^3)	580,000	280,000
Sand (m^3)	2,000,000	820,000
Fill (m^3)	3,500,000	2,500,000
Sheet Piling (tonne)	2,800	960
Excavation (m^3)	220,000	780,000
Concrete (m^3)	12,000	5,700
Reinforcement (tonne)	900	520

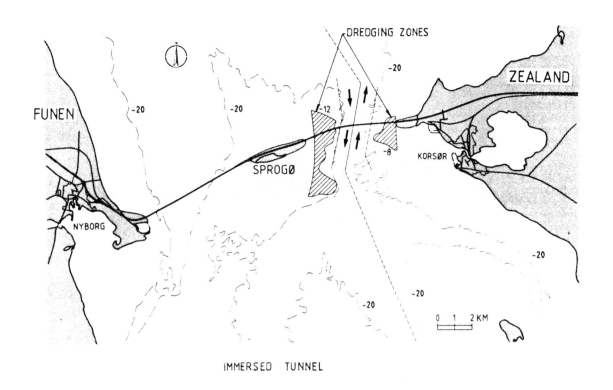

IMMERSED TUNNEL

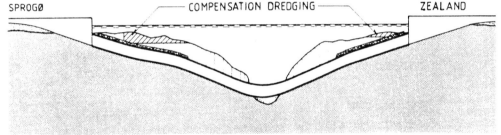

SECTION ALONG IMMERSED TUNNEL

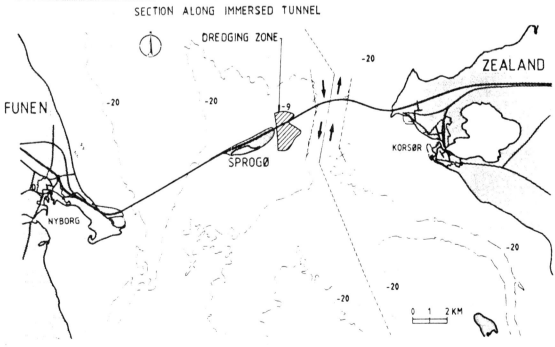

BORED TUNNEL

FIG 10   COMPENSATION DREDGING

133

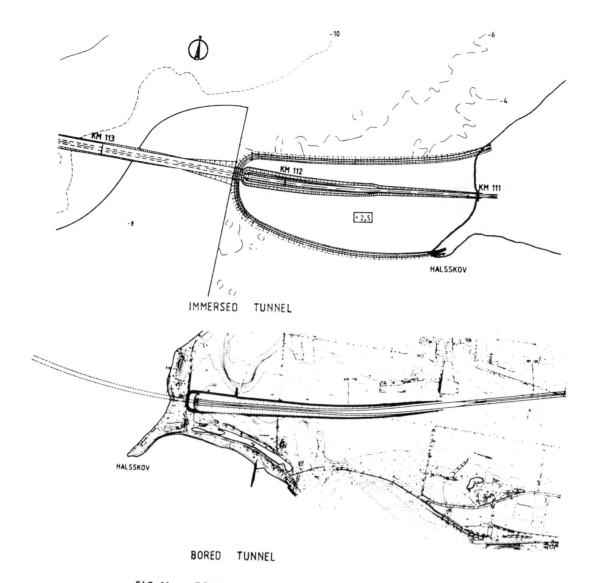

IMMERSED TUNNEL

BORED TUNNEL

FIG 11   ZEALAND OPEN CUT SECTION

PROGRAMME FOR THE FUTURE

The Great Belt Link Company, the AS Storebaeltsforbindelsen, was formed in early 1987 and took over the responsibility for the project from the Ministry of Public Works. Studies and site investigations have continued and at the end of August, Consultants were appointed for the preparation of Tender Documents for both the immersed tunnel and the bored tunnel schemes. The proposed programme is for the two schemes to go out to Tender in February 1988 with construction commencing on the chosen scheme in late 1988 and a completion date in 1993.

ACKNOWLEDGEMENTS

The studies were carried out for the Ministry of Public Works, Planning Department by the following three groups:-

Steel and Concrete Immersed Tunnel	Storebaeltgruppen Cowiconsult, B. Højlund Rasmussen and Rambøll & Hanneman
Concrete Immersed Tunnel	Christiani & Nielsen A/S and ramps for all schemes
Bored Tunnel	Sir William Halcrow & Partners

Permission to write this paper is acknowledged from each of these organisations.

134

Diaphragm wall techniques for the Channel Tunnel shaft-sinking on the French side

G. Evers
C. Hovart
Soletanche, Nanterre, France

INTRODUCTION

The project for a permanent link across the English Channel named: "Channel Tunnel", or "Chunnel", is undertaken by EUROTUNNEL. This joint venture company is the promoter, the designer, the builder and afterwards the operator during 55 years of the railway tunnel. EUROTUNNEL has chosen as general contractor a binational consortium named TRANSMANCHE LINK, whose French partner is TRANSMANCHE CONSTRUCTION (TMC), an association of the firms DUMEZ, BOUYGUES, SAE, SOBEA and SPIE BATIGNOLLES.

The "Chunnel" is made up of two 7.6 m inside diameter main tubes for the railway traffic and one 4.8 m diameter central service tube, the three tunnels having a 15 m centre spacing.

The total length of the "Chunnel" between France and England will be 50 km, with an under water length of 37 km, and an on shore length of 13 km, 3.5 km on the French and 9.5 on the English side.

Almost over the whole length below the sea, the tunnels will be at a depth of 40 m below the seabed and 100 m below the waterlevel.
The tunnels are to be bored using 5 shields on the French side, and 6 shields on the British side.

On the French side, the construction of both the underwater section and the on-shore section will start from SANGATTE, near the shore, where all plant installation required for the tunnelling operations will be set up.

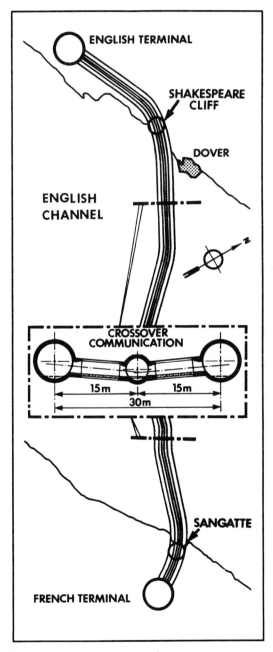

GENERAL ROUTE OF THE PERMANENT LINK

135

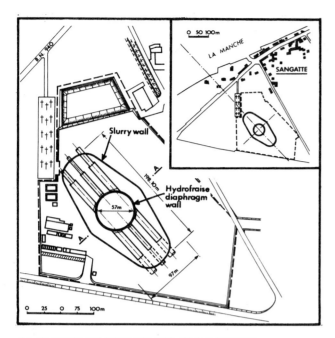

PLAN VIEW OF THE SHAFT AT SANGATTE

At this location, 4 km from the future terminal, the tunnels are at a depth of 45 m below ground level and 30 m below ground water level.

Consequently the works have to start with the realization of a vertical access shaft, 57 m in diameter and 65 m deep.

Roadheaders will then be used for the first 50 m, opening up excavations slightly larger than the dimensions to which the tunnelling shields will be working so as to allow access to the machines in the early stages.

The plan is eventually to have five tunnelling shields on site, which will all start from SANGATTE, three working towards the sea and two towards the French terminal.

Taking into account the geological conditions of the site, important earth retaining and watertightness works were conceived.
TransManche Construction, after submitting the work for tender, chose *Solétanche* to construct these special works.

SCOPE OF SPECIAL WORKS

Objectives

Nearly over the whole length below the sea the tunnels are to be bored in the Cenomanian blue chalk layer, with rather low permeability figures (10^{-7} m/s), but right at

SANGATTE the formation in which the tunnels will start, is a layer of permeable grey chalk (2 to 5. 10^{-5} m/s, i.e. 100 times more than the blue chalk).

The shaft design was based on a major constraint, specified by T.M.C.: to shelter the wall of the shaft from any groundwater pressure during the total duration of the tunnel works, in order to minimize the dimensions of the wall and to ease the design and the construction of it.

Moreover, working with roadheaders and setting up of the tunnelling shields cannot be done within an aquifer. Consequently, during the initial stage of boring, it would be necessary to proceed to dewater to a depth of 30 m.

But the permeable grey chalk layers form a fresh water reservoir for the region, wich is exploited by a pumping station at only 700 m distance from the shaft. A general drawdown of the watertable would reduce the volume of the reservoir, but above all would seriously affect this reservoir: a more than 1.5 m drawdown would cause a salt water intrusion from the sea (which is only at 300 m distance from the shaft) and alter the water quality for a long time.

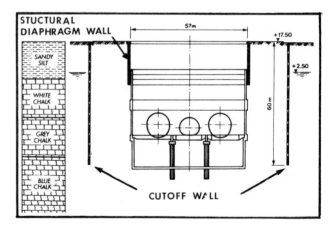

TYPICAL CROSS SECTION

It was therefore necessary to consider:

- *a general impervious barrier around the shaft* and the tunnel accesses such that the total pumping discharge would not exceed 10 l/s (36 m^3/h). This value is much lower than the discharges generally allowable for excavations of this size.

This solution involved special techniques and equipment as will be described below.

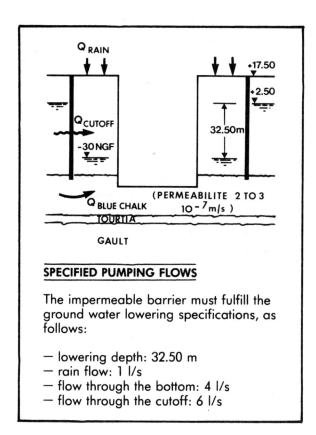

SPECIFIED PUMPING FLOWS

The impermeable barrier must fulfill the ground water lowering specifications, as follows:

— lowering depth: 32.50 m
— rain flow: 1 l/s
— flow through the bottom: 4 l/s
— flow through the cutoff: 6 l/s

- *a pumping system* which would allow the control of the water level inside the enclosure and a piezometer network around the enclosure to record the evolution of the outside water table.

For reasons of optimization, the shaft was to be of a circular form with its wall being 'self-supporting'. Below a depth of 20 m the chalk layers have good mechanical characteristics, and the construction of the wall could be done with successive downwards stages and concreting of the wall as excavation progresses.

But over the first 20 m loose soil layers are encountered and T.M.C. chose to support this height by *a continuous diaphragm wall*.

Together these works: diaphragm wall (approx. 4000 m^2), curtain (approx. 30 000 m^2) and pumping network, were to be completed within 4 months thus allowing work on the tunnel to commence.

PROPOSED SOLUTIONS

Bearing in mind the principal technical objectives *Solétanche* proposed to T.M.C. the following solutions :

Impervious barrier

An enclosing cement - bentonite cutoff wall of a quasi - elliptical form with a perimeter of 482 m anchored 3m into the blue chalk, to a depth of 60m.

This choice was made after a comparative study between several solutions involving grouting.

The diagram on the opposite column illustrates the results, obtained from finite-element calculations , showing the seepage rate across the curtain and under the structure through the blue chalk.

The choice of solutions was dictated by the constraint : to be able to limit the discharge to 10 l/s for a drawdown to -32 m, taking into account the range of permeabilities obtained within the blue chalk (from 2 to 9.10^{-7} m/s).

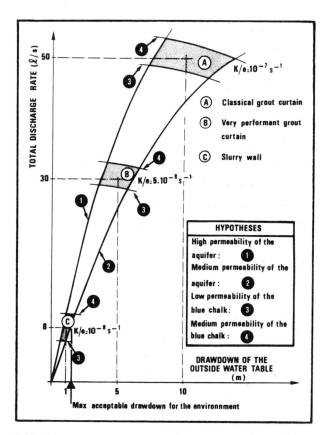

EFFECT OF THE IMPERVIOUS BARRIER PERFORMANCE ON THE DISCHARGE AND DRAWDOWN OF THE OUTSIDE WATER TABLE

The diagram above shows that the performance of the curtain, expressed as the ratio k/e (permeability/thickness), had to be less or equal to 10^{-8}/s.

The performance of a standard grouted curtain in this type of terrain would approximately be: $k/e = 10^{-7}$/s (e.g. 3m thickness and a permeability of 3×10^{-7}) i.e. ten times greater than the allowable value.

As for high - performance type grout curtains it would be difficult to reduce the value permeabilty by more than 2 to 3 times.

In this case, not only was studying a suitable grouting method unrealistic because of high cost and execution time considerations, but furthermore the drawdown of the water table outside the enclosure would reach a minimum of 3 to 5 m, and this would be unacceptable for the environment.

Thus *Solétanche* arrived at the conclusion that a cement - bentonite cutoff wall was the most suitable solution.

The thickness of the wall was fixed at 0.60m which required the permeability of the cement - bentonite to be in the order of 5×10^{-9} m/s ; an ambitious objective but feasible with a curtain in a fractured environment as will be explained later.

For the execution of this curtain *Soletanche* proposed to use the 'Hydrofraise', which is a diaphragm wall excavating machine capable of reaching a depth of 60m through fissured rock, and meeting at the same time the cost, time and quality requirements.

Structural Diaphragm Wall

Solétanche proposed :
- A wall of 1m thickness with 50kg/m3 of reinforcing.
The choice followed from the T.M.C.'s requirements for the wall to have a combined function:
* during the Construction Phase:
Under the effect of the earth pressures and distributed surcharges : to function as a self-supporting, slender arch.
* during the Service Phase:
Under the effect of the same loading but in addition with heavier localized surcharges : to be able to function as a vertical beam supported at the top by a stiff capping beam and at the foot by the facing of the lower shaft.

- To use the 'Hydrofraise' which was capable of producing the quality finish required to meet the very tight geometrical tolerances (vertical deviation of less than 0.5%) and the ability to form joints able to transmit forces without disturbing the arching effect.

Pumping System

Four filter pumps at a depth of 60m would be able to lower and maintain the water level on the interior of the cutoff wall and thus the water pressure would be unable to affect the wall and tunnel access.
For observing the pumping and drawdown induced on the exterior of the wall a group of 30 piezometers were used.

The ' HYDROFRAISE '

The 'Hydrofraise' is an excavation machine powered by three down-the-hole motors, with reverse mud circulation.

A heavy metal frame serving as a guide is fitted at its base with two cutter drums carrying tungsten carbide tipped cutters which rotate in opposite directions and break up the soil.

A pump placed just above the drums evacuates the loosened soil, which is carried up to the surface by the drilling mud. The mud with cuttings is continuously filtered and then poured back into the trench.

A heavy crawler crane supports and manipulates the machine. It carries the power pack supplying the hydraulic power, which is conveyed through hoses to the three down-the-hole motors, two of them driving the cutter drums and the third driving the pump.

The hydraulic cutting device is designed to give the cutter drums a high torque at low speed of rotation.

The guide frame is attached to the crane operated cable, from which it is suspended by a hydraulic feed cylinder, which can be controlled either to give a constant rate of advance or to maintain a constant weight on the cutter drums (the maximum being the weight of the machine, 16 to 20 tons).

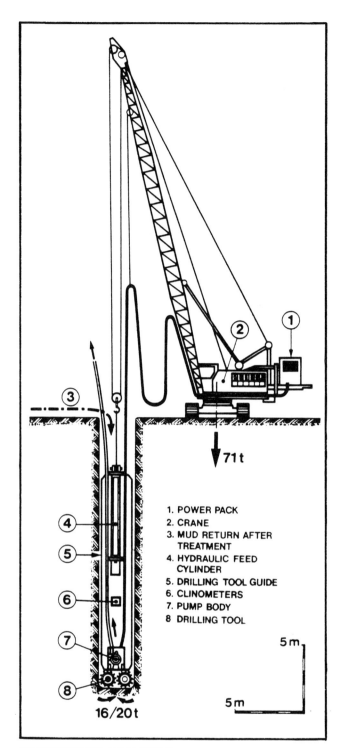

1. POWER PACK
2. CRANE
3. MUD RETURN AFTER TREATMENT
4. HYDRAULIC FEED CYLINDER
5. DRILLING TOOL GUIDE
6. CLINOMETERS
7. PUMP BODY
8 DRILLING TOOL

71 t

16/20 t

5 m

5 m

PRINCIPLE OF OPERATION

The 'Hydrofraise' is able to excavate diaphragm wall elements down to great depths (cut-off walls down to 120 m. depth have recently been performed with it), with a high precision in verticality (a permanent deviation control and adjustable drum positions allow to control and correct the deviation to less than 0.2 % if required), through a very range of soils, from cohesionless soils (silt, sand, gravel and cobbles up to 10 cm) to rock with 100 MPa crushing strength.

EXECUTION

Execution of the cutoff

Taking into account the time limit , two 'Hydrofraise' and two 'Kelly' clamshell rigs were used . The equipment was able to descend to depths of at least 60m and was supplied by a plant which had the capability of treating 600m3 of mud and producing $50m^3$ /h of cement - bentonite slurry.

In order to achieve the optimum use of this equipment, the following operation method was used:

- excavation of the primary panels 2.4 m. long, using the 'Hydrofraise' under bentonite mud. After completion of the excavation down to 60 m, the mud was replaced with a cement-bentonite slurry containing 150 kg/m^3 of cement.

This replacement was done using a special device in order to guarantee the quality of the substitution: a metallic piston with a cross section slightly inferior to that of the excavation, was lowered down to the bottom of the excavation; the cement-bentonite slurry was then introduced below the piston, and the piston raised as slurry introduction progressed. An automatic control allowed to ensure that at any time the quantity of slurry introduced was at least equal to the volume liberated by the piston.

- excavation of the secondary panels, varying between 0.40 and 1.10 m. long, was made using a 'kelly' adapted to the hard terrain.

Execution of the Circular Diaphragm Wall

The reinforced diaphragm wall is 1 m thick, 21 m deep and 57 m in diameter.

The wall was constructed by the 'Hydrofraise' to ensure a perfect verticality of the wall and a good quality of the joints.
Working technique was conventional: bentonite mud excavation, then concreting by the tremie pipe method .
Primary panels were 5.5 m long and 2.2 m apart.
Junction between primary and secondary panels is obtained by cutting 0.1 m from the ends of the primary panels with the 'Hydrofraise', when carrying out the secondary panels.

RESULTS

Execution time

Structural Diaphragm Wall : Work began on the 5th January 1987 , and was completed on the 17th February 1987 , in spite of a shutdown period of nearly three weeks due to a severe frost in January .

Curtain : The cutoff excavation began on the same date with two rigs (1 'Hydrofraise' and 1 'Kelly') and then with four rigs (2 'Hydrofraise' and 2 'Kellies') upon completion of the diaphragm wall .

The total project was completed within four months even after time lost during the cold weather in January 1987. In order to keep on schedule it was necessary to work continuously 24 hours a day , 7 days a week for nearly two months .

Technical achievements

Diaphragm Wall : The geometerical tolerances specified in the contract were wholly satisfied. The measurements made by T.M.C., during construction, showed an 'arching' behaviour as predicted in the theoretical study, demonstrating particularly the excellent functioning of the joints.

Thanks to the very good precision in verticality and the good contact between the concrete of adjacent panels, the 'Hydrofraise' proved to be an excellent equipment for the construction of 'slender-arches', even if the circular wall has exceptional dimensions, as was the case in Sangatte.

The picture of the shaft on the next page was made at the end of April 1987, when the excavation in the shaft reached a depth of 25 m and the the last panels of the cutoff wall were being completed. The picture gives an idea of the exceptional dimensions and the aspect of the diaphragm wall at that moment.

The cement-bentonite cutoff wall :

Characteristics of the slurry:

The table below shows the contractual values and those measured on slurry taken from the site .

	Contractual	Measured on samples
Resistance Rc at 90 days (MN/m2)	0.5	0.6 to 3.0
Permeability k at 90 days. (m/s)	10^{-8}	3 to $5 * 10^{-9}$

It is recalled that the slurry contained 150 kg/m^3 of cement. The performance values were high and varied due to the amount of chalk which was generally present in large quantities in the mud used for the manufacturing of the slurry.

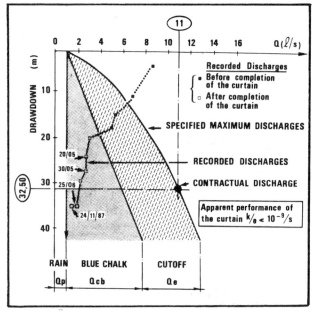

RECORDED DISCHARGES IN FUNCTION OF DRAWDOWN

The chalk was mixed into the mud during excavation of the panels by the action of the cutting teeth. The chalk content reached sometimes the amount of 400 kg/m^3 which influenced in a beneficial way the mechanical and hydraulical characteristics of the slurry after setting.

As a matter of fact an extensive laboratory testing programme, performed before beginning of the works in order to analyse the effect of the chalk on the slurry characteristic, showed the beneficial effect of the chalk, provided appropriate bentonite and cement types are used. It was therefore decided not to eliminate all the chalk from the mud before manufacturing of the slurry, but to maintain the fine particles up to a limit of 400 kg/m^3

CARRYING OUT THE NORTH SIDE CUTOFF AND EXCAVATION OF CIRCULAR SHAFT

The effectiveness of the impervious barrier:

The discharge diagram of the figure on page 6 allows a rapid comparison of the expected discharge (which is obviously a function of the drawdown) and the measured discharge. It can be seen that the measured discharge for a drawdown of 35 m is 2 l/s which is 5 times less than the contactual value. Furthermore these values are for the construction phase. The discharge will probably diminish with time in spite of an increased drawdown.

These results are justified by the quality of the execution which has guaranteed a continuous, homogeneous curtain and quality cement-bentonite slurry whose characteristics have surpassed the expected values. Equally the penetration of mud and slurry into the fissures of the chalk (the distance of penetration being a function of the crack width) have been very effective in zones of severe fracturing. Upon excavation of the shaft it was observed that the cement slurry had penetrated several tens of metres into the cracks.

CONCLUSION

Thanks to its ability to excavate diaphragm wall elements with a high precision in verticality, through a very wide range of soil, from soft soil to hard rock, the 'Hydrofraise, an excavating machine conceived and developed by *Soletanche*, made it possible to meet the very ambitious requirements for the special works of the shaft in Sangatte.

Measurements on the circular 'self-supporting' diaphragm wall showed a perfect 'arching' behaviour, in spite of its exceptional 57 m diameter.

The cement-bentonite slurry wall, with a perimeter of 500 m and a depth of 60 m, proved to be very effective. The recorded discharges were less then 20% of the specified figures, and the apparent permeability of the curtain is less than 10 m/s. The drawdown of the outside water table is limited to not more than one decimetre, thus the protection of the fresh water reservoir is fully ensured.

Some experiences of rapid excavation in Lubuge hydroelectric power tunnel, China

Guo Zongyan
Wan Shengpei
*Water Resources and Hydropower Planning and Design Institute, Ministry of Water Resources and
Electric Power, Beijing, China*

SYNOPSIS

The Lubuge Hydropower Station is on the Huangni
River, a tributary of the Nan Pan River, which is
on the borders of Yunnan and Guizhou Provinces
and the Autonomous Region of Guangxi, China. The
total head used of this station will be 372 m,
with a design capacity of 600 MW (4x150 MW).Pre-
paratory works were mostly carried out in 1982.
Construction of the main structure began in 1984
and the first unit will be in operation in 1988.
The power tunnel, situated on the left bank, is
9382 m long, and its excavation diameter is 8.8-
9.2 m. Rock strata in this area are composed of
dolomite and limestone. Of the total length of
the power tunnel, 8782 m were constructed by Taisei Corporation, Japan. Excavation of the power
tunnel began in November 1984 and was finished in
October 1986. At the beginning of construction,
the power tunnel was excavated at two working
faces simultaneously by a conventional drill and
blast method. At the end of construction, the power tunnel was excavated at one working face. An
average advance rate of 231 m per month for each
working face was achieved. In the following years
of construction, maximum monthly advance rates of
243.7 m, 281 m, 357.4 m and 373.7 m were achieved
in succession. The frequency of blasting was 3
rounds per day at the beginning, and 6 rounds at
the end of construction. The average overbreak
was 16 cm.

GENERAL DESCRIPTION OF LUBUGE HYDROELECTRIC
STATION

The Lubuge Hydroelectric Station is on the Huangni River about 320 KM east of Kunming. The Huangni River is 220 KM long and has a drainage area

of 8264 KM^2. The total available head on the
river is 1328 m; in the lower reaches, a drop of
450 m occurs in a stretch of 43 KM. This station
is the largest project in the Huangni River system, with a generating capacity of 600 MW. The
project is being developed solely for the purpose of power generation.

The site is in a deep gorge, where a natural
drop of 287 m exists in a river stretch of 10.5
KM. The valley is narrow with steep mountain
peaks rising on both banks about 300 m higher
than the river water level. Rock strata in this
area are composed of dolomite, limestone and
other sedimentary rocks. They are, in general,
hard and intact. However, some karstic formation
has developed in the carbonate rocks. The seismic
intensity at the site has been evaluated at about
6 degrees on the Merculli scale.

The dam site has a drainage area of 7300 Km^2.
The annual mean precipitation is 1300 mm. The
climate at the project area is characterized by a
warm temperature, high humidity, abundant rainfall and long wet seasons. The perennial average
discharge and yearly runoff at the dam site are
164 m^3/s and $517x10^3$ m^3 respectively. The maximum
recorded peak flow at the dam site is 2560 m^3/s,
which occured in July 1976. The peak inflow to
the reservoir for a frequency of one in 500 years
is 6460 m^3/s, and 9210 m^3/s for one in 5000 years.
The probable maximum flood (PMF) is estimated at
about 10880 m^3/s. The annual silt load at the dam
site is $3.4x10^6$ t. The dam will raise the original river water level by 85 m. The reservoir thus
formed will have a total storage capacity of 111
million m^3, which is capable of seasonal regulation only. The flow for power generation is

diverted through a 9 km-long power tunnel from the reservoir to the underground powerhouse. The total head used will be 372 m, and the maximum discharge utilized will be 230 m^3/s.

The project comprises three major structure groups, namely, the headworks complex, the hydraulic system and the power house complex (see Fig.1).

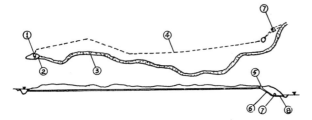

Fig. 1 General layout of the Lubuge scheme (1. dam; 2. intake; 3. Huangni river; 4.power tunnel; 5. surge shaft; 6. penstock; 7. powerhouse; 8. tailrace)

A dam, the surface spillway, the left bank spillway tunnel and the right bank spillway tunnel are the main components of the headworks complex. The dam will be of the rockfill type, with a vertical central core and the following dimensions: maximum height 103.5 m, crest length 216 m, crest elevation 1130 m, total embankment volume 2.1x10^6 m^3.

The powerhouse complex is laid out at the lower end of the gorge. In accordance with local topographical and geological conditions, the main machine hall, the ancillary bay and the transformer bar are all arranged underground on the left side of the river. The main powerhouse cavern will be 125 m long, 19 m wide and 45 m high. To reduce the span of the main chamber, the Francis turbines were specified to rotate in a counter clockwise direction (when viewed from the top), and the penstocks will enter the powerhouse at an angle of 60° to the longer axis of powerhouse chamber. A reinforced concrete beam supported on a rock ledge and anchor bolted to the cavern wall will be used as the crane girder.

The hydraulic system comprises a power intake, a power tunnel, a surge shaft and two penstocks.

The power intake is a reinforced concrete structure located along the left bank immediately next to the upstream face of the rockfill dam. The floor of this power intake is set at an elevation of 1091.5, with a central gate 6 m wide and

9 m high.

The power tunnel is in the mountain along the left side of the valley. Its total length is 9382 m, and its internal diameter is 8 m. In view of the good quality of rock encountered, the power tunnel will be lined with plain concrete to obtain better hydraulic properties. It has only been necessary to use a reinforced concrete lining at a few fault zones.

At the end of the power tunnel is the surge shaft, which will be of the differential type with an upper tank. The height at the surge shaft is 68.5m, and the internal diameter of the main shaft is 13 m.

At the downstream side of the surge shaft two inclined penstocks are connected with steel linings. They are 463 m and 489 m long respectively. Both penstocks have the same inclination of 45° and the same internal diameter of 4.6 m. Each bifurcates before reaching the underground powerhouse, to supply water to the four turbines.

The Lubuge Project Construction Management Bureau was set up to oversee the whole project during construction on behalf of the owner. The hydraulic system is being constructed by the Japanese Taisei Corporation. The headworks and the powerhouse complexes are being constructed by a Chinese construction force – The Fourteenth Construction Bureau.

Preparatory works of the project such as the construction of access roads, camps and auxiliary plants, power lines, and so on, were mostly carried out in 1982. Excavation of the diversion tunnel began in 1983. The Engineer's order to commence construction of the power tunnel was issued on 31 July 1984. Construction of the various components of the project was well under way by 1985. First power is expected to be available from Lubuge by the end of 1988.

CONSTRUCTION OF POWER TUNNEL

The sequence of power tunnel excavation and lining was as follows. The section BA was excavated through the adit N° 2 and the point B to the upstream. It was 3666 m long. When the excavation was completed, the lining was started from the point A to the point B; The section DC was excavated through the adit N° 4 and the point D to the upstream. It was 2589 m long. When the excavation was completed, the lining was started from the point D to the point C. When the excavation of sections DC and BA was finished, the excavation of the section BC was started through the adit N⁰ 2 and the point B to the downstream. It was 2514 m long. When the excavation was completed, the lining of this section was started (Fig.2).

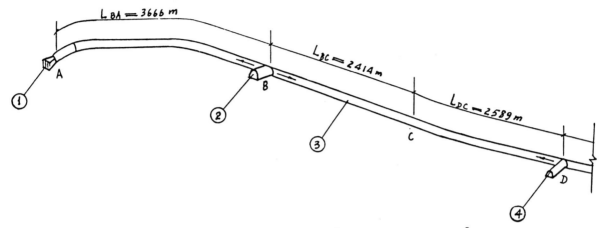

Fig. 2 Sequence of power tunnel excavation and lining (1. intake; 2. adit N⁰ 2; 3. power tunnel; 4. adit N⁰ 4)

The advantages of this excavation and lining sequence as follows. There were two working faces in simultaneous construction. Therefore two sets of excavation construction equipment were enough for the whole construction period; the excavation and the lining were made separately and disturbance between the excavation and lining could be avoided. In this way the speed of the whole tunnel construction could be increased.

The main types of equipment used in each working face are listed in table 1.

Table 1   The main types of equipment used in each working face

No.	Name	Model	Specification	Size	Quantity	Made in
1	Hydraulic drill Jumbo crawler type	JCH3-100C	3-boom	14.17x2.8x4.33 m	2	Japan
2	Wheel type loader	CAT-966D	3.1 m³	8.275x3.085x5.468 m	1	Japan
3	Dump truck	CW-52	12 t	7.315x2.49x3.00 m	6	Japan
4	Hydraulic back shovel	UHO-4	0.4 m³	7.17x2.49x2.60 m	1	Japan
5	High platform car	AS-C2			1	Japan
6	Turn table	ST-30H	30 t		1	Japan
7	Moveable transformer 400 v	3ΦTK400KVA	6kv/420 v		1	Japan
8	Moveable transformer 200 v	3ΦTR200KVA	6kv/210 v		1	Japan
9	Moveable compressor	OSP-75V6AL			1	Japan
10	Francis ventilator	PF-100SW37	1000 m³/min	Φ1230x4212 mm	1	Japan
11	Francis ventilator	PF-50SW15	400 m³/min		1	Japan
12	Laser	SLB			3	Japan
13	Submerged pump		1.5 kw, 200 v	Φ50x30 mm	1	Japan
14	Jeep	Toyota			1	Japan

The excavation in the power tunnel was performed during three 8 hour shifts a day. The working week was six days. Table 2 shows the numbers of workers for one working face.

The drilling and blasting parameters of the power tunnel were: design excavation section, 60.82 m²; average number of drill-holes, 139;

density of drill-hole, 2.29 per m²; drill-hole diameter, 100 mm and 45 mm; average depth of drill-hole, 3.3 m; average advance of the face per cycle, 3.12 m; efficiency of blasting, 89.8%; average charged density of explosive, 1.65 kg/m³; average charged density of detonator, 0.79 per m³. See Fig. 3 for cross section of drill-hole layout.

Table 2 The number of workers for one working face

Number of shift	Type of work	Number of workers	
		One shift	Three shift
	Foreman	1	3
	Drilling	7	21
	Blasting	1	3
Three shifts	Electrician	1	3
	Loading	1	3
	Truckdrivers	6	18
	Jeepdrivers	1	3
Two shifts	Repairman	2	4
	Foreman of labourers	1	1
	High platform operator	1	1
	Crane operator	1	1
One shift	Surveyor	2	2
	Labourers	5	5
	Foreman	1	1
Total			69

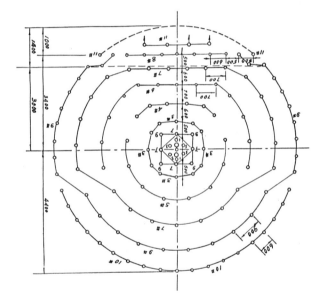

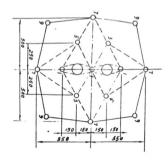

Fig.3 Cross-section of layout of drill-holes

At the beginning of excavation, the average blasting result was 3.08 rounds per day, the average cycle time was 7 hours and 1 min. It includ-

ed following operation times: measuring and arranging the drill-holes, 32 min.; drilling, 124 min.; charging and connecting the wires, 80 min.; demobilization of blasting, 17 min.; ventilation and scaling the arch part, 22 min.; mucking and scaling the bottom, 146 min. At the later stage of excavation , the average blasting number was 6 per day, the average cycle time was 4 hours and 10 min. It included following operation times: laying out of the drill-holes, 10 min.; drilling 75 min.; charging and connecting the wires, 50 min.; demobilization of blasting, 10 min.; ventilation and scaling the arch part, 15 min.; mucking and scaling the bottom, 90 min.

During excavation, smooth blasting and short cycle construction method were adopted. Therefore the quality of excavation was very good.More than 80% of smooth blasting holes remained on the periphery of power tunnel. The average overbreak of tunnel excavation was 16 cm only.

SOME EXPERIENCES OF RAPID EXCAVATION IN POWER TUNNEL

1. Construction adits

In order to increase the excavation speed when the topographic conditions permitted, the use of a construction adit was an effective measure. Whenever one adit was added, two more working faces would be created. However this had always to be paid for in increased costs for the construc-

146

tion of the adit, the amount of construction equipment and the number of labourers. Before construction of the power tunnel was invited by tender, in view of the topographic condition and the average advance rate (120 m per month), five more adits were arranged. After the tender for the construction of the power tunnel was accepted by Taisei Corporation Japan, they decided to use the adits N⁰ 2 and N⁰ 4 only, and the other adits were abandoned. The contractor considered that more than 200 m average advance rate per month could be achieved and the excavation and the lining could be performed separately. To reduce the amount of construction equipment and labour, and to avoid the disturbance between excavation and lining, the constructor decided to use two working faces simultaneously and two sets of excavation equipment only.

In practice reducing the amount of construction adits and working faces reduced the number of labourers, equipment was saved and the excavation speed was increased. After the excavation of the power tunnel commenced normal operation, the average advance rate achieved was more than 200 m per month. The maximum advance rate reached 373.7 m per month. If the tunnel is long enough and the average advance rate is more than 200 m per month and the topographic condition is favourable, one adit per every 4 KM of tunnel is recommended.

2. Selection of type and amount of construction equipment

In view of the narrow working face and the difficulty of changing the construction equipment in the tunnel, the selection of the construction equipment must follow the following principles: the amount of construction equipment must be a minimum; in order to increase the output from each item, the selected equipment must complete a chain; the construction equipment must be multi-purpose.

Two sets of hydraulic 3-boom drill jumbos were used instead of one set of hydraulic 4 or 6-boom drill jumbo in one working face. The manoeuvreability of the drill machine was increased, and the 3-boom drill jumbo was used for the following works: laying out the drill-holes; charging and connecting the blasting wires; scaling of loose rocks at tunnel arch; drilling anchor holes; and installing anchors. Therefore, a special anchoring machine was not required.

A hydraulic back shovel (UH04) was used by the Taisei Corporation for the following works: treating the dangerous rock in the tunnel arch; excavation of the drain ditch; and excavating the underbreak of tunnel section with a vibration pick instead of shovel. Practice showed that the application of multi-purpose equipment resulted in not only an increase in construction speed, but also safety in construction activities.

The construction equipment was regularly maintained. When equipment faults were found, correction was immediate. When the cause of failure was not readily found, the faulty parts were replaced as soon as possible. Holidays and off-days were used as the major time for maintenance and repair of construction equipment. Therefore, the utilization factor of construction equipment was high.

3. Application of short cycle construction method

Determination of the advance length for each cycle mainly depends on the optimum drilling depth of the drilling machine, the drillability of the rock and the duration of each excavation sequence. Recently, along with the development of the drilling machine, the optimum drilling depth was increased. Chinese engineers consider that the optimum drilling depth for a hand-drilling machine is 1.5-2.0 m, But for a hydraulic multi-booms drill Jumbo is 3-4 m. However, when the advance length of each cycle is increased, the overbreak of tunnel excavation is increased also, because when the peripheral holes are drilled, the drilling rod must maintain an angle between the directions of tunnelling axis and the drilling rod. The longer the drill hole, the greater the distance between the peripheral line of the tunnel and the end of drill hole, and the greater the overbreak of the tunnel excavation.

The Taisei Corporation had made a constant improvement of the short cycle method and set the record for advance rate of 357.4 m per month in Oct. 1985. The number of cycles was 131 rounds in that month. The average advance length per cycle was 2.728 m. The average time of cycle was 4 hours 58 min. The maximum advance length per day was 17.5 m. The average overbreak of the tunnel excavation was 16 cm only.

4. Arrangement of temporary dump near the adit portal

In order to reduce the number of dump trucks

and the time of each working cycle, a temporary
dump near the adit portal was an effective measure. When loading in the tunnel, the truckdrivers
dump the spoil in the temporary dump near the
adit portal. Because of the short distance, the
transport of spoil required only a limited number
of dump trucks. When drilling in the tunnel, the
dump trucks and loader load and transport the
spoil from the temporary dump, and transport tne
spoil to the permanent dump further away. The
practice proved that with the application of a
temporary dump, not only was the cycle time de-
creased, but also the utilization factor of dump
trucks and loader was increased.

   5. Full development worker productivity

     During the 8 hours of each shift, under the
unified supervision of the foreman, every worker
and machine had a full task load, and holdups in
the work through poor organization was not allowed. When drilling in the tunnel, the loader was
loading the spoil from the temporary dump or was
maintainning the tunnel road, the hydraulic back
shovel was excavating the drain ditch or treating
any shortage of tunnel section, the dump trucks
were transporting tne spoil between the temporary
and the permanent dumps or transporting other material. When loading in the tunnel, the drilling
and blasting workers are processing the stemming
in a room located near the adit portal. According
to the work performances of every workers, the
foreman had the power to punish or reward the
workers. Therefore the activity of workers was
maintained at top level.

The Aalesund Fjord tunnels

Bjoern Kielland
Selmer-Furuholmen Anlegg a.s., Oslo, Norway

Aerial view of the two tunnels totalling 7.7 km linking Aalesund with Ellingsøy, Valderøy, Giske and its airport at Vigra

SYNOPSIS

This paper is based on experiences from a recent construction of a fjord-crossing near Aalesund, on the West coast of Norway, and discusses different parametres concerning choice between bridge and tunnel.

For this particular crossing, the tunnel alternative was found to be the best solution, and in October 1987 two undersea tunnels, respectively 4,200 m and 3,500 m long, were opened for traffic. Total construction-cost was 325 million NOK and construction time was 22 months.

Norwegian tunnel technology is primarily based on careful selection of optimal machinery and equipment for the particular cross-section and rock quality, combined with efficient management of well trained and experienced crews. Norwegian tunnel crews working at the face seldom exceed 3 persons, dividing the necessary tasks.

In this case, integrated cooperation between the client, the engineer, and the contractor resulted in added efficiency and made it possible to complete the project at lower total costs than budgeted and within shorter (and a record) time.

1. BACKGROUND INFORMATION

Aalesund is a medium sized city on the Norwegian West Coast and a business centre for the region. The regional airport is situated on the Vigra island, directly North of Aalesund.

The airport services approximately 128,000 people from a region which is very dependent on air travel for quick and dependant communication with the rest of the country. Connection between the local population centres and the airport has, until now, been dependent on ferries, but an average daily traffic of 2,500 - 3,000 cars gave basis for a strong demand for ferry-free connections.

The article covers the development of this project, from the first planning phase, up to the present completed project. Fig. 1.

 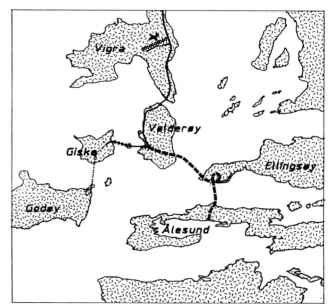

Fig. 1. Location of the tunnel system

2. BRIDGE ALTERNATIVE

During the last part of the 1970s a bridge alternative was analysed technically and economically, and a conceptual design was completed in December 1980 (1) Fig. 2.

The chosen alignment included the Elling Island (Ellingsøy) in order to service the increasing population living on this island. The project therefore included two bridges:

* Total length of bridges   3,500 m
* Longest span   500 m
* Largest clearance height   42 m
* Deepest foundation   - 26 m
* Volume of concrete   100,000 cu.m
* Construction time   4 years
* Estimated costs   730 million NOK
  (adjusted to 1985 NOK)

Because of the high costs, the project was postponed.

3. TUNNEL ALTERNATIVE

Between 1980 and 1984, several undersea tunnels were built in Norway. The most relevant for this project were the Vardoe Road Tunnel (1982) and the Shore Approach Tunnel for the gas pipe from the North Sea at Kaarstoe (1984).

Based on the experiences from these tunnels, and on reports of the good rock quality in the area,

another feasibility study was proposed. The study included two undersea tunnels, with the following main data:

* Total length   7,700 m
* Greatest depth   -140 m
* Minimum rock overburden   50 m
* Steepest gradient   8.5 %
* Volume of excavation
  (solid rock)   530,000 cu.m
* Construction time   3 years
* Estimated cost,   355 million NOK
  (1985)

The preliminary design was based on an existing acoustic profile which had been made in connection with a general survey of deposits in the region.

The low cost estimate brought new life to the development and caused several additional activities to be initiated:

* During the fall of 1984 and the spring of 1985, supplementary seismic surveys were performed, with additional control borings to check critical profiles.
* On the basis of these surveys there was drawn a new, detailed geological profile along the alignment, registering all main weak zones in the rock. Please refer to Fig. 2.

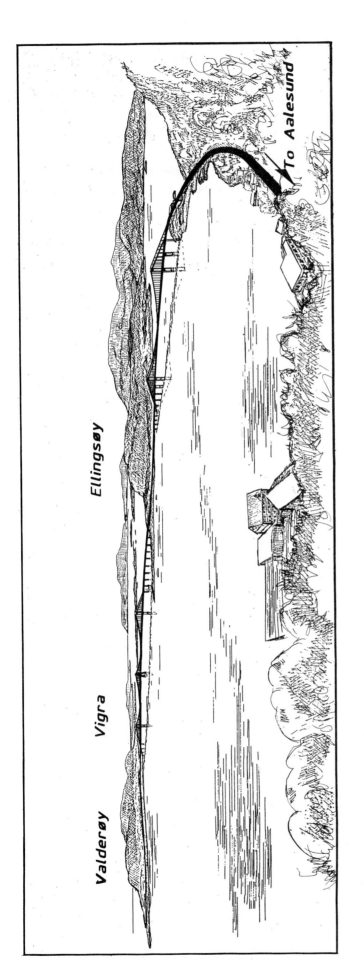

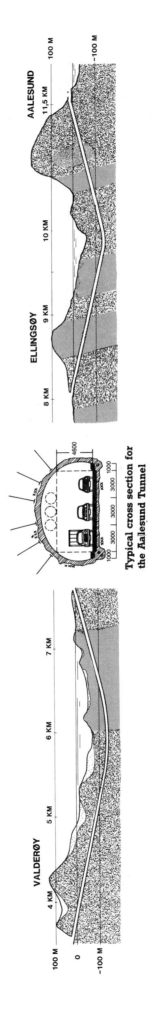

Typical cross section for the Aalesund Tunnel

Fig. 2. Connections between Aalesund and the Vigra Airport. Alternative solutions

* Parallel to the field investigations, the
  present and future traffic was estimated, as
  well as the willingness of the road user to
  accept a toll-road system.
* The formal planning process for the project was
  analysed, and
* The financing of the system was concluded
  through a bank syndicate.

The financing assumes the system to be
amortisized over a period of 15 - 20 years
through collection of a tollroad fee.

Public financing is limited to a lump sum,
representing the saved subsidies to the present
ferry-system. The Public Roads Administration
will undertake the yearly maintenance of the road
system.

The project was debated and decided by the relevant political departments within a very short
time, and the project was sent out for open
tendering.

4. EXECUTION OF THE PROJECT

.1. Schedule for execution

January 1986 Selmer-Furuholmen Anlegg a.s signed
the contract as main contractor for the project.
Later, separate contracts were signed for
lighting, ventilation, and pumping system.

The contract specified the project to be completed by January 29. 1989, i.e. a construction
time of 37 months.

However, during execution of the work, the
construction progress went through a very
positive development. Through open and active
cooperation with the client, the contractor was
able to complete the whole project and officially
open the link between the airport and the mainland on October 20. 1987,
- 15 months ahead of schedule!

.2. Main figures

	Assumed in contract	As built
A. Tunnel	(3,500 m + 4,200 m)	(3,495 m + 4,176 m)
	7,700 m	7,661 m
B. Tunnel-support		
1. Rock bolts	38,200 pc.	51,950 pc.
2. Shotcrete, wet	6,200 cu.m.	7,950 cu.m.
3. Full lining	945 m	326 m.
4. Pre-bolts	500 pc.	450 pc
5. Exploratory drilling	31,200 m	27,700 m.
6. Injection	435 tons	385 tons
7. Sandwich insulation	1,000 sq.m.	3,000 sq.m.
8. Polyethylene foam sheets	42,000 sq.m.	78,000 sq.m.

As may be seen for this project, concrete lining to a large extent was replaced by shotcrete and rock bolts.

It should be mentioned that the standards for the prevention of leakage of salt water onto passing cars was raised, resulting in a near doubling of the volume of polyethylene sheets used.

.3. Economy

Fig. 3. compares the bid price; 277 million NOK (1985), and the final construction costs, 325 million NOK (1987). This last figure does not include financing costs. Roughly, the difference between the two sums may be identified as follows:

	Million NOK
Bid price	277
Increase of volumes for tunnel support	8
Raising of standard	13
Inflation 9%	27
SUM	325

To further emphasize the low costs achieved for the tunnel at Aalesund, it may be of interest to mention that, on an average, a similar road in mountainous terrain in Norway would cost approximately 10,000 NOK per meter.

The tunnel costs at Aalesund ended up at 42,000 NOK per meter, confirming the Norwegian experience that in good rock it is possible to build a road tunnel at 3 to 5 times the cost of a normal surface road.

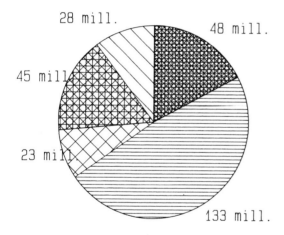

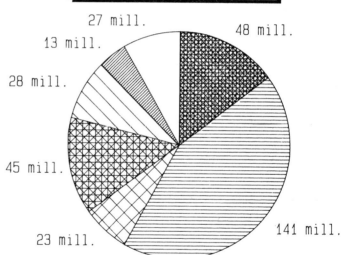

BID SUM : 277 mill. NOK

28 mill.   48 mill.
45 mill
23 mill
133 mill.

CONSTRUCTION PERIOD : 22 MONTHS

FINAL SUM : 325 mill. NOK

27 mill.   48 mill.
13 mill.
28 mill.
45 mill.
23 mill.   141 mill.

⊞ MOBILIZATION AND PRELIMINARY WORKS
☰ BLASTING, MUCKING OUT AND ROCK SUPPORTS
⊠ DRAINAGE, ROAD PAVEMENT.
⊠ PERMANENT ROCK SUPPORTS, PORTALS, TOLL POSTS
◿ LIGHTING, PUMPS, VENTILATION
▨ HIGHER STANDARD CONSTRUCTION
☐ PRICE ESCALATION

Fig. 3. Details of the construction costs

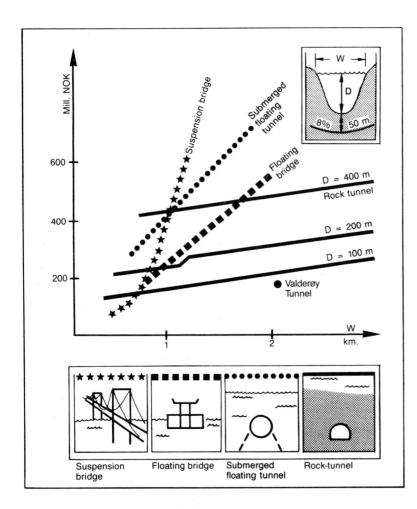

The figure shows costs for various technical schemes as a function of fjord width (W) and water depth (D). Sub-sea tunnels are the more cost efficient with wide crossings.

Fig. 4. Costs for various technical solutions

Figure 4 was developed by the Public Roads Administration, Norway. The diagram shows approximate cost estimates for different types of fjord-crossings in Norway.

The longest tunnel of the project discussed here is plotted on the diagram and shows an advantageous position, economically.

The diagram includes the parameters:
* Width of the fjord
* Depth of the fjord

It omits, however, the third and very important factor, the geo- technical conditions along the alignment:
* Deposits on sea bottom
* Rock conditions
* Fissures and leakages

In the Aalesund region, the rock consists of Precambrian gneiss and is, according to Norwegian standards, classified as a medium-to-good rock, of good stability which is easily subjected to injection. In a broader comparison, the rock may be characterized as exellent, a typical hard rock.

A warning must therefore be given against un-limited extrapolation from the experiences of the Aalesund project onto other projects where the rock is of lower quality, or of the "soft rock" type. It is also important to evaluate the variation of construction methods and utilization of labour from country to country.

.4. Construction experiences

In addition to the regular cycle of blasting and mucking out, the main elements of the undersea tunnelling were:

1. Exploratory drilling
Such drilling was executed according to procedures shown in Fig. 5 (3). For leakages through the borehole exceeding 5 litres/min., the rock was to be sealed by injection before further blasting.

154

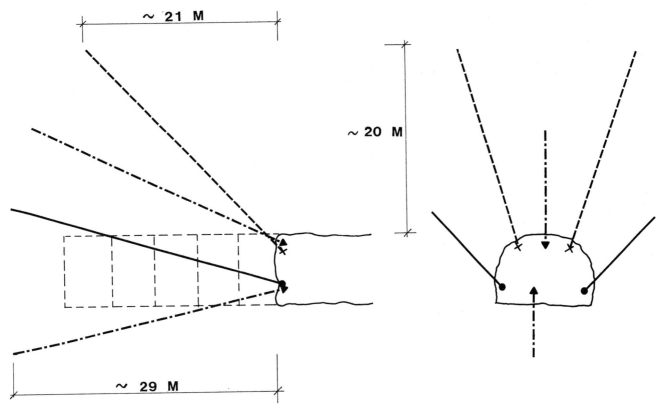

Fig. 5. Procedures for exploratory drillings

Exploratory drilling each fifth blasting.

Level 1. The whole length beneath the sea
i.e. 2 holes of 30 m length

Level 2. Expected weak zones
i.e. 4 holes of 30 m length

Level 3. Rock cover less than 40 m (in weak zones
50 m) 6 holes of 30 m length

Fig. 5. Systematic exploratory drilling with
percussion drill

2. Injection

An injection screen consisted generally of 10 -
20 holes of 18 m length.

Injection pressure varied between 30 and 100 bar.
As the foliation direction of the gneiss
generally was vertical to the tunnel axis, the
rock was easily sealed, even in areas where the
leakages per borehole reached 350 litres per min.
The total pumping necessary today for each tunnel
is approximately 1000 l/min. which shows that the
necessary sealing effect is obtained.

3. Tunnel support

Light support work was achieved through use of
the traditional combination of rock bolts and
shotcrete, mainly with fibre added to the
concrete.

Full concrete lining was undertaken through the
use of self-propelled, expandable steel formwork/
shields.

These shields, designed by Selmer-Furuholmen,
were very efficient for this large cross-section
(70 sq.m.) and infrequent use of full lining.
Because of their mobility and the short time
necessary for positioning, four tunnel sections
were easily served by two shields.

At some places the rock was of such poor quality
that the roof section caved in before the shield
could be placed.

In such areas good results were obtained through
the use of "spiling", or pre-bolting. The 8 m
long bolts, made from deformed reinforcement
bars, were placed with c/c down to 30 cm, and
gave sufficient stability until the concrete arch
had been placed. This was possible in spite of
the fact that in some sections the rock
approached a condition near that of gravel or
sand.

155

Before establishment of this procedure, it
occured an uncontrolled collapse of the roof with
the roof caving up to 10 - 12 m above the theoretical profile. The progression of the collapse,
with the Atlantic ocean as the nearest neighbour,
was somewhat unsettling.

To stop the collapse, the whole cross-section was
filled with concrete for a length of 6 m, partly
mixed with material from the collapsed rock, and
then re-excavated. Fig. 6. 700 cu.m of concrete
stabilized the situation.

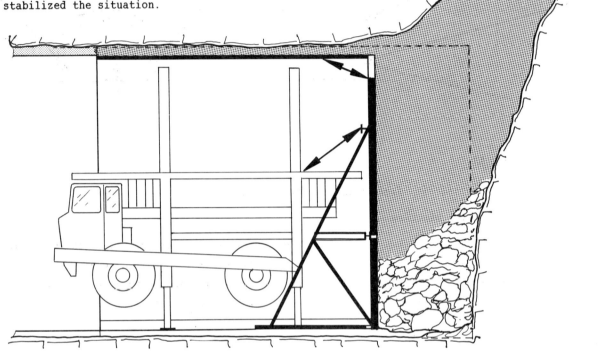

Fig. 6. Sealing of tunnel section (4)

.5. Finishing works
Work which traditionally is performed after the
blasting of the tunnels was done concurrently
with the rock excavation.

This was possible because the large cross-section
of the tunnel allowed machinery and equipment to
pass each other during construction.

The main elements of this work were:
* Ditches and pavement
* Portals and drainage sumps
* Permanent tunnel supports
* Polyethylene foam sheets
* Electrical work

This concentration of work gave a peak work force
of 230 persons. Even though this led to some loss

of efficiency, it took only 13 weeks after breakthrough until the tunnel was finished, compared
with the contract schedule of 40 weeks.

5. TUNNEL LINING

The Norwegian "Low Cost Tunnel" is based on the
following principles:

* Bolts, shotcreting, and full concrete lining
  are only used to stabilize the rock.

* No lining is used for "cosmetic" reasons.

* Small leakages are led away from the pavement
  by use of poly-ethylene foam sheets or sandwich
  plates. Some small leakages onto the pavement
  are allowed.

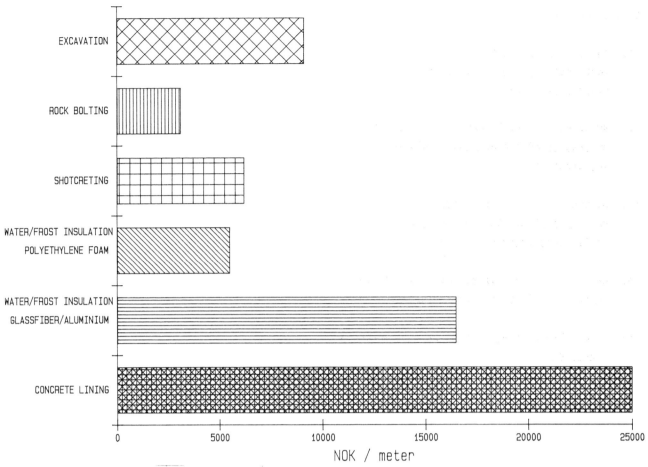

Fig. 7. Cost per metre for systematic use of
different types of tunnel linings

Raising of the standard to full concrete lining
for this project is estimated to an additional
cost of approximately 150 million NOK; - a
cost-increase of nearly 50%. Construction time
would have been increased by approximately one
year.

6. COST OF OPERATION AND MAINTENANCE.

Maintenance costs per year for bridges in Norway
are generally calculated to be between 0.1 and
0.3 % of the construction costs (1). The costs
for tunnels will probably be lower than this.

The cost per year of operating pumps, lighting,
and ventilation machinery is estimated to about
0.5 - 1.5 million NOK per year, representing 0.3
- 0.9 % of the construction cost. The magnitude
is dependent on leakages and the need for ventilation.

7. EXPECTED FUTURE DEVELOPMENTS

The tunnel-link between Aalesund and Vigra
(airport) has already encouraged the planning
work for other fjord crossings.

The Clients, the Bridge/Tunnel Corporation and
the Public Roads Administration, Norway, have
already opened new avenues of political flexibility, financing, and a positive attitude
towards the construction work.

Based on Norwegian tunnel technology, Selmer-
Furuholmen completed the project in record time
and has, in cooperation with the Client, moved
the technical/economical borders for new
projects.

Interest in sub-sea fjord crossings has become
re-vitalized. Just in Norway, more than 50
projects have been proposed, including 70 new
tunnels.

8. References:

(1) Selberg, A./Holt, J. (1980): Kjørbar
    forbindelse Alesund - Valderøy
    NTH/Bruselskapet

(2) Øvstedal, E.Lundebrekke (1984) Forprosjekt
    tunnelforbindelse Alesund - Valderøy
    Vegdirektoratet

(3) Blindheim, O.T. (1986) Ingeniørgeologiske
    under- søkelser Alesund tunneler
    Fjellsprengningskonferansen 1986

(4) Naas, R. (1987) Driftserfaring ved Alesund
    Tunneler Fjellsprengningskonferansen (1987)

(5) Vegdirektoratet High tech low cost Norwegian
    Tunneling

(1) Selberg, A./Holt, J. (1980): Kjørbar
    forbindelse Alesund - Valderøy
    NTH/Bruselskapet

Tunnelling investigation in a highly complex marine-volcanic sequence, Honolulu, Hawaii, U.S.A.

J. K. P. Kwong B.Sc., M.Sc., Ph.D., C.Eng., M.I.M.M.
Dames & Moore, Honolulu, Hawaii, U.S.A. (formerly Geolabs-Hawaii, Honolulu, U.S.A.)
J. W. Mahar B.Sc., M.Sc., Ph.D.
University of Illinois at Urbana-Champaign, U.S.A.
E. J. Cording B.Sc., M.Sc., Ph.D., M.A.S.C.E.
University of Illinois at Urbana-Champaign, U.S.A.

SYNOPSIS

Geological conditions and their potential effect on tunnelling constitute the greatest source of unknowns prior to actual construction of a tunnel project. Proper acquisition and interpretation of geologic information and presentation of the anticipated tunnelling conditions are vital to safe and economical tunnel design and construction. This paper shows that the ability to predict geological conditions improves with the amount, nature, and quality of the geotechnical engineering investigation.

Exploration procedures required to delineate ground conditions for a tunnel differ from those used in normal foundation design. Furthermore special procedures are required inorder to obtain a representative picture of conditions occurring in complex mixed face conditions, such as were present at the Honolulu, Hawaii tunnel site described in this paper.

The multi-phased investigation along the 1.6 Km (5166 L.F.) alignment of the 1.5m (60-in.) I.D. sewer for the City and County of Honolulu, Hawaii included drilling of 41 borings, 2 large (1.05m) diameter observation shafts, installation of 39 piezometers, performing field permeability, grout injection and in-situ electric cone penetration tests and laboratory soil testing.

Due to the complex geology, unusually difficult and variable mixed-face conditions were revealed only after the supplementary phases of investigation were performed and sufficient information was collected to determine ranges of ground conditions and the nature of the materials in various reaches of the alignment.

One third of the tunnel will be constructed in mixed face conditions consisting of highly complex and variable clays and silts (weathered tuff), boulders and layers or masses of basalt rock, cinder sand and reworked cinder sand, marine sediments and remnants of coral reefs. The section is anticipated to have water in the invert and perched water and local water in-flows in the tunnel face.

GENERAL GEOLOGICAL SETTING

Oahu, the third largest in the eight major islands of the Hawaiian Archipelago, covers a land area of approximately 1560 square kilometres. The island was formed generally by the volcanic activity of two large shield-type volcanoes.

The island of Oahu is divided into four geographic areas: the Waianae Range on the west, the Koolau Range on the east, the central Schofield Plateau, and the southern coastal Honolulu Plain (Figure 1). The project site is

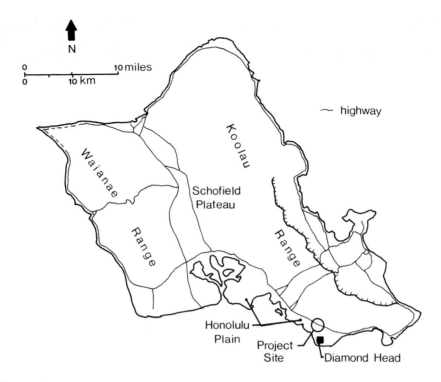

Figure 1.   General project location plan.

located on the southern flank of the Koolau Range and lies on the interface of the volcanic and marine sequence (Figures 2 and 3).

The stratigraphic history of the Manoa-Makiki area is complex because of numerous sea level changes and secondary volcanic activity that are superimposed on the rocks and soils of the Koolau Range. There were many sea level changes during the Pleistocene. The higher sea level stands allowed accumulation of coral reef deposits at corresponding higher elevations. The lower sea stands caused streams to carve valleys through the sediments and reef deposits, and a long line of sea cliffs were formed along the southern coasts (approximately Elevation 12m).

After a period of stable geological time, a new period of volcanism began in the southeast portion of the Koolau Range. Although these eruptions were small compared to the major volcanic activity of the Koolau dome, more than 30 seperate eruptions formed cinder, ash, and spatter cones and poured lava flows over the eroded topography and onto some of the fringing coral reefs. This period of post-erosional

volcanism, known as the Honolulu Volcanic Series, spanned about one-half million years, roughly from mid-Pleistocene to recent time (MacDonald et al.[3] and Sterns.[5]). About 6 or 7 of these eruptions have affected the study area.

Review of the available published literature and reports indicated that the project area was expected to primarily contain normally to over consolidated alluvial deposits, volcanic cinder (black sand), and weathered tuff.

PROJECT EXPLORATORY PROGRAM

The field exploration program consisted of the following:

a.   Inspection of surface soil and rock exposures to confirm the regional geology of the project area.

b.   Initial (Phase I) test borings, sampling, installation of piezometers, and in-situ permeability tests at 20 locations, to delineate the general geologic conditions along the proposed

160

Figure 2. High oblique aerial photograph showing the upper
Honolulu Plain in the foreground, and volcanic cones in
the background.

sewer alignment. Most of the borings
were spaced 75m to 150m apart and in
general are close to shafts, manholes
and where Makiki Stream was located.
These borings were drilled between
December 1985 to February 1986.

c. Nine additional (Phase II) borings were
drilled between March to April, 1986,
to better define ground water
conditions and contact zones between
geologic units. Selected borings in
Phase II were placed in areas of known
complicated geologic contacts, boulders
and possible lava flows.

d. Six pump test observation wells were
placed and pumping and grout injection
tests were performed (Phase III) in
June, 1986.

e. Two large (1.05m) diameter observation
shafts were drilled in July, 1987, to
provide direct observation of ground
conditions and geotechnical data for
design and construction. Windows and
ladders were installed on shaft casings
and the shafts are left open to allow
observation by prospective contractors.

Continuous sampling procedures were used in
most of the borings to provide a continuous log
of subsurface conditions, and to obtain adequate
sampling of geologic units, particularly at and
near the tunnel level. Sketches were prepared
of each sample and stratigraphic details were
noted on the logs. These sampling and recording
procedures were necessary because of:

a. The complex stratigraphy in the
volcanic, alluvial, and marine sequence
along the alignment of the proposed
sewer.

b. The importance of detailed lithological
variations, such as the interbedding of
uncemented cinder sands and weathered
tuff (clayey silt) on the performance
of the tunnel, and the ability to grout
or dewater the subsurface materials.

c. the need to realistically identify
boulder bearing unit and mixed-face
conditions at the proposed tunnel
level; and

d. the need to identify potential perched
water conditions near and at the
proposed tunnel level.

161

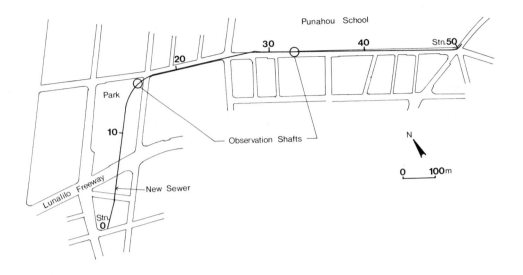

Figure 3. General alignment of the new sewer tunnel.

For the most part continuous sampling was obtained by alternate use of ring and split spoon samplers. In selected borings, a Triefus Triple tube core barrel or a wireline (HQ) rock coring system was used. The Triefus Triple tube core barrel was used to recover rock, boulders and cemented soils. The undisturbed samples obtained by the Triple tube barrel were compared with Standard Penetration test results and split spoon samples in adjacent boreholes.

Photographs of all the opened split spoon samples and of the cores were obtained in the field prior to taking bagged samples for laboratory testing and provided an accessible permanent record of the details of the stratigraphy.

Falling head permeability tests were carried out to estimate in situ hydraulic conductivity of the interbedded cinder sand and tuff layers and in the coral units (Hvorslev, 1951). The laboratory method was not used because of problems with sample preparation and large anticipated difference in vertical and horizontal permeability in the field.

Pump tests were performed in the 1.05m diameter observation shaft at Station 33+00 (1006m). Thirty-nine piezometers were installed in 35 boreholes to allow long-term monitoring of

groundwater levels. Multi-level piezometers were installed in 4 selected borings to monitor the perched as well as ground water conditions.

Electric cone penetrometer (ECP) tests were carried out in two selected locations. The cone penetrometer was used because of the potential difficulties in obtaining undisturbed samples of loose and/or uncemented cinder sand. The values of the tip resistance and friction ratio (sleeve friction over tip resistance) were used to estimate soil strength (Robertson and Campanella[3]).

Comparison of in situ test data (SPT and ECP) with direct shear and unconfined compressive strengths obtained on samples of cemented cinder from the Triefus Triple tube core barrel and ring sampler were carried out and summarized in Table 1.

Grout injection tests were carried out in two Phase III borings. Cement grout was injected at different consistencies to provide information on the groutability of the soils at one of the crossover locations of the existing sewer (Station 27+00/823m). The grout test results indicated that clean cinder sand can be grouted with neat cement mixes from 1m above the existing tunnel in the Punahou Street crossover area. The test results also revealed that

162

cement grout cannot be effectively injected into the interbedded cinder and silt deposits. Thus grout stabilization was not recommended for sections of tunnel such as the crossing beneath the Lunalilo Freeway.

Detailed description and discussion of electric cone penetration and grout injection test methods are beyond the scope of this paper, and are not included in this presentation.

Laboratory tests included Atterberg limits, direct shear, unconfined compression, swell pressure, Schmidt hammer, Scleroscope and abrasive hardness tests.

SUBSURFACE CONDITIONS REVEALED IN THE PHASE I INVESTIGATION

The Phase I borings indicated that the following geological units were expected along the proposed sewer alignment:

a. Recent MUDFLOW and ALLUVIAL deposits - gravelly clay (CH), gravelly clayey silt (MH), and gravelly sand (SP); all with cobbles and boulders.

b. Weathered TUFF - primarily clayey silt (MH), some clay (CH) with gravel, cobbles, and boulders, fissured in places. In local areas, the tuff is fused and unweathered.

c. Interbedded CINDERS and weathered or reworked TUFF - silty sand (SM, SM-SP), gravelly sand (SP) to sandy gravel (GP) interbedded with thin layers of silt to gravelly silt. The cinder sands are generally loose to dense, and are uncemented to locally slightly cemented or cemented.

d. Marine CLAY - clayey silt (MH) and clay (CH), with gravel to boulder sized inclusions, fissured in places; and

e. Coral - sandy silt, sandy gravel, to hard coral and cavities.

A generalized cross section showing the initial interpretation of the subsurface conditions along the new tunnel alignment is presented in Figures 4 and 5a. Some engineering properties and characteristics of the above described geological materials are summarized in Table 1.

Table 1.   Summary of selected geotechnical engineering properties.

Soil Type	Total Unit Weight (Mg/m³)	Friction Angle (Degree)	Cohesion (kPa)	Unconfined Compressive Strength(MPa)		Ring Swell (%)		SPT "N" (blows/ft)
				Average	Range	Average	Range	
Alluvium (clayey silt/ silty clay)	1.76*	18*	0*	---	---	--	--	10 to 35
Weathered Tuff (clayey silt)	1.76*	22*	0*	0.2	---	4.0	0.4-7.4	15 to 60
Cinder: a. uncemented b. cemented c. with scoria	1.6*	34*+ 34+ 39+	0* 0 20	1.38	1.0 to 1.9	N/A	N/A	4 to 30 40 to 52 51 to 91
Marine Clay	1.76*	13*	0*	---	---	17.0	16.7-22.2	9 to 40
Coral: a. Gravel & Sand b. Silty sand c. Reef	1.9* --- ---	30* --- ---	0* --- ---	--- --- ---	--- --- ---	N/A N/A N/A	N/A N/A N/A	---- 2 to 9 16 to 50
Basalt (vesicular to dense)	2.2*	N/A	N/A	95.8	64.8 to 143.4	N/A	N/A	Refusal

Note:

* Recommended parameters for earth pressure calculation, based on direct shear tests.

+ A $\phi'= 34°$ to $42°$ range was obtained using electric cone penetration.

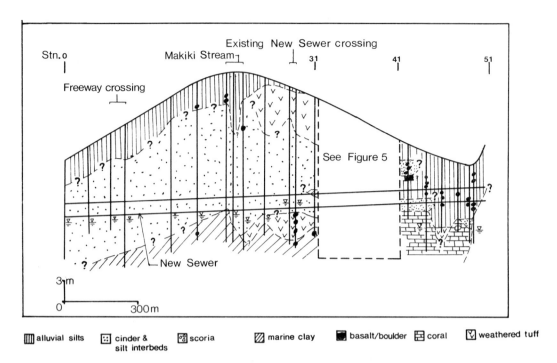

Figure 4. Generalized subsurface profile along the new sewer
new sewer alignment.

Generally, the first 900m of the proposed
sewer traverses across the higher elevations of
the Honolulu Plain. The stratigraphy here is
relatively simple and consists of three basic
geologcal units: alluvium, cinder sand with or
without weathered or reworked tuff interbeds,
and marine clay. The cinder sand is typically
12m to 48m thick and is deposited on a
relatively flat, basal marine clay or coral
surface (Figure 4). Alluvium, weathered tuff,
and mudflow deposits overlie the cinder sand at
the top of the profile.

The remaining portion of the new sewer,
approximately 700m (about Station 29+00/884m to
51+61.1/1573m) of the new sewer, crosses along
the southerly flank of Rocky Hill (an extinct
volcanic cone). The initial Phase I borings
indicated that the anticipated tunnelling
conditions may include excavation in interbedded
cinder and bouldery weathered tuff deposits, and
marine clay (Figure 5a). The investigation team
requested additional field exploration, because
of difficulties in correlation of lithological
units and the possible presence of lava flows in
the profile (Figure 5a).

PHASES II & III INVESTIGATIONS
The 9 additional Phase II borings showed the
presence of a complex sequence of volcanic,
alluvial, mudflow, marine sediments, and rock at
the eastern portion of the new sewer alignment.
The soil and rock conditions are highly variable
and correlations between boreholes in this
section are still tenuous (Figure 5b). The
extra borings indicated that the eastern portion
will be the most difficult to construct because
of the large variability and potentially adverse
ground conditions which range from boulders and
flowing ground to a full face of hard basalt.

Based on the additional borings, the ground
conditions between Station 29+00 to 35+00 change
from a relatively uniform sequence of recent
sediments, cinders and tuff, and marine clay to
highly complex soil and rock conditions.
Mixed-face tunnelling is anticipated throughout
much of the section (Figures 5b and c).

The complex geologic conditions occur as a
result of the tunnel alignment being at the
interface between the Rocky Hill volcanic cones
and a marine coastal sequence that has
experienced several fluctuations in sea level.

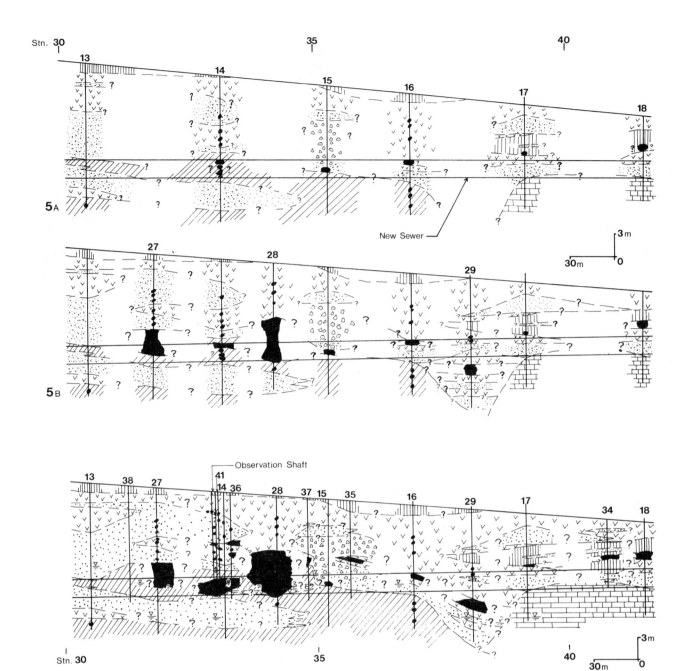

Stn. 30   35   40

5A   New Sewer ─┘   3m
          30m ─┘ 0

5B

Observation Shaft

13 38 27 41 14 36 28 37 15 35   16   29   17   34 18

5C
Stn. 30   35   40   3m
          30m ─┘ 0

| ▥ alluvial silts | ∷ cinder & silt interbeds | ⌂ scoria | ▨ marine clay | ■ basalt/boulder | ⊞ coral | ⍓ weathered tuff |

Figure 5. Idealized subsurface profile between Station 30+00
          (914m) to 44+00 (1341m) based on boring data from
          Phase I (5a), Phase I & II (5b), and Phase I to III (5c)
          (Water levels shown were highest measured during field
          exploration)

Between approximate Station 29+00 (884m) and
35+00 (1067m), the thick (up to 13m) cinder sand
deposit appears to interfinger with marine
sediments (1.5m to over 4m thick) and weathered
tuff units and pinches out at the southern edge
of Rocky Hill (about Station 35+00/1067m). The
basal marine sediments were dissected subsequent
to deposition and a drop in sea level, and

erosional depressions were in-filled by basalt
flows, most likely from the rocky hill cones.
Three main lava flows (minimum 3m to 6m thick)
and numerous thinner flows (about 0.7m to 1.2m)
were identified in the Phase II and III of the
field investigation (Figure 5c).

          Lava flows were typically slightly
weathered to fresh, dense to vesicular basalt.

165

Clinker and broken zones with brown silty clay
seams of up to 0.15m thick were also present in
the basalt flows. Clinker is formed as a
cooling crust of slow moving aa lava flows. The
result is a discontinuous layer on the top and
bottom of flows that is composed of blocky loose
and partially welded lava fragments. Since
basalt flows tend to follow pre-existing
topographic depression, test borings drilled on
15m to 65m spacings do not provide a complete
picture of the locations of the flows in the
tunnel section. Furthermore other flows not
intersected by the borings are anticipated.

In order to view the soil and rock
conditions directly, a 1.05m diameter
observation shaft was drilled in the area of
complex geology (Figures 3, 5c, and 6). Two
basalt flows were encountered in the shaft. One
of the flows does not extend across the full
width of the shaft, and appears to have formed
in a narrow gully. Thus, the location and
extent of the flows will be variable. Zones of
weathered tuff and cinders with silt, were also
encountered in the shaft. In general, the
materials in the shaft walls stood without
support because the cinder was slightly
cemented. However, cementation of the cinders
is highly variable and in some places the

Figure 6b. Clay to basalt interface exposed
in observation shaft.

cinders may not be cemented. For example,
saturated cinder and clinker zones below and
within the basalt flow were unstable during
shaft excavation. Water was encountered above
the marine clay at the bottom of the shaft. In
observing ground behaviour in vertical shafts it
must be remembered that stable materials in
shaft walls may be unstable in a tunnel
excavation.

Highly variable mixed-face conditions are
anticipated at the tunnel level between Station
29+00 (884m) and 35+00(1067m). Conditions are
likely to range from an entire face of cinder
sand to a complex sequence of cinders and marine
sediments to marine sediments, basalt flows and
thin cinder layers (Figure 5c). Other
combinations of soils and rocks with large
variations in material properties are expected.
All nine borings drilled along this section of
the alignment encountered hard boulders.

Further eastward, mixed-face tunneling is
also expected between Station 35+00 (1067m) to
39+00 (1189m). Stratigraphic units along this
portion of the alignment include:

a. probable occurrence of local volcanic
   spatter and cinder cone (about
   Station 35+00/1067m to 37+00/1128m);

b. basaltic lava flow(s) interlayered with
   tuff and cinder/volcanic ejecta
   sequences (about Station 35+00/1067m to
   39+00/1189m);

Figure 6a. Installation of large diameter
observation shaft.

166

c. possible wave-eroded bluff and wave-cut platform in marine sediments which were later buried by locally wave-reworked cinder deposits (about Station 35+00/1067m to 37+00/1128m); and

d. a buried channel at and near Station 38+00 (1158m) area.

The conditions are expected to be variable, and unknown conditions may be encountered even where borings were spaced approximately 20m to 35m apart.

FIELD PERMEABILITY

Falling head permeability (hydraulic conductivity) tests in the cinder sand yield values of 1.8×10^{-5} m/sec. to 6.8×10^{-8} m/sec. Falling head tests carried out in thick zones of relatively clean cinders yield values of 1.1×10^{-6} m/sec. and 1.8×10^{-5} m/sec. Lower values of 6.2×10^{-8} m/sec. and 6.8×10^{-8} m/sec. were obtained in interbedded cinder and silt units. The low permeability values may be largely due to a). the presence of clayey silt interbeds; b) clogging by fines; and c) presence of unsaturated conditions in the test material.

Hydraulic conductivity measured in the coral unit at Station 39+00 (1189m) was estimated to be 3.8×10^{-6} m/sec.

Hydraulic conductivities measured in the basalt flows were estimated to be 2.8×10^{-6} m/sec. and 1.4×10^{-6} m/sec.

Pump-out tests performed at approximate Station 33+00 (1006m, observation shaft CH-2) indicate that the basalt flow unit there is hydraulically connected within the vicinity of the test site, and construction dewatering would be feasible.

During the pump test, because of the slow rate of recharge recorded subsequent to drawdown, steady state flow cannot be practicably established during the field test, and the hydraulic properties of the basalt flow unit tested was not calculated.

IMPORTANCE OF THE EXPLORATORY PROGRAM

To prepare proper specifications for a tunnel project, the designer must not only obtain information that permits sizing of the lining, but, more importantly, the exploratory results should provide the needed data to select the most desirable vertical and horizontal alignment, and to establish appropriate criteria for tunnelling, controlling ground movements, and damage to structures. Furthermore, the exploratory information should be presented to assist propective contractors in preparing responsive bids. The exploratory program should be planned so that the results will assist in the selection of equipment and procedures, including the tunnelling machine and shield, dewatering systems, and other ground control measures. The exploratory results must be adequate to determine the range of expected conditions.

Mixed ground conditions, including mixed face tunnelling, such as those anticipated between Station 29+00 (884m) and 45+00 (1372m) are some of the most difficult conditions in underground work because of the multiple ground behaviours combined with hard cobbles, boulders and rock. One of the main difficulties lies in maintaining a stable face yet providing access to the face to remove obstructions (cobbles, boulders and rock).

Conditions similar to those described in the preceeding paragraphs have caused abandonment of other tunnels because of alignment, excavation, support and/or ground loss problems. Dewatering, local treatment of the ground by consolidation grouting, and reinforcement of the rock above the crown using rebars grouted in from the ground surface may be needed to stabilize the soils in and above the tunnel interval in the difficult mixed face section.

It can be seen from the above case that the details of the stratigraphy and other minor variations in geologic profile can have a significant effect on tunnelling conditions and on the construction contract. Cording et al [1] showed that such small engineering geological variations can have a strong influence on behaviour of the soil in a tunnel face and around the tunnel. Therefore the emphasis in the exploratory program for a tunnel should differ from the emphasis for a foundation investigation, and continuous samples of soil and rock materials should be obtained and logged in detail, rather than relying on samples obtained at intervals, such as 1.5m. in the borehole.

The importance of a qualified and experienced field crew to the proper implementation of the field exploratory program cannot be overemphasized. The geologic engineer or engineering geologist responsible for the field operations must be knowledgeable on drilling techniques and procedures, have ample experience in identifying geologic materials and tunnelling, foresee potential sampling problems, and be able to work with the drill crew.

In view of the varied tunnelling conditions, all pertinent and available information obtained during the geotechnical engineering investigation phase of the project were available for examination by the bidders for the tunnel construction. Files relating to the project in the G. E. office were available for review by the bidders. A detailed geotechnical engineering report was included as part of the construction contract document.

In particular, during the pre-bid meeting, the bidders were able to inspect the two large diameter observation shafts, and examine the soil and rock samples obtained.

ENGINEERING GEOLOGICAL FACTORS SIGNIFICANT TO TUNNELLING

Some of the engineering geological factors that have a strong effect on ground behaviour in soft ground tunnelling are:

    a.   cohesion and cementation of soils/weak rock,

    b.   size and frequency of rock or boulders,

    c.   groundwater conditions.

Even with a detailed field exploration, the above features may be difficult to predict beacuse of geological variability.

Degree of Cementation

Collapse of cinder sand around the 4-inch diameter drill casing indicates that certain portions of the cinder deposits in the Honolulu project area are uncemented. However, based on the triple tube core barrel samples and the observation shaft results, most of the cinders are cemented (Figure 7).

The degree of cementation is difficult to determine by inspection of samples obtained by the split spoon or ring sampler. The apparent lack of cementation was the result of sampling disturbance, particularly in weakly cemented soils and rocks with a high void space. High cuts in cinders exposed in volcanic cones north of the project area are weakly cemented and appear to be similar to cinders recovered in the core barrel and observed in the shafts. However, the cinder/tuff sequence between Station 0+00 (0m) and 10+00 (305m) appears to be reworked and deposited in a nearshore marine or coastal plain environment where reworking by waves and fluvial processes have destroyed any bonds between the angular volcanic sand grains.

The cinder sand is expected to primarily exhibit firm to running behaviour. For the most part the cinder sand should be stable in the tunnel face, particularly where the cinders are cemented. However, running will occur in uncemented cinders and some local ravelling may develop in cemented sections. These conditions can be controlled by a properly designed shield and careful workmanship. The shield should be able to support running soils in the face as well as provide adequate space to excavate hard, cemented cinders. Flowing conditions are expected to occur where the groundwater level is at or above the tunnel invert or where perched water is present at tunnel level. Cemented cinders should not flow and should provide some face support, whereas uncemented cinders will flow rapidly from the face.

Identification of Thin Basalt Flows and Boulders

DRILLING METHOD & EQUIPMENT	SEWER TUNNEL RELIEF INCREMENT 2	BORING NO. G-13

<table>
<tr><td colspan="2">DRILLING METHOD & EQUIPMENT
CME 55, 4 IN. SOLID STEM AUGER, 4 IN.
CASING, 140 LB. HAMMER, 30-INCH DROP</td><td rowspan="2">SEWER TUNNEL RELIEF
INCREMENT 2
CARTWRIGHT FIELD TO METCALF STREET
HONOLULU, OAHU, HAWAII
DIVISION OF WASTEWATER MANAGEMENT
DEPARTMENT OF PUBLIC WORKS
CITY AND COUNTY OF HONOLULU</td><td colspan="2">BORING NO. G-13</td></tr>
<tr><td colspan="2">SAMPLING METHOD
TRIEFUS TRIPLE TUBE, SHELBY 2½ IN.,
2-INCH SPLIT SPOON, 3-INCH RING SAMPLER
LOGGED BY J. KWONG S. LATRONIC</td><td colspan="2">SHEET 2 OF 3
W.O. 1618-00
DATE STARTED 1/23/86
DATE COMPLETED 1/24/86
TOTAL DEPTH 56.5 FEET
SURFACE ELEV. 55.94 FEET</td></tr>
</table>

SAMPLE NO.	RECOVERY(%)	BLOWS PER 6-IN. RS	BLOWS PER 6-IN. SS	N (BLOWS PER FOOT)	SAMPLE B	DEPTH (FT.)	GRAPHIC LOG	LAB USCS	MATERIAL DESCRIPTION	MOISTURE CONTENT(%)	qu (KSF) Pp	LAB TEST	NOTES
TT 13	100					26			BLACK MEDIUM TO COARSE SAND WITH SOME GRAVEL, UNCEMENTED TO LOCALLY CEMENTED, WET (CINDER)				WATER RETURN: CLEAR TRIEFUS SAMPLE: 24.5 TO 27.5 FEET 33 SECONDS PER FOOT 30 SECONDS PER FOOT 28 SECONDS PER FOOT
						27							
TT 14	62					28							WATER RETURN: CLEAR TRIEFUS SAMPLE: 27.5 TO 29.5 FEET 36 SECONDS PER FOOT 43 SECONDS PER FOOT
						29							RUN CASING TO 29.5 FEET
TT 15	100					30			SLIGHTLY CEMENTED AT 30.0 TO 34.5 FEET				
						31				●			
						32							
TT 16	100					33							WATER RETURN: CLEAR TRIEFUS SAMPLE: 32.5 TO 34.5 FEET 22 SECONDS PER FOOT 20 SECONDS PER FOOT
						34							
						35							WATER RETURN: CLEAR TO 38.0 FEET THEN CHANGED TRIEFUS SAMPLE: 34.5 TO 39.0 FEET 30 SECONDS PER FOOT 30 SECONDS PER FOOT 20 SECONDS PER FOOT 40 SECONDS PER FOOT 25 SECONDS PER 6-INCH
TT 17	26					36							
						37							
						38							
						39			BLUISH GRAY TO TAN SILTY CLAY WITH POCKETS OF WEATHERED CORAL, SOFT, WET (MARINE SEDIMENT)				
ST 18	100	300PSI 400PSI 700PSI				40							
		750/2"				41			BROWN COARSE SAND (CINDER) AND TAN HIGHLY WEATHERED TUFF				REFUSAL TO SHELBY PENETRATION AT 40.5 FEET
TT 19	89					42			BLACK COARSE TO MEDIUM CINDER SAND, UNCEMENTED TO LOCALLY CEMNETED, WET (CINDER)				TRIEFUS SAMPLE: 41.5 TO 43.5 FEET 38 SECONDS PER FOOT 29 SECONDS PER FOOT 25 SECONDS PER FOOT
						43			SLIGHT CEMENTED: 42.3 TO 45.2 FEET 45.5 TO 46.6 FEET				
SS 20	83	24 25 22		47		44							
						45							WATER RETURN: SLIGHTLY MUDDY TRIEFUS SAMPLE: 45.0 TO 48.0 FEET 41 SECONDS PER FOOT 40 SECONDS PER FOOT 70 SECONDS PER FOOT
TT 21	94					46							
						47							
						48							
SS 22	83	17 10 17		27		49			BROWN TO GRAY SILTY CLAY WITH SOME GRAVEL, MOIST (WEATHERED TUFF)				
						50							

Figure 7. Log of boring showing alternating use of triple tube coring and SPT in sampling interbedded cinder and weathered tuff.

Cobbles, boulders and rock are notorious for causing difficulties in "soft ground tunnelling". They can result in delays, lost ground, face instability, and alignment difficulties. Most shield machines cannot efficiently handle large boulders. They can only proceed after the boulders are pushed outside the perimeter, are broken, or are removed by hand from the front of the shield. Often, in the attempt to remove a boulder, the exposed soil surrounding the boulder becomes unstable and either runs or flows into the tunnel face. The magnitude of the problem depends on the soil characteristics: the nature of the materials surrounding the boulders, the groundwater levels above tunnel invert, and the frequency and strength of the boulders. Problems are more likely to occur when the size of the obstruction is large in comparison to the size of the opening (greater than 10 to 20%).

Although the identification of boulders and rock in soft ground is of paramount importance in pre-bid tunnelling investigations, valid evidence of the presence of cobbles and boulders may not be always apparent or recognized. Drilling and split spoon refusal often do not ocurr in materials containing cobbles and boulders less than 0.45m in size. Yet cobbles and boulders in the 0.15 to 0.45m size range have caused difficulties in soft ground tunnelling project (Cording et al. 1987). The presence of cobbles and boulders should not only be determined by refusal, but also by criteria such as rig chatter, drill bit scrapping noise, slow rate of drill advance, angular fragments and shards in the drill cuttings, high blow counts and recovery of angular rock fragments, and obstruction in the borehole that cause difficulty in raising and lowering drilling tools. The depth of each cobble or boulder hit should be noted and shown in the boring log. Where refusal is encountered, the obstruction should be cored to determine the nature and composition of the rock block or slab. Figure 8 illustrates some of the procedures and techniques used in identifying the presence of cobbles and boulders.

Tunnelling progress through the mixed-face section described earlier will be slow and difficult. The contract specifications required that a full circle open face shield may be used in this section. Wheel-type excavators were not allowed. Pipe jacking methods were not permitted. Partial shield or no shield methods were allowed between Stations 30+15 (919m) and 41+70 (1271m) if they are capable of providing continuous and complete support of the face, are capable of maintaining a stable invert, and are capable of providing support ahead of the face to prevent collapse and minimize ground loss and inflow of soil.

The shield should be able to excavate cemented zones, capable of accomodating large boulders and layers of rock that may be encountered during excavation and should be designed to allow excavation through a full face of rock that requires blasting.

The tunnelling equipments must have capabilities for spiling or forepoling ahead of the face and for complete breasting of the face in order to support running or flowing soils and also permit excavation of rock. Ground losses will tend to be more severe where rock is present, in combination with running or flowing soils, requiring exposure of the ground at and ahead of the face in order to remove the rock or boulders. The unstable running or flowing soils will need to be supported in the face while the rock is excavated.

Groundwater

The geologic units within the project area make up a variable and complex aquifer/aquitard system (Figures 4 and 5c). The tunnel excavation will encounter groundwater in permeable cinder layers and basalt lava flows. Some water will be perched on weathered tuff or marine clay layers. Dewatering wells will need to be at least 13m to 34m deep in the mixed-face section, and to be effective will require use of a vacuum system and submersible pumps. Dewatering in this section can also be accomplished by allowing the water to flow

DRILLING METHOD & EQUIPMENT CME 45, 7¼-INCH HOLLOW STEM AUGERS 0 TO 29 FT., 4-IN. CASING:29.0 TO 54.0	**SEWER TUNNEL RELIEF INCREMENT 2** CARTWRIGHT FIELD TO METCALF STREET HONOLULU, OAHU, HAWAII	**BORING NO. G-27**

SEWER TUNNEL RELIEF
INCREMENT 2
CARTWRIGHT FIELD TO METCALF STREET
HONOLULU, OAHU, HAWAII
DIVISION OF WASTEWATER MANAGEMENT
DEPARTMENT OF PUBLIC WORKS
CITY AND COUNTY OF HONOLULU

DRILLING METHOD & EQUIPMENT
CME 45, 7¼-INCH HOLLOW STEM AUGERS
0 TO 29 FT., 4-IN. CASING:29.0 TO 54.0

SAMPLING METHOD   FEET
2-INCH SPLIT SPOON, 3-INCH RING
SAMPLER, TRIEFUS TRIPLE TUBE

LOGGED BY J. KWONG
           S. LATRONIC

BORING NO. G-27
SHEET 2 OF 3
W.O. 1618-10
DATE STARTED   3/11/86
DATE COMPLETED   3/13/86
TOTAL DEPTH   57 FEET
SURFACE ELEV.   54.63 FEET

SAMPLE NO.	RECOVERY (%)	BLOWS PER 6-IN. RS	BLOWS PER 6-IN. SS	N (BLOWS/FOOT)	SAMPLE & DEPTH (FT.)	GRAPHIC LOG	LAB USCS	MATERIAL DESCRIPTION	MOISTURE CONTENT (%)	qu (KSF)	NOTES
SS 15	83		17 33 35	68	26–			BLACK GRAVELLY COARSE TO MEDIUM SAND, WITH BASALT COBBLES/BOULDERS (CINDER)			AUGER CHATTER: 24 TO 27 FEET
SS 16	50	23 50/5"			27– 28–			COBBLE OR BOULDER AT 27.0 FEET			SPLIT SPOON REFUSAL AT 27.9 FEET
RS 17	100	50/6"			29–						SS-18 REFUSAL AT 29 FEET CASING TO 29 FEET
TT 1	83				30–			BLUISH GRAY, HARD, VESICULAR BASALT, CLOSELY JOINTED, MODERATELY TO SLIGHTLY WEATHERED, WITH IRON STAINED FRACTURES AND WEATHERED SEAMS (LAVA FLOW)			CORING RATE: 4 MINUTES/2 FOOT RUN WATER RETURN: BROWN/GRAY
					31–			RQD = 0%			SS-19 REFUSAL AT 31 FEET WATER RETURN: BROWN TO 32 FEET NO WATER RETURN 32 TO 34
TT 2	86				32– 33–						CORING RATE: 31 TO 32 FEET: 4 MINUTES 32 TO 33 FEET: 1 MINUTE 33 TO 34 FEET: 8 MINUTES
					34–			RQD = 0%			SS-20 REFUSAL AT 34 FEET WATER RETURN: BROWN 34 TO 37 FEET
TT 3	116				35– 36–						CORING RATE: 34 TO 35 FEET: 3.5 MINUTES 35 TO 36 FEET: 2.5 MINUTES 36 TO 37 FEET: 3.0 MINUTES NO WATER RETURN 37 TO 40 FEET
					37–	▽		RQD = 0%			
TT 4	100				38– 39–						CORING RATE: 37 TO 38 FEET: 6.0 MINUTES 38 TO 39 FEET: 6.5 MINUTES 39 TO 40 FEET: 6.0 MINUTES
								RQD = 0%			HOLE TENDING TO CAVE WHEN BARREL PULLED AT 40 FEET
RS 21	100	28 32 43			40– 41–			INTERBEDDED GRAY COBBLY CLAY AND SANDY GRAVEL (MARINE CLAY)	●		
SS 22	83		11 9 18	27	42–		CH	GRAY TO BROWN CLAY WITH CORAL FRAGMENTS, VERY STIFF, WET (MARINE CLAY)	● ├─●─┤	8.0	
RS 23	78	10 12 38			43– 44–			BASALT COBBLES/BOULDERS AT 43.0 TO 44.2 FEET	●		SLOWER PENETRATION FROM 44.2 TO 44.5 FEET
SS 24	67		23 27 48	75	45– 46–			BLACK MEDIUM TO COARSE SAND, WITH SOME SILT, UNCEMENTED TO LOCALLY CEMENTED, MEDIUM TO VERY DENSE, WET	●		
SS 25	67		45 28 25 25	53	47– 48–			THIN LAYER OF SILTY FINE SAND: 47.8 TO 48.0 FEET	● ●		
					49– 50–	▽					SAND GRIPPING CASING, USED DRILL MUD (REVERT) TO CLEAN TO 49.5 FEET

Figure 8. Log of boring showing techniques used in obtaining a continuous log of soil and rock sequence.

downward. If downward dewatering is used, the wells will have to be drilled and screened deep enough to intersect the permeable cinder and coral layers which have water levels below tunnel invert.

CONCLUSIONS

1. The complex geological conditions along the Kaimuki-Manoa Sewer Tunnel Relief (Increment 2) alignment occur as a result of the tunnel alignment being at the interface between volcanic cones and marine coastal sequences.

2. Some of the mixed ground conditions identified along one-third of the tunnel are considered to be some of the most difficult conditions in underground work because of a combination of the small size of the tunnel, the need to stablize running to flowing ground conditions, and at the same time access to the face has to be maintained to remove obstructions such as hard cobbles, boulders, and rock.

3. This case shows that an adequate tunnelling investigation is different from a typical foundation investigation. The factors and exploratory techniques that were found to be of paramount importance in obtaining reliable information for tunnel design and construction include:

    a. continuous sampling using a combination of drive samplers and triple tube core barrels to obtain information in intermixed soil and rock sequences;

    b. alternating use of the Standard Penetration Test and triple tube coring to obtain pertinent information on, and less disturbed samples of, weakly cemented soils;

    c. detailed logging of the borings and making photographic record of each sample obtained;

    d. use of large diameter observation shafts in critical locations to observe the nature and behaviour of in-place materials;

    e. testing possible construction procedures, such as pump tests and grout injection tests, during field exploration;

    f. the use of qualified and experienced personel in the implementation of the exploratory program.

4. The exploratory borings provided an indication of the probable range of geological variations along the tunnel alignment. Several closely spaced borings showed that variations in geological conditions can be abrupt. However, the borings may not delineate all geological variations along the alignment, and the actual conditions at all points along the tunnel may not be known until after construction.

5. The proper acquisition, interpretation, and presentation of the anticipated tunnelling conditions benefit the owner, and the contruction contract, by allowing:

    a. safe and economical tunnel design and

    b. the bidding contractors to be fully aware of the potential construction difficulties at the pre-bid stage.

Acknowledgements

The Manoa-Kaimuki Sewer Tunnel Relief is jointly funded by the City and County of Honolulu, and the Environmental Protection Agency.

The design team for Increment 2 of the new sewer includes Park Engineering, Dr. E.J. Cording and associates, and Geolabs-Hawaii. Air photograph used was taken and provided by Park Engineering and is gratefully acknowledged. Mr. U.K. Ung performed the electric cone penetration tests.

References

1. Cording E.J., Brierley, G.S., Mahar, J.W., and Boscardin, M.D., 1987. Controlling Ground Movements During Tunnelling. In Proc. Symposium on Art and Science of Geotechnical Engineering at the Dawn of the 21st Century. Published by Prentice Hall (in press).

2. Hvorslev, 1951. Time Lag and Soil Permeability in Groundwater Observation.

172

Bulletin No. 36. Waterways Experiment Station,
Corps of Engineer. Vicksburg, MISS.

3. MacDonald. G.A., Abbott. A.T., and Peterson,
F.L.. 1983. Volcanoes In the Sea. Second
edition. University Press, Honolulu.

4. Robertson, P.K. and Campanella, R.G., 1984.
Guidelines for use and Interpretation of the
Electric Cone Penetration Test. University of
British Columbia Press.

5. Stearns. H.T.. 1967. Geology of the
Hawaiian Islands. Bulletin 8. Hawaii Division
of Hydrography.

Excavation and support of the Cern point 4 experimental zone

C. Laughton B.Sc., A.R.S.M., M.Sc., C.Eng., M.I.M.M.
CERN, Geneva, Switzerland

SYNOPSIS

CERN, the European Laboratory for Particle Physics, is, at present, constructing a Large Electron Positron (L.E.P.) collider adjacent to existing laboratory facilities under the plain of the Leman basin, near Geneva.

The L.E.P. machine is installed in a twenty seven kilometre long, quasi-circular tunnel, composed of eight arc and eight straight sections. Within four of the straight sections are developed experimental zones, constructed to house the large volume of detection apparatus necessary to study the behaviour of particles produced by high energy collision of electrons and positrons travelling at speeds approaching that of light.

This paper describes the techniques adopted to effect the excavation and temporary support of one of the main horse-shoe profile caverns, using roadheaders and a combination of passive bolting and reinforced, sprayed concrete for temporary rock support.

The first phase of the LEP machine operation will involve the installation of a magnet and vacuum system capable of accelerating and storing electrons and positrons at energies of over 50 GeV. Four large underground caverns at Points 2, 4, 6 and 8 are sited around the tunnel network see figure 1; at these points particle-detection apparatus will be mounted and aligned to study the behaviour of elementary particles.

The layout of the Point 4 cavern and its associated structures is shown in figure 2. The longitudinal axis of the horseshoe profile UX experimental cavern (lined roof diameter of 21.4 m) is aligned at right angles to the LEP tunnel with access provided by three vertical shafts, PZ, PM and PX, respectively of 5, 9 and 10 m, diameter.

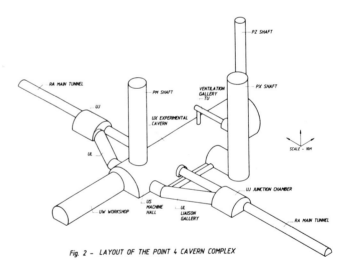

Fig. 2 - LAYOUT OF THE POINT 4 CAVERN COMPLEX

GEOLOGY

The excavation works for the LEP project are sited at depths of 50 to 170 m and link up to an existing CERN tunnel complex, the Super Proton Synchrotron (SPS). The main tunnel lies, for nine-tenths of its length, in the bedrock strata of the Leman basin and for one-tenth, in the mainly limestone strata of the Jura Mountains.

In the Leman basin, the "Molasse", which forms the bedrock in the region, is overlain by a series of Quaternary glacial

Fig. 1 -
AERIAL PHOTOGRAPH SHOWING THE IMPLANTATION OF THE LEP RING AND POINT 4.

175

moraine deposits. Access to the LEP tunnel and experimental zones is provided by a set of twenty vertical shafts, varying in finished diameter from 5 to 23 m.

At Point 4 the experimental cavern and its associated underground openings were excavated at depth in the molasse strata. The roof of the cavern has a total overburden and rockhead cover of approximately 135 and 87 m, respectively.

Molasse Lithology :

The Molasse is a series of Tertiary perideltaic deposits consisting of alternating sandstone and marl bands of varying composition (ref. 1). The individual beds in the irregular series of molasse strata vary in thickness from 0.1 to 3.0 m.

A simplified classification and description are given below :

I. marls, well consolidated strata, containing a high fraction of argillaceous material, often including a proportion of Montmorillonite. The marl beds possess a significant amount of oblique, closed fracturing, the surfaces of which are slicken and striated. These beds presented a particular problem insomuch as the presence of the clay element renders the rock relatively sensitive to alteration. When left exposed to air or water, these strata are subject to desiccation on hydration which can rapidly lead to a marked degradation in the mechanical properties of the rock.

II. intermediate facies, representing the marl/ sandstone transition, relatively compact strata containing a small amount of oblique fracturing;

III. coarse-grained, poorly cemented sandstones, containing a considerable amount of sub-vertical fracturing;

IV. fine-grained, well cemented sandstones, a set of compact beds containing a limited degree of fracturing;

Structural Geology

The series of molasse strata lying in the Leman basin were subjected to folding activity during the Jurassic period. The associated earth movements of this era generated three folds, aligned with those of the Jura massif. The Plain strata dip generally stays near horizontal, however close to the Molasse/Jura unconformity, the strata dip increases to reach 15 to 20 degrees and the bed fracturation becomes more pronounced. At Point 4, the strata are inclined at an angle of approx. 6 degrees away from the Jura (SSE), the true dip being roughly aligned with that of the longitudinal cavern axis (see figure 3).

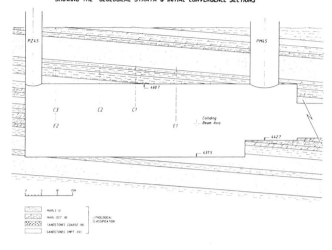

Fig. 3 - SIMPLIFIED LONGITUDINAL SECTION OF THE POINT 4 CAVERN SHOWING THE GEOLOGICAL STRATA & INITIAL CONVERGENCE SECTIONS

MARLS (I)
MARL-SST. (II)
SANDSTONES (COARSE (III))   LITHOLOGICAL CLASSIFICATION
SANDSTONES (MPT (IV))

Owing to the presence of the Quaternary overburden cover, which unconformably overlies the Molasse, the detection of fault zones was rendered difficult. Four main fault sets were known to exist in the Jura and Leman basal structures, but the underground works performed in the strata had not encountered any open faulting.

Rock Mass Condition

Before the letting of the Civil Engineering contracts the molasse formation was investigated, in-situ, by borehole and an exploratory tunnel, located to intersect the Jura-Plain transition zone. Additional information, gathered during the excavation of other CERN tunnels sited in the same rock formation, notably that of the 8 km long SPS collider, was also used to give an accurate assessment of rock mass conditions.

To establish the lithology and in-situ conditions at Point 4, three vertical boreholes were core-drilled into the bedrock. As previously mentioned, the proximity of the Jura massif did slightly influence the strata; the dip angle and fracturing being higher than normally observed in the Plain and, at the depth of interest to the cavern site, coarse-grained sandstone horizons were absent; the "large-scale" homogeneity and conformity of the molasse formation was, however, confirmed.

Hydrology

The results of the in-situ Lugeon tests carried out showed the constituent strata to be of low permeability, only the poorly cemented, coarse-grained sandstones had a significant primary permeability. Secondary permeability existed in the superficial layers of the Molasse where the formation contained open fractures and was in contact with aquifer-bearing moraine deposits. Water inflows, at depth, within the molasse structure were not encountered either during investigation on excavation at Point 4.

Geotechnical Characteristics

The geotechnical characteristics of the molasse "lithotypes" at Point 4 were obtained by a series of tests and measurements performed on borehole cores; the main characteristics are summarized in the table given in figure 4.

Charact.	Unit	Marls	Marl/Sst.	Sst. Coarse	Sst Cmpt.	Molasse (Pt 4)
R.Q.D.	%	64 - 94	89 - 100	91 - 96	94 - 100	90
Bulk Density	kN/m3	24.5	25.4	23.9	25.7	25.3
Permeability	Lugeons	≪ 0.1	≪ 0.1	0.1	< 0.1	0.1
U.C.S	MPa	8.5	13.6	8.5	20.7	15.2
U.T.S.	MPa	0.7	1.4	0.6	2.2	1.5
E (tang.)	MPa	730	1270	1300	2680	1700
Occurence (Pt 4)	%	25	35	0	40	-
Ave. bed thickness	m	1.10	1.09	1.15	1.53	1.27
CSIR Rating	-	39	52	56	82	72
Hardness (CERCHAR)	-	n/a	n/a	5.6	9.6	-
Abrasiveness (CERCHAR)	-	n/a	n/a	0.3	0.4	-
Lithological classification		I	II	III	IV	

Fig. 4 - *MAIN GEOTECHNICAL CHARACTERISTICS OF THE MOLASSE LITHOTYPES*

Care was taken to limit the alteration of the rock cores after extraction owing to the sensitivity of the marl strata to alteration. Equal care was necessary throughout the excavation and support phase of the cavern development to ensure that a minimum time elapsed between exposure of the rock profile and application of a protective shotcrete layer.

At Point 4, the lithotypes, as given by reference to their CSIR ratings (ref. 3), were classified as "very good" for the compact standstones, "fair" for the beds of intermediate composition and "poor" for the marls. As the average strata thickness (1.27 m) was small in comparison to the excavation size (27 m height), the characteristics of the individual rock strata were combined to obtain a unique data set representative of the Molasse. This set of "homogenised" rock mass characteristics was used to create a failure envelope and boundary element model using the Hoek and Brown criteria and

programme (ref. 8). The model pinpointed zones of instability within the surrounding mass during the initial design study and allowed a comparison to be made between predicted and observed ground movements throughout the period in which rock support was given by New Austrian Tunnelling Method (NATM) mechanisms. The failure envelopes of the individual strata and rock model are shown in figure 5.

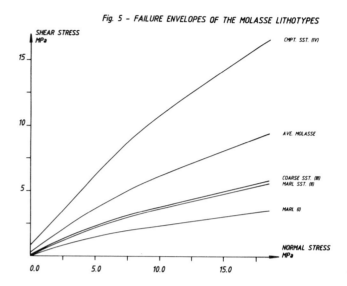

Fig. 5 - *FAILURE ENVELOPES OF THE MOLASSE LITHOTYPES*

For the purposes of the boundary element modelling the temporary support, rockbolting and shotcrete, was not considered to improve the rock mass or provide a confinement pressure to the cavern wall. The support mechanisms were deemed to increase the homogeneity of the Molasse around the opening and protect the sensitive rock strata against alteration.

In parallel to the use of the boundary element model, as used to look at the overall conception of the phases of excavation, an analysis of local instability problems was carried out (ref. 4 and 5). The support problems analysed were those associated with "bed separation", beam, block and wedge failure in the roof, sidewalls and intersection zones. For the purposes of the analysis, the local rock strata and cavern geometries were combined so that an individual assessment could be made of potential failure mechanisms, and anchorage designed accordingly.

In-situ Stresses

The determination of the primary state of stress in the Molasse at Point 4, prior to the cavern excavation, proved to be problematic, as no in-situ measurements had been obtained in the region.

Reference was made to a deformation study carried out in a gallery excavated by Tunnel Boring Machine (TBM) in the Molasse under Geneva (ref. 15). This study indicated the presence of a hydrostatic stress field equal to that of the overburden loading. This gallery was, however, at shallow depth in the Molasse and sited well away from geological unconformities.

At Point 4, the effects of over-consolidation, due to glacial loading of up to 400 m and the proximity of the Jura massif, were thought to have created a horizontal-vertical stress ratio (K) greater than one.

For an initial assessment of cavern stability, using the two dimensional model, a large range of stress field conditions (K = 0.5 to K = 2.0) was analysed taking the vertical stress as being equal to the overburden load. Once the excavation of the first phase of the cavern began, convergence measures were obtained to allow a correlation between the observed ground movements and the model behaviour under various boundary-loading conditions. This operation permitted a more accurate definition of the in-situ stress values to be adopted for subsequent on-site analysis during the cavern development.

Evolution of the Rock Structure

Given the nature of the rock mass, a certain amount of "delayed internal relaxation" of the surrounding structure, after completion of the initial elastic-plastic movements was expected, (ref. 6, 13 and 16).

The short-term and time-dependent displacements, both superficial and at depth in the reinforced rock formation, were monitored by a combination of convergence and extensometer measurements. As previously mentioned, convergence measurements were undertaken during the initial stages of the cavern development using an Interfels KM 15. Once the cavern section was sufficiently developed, two sets of five 6.0 m extensometers (type Distofor made by Telemac) were installed, radially to the arch, to give relative displacements at depths of 0.5 m, 2.0 m, 3.5 m and 4.5 m with respect to the 6 m anchorage (see figure 6).

EXCAVATION AND TEMPORARY SUPPORT

Owing to the relatively soft and non-abrasive qualities of the constituent rock strata excavation of the LEP caverns was undertaken by a combination of roadheader plant (Voest Alpine AM50, AM100, Demag H41, Paurat E134 and Westfalia Lunen Buffel WAV 170). The use of explosives was not excluded for bulk blasting in the main body of the cavern, but to avoid opening fractures within the rock mass, the final cavern profile was, in all cases, to be formed by mechanical breakage.

At Point 4, the cavern was completely excavated by roadheader, working from the roof down, in passes of 3.5 to 5.5 m in height (see figures 7 and 8). The opening was developed from the centrally aligned machine shaft (PM 45), initially using an AM 50 roadheader. Front End Loaders were used for horizontal transport and a combination of tower and gantry crane was used to give the cavern and shaft muck haulage.

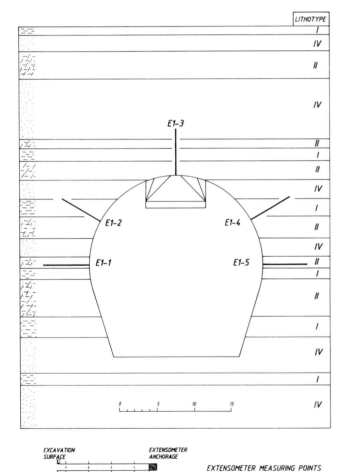

EXTENSOMETER MEASURING POINTS

Fig. 6 - CAVERN CROSS-SECTION SHOWING CONVERGENCE & EXTENSOMETER CONFIGURATIONS

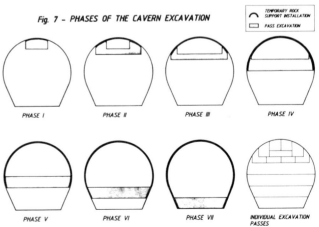

Fig. 7 - PHASES OF THE CAVERN EXCAVATION

178

Fig. 8 - DEVELOPEMENT OF THE POINT 4 CAVERN BY ROADHEADER.

Temporary rock support was achieved by a combination of reinforced shotcrete and rock-bolting (see figure 9). A systematic approach was adopted for the installation of temporary support owing to the frequent change in ground conditions given by the limited thickness and inclination of the strata. The rock-bolt density and length was increased locally to limit the propagation of bedding failure, where the weaker marl strata failed in beam or wedge mode upon excavation, and to give additional support at tunnel and shaft intersections.

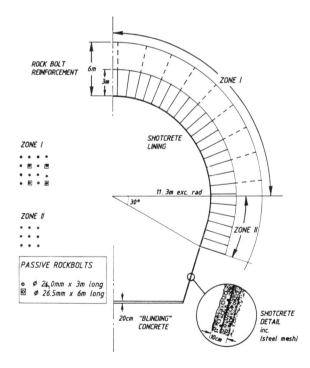

Fig. 9
CAVERN TEMPORARY ROCK SUPPORT MECHANISMS

In the crown, drivage was performed by advance cycles of 3 to 5 m, thus ensuring that the roadheader driver remained in the previously supported zone. This precaution was necessary as the identification of weak strata in the

roof, prone to failure, was not always evident upon excavation. Once the profile was obtained an initial protective layer of shotcrete was applied followed by the installation of fully bonded passive rock-bolts, wire mesh and a second layer of shotcrete. This combination of NATM support systems, placed rapidly after excavation, protected the rock against alteration and was designed to allow the formation of an actively reinforced support zone in the shotcrete and surrounding rock mass before completion of the short-term deformations.

During Phase I, the completion of the support system was deferred so that the 6 m rock-bolts could be placed in a single pass; elsewhere the bolting pattern and reinforced shotcrete lining were completed on advance. In the footwall levels a berm of approximately 1 m width was left in place between the bulk excavation and the final cavern profile : this allowed the Contractor to separate the production and support activities within the cavern. After completion of the bulk excavation, the berm was removed, the rock profile formed, and the support systems applied with a minimal delay.

ON-SITE MONITORING OF THE ROCK MASS BEHAVIOUR

General

To observe the displacements in the rock mass around the opening, a certain amount of instrumentation was installed. Information on ground movements had previously been obtained during the excavation of other experimental caverns in the Molasse, but, given the importance of the excavation, the uncertainty that existed as to the local in-situ stress levels, the small scale heterogeneity of the rock mass and the choice of a relatively light, flexible support mechanism, rock instrumentation was considered necessary.

For the initial excavation phase, convergence sections were installed to record rock surface movements and enable the in-situ stresses to be assessed more accurately. Three convergence sections were placed in the crown of the cavern to provide a short-term indication of the magnitude and evolution of the cavern profile deformations. It was seldom possible to maintain convergence stations for long periods due to their destruction on removal of the temporary sidewalls. Continuity of ground movement monitoring was obtained by the placement of extensometers; these were installed once the opening was sufficiently developed and maintained up until the casting of the final concrete lining.

Convergence Measures

A convergence section and measurements are shown in figure 10. The 30 cm bolts were cemented into identified rock strata approximately 20 cm behind the face, in parallel with

179

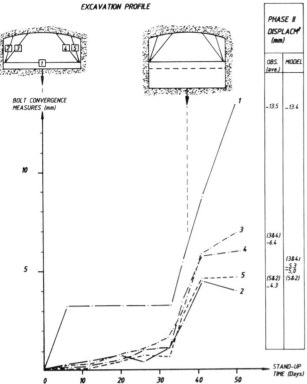

EXCAVATION PROFILE

BOLT CONVERGENCE
MEASURES (mm)

	PHASE II DISPLACM^t (mm)	
	OBS. (ave.)	MODEL
1	-13.5	-13.4
(3&4)	-6.4	(3&4) -5.3
		-5.0
(5&2)	-4.3	(5&2)

STAND-UP TIME (Days)

Fig. 10 - CONVERGENCE MEASURES OBSERVED AT ROOF SECTION C-3

rock support activities. Short-term movements were then noted once the heading was advanced and during excavation of subsequent passes, up until substitution of the sidewall bolts.

For the determination of in-situ stress levels one-third of the short-term deformation was assumed to have taken place prior to the placement of the convergence bolts. This figure was obtained by reference to the deformation study performed in the Molasse during a TBM excavation (ref. 15). On excavation of subsequent passes, the model-loading conditions, as were given from a fitting of the model and observed convergence during the initial passes, were checked. Using mean values given by this technique, the in-situ stresses were fixed as 2.8 and 3.0 MPa in the vertical and horizontal direction, respectively, thus giving a K value of just over one. These boundary loads were considered to be independent of depth for the height of the cavern when applied to the boundary element model.

Extensometers

The extensometers, which were installed after completion of the temporary support, allowed the medium term rock mass deformation in the crown to be monitored during development of the cavern.

A certain delay was evident between the profile excavation and installation of the instrumentation, particularly in the footwalls, thus the majority of short-term movement had

taken place before the extensometers were in operation. Only relatively small short-term movements, induced by subsequent floor excavations, were recorded. The extensometer heads were also equipped to allow convergence measurements to be taken across the section, thus making it possible for a correlation between partial and absolute deformations to be obtained. This was necessary as a significant amount of the overall rock deformation occurred outside the monitored zone.

Figure 11 shows the relative displacement of the reinforced rock structure with respect to the extensometer anchorage at different depths, during the latter excavation phases. For all the extensometers in the section a deceleration in the rate of ground displacement, towards a convergence-confinement equilibrium, was noted prior to the placement of the cast-in-situ soffit. A certain amount of "medium-term", differed ground movement was observed after completion of the excavation and support activities. These movements were more pronounced in certain zones, probably owing to the small scale ground heterogeneity, but remained within the displacement limits predicted by the B.E. model.

Fig. 11 - EXTENSOMETER MEASUREMENTS (SECTION E1)

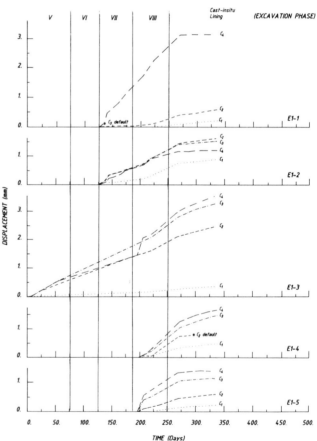

FINAL LINING

General

All the permanent structures excavated at CERN in the Molasse receive a secondary, cast-in-situ concrete lining. It is necessary to introduce a more rigid lining capable of resisting delayed or long-term deformations in the rock. Sensitive marls have been shown to possess potential swelling pressures of up to 2 MPa in laboratory-testing, and have generated displacements of over 10 cm in the shotcrete and blinding concrete during the execution of temporary works. Even millimetric displacements of the LEP foundations would be sufficient to require realignment of the machine, thus a comparatively rigid lining is essential to ensure LEP's long-term stability. A final concrete crown lining with a nominal thickness of 50 cm, incorporating a gantry crane support system was poured in-situ (see figures 12 and 13). For simplicity of execution in the floor section reinforcement was kept to a minimum and a mass concrete slab of over 3.5 m in depth was placed to resist against possible floor swelling pressures.

Fig. 13 - THE LINED POINT 4 EXPERIMENTAL CAVERN.

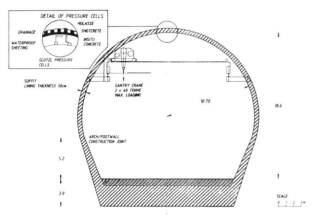

Fig. 12 - FINAL CAST-INSITU CAVERN LINING INCORPORATING GANTRY CRANE SUPPORTS

A rock-bolt and shotcrete lining provides the permanent support in the flat end-walls of the cavern where the final lining was constructed independently, leaving a minimum void of 20 cm between shotcrete and concrete; thus relatively large, local, long-term deformation is permitted in the rock mass while reinforcement of the concrete walls is reduced. Prior to placing the footwall and crown linings, a drainage and waterproofing complex was installed against the shotcrete. This umbrella system avoids the possibility of water infiltrating from the moraine levels and rock matrix through the roof concrete into the cavern and ensures that no hydrostatic pressure is applied.

Long-Term Monitoring of the Cavern Structure

Originally it had been intended to monitor rock mass movements around the opening for the life of the cavern, using the extensometers previously installed. Unfortunately during the application of the drainage and waterproofing complex most of the extensometer equipment was damaged beyond repair. In the absence of the rock mass measurements, a limited number of concrete pressure cells were installed in the soffit pours and it is hoped that any future evolution of the rock loading will be indicated by means of these cells, once the drainage and waterproofing complex has been confined.

CONCLUSIONS

Given the size of the cavern in comparison to the small scale heterogeneity of the rock structure, it was decided to check the global cavern stability, during development, using an average set of rock characteristics, applied to a boundary element programme. The relatively light set of support mechanisms, installed systematically across the section, were considered to create a reinforced, "homogenous" zone around the cavern periphery. Locally, block and wedge stability in the roof and intersection zones was ensured by reinforcement and extension of the rock bolt pattern and length respectively.

Great importance was placed upon the rapidity with which the temporary support mechanisms were installed. The application of an initial shotcrete layer minimised the time of exposure of the excavation surface to air; which, in the case of the argillaceous strata could have led to hydration or dessication of the rock. The rapid installation of the passive rock bolts permitted the development of an actively reinforced zone before the completion of the short-term rock displacements and arrested the onset of bed separation.

By means of the on-site instrumentation it was possible to follow the evolution of the convergence movements during development of the section up until the placement of the final lining. Ideally, instrumentation of the rock mass placed, at depth, prior to, and directly upon excavation and maintained for the life of the project, would have allowed a more complete history of the rock mass deformation to have been established. However, the limited amount of relatively shallow instrumentation installed, in a site environment, did permit the cavern stability and the order of magnitude of ground movements to be followed from an early stage of excavation thus enabling subsequent development of the cavern to be undertaken with greater confidence.

ACKNOWLEDGEMENTS

Thanks are due to the Contractor
(Eurolep, a consortium of five Civil Engineering
Companies, Astaldi (I), Entrecanales (Sp.),
Fougerolle (F), Philipp Holzmann (WG) and
Rothpletz Lienhard (CH)), the design office
(Simecsol, Paris) and Messrs Danesin and
Lallement without whose assistance and persever-
ance the rock mass monitoring, would not have
been so comprehensive.

REFERENCES

1. Amberger G.   - La molasse du bassin gene-
                       vois. Thema : La recherche
                       scientifique dans les hau-
                       tes écoles et uiversités
                       suisses, 1986, p. 5-8.

2. Association Française des Travaux en Sou-
                       terrain - Working group
                       7. Recommandations sur
                       l'emploi de la méthode
                       convergence - confine-
                       ment. Tunnels et ouvrages
                       souterrains, No 59, Sept.
                       - Oct., 1983, p. 218-238.

3. Bieniawski Z.T. - Rock mechanics design in
                       mining and tunnelling.
                       (Rotterdam : A.A.
                       Balkema, 1984), 272 p.

4. Dejean M. and Raffoux J-F. - Choix des pa-
                       ramètres d'un soutènement
                       par boulonnage. Industrie
                       Minérale - Mine, October
                       1978, p. 149-160.

5. Etienne M.   - Rôle et emploi du boulon-
                       nage. Tunnels et ouvrages
                       souterrains No 72, Nov. -
                       Dec. 1985.

6. Gosler J.   - The New Austrian Tunnell-
                       ing Method (Theoretical
                       background practical
                       experience). In Proceed-
                       ings of the Engineering
                       Foundation Conference -
                       Shotcrete for Ground Sup-
                       port, Maryland 1976
                       (Detroit : American Con-
                       crete Institute, 1977) p.
                       323-347.

7. Hingant P. and Legrand M. - Ten years of
                       French motorway tunnels.
                       In Tunnelling '82, Jones
                       M.J. ed. (London :
                       I.M.M., 1982), p. 19-29.

8. Hoek E. and Brown E.T. - Underground excav-
                       ations in rock (London :
                       I.M.M., 1980), 527 p.

9. Jaeger J.C. and Cook N.G.W. - Fundamentals
                       of rock mechanics (Lon-
                       don : Chapman Hall,
                       1969), 593 p.

10. Lang T.A. Bishoff J.A. - Stability of
                       reinfored rock struc-
                       tures. In Proceedings of
                       the I.S.R.M. Symposium
                       Design and performance of
                       underground excavations,
                       Brown E.T. and Hudson
                       J.A. ed. (London : B.G.S.
                       1984) p. 11-17.

11. Laporte H.   - Le L.E.P. Grand project
                       souterrain. Tunnels et
                       ouvrages souterrains No
                       63, May - June 1984, p.
                       115-122.

12. Leblais Y.   - Conception et realisation
                       des grandes cavités du
                       projet L.E.P. (C.E.R.N.).
                       In Work Study Session no
                       280. Evolution des tech-
                       niques dans les grands
                       chantiers européens en
                       conditions difficiles.
                       (Paris : Centre d'études
                       d'information et de for-
                       mation pour les ingé-
                       nieurs de la construction
                       et de l'industrie, 1987).

13. Lombardi G.   - Quelques remarques au su-
                       jet de la méthode conver-
                       gence - confinement.
                       Tunnels et Ouvrages Sou-
                       terrains no 32, March -
                       April 1979, p. 87-92.

14. Londe P.   - Mesures in-situ dans les
                       tunnels. La Revue Fran-
                       çaise Géotechnique no 4,
                       June 1978, p. 49-62.

15. Odier M.   - Mesures in-situ exécutées
                       dans la molasse; Gaine
                       Technique entre St-Jean et
                       Nations. Rapport
                       d'activité du Laboratoire
                       de Géotechnique de l'Ecole
                       Polytechnique Fédérale de
                       Lausanne, April 1974.

16. Panet M   - Les déformations différées
                       dans les ouvrages souter-
                       rains. In Proceedings of
                       the 4th International
                       Congress on Rock Mecha-
                       nics (Montreux : ISRM,
                       1979), vol. 3, p. 291-
                       201.

Underground civil works in Texas

B. Kent Merritt B.Sc., M.Sc., C.Eng., P.Eng.
Robert M. Valentine B.Sc., M.Sc., P.Geol., C.Geol.
Woodward-Clyde Consultants, Houston, Texas, U.S.A.

SYNOPSIS

During the past fifteen years the State of Texas has discovered the art of tunnelling as a solution to many construction problems in congested urban or environmentally sensitive areas. Contractors are still learning to deal with the various ground and rock conditions underlying the State's major cities. However, agencies are supplying ample opportunities with over 200 km of tunnels under construction or recently completed, and another 200 km being designed, planned or conceptualized. Groundwater in the soft ground and variations in lithology in the soft rock have been the major problems for contractors. As the contractors learn to deal with the Texas underground, engineers are aggressively designing projects that a decade ago would not have been considered. An interesting relationship between the estimated unit costs of tunnelling and the length of the heading has been developed.

INTRODUCTION

Until recently the infrastructure development of the State of Texas, U.S.A. has had little need for the use of tunnels as part of civil works programmes because of the great expanses of flat to gently rolling terrain, the frequency of low velocity rivers, and extensive development of surface transportation. However, beginning in the 1970s, owing to congestion in major urban areas such as Dallas, Austin, San Antonio and Houston, tunnelling has become a viable and economically competitive option for the transmission of water, wastewater, stormwater and to a lesser extent, transportation. During this 15 year period, over 200 km of tunnels have been driven in urban areas and a similar length is being designed or planned. The diameter of these tunnels varies from 250 mm to nearly 8 m.

Significant projects which are the basis for this paper are the Northside Sewer Relief Program (22.5 km) and the East Water Program (16-20 km) tunnels in Houston, the Crosstown (17 km), Onion Creek (15 km), and Govalle (13 km) wastewater tunnels and the Lake Travis multiple-tap, intake and transmission tunnels (13 km) in Austin. These projects are all in various stages of design and construction or have recently been completed. These and other Texas underground projects, such as the San Antonio River and San Pedro Creek tunnels (6 km) in San Antonio, the Jefferson Avenue tunnel (3 km) and DART tunnels (5± km) in Dallas, will be referenced in this paper.

GEOLOGICAL SETTING

Texas is dominated by the Cenozoic age, Gulf coastal plain and by inland plains of Mesozoic and Paleozoic sediments.[1] (Fig. 1).

The City of Houston is the heart of soft ground tunnelling activity. Houston is situated on the Beaumont Formation, the youngest of the Pleistocene depositional units that were deposited as fine-grained alluvium during the last approximately 30,000 years. Principal deposition was deltaic and interdeltaic as sediment laden streams migrated across the coastal plain. The resulting formation, taken in section,

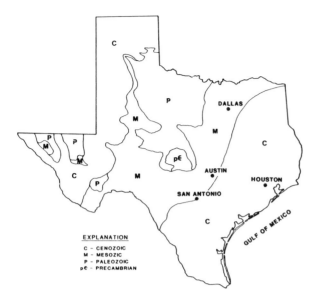

FIG.1 GEOLOGIC MAP OF TEXAS

EXPLANATION
C - CENOZOIC
M - MESOZIC
P - PALEOZOIC
pЄ - PRECAMBRIAN

These soils classify as SP, SM, SC, and ML. Most deposits have a relatively low coefficient of permeability and the static water table is generally present from 2 to 5 m below the ground surface. Most granular deposits regardless of depth share a

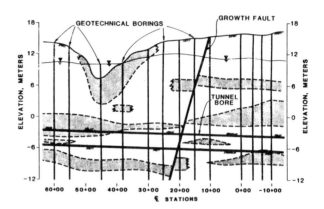

FIG. 2 TYPICAL HOUSTON STRATIGRAPHY

displays a clay matrix, with almost randomly located and oriented lenses, layers, and channels of granular soil (channels, cheniers, beach deposits, etc.). A typical section of the Beaumont Formation is shown in Fig. 2. The clays typically have been overconsolidated by the process of desiccation. The plasticity of these clays and, correspondingly, the degree of secondary structure (joints and fissures) generally increases towards the Gulf of Mexico.

The density and mechanical properties of the clays are dominated by stress history. As a result of the expanding lattice structure of the principal mineral montmorillonite and the "locked in" strain energy as a result of desiccation, the clay has a moderate propensity for swelling on unloading or moisture increase. Undrained shear strengths typically range from 40 to 300 kN/m^2 or more. The overconsolidation ratio (at typical tunnel depth) is in the range of 2 to 8, with a measured at-rest coefficient of lateral earth pressure in the range of 1.0 to 1.5 or greater.[2,3] Total unit weight is often assumed as 2,000 Kg/m^3. The clay typically classifies as a CH in the Unified Soil Classification System.

The granular soils contained in the Beaumont Formation are predominantly medium dense to very dense, very fine sands, silty fine sands or silts, occasionally with minor amounts of plastic clay.

common phreatic surface. Consequently, nearly all deposits of non-cohesive soil encountered in Houston tunnels are under excess hydrostatic pressure.

Of particular concern to tunnelling in the coastal plain is the presence of "growth faults" or contemporaneous faults (Fig. 2). These are actually the slide planes of massive landslides that occurred during sedimentation. Some of these features are still active and differential movement occurs across the fault plane owing to subsidence caused by overpumping shallow groundwater or oil and gas reservoirs. Movement is slow, from a few millimeters to several centimeters per year. However, the movement racks apart surface structures and poses similar problems to tunnel lining.

The other principal tunnelling locales, San Antonio, Austin, and Dallas, are situated along the boundary of the Mesozoic and Cenozoic age units (Fig. 1). The Balcones Fault escarpment marks this boundary in the San Antonio-Austin area with the cities divided between Plains on the east and "hill country" to the west.

Tunnelling is in Cretaceous age units, principally claystones, siltstones, and soft limestones. Some tuffaceous deposits are present in limited areas that

184

originated from small local volcanoes. All of the rock units are categorized as "soft rock", ranging from 0.7 MPa to 50 MPa in unconfined compressive tests, with the claystones and siltstones at the lower end, tuffaceous deposits intermediate (5 to 12 MPa) and limestones representing the stronger fraction.[4] A variety of calcareous deposits are present, ranging from chalk and marl to relatively hard dolomitic limestone.

Owing to the large uplift along the Balcones Escarpment, faults are common. However, the nature of the gravity-type faults and the location of many of the tunnels at relatively shallow depths have combined to negate major impacts on tunnelling to date. In fact, the Cretaceous rocks provide some near ideal tunnelling conditions. The rocks generally can be mined without excessive bit wear or large horsepower requirements; standup time is good; the rocks are quite tight and groundwater has not been a consistently difficult problem.

SOFT GROUND TUNNELLING

Houston's Northside Sewer Relief Programme (NSRP) consists of 22.5 km of relief and interceptor gravity wastewater mains ranging in finished diameter from 1.7 to 4 m. Construction of this programme will be substantially complete in 1989. The NSRP coupled with the Northside Sewer Rehabiliation Programme is designed to relieve the surcharged condition of the old sewer system which exists in areas north of downtown Houston.

With the exception of the downstream 2.5 km of the NSRP, the tunnels in this program are all of the order of 20 m deep. The water table is typically at a shallow depth of 2 to 5 m below the ground surface. Therefore, most of the mining for this programme has been conducted under more than 15 m of hydrostatic head. The dominant single consideration in mining this and other Houston tunnels has been groundwater.

In the stratigraphy (as previously described) the combination of relatively high hydrostatic pressure and the low transmissivity of the included granular deposits makes dewatering difficult. It is nearly impossible and economically unreasonable to "dry out" these deposits. Consequently, the objective of dewatering becomes depressuring or "taking the head off" the granular deposits. Most contractors have come to agree that a Tunnel Boring Machine (TBM) with bulkheads and closure doors is the preferred mining technique for these soils. Even these machines are not completely effective if the flood doors cannot be closed when flowing ground is encountered.

From a contractor's point of view, learning to deal with the soft ground of the Gulf coastal plain requires experimentation with shields, excavation methods, groundwater control techniques and liner materials. One contractor, on the first of several contracts awarded to him, began mining with an open-faced TBM. Because of his inability to close off or completely breast the face, he often experienced excessive ground loss when he encountered water charged cohesionless soils. He also experienced difficulties in negotiating curves on the alignment. With these problems, his mining rates fell well below those on which his bid was based, leading to threatened claims of differing site conditions. His true difficulties were, however, discovered when the curves on his alignment were superimposed on a graph of his mining rates (Fig. 3).

An analysis of Fig. 3 indicates that the contractor averaged only 20 m/wk during the first five weeks while he assembled the trailing gear, installed rail switches, and became familiar with the ground. However, on the remainder of the alignment he averaged 135 m/wk while on tangent alignments, but dropped back to only 55 m/wk while mining through curves. From another perspective, and discounting the first five weeks, he required only 11 weeks to mine approximately 1525 m along tangents, but 13 weeks to mine approximately 550 m on curved headings.

On subsequent contracts, this contractor has employed TBM's equipped with bulkhead and closure doors for full breasting of the face and an improved steering mechanism. The result has been substantially increased mining rates.

The NSRP, being the largest tunnelling project yet undertaken in Houston, has allowed contractors to

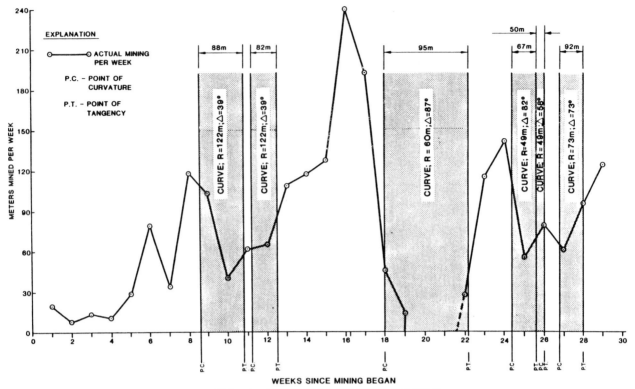

FIG. 3 WEEKLY MINING RATES

learn from the use of different types of TBM's and mechanical shields. Three of the mining machines used on various NSRP contracts are shown in Fig. 4. Currently, all active contractors are using TBM's similar to the one on the right of this figure.

On a recent project, one contractor installed 68 deep wells with submersible pumps along a 250 m reach of his alignment which contained a large, fine-sand body at tunnel depth. Production from the wells varied almost randomly from about 1 l/min to almost 400 l/min. Even the numerous wells in combination with an appropriate TBM did not prevent two stopes (cave-ins) as the contractor mined this heading. Both were the result of flowing ground in the large sand body.

Another contractor was more successful on a much shallower heading when he approached a water bearing granular lens with an open-faced TBM.[5] The contractor installed five wells with submersible pumps to dewater this shallow sand lens and six piezometers to monitor the drawdown (Fig.5). After pumping for five days with a total production of about 40 to 60 l/min, the groundwater level had dropped about 1 m and stabilized. In an attempt to

increase production of the wells, the contractor added a small vacuum, 24 cm of mercury, to the wells. After an additional five days of pumping the water table had dropped a further 3 m to near the bottom of the lens. One should note in Fig. 5 the steep gradients developed between the piezometers and the wells. These steep gradients further demonstrate the reluctance with which the very fine granular soils release the water.

A third contractor could not control groundwater inflows well enough to complete sinking of a starting shaft. Subsequently, the contractor was terminated and the contract was awarded to another contractor, who, using different techniques, has successfully excavated the necessary shaft. The two contractors who were awarded the most recent Houston contracts have employed extensive dewatering with deep wells and have purchased Earth-Pressure Balanced (EPB) TBM's.

The active growth faults commonly found along the coastal plain provide challenges of another type for tunnelling, particularly for the designers. As discussed, these faults are nontectonic, but the

186

FIG. 4   N.S.R.P.   SHIELDS

downthrown side can displace as much as 2 cm or more per year. Over the years, engineers have developed many designs intended to protect shallow conduits, emplaced by opencut techniques, from the shearing forces resulting from fault movements. Unfortunately, all of these techniques require access from the surface during construction and are not applicable to tunneled conduits.

The Pecore fault was identified early in the NSRP route selection process. Originally the route crossed the fault three times, but minor adjustments in the alignment eliminated two of the crossings. Even with one crossing of this active fault, it was necessary that a solution be devised to protect the conduit from the projected 0.3 m of movement during its 40-year design life. Owing to the deformation adjacent to

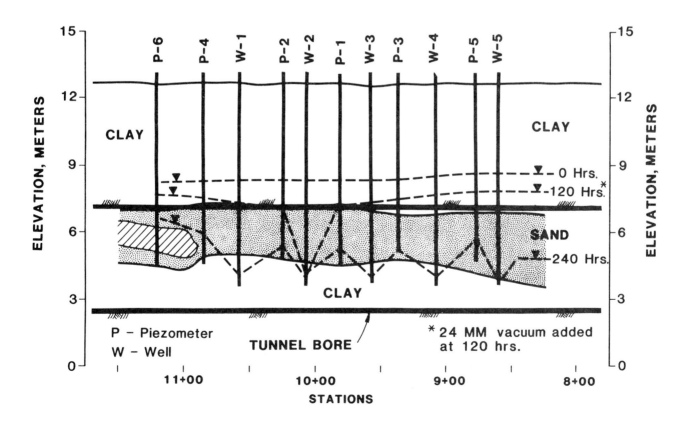

FIG. 5 DEWATERING WITH VACUUM ASSIST

the fault's shear plane, a horizontal zone of disturbance of 30 m was projected for this fault. Additionally, since the fault plane dips at an angle, the fault's movement has both vertical and horizontal components.

The design solution was to place the sewer conduit within a sacrificial outer liner with the annular space between the inner conduit and outer liner filled with a compressible "foamcrete" grout. This compressible grout is intended to prevent the transmission of shear stresses to the inner conduit. Details of this "double pipe" are shown on Fig. 6.[5] Translation of the joints of the inner pipe is accomodated by inclusion of a polyvinyl chloride sheet at each joint. The double liner has recently been installed and is heavily instrumented. However, it will be many years before its effectiveness can be evaluated.

Basically, two tunnelling techniques have been employed in construction of the NSRP: TBM tunnelling with steel ring beams and hard wood timber lagging employed as the primary lining and cast-in-place reinforced concrete as the final lining; or shield or TBM mining carried out ahead of jacked

pipe. With the former technique, piping of fine-grained soils through the openings in the ring beams and timber lagging had been a problem. Officials were concerned that the piping would contribute to excessive lost ground expressed as unacceptable surface settlement. The piping problem has largely been overcome by the use of geotextile filter-fabric placed behind the lining (Fig. 7). Detrimental surface settlement as a result of mining on NSRP contracts has been minimal. By way of example, settlement monitored during and approximately five months after mining beneath an eight-lane freeway ranged from 6 to 34 mm with an average of 17 mm.

TBM or mechanical shield mining ahead of jacked-pipe has been used on three of the contracts. Pipe jacking, however has limited applicability in an urban area. One of the objections to this technique is the necessity of frequent shafts, typically on a 250 to 350 m spacing. One contractor overcame this limitation by the use of intermediate jacking rings allowing him to jack a 3 m pipe a record distance of approximately 635 m between shafts. The main problem encountered during this push was the use of a single-skip mucking system which left him muck-bound through much of the distance.

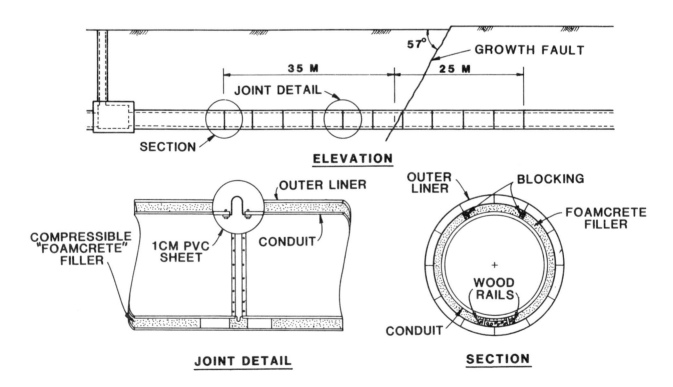

FIG. 6 DETAILS OF TUNNEL ACROSS AN ACTIVE GROWTH FAULT

FIG. 7 PLACEMENT OF FILTER FABRIC BEHIND TIMBER LAGGING.

Houston EWP

The second major programme which is currently underway in Houston is the East Water Programme (EWP), which includes both the Northwest Lateral Pipeline Conveyance System (NWLPCS), a 12 km raw water line into the East Water Purification Plant and a 160 km transmission-distribution pipeline which ranges in finished diameter from 0.7 to 2.7 m. The NWLPCS includes approximately 3 km of tunnel in which 3 m carrier pipe will be installed. The transmission-distribution system includes between 15 and 20 km of tunnel emplaced conduit. This system will ultimately distribute approximately 1.1 trillion l/day of potable water to the City of Houston.

Although not as yet under contract, the raw water pipeline will pass beneath the Houston Ship Channel and a major bayou (river). The combination of these two subaqueous crossings will result in approximately 3 km of shield driven tunnel. The tunnels will be the deepest ever driven along the Texas coastal plain, with both headings in excess of 33 m deep. The crossing beneath the Houston Ship Channel will be of particular interest because of the relatively weak clays through which the alignment passes.

For the heading beneath the Ship Channel, the calculated overload factor (OF) (the ratio of the effective overburden load to the average undrained shear strength of the clay through which the heading passes) varies between 8 and 11.5. When one considers that local shear failure of the clay surrounding a tunnel begins at an OF of 4.5 to 5 and general shear failure occurs at about 7, the potential problems of mining this heading are obvious. Attempts at compaction and/or penetration grouting have never been successful in the soils along the Texas coastal plain and freezing of the soils comprising this heading appear to be operationally and economically impractical. The most practical methods of mining this heading appear to be with the use of compressed air and/or with EPB or slurry shield TBM's.

Because of the variable soil conditions and the treacherous groundwater conditions found along the Texas coastal plain, many state-of-the-art and innovative designs and construction techniques for soft ground tunnelling are currently in use for completion of these and other projects. To date tunnels in the Houston stratigraphy have not been instrumented, however, this situation is currently changing. Many questions with respect to short and long-term earth loads, settlement due to tunnelling and lateral ground movements have dictated instrumentation of future projects.

SOFT ROCK TUNNELING

Outside Houston, more tunnels have been driven and more are planned in Austin than anywhere else in the state. The city has recognized the environmental advantages of tunnelling over cut-and-cover construction and has employed tunnelling for a wide variety of projects. The project that initiated this interest was the Crosstown Interceptor Tunnel, an approximately 17 km tunnel constructed across the city to convey wastewater to a new sewage treatment plant. That work was conducted in the mid 1970s and construction was so successful that tunnelling was designated when the city initiated a major construction program in the early 1980s.

Onion Creek Inteceptor

Onion Creek, a 15 km tunnel was the first project of

this new programme. It was designed to carry wastewater from an outdated treatment plant round the edge of the city to a new plant. The tunnel was driven principally through claystones, siltstones, and limestone. Substantial problems were encountered by one contractor when tuffaceous deposits were in an interbedded, and intermixed condition, with the claystones and chalks (Fig 8). The tuffaceous materials were decomposed and, of themselves, not difficult to mine. Unfortunately they were usually of a different strength than their host or adjacent rock. Consequently the contractor was either confronted with a mixed face condition or with a decision of changing from disk cutters for the chalk to clay teeth for the claystone and tuffs.

FIG. 8 TUFFACEOUS INCLUSIONS IN THE CLAYSTONE HEADING.

The other major problem that was experienced related to the shallow cover beneath several river crossings. In one case, cover was only one m but the crossing was in limestone and no problems were encountered. Another crossing was not so fortuitous. In that case, the contractor used a temporary plywood lining system consisting of two layers of 9.5 mm thick plywood sheets, which were prestressed and forced out against the rock.[4] The sheets were butted together and joints between sheets in the inner and outer layers were staggered (Fig. 9). The sheets were anchored to the claystone with steel nails driven into the rock below springline. The plywood was to act as a "membrane" providing nominal support and protection against fallout and claystone deterioration. The plywood was

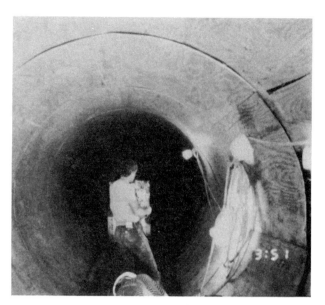

FIG. 9 PLYWOOD SHEETS AS A PRIMARY LINING IN AUSTIN TUNNEL.

installed a short distance behind the TBM thrust ring, about 9 m behind the cutterhead.

At the first creek crossing using this preliminary support system, rock conditions were suitable and the plywood performed well. As the TBM approached the second crossing, rock conditions deteriorated, and immediately past the second crossing, terrace gravels that overlay the claystones were encountered along with considerable water. The resulting crown failure required a temporary shaft to recover the machine. Thereafter, the plywood was used intermittently but never provided the speed and low cost that had been projected by the contractor.

Overall, advance rates for the Onion Creek tunnels averaged about 37 m per day in the claystones, 26 m per day in the tuffaceous deposits, and about 16 m per day in the limestone and chalk using modified and upgraded soft ground machines.[6]

The Govalle tunnel of some 13 km was recently completed in similar types of materials as Onion Creek. However, that contractor profited from the knowledge gained from Onion Creek and under near ideal conditions averaged from 60 to 65 m per day.

Lake Travis Project

Another major project just beginning construction, the Lake Travis Tap and Intake Tunnel (Fig. 10) will set another milestone in the U. S. The City of Austin is constructing multiple deep lake taps and a pumping system to provide potable water in new parts of its water distribution network. The project involves: three lake taps including the deepest tap in the U.S., approximately 50 m; a shaft and gate chamber; a 3 km intake tunnel; a pumping chamber with pump shafts; and a treatment plant and a distribution system comprising over 15 km of tunnels.

of the 7.5 m inside diameter San Antonio River and San Pedro Creek Tunnels (6 km) in San Antonio to direct floodwaters beneath the downtown, specifically to protect the historic and picturesque River Walk. These tunnels are the first tunnels in Texas designed specifically for flood diversion and will also be the first Texas tunnels to employ segmental concrete lining. A similar project, the Shoal Creek Tunnel, is in the planning stage in Austin. These tunnels will provide diversions needed to handle the rapid run off from high intensity rains that fall on the limestone bedrock surface in the hill country north and west of these central Texas cities.

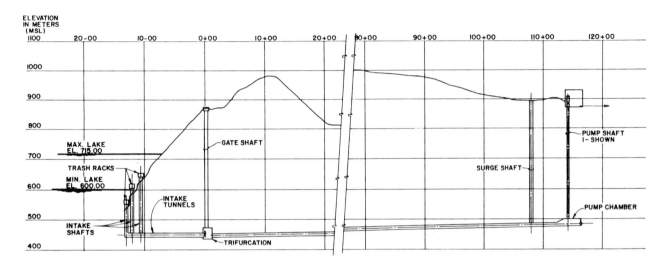

FIG. 10 LAKE TRAVIS TAPS AND INTAKE TUNNEL

Lake Travis, from which the project originates, is a major recreation facility in the area and hidden lake taps were dictated for environmental reasons. The multiple lake intakes also allow mixing of waters with various temperatures and qualities from the various reservoir elevations.

The rock conditions here are somewhat harder limestones, marls and dolomites than were encountered in previous tunnelling. A variety of equipment is expected to be employed to excavate the shafts, tunnels and taps.

San Antonio Tunnels

The Corps of Engineers has commenced construction

Dallas Tunnels

One of the most ambitious tunneling projects is in Dallas where a heavy rail transportation system is being designed. Although the majority of the system will be on the surface, the downtown and adjacent areas along freeways are proposed to be a system of subways. These facilities will be principally excavated in chalk and soft limestone that are expected to be easily bored and practically self-supporting.

Tunnelling to date in Dallas has consisted mostly of short utility bores a few hundred m in length. The first major tunnel to be constructed for recent infrastructure improvement is expected to be Trinity

191

River Authority's 3 km Jefferson Avenue wastewater line. Cretaceous age claystones and sandstones are expected to provide excellent tunnelling conditions.

As in Houston and Austin, the advantages of tunnelling, as shown by the recent projects, are developing increased interest in Dallas and San Antonio. These cities are seriously considering additional underground projects as their infrastructure is enlarged and expanded.

COST OF TEXAS TUNNELING

A review of bid prices for recent tunnels in Texas (1982-1987) provides several interesting parameters that will be useful in projecting the costs of future tunnels. The cost of excavation, primary and/or final liners and construction shafts were extracted from bid tabulations from 15 recent projects. From this information a cost parameter, cost per meter of tunnel per meter of finished diameter, was calculated. When this cost parameter was compared

to other project characteristics, several interesting trends were observed.

1. The average cost of tunnelling throughout this period appears to be approximately $700/m of tunnel/m of diameter.

2. There is no clear indication that the cost of Texas tunnelling has substantially increased during this five year period.

3. Tunnelling costs appear to be independent of the type of material through which the heading is driven, e.g., soft ground or soft rock.

4. There is a non-linear inverse proportionality between this cost parameter and the length of the contract heading (Fig. 11).

Of these observations, the last is the most interesting. The relationship is logical when one

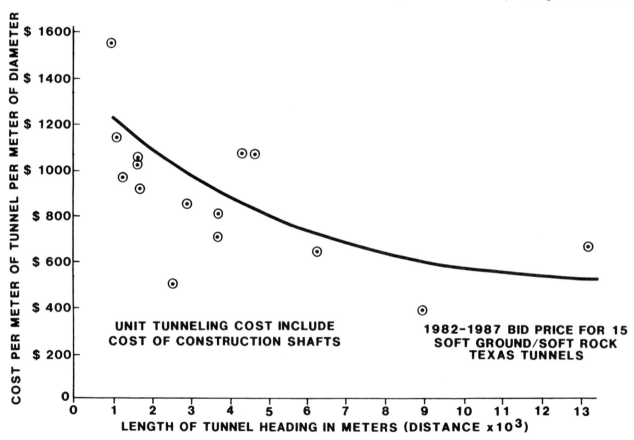

FIG. 11 UNIT COST OF TEXAS TUNNELING "VS" LENGTH OF HEADING

192

considers the front-end costs, i.e. cost of the TBM or shield, mobilization, crew training, etc. The longer the heading over which these costs may be amortized, the lower the unit cost of tunnelling.

SUMMARY

The history of tunnelling in Texas goes back more than 50 years. However, tunnels have generally been considered unnecessary for urban development until the last 10 to 15 years. Conflicts posed by shallow existing utilities and the desirability of minimizing disruption to surface activities in congested urban or environmentally sensitive areas has brought about the recent emphasis on tunnelling.

As engineers become more familiar with the design requirements for underground projects and contractors gain experience in dealing with ground, rock and water conditions, tunnelling is becoming a viable component of the infrastructure renovation in Texas. Control of groundwater and prevention of flowing ground are still the biggest construction problems in tunnelling on the coastal plain. However, with deeper tunnels such as the NWLPCS, steerage and squeezing ground are likely to provide a new set of problems. In the soft rock underlying many of the major Texas cities variations in the lithology present the biggest concern.

Early use of mechanical shield and roadheaders in the soft ground has given way to modern TBM's capable of full face closure. The early use of hard rock moles was demonstrated to be inefficient and nearly all of the soft rock mining is now done with TBM's with bull gear and pinion drives. The only exception is the use of roadheaders for short, specialized purposes. Also, all soft ground and most soft rock tunnels are supported by a primary liner erected in the tail shield. Drill and blast techniques are occasionally employed in soft rock and hand mining with spiling is sometimes used in soft ground, although generally for short reaches such as tail tunnels and utility crossings.

No appreciable increase has been noted in the cost of Texas tunnelling over the past 5 to 7 years. This may, however, be due to experience and confidence gained by underground contractors in Texas which offsets the normal escalation of construction costs with time. Based on the demonstrated trend to lower unit costs as alignments become longer, many recent advertisements allow contractors to bid on individual contracts or multiple contracts as one unit. In every case, to date, the bid for multiple contracts has been lower than the bid for individual contracts.

With acceptance by governmental agencies at all levels and maturing experience on the part of contractors, underground construction has a bright future in Texas.

References

1. Geologic Highway Map of Texas. The American Association of Petroleum Geologists, Tulsa, Oklahoma.

2. O'Neill M. W. and Maher L. J. Geotechnical Characterization of Desiccated Clay. Journal of Geotechnical Engineering, ASCE. Vol. 109. No. 1. Jan., 1983. p. 56-71.

3. Merritt B. K., Davidson R. R. and Baker G. L. Menard Pressuremeter Experience in Beaumont Clay. Paper presented at Spring Texas Section Meeting, ASCE, Austin, Texas, 1979.

4. Lentell, R. L. and Valentine R. M. Interpretive Geotechnical Investigation for Onion Creek Wastewater Interceptor Tunnels, Austin, Texas. Rapid Excavation and Tunneling Conference Proceedings, Volume 2, 1985, p. 611-630.

5. Merritt, B. K. and Valentine R. M., Houston Underground. Paper presented at Woodward-Clyde Consultants Central Symposium. St. Louis, Missouri, 1986.

6. Nelson, P. P., Case Histories In Tunneling: The Onion Creek Wastewater Interceptor Tunnel, Sections II and IV Contract. Geotechnical Engineering Report GR-86-9. The University of Texas at Austin, 1986.

The Los Angeles Metro Rail Project—planning and design of tunnels in gassy ground

Krishniah N. Murthy P.E.
Parsons, Brinckerhoff, Quade & Douglas Inc., Los Angeles, California, U.S.A., and
Facilities Division, Metro Rail Transit Consultants, Los Angeles, California, U.S.A.

SYNOPSIS

The Los Angeles basin, with a population of approximately 11 million, is one of the world's largest conurbations. After decades of studies and planning, the City of Los Angeles has finally embarked on the construction of a heavy rail system called the Metro Rail project, as well as two light rail projects called respectively the LA-Long Beach Light Rail project and the Century Freeway project (the latter light rail is in the median of the Century Freeway).

The Metro Rail project, begun as a 30-kilometer starter line subway (Fig. 1), is now a 36-kilometer subway/aerial combination with 17 stations (Fig. 3). At certain locations, the subway route will either skirt or cross old oil fields. The presence of hydrocarbons due to oil deposits mandates that the design consider and specify construction techniques to restrict hydrocarbon infiltration and to build and operate a safe transit system. Further, the presence of old oil fields means the possible presence of oil wells that the explorers have used for commercial purposes.

The majority of oil exploration along the subway route took place in the early 1900s, with little or no record of the exact location of oil wells. The possibility of encountering such a well, or wells, requires that the designer consider this aspect in the contract documents.

The presence of hydrocarbon gases, the possibility of encountering abandoned old oil wells, the treatment of contaminated underground water prior to discharge, and the high seismic activity in the region makes this Metro Rail project a unique tunneling design.

To overcome these challenges, the design requires that the contractors conduct a magnetometer survey ahead of the tunnel face, install a high density polyethylene membrane to wrap the tunnels and stations to prevent gas intrusion (hydrocarbon resistant coating to be applied if precast concrete liners are chosen for the subway), and chemically treat the dewatered water prior to discharge. These out-of-the-ordinary requirements must be conveyed to the bidders in clear terms so that a competitive bid for the job is received by the owners. The object of this paper is to discuss the design parameters, actual design, and specifications developed for competitive bidding, all of which can be used as a guideline for tunneling projects under similar conditions.

INTRODUCTION

The California State Legislature created an agency called the Southern California Rapid Transit District (SCRTD) in 1964 with a legislative mandate to design, construct, and operate a rapid transit system within the Los Angeles county area. Authorization to use a portion of the state gasoline tax for transit planning and construction was given by the voters of Los Angeles County in June 1974. Starting with 16 transit corridors for the Los Angeles Metropolitan area, the SCRTD Board of Directors selected a locally preferred alternative for the Metro Rail project. The alignment extended from the Central Business District through the Wilshire Boulevard area to Fairfax Avenue, and then north through Hollywood to North Hollywood (Fig. 1). Since then, the project has successfully completed preliminary engineering, continued preliminary engineering and final design for the initial minimum operable segment (MOS-1), and advertised major facilities and systems contracts for MOS-1 construction (Fig. 2).

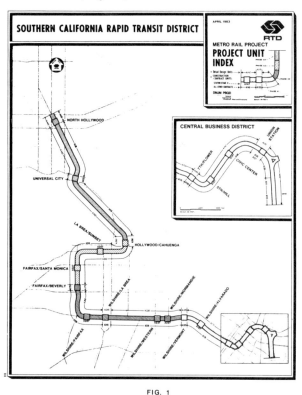

FIG. 1

On March 24, 1985, a methane gas explosion and fire occurred in the Fairfax area (in the vicinity of Fairfax/Beverly Station - See Fig. 1) because of ignition of methane gas in a department store. The methane gas had entered the building through small openings between the floor slab and the foundation walls of the building. The gas was contained in a room without ventilation and with a source of ignition. The explosion site and the Metro Rail route through the area are located on a portion of an old and abandoned salt lake oil field (See Fig. 4). Decomposed organic matter nearer to the surface and the abandoned oil field are the source of methane gas that is trapped in gas pockets below

the surface. The extensive asphalt or concrete paving of the area has sealed off many natural vents to the surface thus causing a buildup of pressures in these gas pockets. It is acknowledged that a random movement of methane gas through the path of least resistance to the surface is occurring and will occur indefinitely in the future. The explosion and the well-publicized gas presence in the area caused the local Congressman to approach Congress, which enacts legislation to appropriate major funds for the Metro Rail project, to enact a law that would prohibit tunnelling for Metro Rail through the Fairfax area.

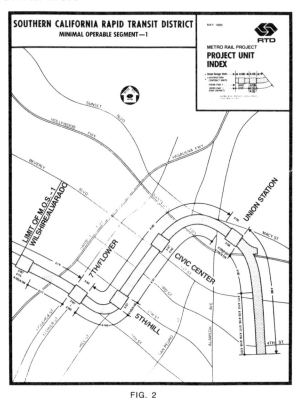

FIG. 2

As a result, in December of 1985 the U.S. Congress enacted a law that required the Southern California Rapid Transit District to re-study any segment of the Metro Rail alignment that would require tunnelling in areas identified as potential risk zones or potential high risk zones because of the subsurface methane gas conditions. To comply with the law, the SCRTD initiated a congressionally ordered re-engineering (CORE) study. The study identified the alignments and assessed the environmental impacts. In April 1987 the Board selected an alignment that will provide service to the Los Angeles regional core comparable to the service that was to be provided by the original locally preferred alternative connecting the Wilshire corridor to Hollywood and North Hollywood (Fig. 3).

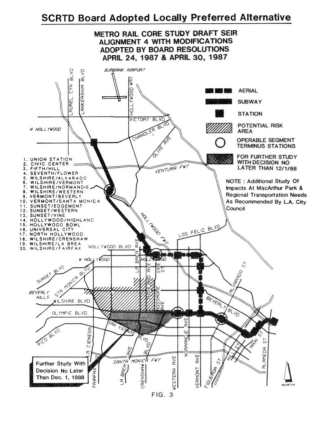

SCRTD Board Adopted Locally Preferred Alternative

METRO RAIL CORE STUDY DRAFT SEIR
ALIGNMENT 4 WITH MODIFICATIONS
ADOPTED BY BOARD RESOLUTIONS
APRIL 24, 1987 & APRIL 30, 1987

- ▬▬▬ AERIAL
- ▬▬▬ SUBWAY
- ■ STATION
- ▨ POTENTIAL RISK AREA
- ○ OPERABLE SEGMENT TERMINUS STATIONS
- ▩ FOR FURTHER STUDY WITH DECISION NO LATER THAN 12/1/88

NOTE : Additional Study Of Impacts At MacArthur Park & Regional Transportation Needs As Recommended By L.A. City Council

1. UNION STATION
2. CIVIC CENTER
3. FIFTH/HILL
4. SEVENTH/FLOWER
5. WILSHIRE/ALVARADO
6. WILSHIRE/VERMONT
7. WILSHIRE/NORMANDIE
8. WILSHIRE/WESTERN
9. VERMONT/BEVERLY
10. VERMONT/SANTA MONICA
11. SUNSET/EDGEMONT
12. SUNSET/WESTERN
13. SUNSET/VINE
14. HOLLYWOOD/HIGHLAND
15. HOLLYWOOD BOWL
16. UNIVERSAL CITY
17. NORTH HOLLYWOOD
18. WILSHIRE/CRENSHAW
19. WILSHIRE/LA BREA
20. WILSHIRE/FAIRFAX

Further Study With Decision No Later Than Dec. 1, 1988

FIG. 3

MOS-1 is a conventional two-track, steel wheel, steel rail system. It will serve a route approximately 7 kilometers long, extending from Union Station to the Wilshire/Alvarado Station with subway and surface tracks connecting to the Yard southeast of the Union Station. MOS-1 includes Yard and Shop facilities planned for the 30-kilometer system, with the exception of Yard Storage tracks which will be installed as the system expands.

MOS-1, with five stations, begins at Union Station and travels through the Central Business District along Hill Street, turning on Seventh Street towards Wilshire/Alvarado Station by passing under the Harbor Freeway. Two double crossovers at Union Station and one at Wilshire/Alvarado Station are provided for operational flexibility. MOS-1 is entirely in subway, with line sections constructed by tunnelling methods and stations constructed by cut-and-cover construction techniques.

GEOTECHNICAL CONSIDERATIONS

Los Angeles is one of those rare cities with relatively uniform geology over large areas. It consists of alluvium overlying miocene-pliocene sandstone, siltstone, and shale of the Puente, Fernando, and Topanga formations (Fig. 4). The formations and most of the alluvium are firm and well consolidated materials. The ground water table is, for most of the alignment, below the proposed subway grade. The geological conditions and the low water table encouraged the designers to adopt a construction schedule that assumed usage of high-speed mechanical tunnel boring machines for the majority of the alignment.

As planned, the Metro Rail corridor lies in heavily urbanized areas with multistory structures. The geology obtained for the construction of these structures provided considerable geologic information pertinent to the subway route. A U.S. Geologic Survey report (Yerkees, 1977), that compiled the logs of more than 200 boring in the downtown area also helped the designers to evaluate the geology of the area. Table 1 summarizes the local geology relative to the subway.

Table 1 Geologic units to be encountered along the L.A. Metro Rail Starter subway

Formation	Lithology	Route Length (Meters)	Proportion (Percent)
New alluvium	Loose alluvium	609.6	7
Old alluvium	Firm alluvium	3352.8	36
Tertiary formation	Shale, sandstone, siltstone	3472.0	50
Topanga basalt	Basalt	609.6	7
Total		9144.0	100

197

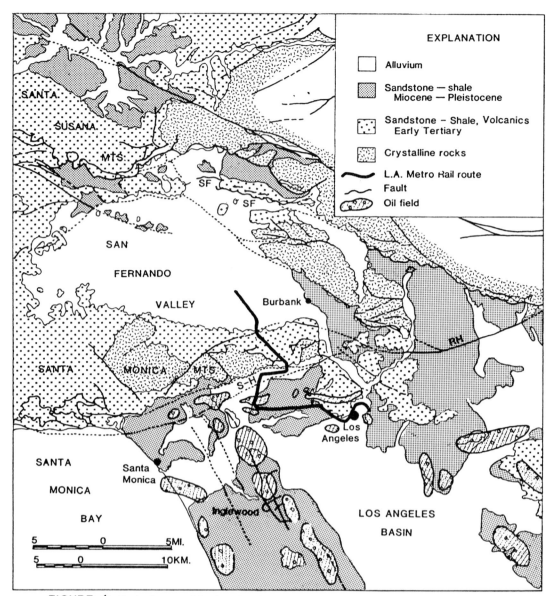

FIGURE 4 Geologic map of the Los Angeles area showing Metro Rail route, major faults and oil fields. Identified faults are MC, Malibu Coast; RH, Raymond Hill; SF, San Fernando; S-H, Santa Monica-Hollywood; SM, Sierra Madre. West end of subway route shown crossing Salt Lake oil field.

GEOLOGIC EXPLORATORY PROGRAM

Converse Consultants, a geotechnical firm working in conjunction with Earth Sciences and GeoResources Inc., produced a geotechnical report (1981) after a year of field investigations and laboratory work that included:

- o Core borings
- o Man-sized auger borings
- o Piezometer installations
- o Water pressure testing
- o E-Logging
- o Seismic refraction surveys
- o Micro-gravity surveys
- o Gas and petroleum analyses

- o Water quality analyses
- o TBM manufacturers' rock testing results
- o Petrology of certain rock cores
- o Laboratory tests for engineering properties.

All station sites were investigated during the engineering design (1982-1985), with at least six borings at each site. To estimate dewatering quantities, aquifer pump tests were performed at selected locations. Man-sized auger borings (915 mm diameter) were excavated and cased, with windows provided in the casing to allow visual inspection (from 15 to 30 meters deep). The core boring program was tailored to identify the geologic complexity of the area so that the

198

tunnel designers could use the specific details identified by the geologists.

While conducting core borings, it was evident that the hydrocarbon gases were present at different levels of concentration along major sections of the subway route. To supplement the gas chromatography analysis performed by the geologists, Engineering Science, a consulting firm, was engaged in 1983 to drill an additional 66 probes along the subway route to perform gas analyses and pressure readings.

GAS TESTING FOR LOS ANGELES METRO RAIL PROJECTS

Engineering Science installed gas probes in the 66 borings along the alignment. Field samplings at each probe consisted of quantitative and qualitative aspects of the following information:

- o   Pressure
- o   Methane
- o   Carbon dioxide
- o   Oxygen
- o   Hydrogen sulfide.

The field sampling was performed during the installation of the probes and subsequently, a week after the installation. Fig. 5 shows a detail of the probe installation. Sampling was performed at least three times in each probe. The samples were collected in laboratory flasks and taken to the laboratory for the following analysis:

- o   High hydrocarbon
- o   Methane
- o   Carbon dioxide
- o   Oxygen
- o   Nitrogen
- o   Carbon Monoxide
- o   Hydrogen.

A portable oxygen and combustible gas indicator with two meters was used to monitor for combustible gas concentrations. Pressure measurements up to 76 mm of water column were made with a slant tube manometer. Where pressure exceeded the

upper reading capabilities of the slant tube, a mechanical pressure gauge was fitted to the top of the probe.

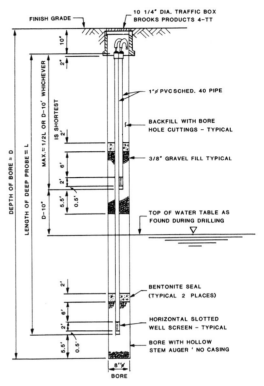

FIG. 5 - PROBE INSTALLATION DETAILS

Hydrogen sulfide readings were made with a hand-held vacuum pump apparatus which draws a sample from the top of the probe through a glass tube. The tube contains an absorbing and reacting material that is calibrated for hydrogen sulfide. Hydrogen sulfide was measured at the top of the probes where "sniff test" was proved to be positive. The field monitoring person is the conductor of the sniff test, and he attempts to smell the odor before the test is conducted.

Carbon dioxide readings at the tops of the probes were performed with an instrument which measures displacement of a special liquid indicator after drawings are obtained from a sample with a small built-in hand pump. Although the quality of the sampling was not always representative because of the draw-off technique, the general objective of identifying the components of the combustible gas was achieved.

Field testing for hydrocarbon gases revealed the following results:

o   Combustible gas concentrations exceeding 2.4 percent by volume in air were found in 18 probes.

o   Pressures ranging from 1.068 to 1.476 atm.abs were found in three probes.

o   Hydrogen sulfide in concentrations of 160 ppm was found in three probes, and a 60 ppm reading was found in one probe.

Fig. 6 schematically shows the results of the testing program compared to the various reaches of the original Metro Rail project. The following information is shown under each reach:

o   Methane gas concentration in ranges of percentage as defined in the legend

o   Methane gas pressure in inches of water column as defined in the legend

o   Locations where seismic considerations control the design

o   Tar sands location

o   Ventilation requirements compared to that provided. Ventilation criteria was to dilute the hydrocarbon gases to 0.25 percent.

TUNNEL DESIGN

As the geology of the alignment indicates, soft ground tunnelling for the Metro Rail project is extensive. Soft ground for this project is defined as tunnelling in soils and weak rocks using shield tunnelling. The total length of soft ground tunnelling, for the revised alignment, including hard rock tunnelling through the Santa Monica Mountains, is as follows:

16,292± meters of tunnel in soft ground
4,877± meters of rock tunnel
11,792± meters of cut/cover, aerial and at grade line.

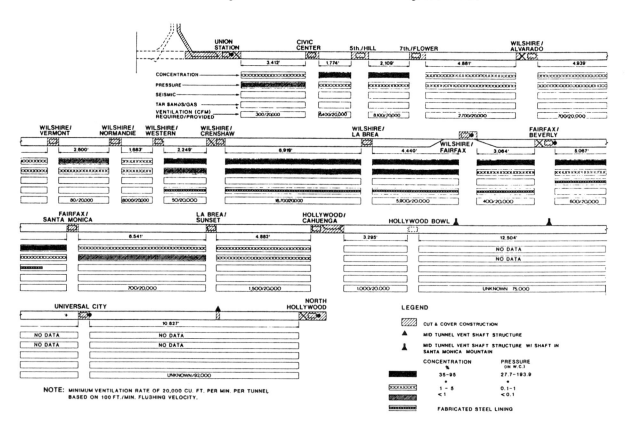

FIG. 6 - GAS INFORMATION BY REACHES

200

Groundwater levels generally occur within the Fernando and Puente bedrock. Perched water can occur locally within the geologic units. Tunnelling depths and general groundwater levels are shown in Fig. 7. Generally, the following classifications can be made concerning soft ground tunnels to be constructed in slightly different geologic conditions:

o   One half of all tunnelling will be in old alluvium.

o   The other half will be in soils such as Young alluvium, Fernando, and Puente.

From the start of the project, it was intended that the choice of liners for the tunnel be decided by a competitive bidding process. Therefore, two designs were presented in the contract documents for the lining. Pre-cast concrete tunnel lining and cast-in-place concrete tunnel lining were the two options designed, assuming traditional shield tunnelling methods and the most severe loading the tunnel might experience at the time of construction. The criteria for structural adequacy of both the liners are governed by the following:

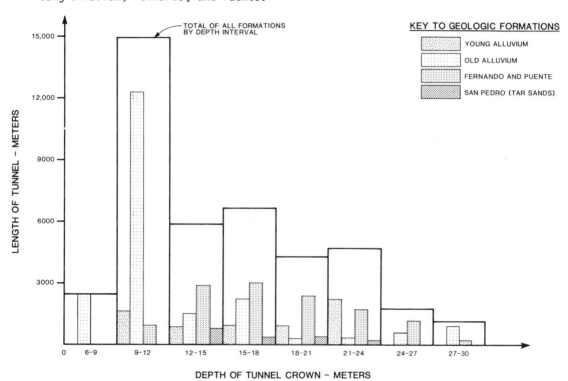

**SUMMARY OF SOFT GROUND TUNNELING BY DEPTH AND GEOLOGIC FORMATION
LOS ANGELES METRO RAIL PROJECT**

FIG. 7

The cover for the above tunnels is in the following ranges:

o   One-third of all tunnelling will be with from 9.0 meters to 12 meters of cover.

o   Portions of tunnelling will be with from 6 meters to 9 meters cover.

o   Maximum cover is 31 meters.

o   Flexibility to deform to an unbalanced load in case of precast liners with adequate strength for contact grouting in case of cast-in-place lining

o   Sufficient strength for combined thrust and bending/strength to accommodate future stress changes

o   Minimum thickness for concreting/constructability.

201

Further, as the Los Angeles basin is seismologically active, the effect of earthquakes on underground structures is one of the prime concerns. There is no code to date that governs the seismic design for underground structures. Therefore, Metro Rail Transit Consultants developed an in-depth criteria, "Seismic Design of Underground Structures," to be followed by the designers. As the tunnel is a standard element for the entire length, it was decided that Parsons, Brinckerhoff, Quade and Douglas, one of the joint venture partners with extensive expertise in tunnel designs, develop a standard design for the pre-cast liners as well as for the cast-in-place lining options.

The two broadly grouped concerns in the seismic design are shaking and faulting.

Shaking, produced by earthquake motion of bedrock, generates shear and compressive waves which cause displacement of the ground transverse and parallel to the axis of wave propagation. Waves propagated either parallel to the subway or transverse to the subway project different effects on the tunnel.

Faulting, the primary shearing displacement of bedrock passing through overburdened layer(s), does not permit the designers to restrain major soil displacements. Accepting the displacement, localizing and minimizing damage, and providing means to facilitate repairs are some of the available design choices.

The general design parameters used for the tunnel lining/liner design are:

o   Providing sufficient ductility to absorb the imposed deformation without losing capacity to carry the static loads.

o   Taking into account that although the absolute amplitude of earthquake displacement may be large, the displacement is spread over a longer length and the gradient of earthquake distortion is often within the elastic deformation of the structure.

o   Designing the circular lining for static loading conditions but checking

Table 2 Design highlights of the two liner types

	Precast tunnel liner (Figs. 8, 9, 10)	Cast-in-place tunnel lining (Fig. 11)
Structural Capacity	American Concrete Institute ACI 318-83 requirements.	American Concrete Institute ACI 318-83 requirements.
Concrete Strength	F'_c = 457 kilograms/sq.cm.	F'_c = 281 kilograms/sq.cm.
Reinforcing Steel	F_y = 4218 kilograms/sq.cm.	F_y = 4218 kilograms/sq.cm.
Thrust Capacity	Equivalent of 45.72 meters of soil cover.	Equivalent to 30.48 meters of soil cover.
Flexibility	20.32 cm thick segmented lining, flexible for all ground conditions considered.	30.48 cm thick Cast-in-Place lining, exceeds strength requirements, assumed that cracking will redistribute the bending moment allowing the lining to deform and relieve the build-up of load.
Analysis Methods Used	°Empirical method °Closed form continuum mechanics equations. °Beam-spring analysis method.	°Empirical method °Beam-spring analysis method.
Influence of ground water	It is assumed that bending moment by ground water is small and is not considered critical for design.	

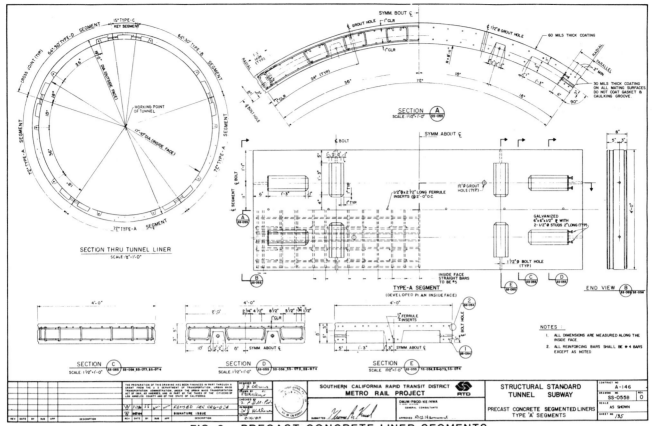

FIG. 8 - PRECAST CONCRETE LINER SEGMENTS

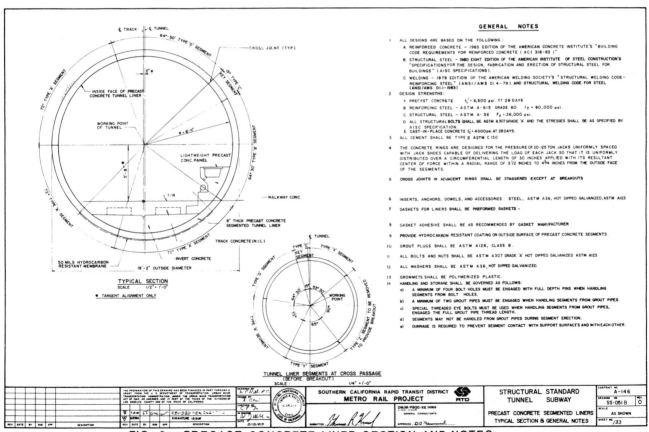

FIG. 9 - PRECAST CONCRETE LINER SECTION AND NOTES

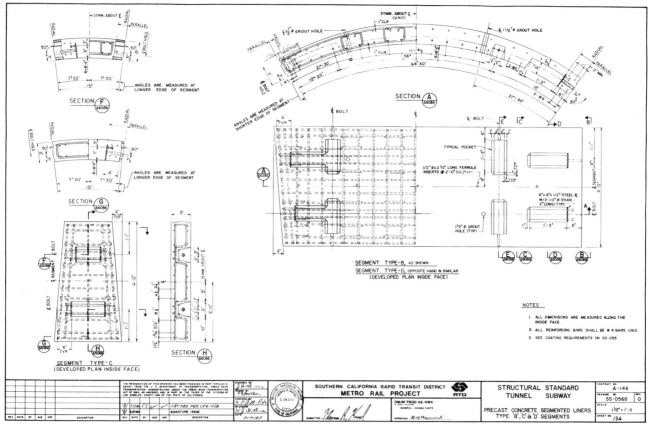

FIG. 10 – PRECAST CONCRETE SEGMENTS

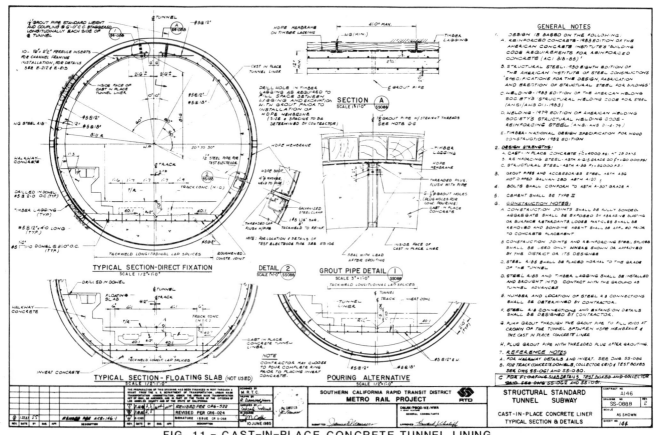

FIG. 11 – CAST-IN-PLACE CONCRETE TUNNEL LINING

204

for dynamic loading conditions, considering the shear wave velocity, induced longitudinal strains, strains due to rocking deformation, and lateral distortion; and analyzing the tunnels for "gravity loading" resulting from the weight of a zone of loosened material above the ground.

o   Considering liquefaction and landslide effects on the structures, where dictated by the geotechnical reports.

The three MOS-1 contractors for the three sections of the tunnels have opted to construct tunnels with cast-in-place concrete lining. Two sections of the tunnels to be constructed by the same contractor (Shank-Obyashi) will use unreinforced, unbolted precast liners as initial support while proceeding with tunnelling operations. The contractor for the first tunnelling section (Tutor, Saliba/S.J. Groves) has opted to use ribs and lagging as his primary supports. The type of tunnelling machines chosen by the two contractors, including probe and magnetometer equipment, are shown in Figs. 12, 13, and 14.

GAS FLOW INTO TUNNELS AND INFLUENCE ON TUNNEL DESIGN

The gas testing revealed a wealth of data and the information has to be effectively used to (a) calculate estimated gas flows into tunnels, and (b) design construction and operational requirements using collected data. Gas, like water, may enter into tunnels through joints or cracks in concrete, and by diffusion. The flow rate of gas (Q) through the joints and cracks is estimated by the equation Q = AV and from the Darcy-Wiesback equation:

$$V = \sqrt{\frac{\Delta p D 2 g}{f \int L}} \qquad (1)$$

Δp = pressure differential

D = hydraulic diameter

g = acceleration due to gravity

f = friction factor

∫ = density of fluid

L = flow path length

V = velocity - velocity of gas through joints and cracks

A = area of opening of joints and cracks

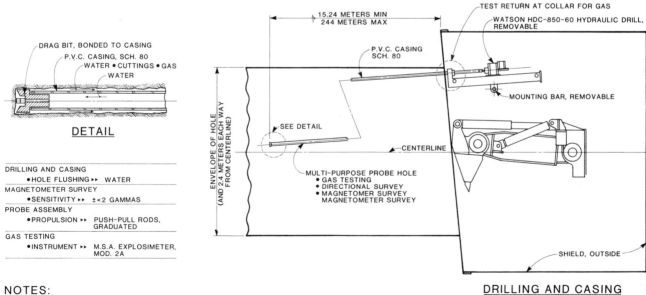

DETAIL

DRILLING AND CASING
  • HOLE FLUSHING ▸▸ WATER
MAGNETOMETER SURVEY
  • SENSITIVITY ▸▸ ±<2 GAMMAS
PROBE ASSEMBLY
  • PROPULSION ▸▸ PUSH-PULL RODS, GRADUATED
GAS TESTING
  • INSTRUMENT ▸▸ M.S.A. EXPLOSIMETER, MOD. 2A

NOTES:
1. HOLE TO BE DRILLED, CASED, TESTED, SURVEYED ON DAY SHIFT, EXCAVATED ON SWING AND GRAVEYARD SHIFTS
2. GAS TESTING BY CERTIFIED TESTER PER CAL-OSHA
3. MAGNETOMETER SURVEY BY APPROVED PROFESSIONAL GEOPHYSICIST

DRILLING AND CASING

PROBE AND MAGNETOMETER

FIG. 12

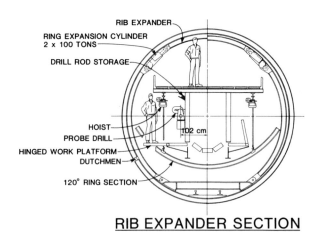

RIB EXPANDER SECTION

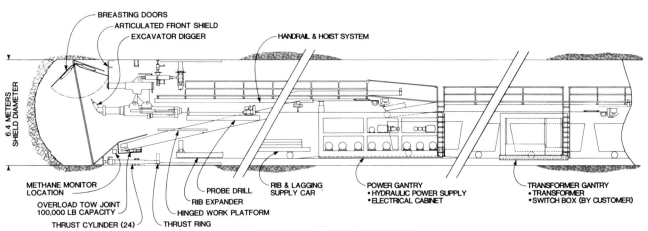

DIGGER AND SHIELD
FOR CONTRACT A141
FIG. 13

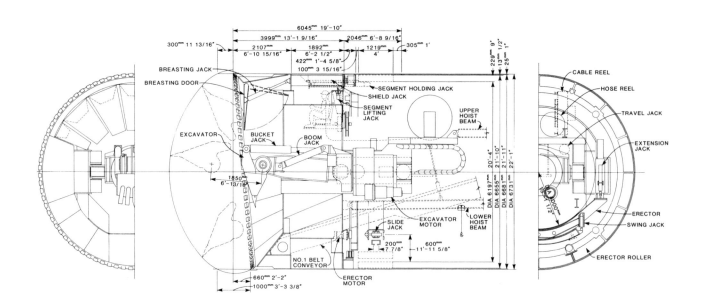

MANUAL SHIELD WITH EXCAVATOR
FOR CONTRACTS A146 & A171
FIG. 14

206

"A" in the above equation is indeterminate and depends on fabrication and construction of tunnels and details such as gasket installation, caulking, and quality of concrete. To estimate the flow of gas, it was decided to use extensive research and field measurement data found in "Guidelines for Tunnelling Design" (Rourke, 1983) and "Special Study of Precast Concrete Tunnel Liner Demonstration" (Weightman et al., 1980). This basis of calculation cannot allocate individual flows to the three sources of leakage (diffusion, joints, and cracks) but provides a method to estimate gas infiltration.

The equation for water and gas can be written as:

$$Q_g = Q_w \sqrt{\frac{\Delta P_g D2gf_w \sqrt{w}L}{\Delta P_w D2gf_g \sqrt{g}L}} \times A/A$$

The flow being in the turbulent range with Reynolds number being greater than 4000 and approximately $f_g = f_w$ equation (2) is simplified to:

$$Q_g = Q_w \sqrt{\frac{\Delta P_g \sqrt{w}}{\Delta P_w \sqrt{g}}}$$

Q_w = Water flow rate
Q_g = Gas flow rate
P_g = Gas pressure
P_w = Water pressure
$\int w$ = Gas density
$\int g$ = Water density

Assuming ΔP_w = 98.43 x 10^2kg/m² as the most conservative case consistent with the above reported data and substituting the densities:

$$Q_g = 0.386 \ Q_w \sqrt{\Delta P_g} \qquad (2)$$

where ΔP_g is in Kg/cm²

Q_w (Water flow into the tunnel)
    = 0.02gal/ft²/day
      (Reb.Weightman et al)
    = 9.43 x 10^{-3} cm³/sec/m²

for 5.334m diameter tunnel and a length of 1524m.

$$Q_w = [\pi \ x5.334 \ x1524 \ x9.43 \ x10^{-3}] cm^3/sec$$
    = 240.8 cm³/sec.

Substituting in equation   (2)
at ΔP_w = 98.43 x 10^2Kg/m²

$$Q_g = 0.386 \times 240.8 \sqrt{98.43 \times 10^2} \ cm^3/sec$$
    = 9220.5 cm³/sec.

It was decided that we design our system considering the possibility of leakage through cracks and joints, and provide ventilation to dilute the infiltered gas to levels that are considered to be safe (gas concentrations not to exceed 0.25 percent in air). Research done by Donaldson, Katz, and others indicated that the gas flow calculation into tunnels by diffusion is very approximate and is not an exact science at this stage. Our estimates in conjunction with Engineering Science indicated that diffusion through concrete is approximately 15 percent of the total flow and therefore negligible. Ventilation equipment designed for this project will handle 23600 cu.cms./sec gas infiltration in a tunnel section of 1524 meters.

To eliminate most of the gas flow through cracks and by diffusion, it was decided to test gas-resistant membranes for use in the tunnels. Matrecon Inc., a firm specializing in testing, was selected to perform screening and testing of these types of material membranes. Screening of many membrane samples resulted in two usable candidates. The selected membranes were shown to be approximately 99 percent effective in stopping the gas. To be conservative, design assumed 90 percent efficiency. The balance of infiltration into the tunnels, if any, will be diluted and removed by ventilation. Similarly, a gas barrier coating was selected to be applied on the outside face of precast concrete liners. The gasket between the liners is a dense elastomeric, manufactured as one continuous ring with molded gasket corners mitered and vulcanized to provide constant gasket thickness along the entire length.

MONITORING FOR GAS DURING AND AFTER CONSTRUCTION

Based on geological data and gas probes, CAL/OSHA (California Occupational Safety and Health Hazard Agency) designated the entire MOS-1 as "gassey." An explosion and fire that occurred at Third Street and Ogden Drive on March 24, 1985, in the Fairfax area not only increased the awareness of gas in underground construction but also forced the United States Congress to change the rail alignment in that area, now declared high risk by the local fire marshall. The CAL/OSHA gassey classification requires that the contractors use explosion-proof equipment in mining operations, install ventilation that will provide a minimum air velocity of 30.48 meters/minute during construction, and monitor the face and other areas of the tunnel for gas. As a long term measure, designers had to work out details to monitor subway and stations for gas presence and ventilation control. A study was conducted comparing local versus centralized monitoring methods. The conclusion was to use an industrial-grade central analyzer technology. Based on this conclusion, a centralized gas monitoring subsystem has been developed for Metro Rail. The technology adopted is a combination of techniques used to monitor carbon monoxide inside dust collectors of coal-fired processors, atmospheric and emission monitoring used by environmental protection agencies, and other such monitoring techniques used by chemical and petroleum industries.

Each central analyzer has a microprocessor-based control unit to control functions, ensure warning/alarm integrity, perform diagnostic checks, and communicate with the central control facility (CCF) through Supervisory Control and Data Acquisition (SCADA). Each control analyzer automatically communicates the following information to CCF:

o   Methane measurement of each sample
o   Hydrogen sulfide measurement of each sample
o   Warning annunciations
o   Alarm annunciations
o   Trouble annunciations.

Each control analyzer responds to some of the following requests from CCF:

o   Selection of next sample to be analyzed
o   Calibration of methane gas measuring equipment
o   Calibration of hydrogen sulfide gas measuring equipment.

Equipment in the CCF will perform the following functions:

o   Record all gas measurements on a 24-hour active memory

o   Record the highest gas measurement of sample line each day, on a 30-day memory

o   Record 30-day memory data on microfilm

o   Make a hard copy of all warning, alarm, and trouble annunications

o   Provide an inpanel display of each warning/alarm and trouble annunciation.

GAS PURGING BY VENTILATION

The concentration of gas in the tunnels, as stated earlier, will not be allowed to be more than 0.25 percent and the inflow of gas shall not exceed 23600 cu.cms/sec. for 1524 meters of the tunnels. When the system is in operation (revenue service hours), the piston generated air flows can adequately disperse and dilute any methane present in the tunnels. During the shut-down period, ventilation is one of the main options to mitigate gas accumulation. Air velocity of at least 30.5 meter/min. is to be maintained to prevent the formation of methane layers at the crown of the tunnels. Forced tunnel ventilation is limited to long tunnels, and to accomplish this, mid-tunnel ventilation systems are designed to be installed.

In general, based on extensive studies of the ventilation and gas purging for stations and tunnels, ventilation equipment consists of the following:

Stations o   To minimize the construction cost, it was decided to use the ventilation equipment provided for other purposes for gas purging also. Consequently, mezzanine smoke exhaust systems are sized at 23600 cu.cms/sec/0.093 sq. meters.

o   Four 17.7 cu.m/sec. air supply units for public space can also be used for future air conditioning.

o   One 30.2 cu.m/sec. underplatform exhaust fan at each platform end and ancillary areas are handled by independent equipment.

Tunnels o   Presently there are no mid-tunnel ventilation shafts in MOS-1 because of the short distance between stations. However, when a mid-tunnel vent shaft is required in the future, it is anticipated that three fans of minimum 71 cu.m/sec. capacity will generate adequate ventilation.

SPECIFICATIONS

The contracting practices in the United States dictate that engineers prepare contract documents to encompass all information so that the contractors are able to bid the job in a competitive atmosphere. The project owners require that engineers be exact in their requirements and contractors be precise in their costs, so that the owner does not have to revise or negotiate the changed conditions and settle the claims. However, the real world is different, and there are many situations where the owner, in response to contractors' claims, has to negotiate and settle the claims.

For the Metro Rail tunnels, the specifications follow the Construction Specification Institute

format, which is divided into four sections. The bid form and other associated forms to be filled out by the contractor as a part of his bid (example: Insurance Bond, Distribution of Work to Others, etc., etc.) comprise Part One of the specifications. Part Two consists of General Conditions and Special Conditions. Parts Three and Four are General Requirements and Technical Specifications, respectively. The Special Conditions not only inform the contractor of time of completion and liquidated damages for prolonging the work, but also carry important information, such as the classification of ground as "gassey," and instructions to stop work and ask the owner for further instructions if hazardous materials or asbestos is encountered during construction.

Under "Shield-Driven Tunnels," the Technical Specifications provide the option to choose either a cast-in-place lining system or pre-cast segmented liners. To provide for a safe tunnel construction operation, the contractor is required to drill magnetometer survey exploratory holes, install casing, conduct a location survey of the exploratory hole, perform magnetometer surveys ahead of the tunnel face to locate possible abandoned oil well casings, and test the exploratory hole to detect the presence of gas. The contractor is also instructed that should the magnetometer survey show a magnetic anomaly indicating the possible presence of abandoned oil or gas wells, he may be directed to proceed with hand excavation of the tunnel, with extra pay as a change condition. Monitoring for gas is to take place at the collar of the exploratory hole, and readings are to be recorded at maximum five-foot drilling intervals. Magnetometer data is to be recorded at one-foot intervals using an instrument having two three-axis magnetic sensor packages separated along the instrument length in a gradiometric measurement configuration. The contractor is also required to compare the magnetometer readings from the second tunnel with those of the first one to achieve the best possible interpretation of probable locations of oil wells.

The contractor is also instructed that he will be

paid extra as a change order for the time lost in plugging the oil wells or the gas well, and that the payment will include costs for equipment and labor.

We believe the explicit instructions detailed above have prompted contractors not to add contingencies in their bids.

Further, to ensure proper ventilation in the tunnel during construction, the contractor is instructed to maintain and operate a temporary ventilation system which will deliver 472×10^5 cu.cms/sec of fresh air at each tunnel face during the excavation period. The ventilation system is required to have the capacity to dilute the explosive gas to less than 10 percent of the lower explosive limit (LEL) in the exhaust duct and satisfy the minimum requirements set by the CAL/OSHA in regard to air velocity in tunnels and underground chambers. The contractor is also advised to have an emergency power source to operate the system on a continuous basis. In a conference before the bid opening, contractors were encouraged to tour the site and to meet for discussion with CAL/OSHA so that they are famil- iar with all the site conditions as well as the requirements. For treatment of dewatered water, contractors were provided with levels of contami- nation acceptable in discharge water, and they were also provided with pump test results so that they could independently calculate the quantity of water to be pumped and discharged. Chemicals required for treatment of the water were listed on the bid form with estimated quantities.

BIDS

The detailed drawings and specifications which cover many, if not all, of the unforeseen condi- tions, and a very competitive market have result- ed in the following bids, which are very favorable to the owners:

Table 3 Contractor's Bids

Contract No.	Description	Engineers' Estimate (U.S. $)	Contractors' Bid (U.S. $)
A141	Line Tunnels from Union Station to 5th/Flower Station including Stage I of Civic Center Sta- tion and crosspassages. Length of Twin Tunnels 3385 meters	76,293,000	61,471,225
A146	Line tunnel from 5th/- Hill Station to 7th/- Flower Station includ- ing crosspassages. Length of Twin Tunnels 1388 meters	20,513,000	18,221,800
A171	Line tunnels from 7th/- Flower Station to Wil- shire/Alvarado Station. Length of Twin Tunnels 3248 meters	38,500,000	26,340,078

CONCLUSIONS

President Truman once stated "I am not afraid of making decisions because I can always change my mind." The contracting practices in many coun- tries do not allow designers to change their minds once the contract documents are bid. But it is important that engineers address all known issues before the bid. It is evident from the bids received to date that given all the known facts, the contractors will be responsive to the known conditions. Unknown risks must be clearly identified: Letting the contractors know that the owner will negotiate if and when a change conditions situation occurs takes away unaccount- ed contingency funds from the bids.

More importantly, this project establishes that urban tunnelling in gassey ground can be designed for the safe construction and operation of a transit system. Los Angeles has embarked on this project; construction on all the tunnels for MOS-1 is now underway.

ACKNOWLEDGEMENTS:

Portions of the text for geology and the gas testing including the figures are extracted from a paper published by J.E. Monsees and R. Proctor in the 1985 RETC Conference (Volume I, Pages 488 through 505).

REFERENCES

1.   J. Monsees and R. Proctor 1985, "Los Angeles Metro Rail Project - Design Issues Related to Gassey Ground." Published in RETC proceedings. Volume I, Pages 488 through 505. References listed by the above authors for their paper are also acknowledged as references to this paper.

2.   J.E. Crawley, 1987, "Los Angeles Metro Rail Update." APTA Rapid Transit Conference.

3.   W.H. Hansmire, 1985, "Structural Requirements for Concrete Tunnel Liners - Metro Rail Project."

4.   K.V. Sain, Metro Rail Transit Consultants, 1987, Report "Mitigating Subsurface Gas by Ventilation In Subway Tunnels."

5.   Metro Rail Transit Consultants, "Supplemental Criteria for Seismic Design of Underground Structures."

6.   Metro Rail Transit Consultants, "Baseline Specifications."

Longer rounds to improve tunnelling and development work

Bengt Niklasson
Swedish Detonic Research Foundation (SveDeFo), Stockholm, Sweden
Roger Holmberg
Nitro Nobel AB, Gyttorp, Sweden
Kenneth Olsson
LKAB, Malmberget, Sweden
Stefan Schörling
Atlas Copco MCT AB, Stockholm, Sweden

INTRODUCTION

This paper describes a project carried out by SveDeFo, the LKAB mining company and Atlas Copco concerning the possibilities of pulling tunnel and drift rounds 7 meters long.

The background of the project was the change of scale in Swedish sublevel caving. Today LKAB, the major iron ore producer in Sweden, is changing over from 15 to 20 meters between the sublevels and using 102 mm diameter holes instead of 57 mm ones. By this the development work is using larger and fewer faces. See figure 1. In order to make development work more effective efforts have been made to analyze the different operations in drifting, namely drilling, blasting, scaling, loading and transport.

The analysis of the drilling operation showed that the availability of the existing drill rigs was not ideal and that the set-up times were long. A possible change over to longer drift rounds was considered to be of great interest because this also affected set-up times for other operations in the cycle.

PRELIMINARY TESTS

Before the full scale tests took place a series of trials were conducted to detect and deal with problems connected with the technique. One of these preliminary tests concerned the cut.

Four 0.7 by 0.7 m cuts were blasted to investigate the possibility of pulling a seven meter long cut. Since the blasting of a cut is

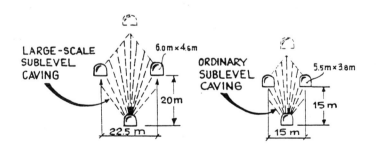

SUBLEVEL CAVING

DATA

	LARGE-SCALE	ORDINARY
* DEVELOPMENT		
TONS/m DRIFT IN THE ORE	2000	1000
* FAN DRILLING		
TONS/DRILLED METER	25	10
* HOLE DIAMETER (mm)	105	57
* BURDEN		
(DISTANCE BETWEEN FANS)	2,5	2.0
* TONS/FAN	5000	1900
* CHARGE CONCENTRATION (kg/ton of ore)	0,30	0,22
* KG OF EXPLOSIVES/FAN	1500	440
* DRILLING CAPACTITY (m/day)	250	600

Figure 1. Large scale sublevel caving in the Malmberget Mine.(Ref.1).

213

the fundamental event in a tunnel blast the result from these cuts would give an indication of the viability of the project. Drilling accuracy was also recorded in this test.

The results from the parallel cut test showed a lot of problems but were encouraging enough to go on with the full scale production tests.

PRODUCTION SCALE TESTS

Five production rounds were drilled and blasted in the LKAB Malmberget Mine in Sweden. Malmberget is situated in the northern part of Sweden close to another large iron ore mine, the Kiruna Mine, which is also operated by LKAB mining company. See figure 2.

After describing the geology the drilling, ignition and charge configurations for the five blasted rounds will be presented. The results from measurements made in order to register the different time of initiation of each charge in the cut as well as in the total round are also presented.

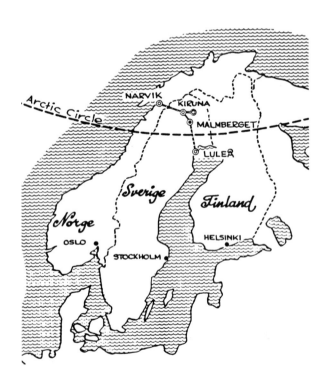

Figure 2. Malmberget and Kiruna are shown on this map of Sweden.

The Malmberget geology

The ores in the Malmberget ore field form a more or less continuous, five km long, undulating band of lens-shaped bodies (Stora Malmlagret). The ores of the eastern part (Yttergruvorna) exhibit a more complicated tectonic structure. Parallel ore-zones also occur. The orebodies plunge 45° to the south. The thickness varies between 10 m and 100 m. The country rocks are recrystallized volcanics, now appearing as "leptites" (fine-grained feldspar-quartz rocks and gneisses). See figure 3.

The ores are medium to coarse grained. The ore mineral is mostly magnetite, but in the western part a few hematite-dominated ore bodies occur. The apatite content varies between and within the different ore bodies and is less than 1% P. Actinolite and, to a lesser degree, biotite, feldspar and quartz occur as gangue minerals.

The parallel cuts

Two different large hole parallel cuts were used in the tests. Round No.1 and 2 used one empty hole with the hole diameter 152 mm. Round No. 2, 3 and 5 had two empty holes with the diameter 127 mm. See figures 4 and 5.

Drill and rod adding system

Atlas Copco developed a prototype of this system. The components consisted of the rod adding device, which was mounted on a BMH 614 feeder and the hydraulic control equipment necessary for running the system. This system was mounted on a rig earlier used for other testing.

To enable accurate positioning of the boom a ILMEG-ANGIE V/H system, which is a direction indicator for both horizontal and vertical angles, was mounted on the rig.

214

THE IRON ORE FIELD OF MALMBERGET

Geological map of the 600m level

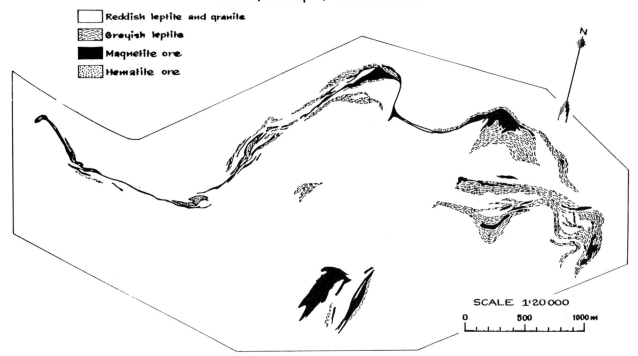

Figure 3. The iron ore field of Malmberget.

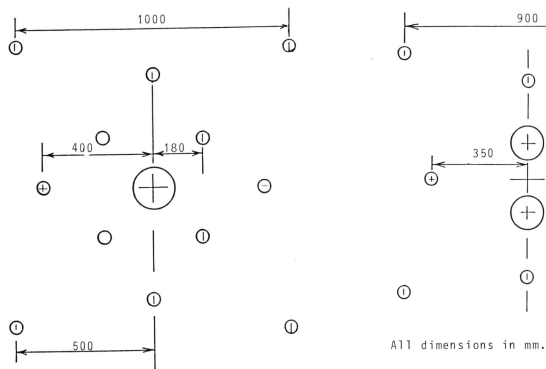

Figure 4. The cut type used in test
round No.1 and 4.

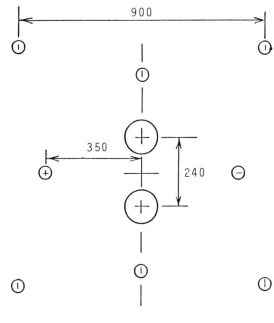

All dimensions in mm.

Figure 5. The cut type used in test
round No. 2, 3 and 5.

Further data on the rig:

Carrier: Carman
Boom: BUT 30
Hydraulics: BMU-38 P-02
Drill machine: COP 1238
Rods: Sandvik Speedrod R32, H32, R32
Sleeve: Diameter 45.5-47.5
Bit: Sandvik Guidebit Ø 51 mm X-bit

The BUT 30 boom is a tripod type of boom with built in parallel holding.

In order to handle the second rod two transfer arms are mounted on the side of the feeder. The two arms together with a hydraulic drill steel support, openable, enables the joining of the two rods. See figure 6.

Blast performance control

It was of very importance to conduct blast performance control of the various test rounds during the field test.

This control was carried with the aid of accelerometers mounted on the wall in an adjacent drift. Measurements were taken in various directions. The signals from the accelerometers were amplified by charge amplifiers and registered on an UV-recorder.

The non-electric NONEL GT System was used for initiation. The NONEL System utilizes 25 different delay intervals ranging from 25 ms up to 6000 ms. Table 1 shows technical data for the NONEL detonators.

As the number of holes for each round exceeded 60, and only 25 delay intervals were available, it was obvious that some delay intervals must contain several detonators. The 16 first initiated holes, i.e. the 4 first quadrangles in the parallel hole cut, were all separated in time. In this way the most critical time phase in the round could be properly monitored and evaluated. The delay time intervals for the remaining holes in the round contained several detonators separated in time only by the space

ROD ADDING SYSTEM

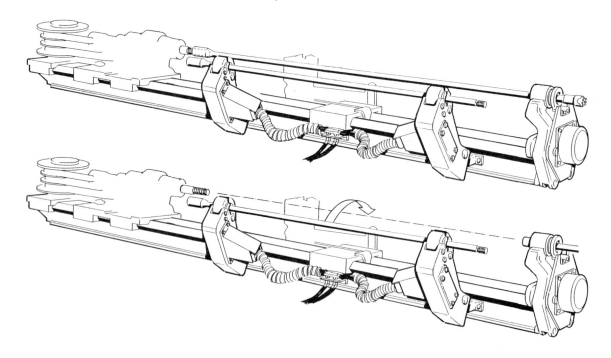

Figure 6. The rod adding system used in the five test rounds.

Table 1. Technical data for the NONEL-detonators.

Tube diameter   3 mm
Tube weight   5.5 g/m
Charge quantity   0.02 g/m
Shock wave velocity 2000 m/sec
Detonator strength   No. 8

NONEL model period no.	Delay range ms	Interval time ms	Standard length m
NONEL GT/MS			
3-20	75-500	25	3.0,4.8,7.8,15.0
NONEL GT/T			
0	25	-	6.0,7.8
1-12	100-1200	100	6.0,7.8
14,16,18,20	1400-2000	200	6.0,7.8
25,30,35,40	2500-6000	500	6.0,7.8
45,50,55,60			

between each delay time. Because of this it is difficult from the analysis to exactly point out how many holes really detonated in each interval. As several holes could have been initiated within a few ms, the analysis most probably understates the number of holes that were initiated in reality.

Data for round No.3 only are shown in this paper. Data for the other rounds can be found in ref.2. Figure 7 shows the drilling and ignition pattern for round No.3 and table No.2 the blasting data.

Figures 8 and 9 show the performance control results from round No.3. The diagrams show at what time, from the moment of initiation, detonated holes are found in the analysis. The width of each bar represents the time space where all detonated holes were found on the recording. On top of each bar the delay interval number is given as well as the ratio between the number of caps per interval utilized in the round and the number of caps found from the analysis. Figure 7 covers the time interval 0-2500 ms, that is i.e. cap numbers 0-25, and figure 8 covers the time period 2500-6000 ms, i.e. cap numbers 25-60.

Table 2. Blasting data for round No.3.

Site   Parta 530, drift No. 500
Drift size   6.0 * 4.65 m
Date   860611
Advance   7.5 m

Cut alternative 2.

2 empty holes   Ø 127 mm
63 drill holes   Ø 51 mm

Explosives

Cut and stoping holes   ANFO
Contour holes   Watergel Ø 22x1000 mm
Lifters   Dynamite Ø 32x1100 mm
Ignition system   NONEL GT/T with tube
                        length 9 m

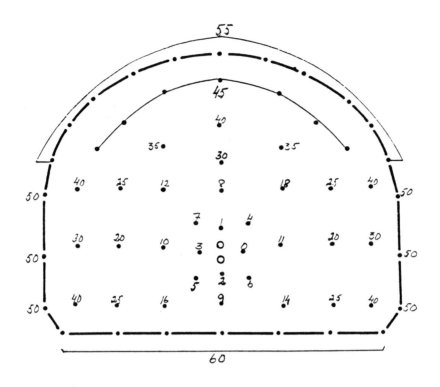

Figure 7. The drilling and ignition pattern for round No.3.

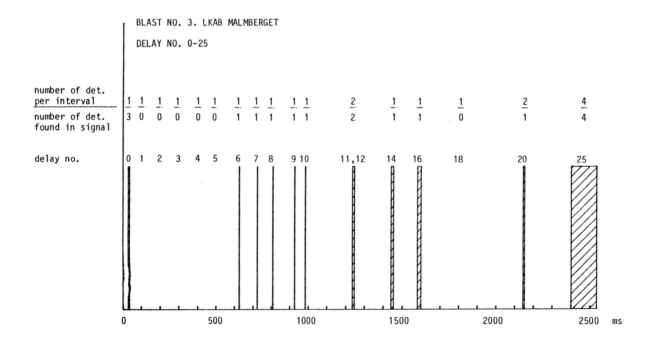

Figure 8. Initiation results for delay no. 0-25 in round No. 3.

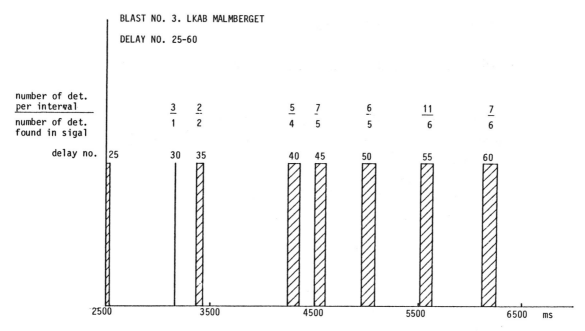

Figure 9. Initiation results for delay no.25-60 in round No.3.

RESULTS

Round number 3

Round No.3 was initiated by one cap per hole at intervals up to time delay interval number 18. The measurements showed that the cut was not working properly. Figure 8 shows that the analysis indicates 3 detonated holes for interval No.0, which indicates that sympathetic detonation might have occured. The numbers 1, 2, 3, 4, and 5 could not be found. Number 11 and 12 detonated at the same time. Number 18 is missing totally. Otherwise it was found that most of the higher time delay intervals could be found at the expected times.

In table 3 the data for all five test rounds are given as well as the data for the previously used conventional rounds.

DISCUSSION

The diagram in Figure 10 shows the percentage of detonated charges for each cut, which were found in the analysis. The results from round No. 1 and 3 indicate that only about 60 percent of the charges were detonated at the expected time. For rounds No.2, 4 and 5 this figure is around 90 percent.

Why do we have this difference? What is specific for round No.1 and 3? Both types of cuts are represented in these two rounds. Round No.1 had one empty hole and round No.3 had two empty holes. Round No.1 had NONEL detonators with a short tube length, e.i. that the primer was positioned in the middle along the drill hole, but round No.3 had the primer in the bottom part of the drill hole. The drilling precision was about the same for all the rounds. All these events indicate that there is no obvious reason why rounds No.1 and 3 were functioning worse than the others. The rock structure is of course one of the major parameters in all rock blasting and is therefore a most potential reason for the result although not controllable in this case.

In spite of the questionable way the cuts were functioning, the advances and the fragmentation results were very good for all rounds. Round No.3 shows the best advance of the five rounds. This might indicate that the drilling and blasting precision in the parallel hole cut is not necessarily of great importance.

The specific charge is approximately the same for the test rounds as for the conventional rounds even though the hole diameter was changed from 48

219

Table 3. Data for five test rounds.

Round:	1&4	2,3&5	Conventional
Hole depth (m)	7.5	7.5	3.7
Advance (m)	5.5-6.0 & 7.3	7.0,7.5 & 7.3	3.5
Area (m²)	24.0	24.0	24.0
Volume (m³)	175	175	84
Hole diameter (mm)	51	51	48
No. of holes	67-68	63	63
Ø empty hole (mm)	152	127	102
No. of empty holes	1	2	1
Explosives:			
Watergel (kg)	48.8	48.8	22
Dynamite (kg)	68.8	68.8	33.6
ANFO (kg)	468.0	416.0	194
Total (kg)	585.6	533.6	249.6
Spec. charge (kg/m³)	3.3	3.0	3.0
Spec. drilling (m/m³)	2.8	2.6	2.8

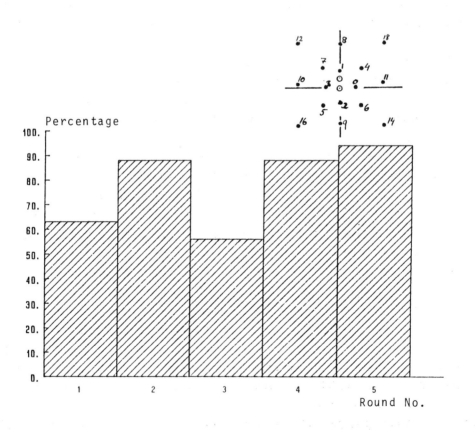

Figure 10. The percentage of working holes in the cuts of the five
tested rounds, the cut beeing defined as 16 holes.

to 51 mm. The purpose of these tests was not to reduce the specific charge but to increase the length of each round, therefore as many parameters as possible were unchanged to be able make a comparison with conventional blasting results from the mine. For this reason drilling, charging and initiation patterns were almost identical with standard Malmberget blasting practice.

Calculations made on the basis of the results in this test show the economic potential of the technique. According to the calculations, costs for drilling increases about 7% for a 7 m long drift round compared with a 3.8 m long one. Costs for charging, loading, transportation and scaling decrease about 15 - 20% in the same comparison.

THE CONTINUATION OF THE PROJECT

This project has led to two main conclusions. The first one is the possibility of pulling 7.5 meter drift rounds.

The second one may be even more interesting. Since following an initiation sequence of a cut by P-wave arrival measurements establishes the fact that only 60% of the charges in the cut detonated at the proper times but still obtained good advance, this leaves many questions to be answered. These questions concern charge concentration, accuracy in drilling and initiation sequence, and they need to be investigated.

SveDeFo has within its long range research program a continuation of this project. In it further studies on long drift rounds will be carried out and detailed work on the cut function will also be conducted. One example is high speed filming of cuts which already has been started and which shows very interesting results.

This work will also continue within another large underground mining research program called "Mining Technology 2000" which is a five year program where the government, the mining industry, the explosives industry, the mining machinery industry and research organisations in

Sweden will together pool their recources to reduce mining costs. The total program is divided into twelve projects. One of them is "Improved drifting".

These two projects will hopefully result in a better understanding of the functions behind drilling and blasting in tunnelling and drifting and also reduce the associated costs in the near future.

REFERENCES

1. Alatalo R., Hedén H. and Rönnbäck L. Large Scale Sub Level Caving in LKAB Malmberget Mine. Proceedings Large Scale Underground Mining, p. 139, Ed. G. Almgren, CENTEK publisher, Luleå, Sweden, 1985.
2. Niklasson B., Olsson K., Schörling S. and Holmberg R. Långa Salvor - för effektiviserad tillredning. In Swedish. SveDeFo report, DS 1986:4, Stockholm.

Borehole radar applied to site investigations prior to tunnelling

O. Olsson Ph.D., C.Eng.
S. Carlsten B.Sc.
L. Falk B.Sc., Ph.D., C.Eng.
B. Niva C.Eng.
E. Sandberg M.Sc.
Swedish Geological Company, Uppsala, Sweden

SYNOPSIS
A recently developed borehole radar system, RAMAC, opens new possibilities for obtaining detailed information about the rock structure at large distances from investigation boreholes. The radar uses electromagnetic waves concentrated in a short pulse (5-10 m) to probe the rock. The RAMAC system can be applied both in single hole and crosshole investigations which provides flexibility in the design of an investigation program. In a number of applications the radar has proven its capability to detect fracture zones, dykes, old boreholes and tunnels. Some case histories related to tunneling will be presented. The borehole radar is a unique instrument for mapping structures in rock since it combines high resolution, on the order of meters, with investigation ranges on the order of a hundred meters.

THE RAMAC RADAR SYSTEM

The RAMAC borehole radar system was originally developed within the Crosshole program of the International Stripa project on the disposal of nuclear waste[1]. The main objective of that program was to develop instruments capable of detecting and mapping fracture zones in crystalline rock in order to define accurately the possible flow paths of water. The radar has been very successful in solving that problem; radar pulses are reflected by discontinuities in the electric properties and these are directly related to the increased water content in fracture zones[2]. In order to achieve pulse propagation in rock and at the same time have acceptable resolution the radar must use very broad band signals in the frequency range 10-60 MHz. The pulses are transmitted by special borehole antennas to avoid ringing.

The radar system[1,3] (RAMAC) consists of five different parts;

- a microcomputer with two 5 inch floppy disc units for control of measurements, data storage, data presentation and signal analysis.

- a control unit for timing control, storage and stacking of single radar measurements.

- a borehole transmitter for generation of short radar pulses.

- a borehole receiver for detection and digitization of radar pulses.

- a motordriven cable winch with an optical borehole cable for transmission of trigger signals to the borehole probes and data from the receiver to the control unit.

The RAMAC system works as follows[3]: A short current pulse is fed to the transmitter antenna, which generates a radar pulse that propagates through the rock. The pulse is received by the same type of antenna, amplified, and registered as a function of time. The receiver may be located in the same borehole as the transmitter or in any other borehole. From the full wave

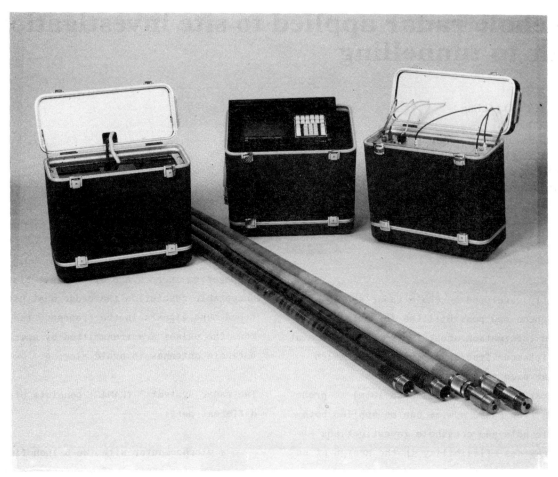

Fig.1 The RAMAC borehole radar system consists of two antennas supported by batteries, a control unit (right) supported by computer (middle) and an optional Winchester disc (left).

record of the signal the distance (travel time) to a reflector, the strength of the reflection, and the attenuation and delay of the direct wave between transmitter and receiver may be deduced.

The radar can determine the position of a reflector within a fraction of a meter. This may appear surprising since the pulse length and also the wave lengths involved are several meters but one has to remember that the resolution in time is about 1 nsec. Since the speed of wave propagation is considerably reduced in rock this corresponds to about 0.1 m in distance. One can thus easily study details within the pulse to investigate the reflection process. However, corresponding limitations appear on the positioning of the equipment: during tomographic work the form of the boreholes must be known to within 0.2 m.

Optical fibers are used for transmission of trigger signals from the computer to the borehole probes and also for transmitting data

from the receiver to the control unit. The optical fibers have no electrical conductivity and will not support waves propagating along the borehole. Another advantage of optical fibers is that they do not pick up electrical noise and as the signal is digitized down-hole there will be no deterioration of the signal along the cable. The quality of the results is thus independent of cable length.

There is no direct connection between the transmitter and the receiver (Figure 1). The transmitter and the receiver can thus be used in separate boreholes. In other words the radar may be used both for singlehole and crosshole measurements. The system provides absolute timing of the transmitted pulses and a calibrated gain in the receiver which makes it possible to measure the travel time and the amplitude of the radar pulses in a crosshole measurement and hence provide data for a tomographic analysis.

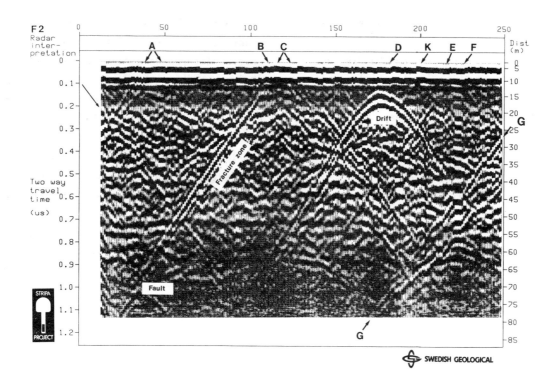

Fig.2 Radar map from Stripa displayed as a function of the position of the radar in a borehole. Fracture zones indicated by capital letters and a tunnel (drift) are clearly seen.

SITE INVESTIGATION WITH RADAR

The detection and mapping of fracture zones using the borehole radar is a straightforward procedure and measurements have been performed at many places all over the world. In the simplest measurements the transmitter and receiver are moved down a borehole at a constant distance from each other. Measurements are usually performed every meter and the signals showing the distance to the reflectors are displayed in radar maps.

Figure 2 from Stripa mine[a] shows that fracture zones (designed by capital letters) are observed as well defined objects in the radar maps. The results agree closely with the theoretically calculated shapes for plane reflectors demonstrating that fracture zones in granite are usually plane structures extending over many hundred meters. When the fracture zones are nearly parallel to the borehole one can however observe that they are sometimes slowly undulating. The degree of fracturing can be estimated from the amplitude of the reflected pulse. It has often been observed that the thickness of a zone may vary considerably over the fracture plane.

Using the RAMAC radar detailed models have been constructed of several sites, both as tests of already investigated areas and as investigations prior to further construction work. A number of techniques have been developed and tested in order to extract as much information as possible from the radar measurements: in an increasing order of complexity they are singlehole reflection measurements, crosshole reflections and tomography, the latter based both on velocity and attenuation measurements on the pulse. Numerical analysis of the collected data is indispensable to extract all the available information contained in the data.

The antennas are cylindrically symmetric dipoles and it is therefore impossible to determine the direction to a fracture plane from a singlehole measurement; only the point of intersection and the angle between the plane and the borehole can be deduced in this way. However detailed models of the investigated sites can be obtained by using data from several boreholes. Directional antennas are presently under development and will further simplify the analysis, especially if there are only a few boreholes available.

Tunnels and even boreholes can be discovered by radar as seen in Figure 2. A tunnel passing about 15 m from the borehole appears as a very strong reflector in this radar map. The reflection is caused by the great difference in dielectric constant of air and rock at radar frequencies. The reflections are enhanced by conductors such as rail way tracks and ventilation shafts in the tunnel.

Using a shorter wavelength for better resolution one can even observe single boreholes. The diameter of the boreholes at Stripa is 76 mm, which is much less than the wavelength, but due to water in the boreholes the electric contrast is considerable. Using the radar it is thus quite easy to locate unmapped tunnels etc. The radar technique is however even more valuable during tunnel construction, since it is possible to tell in advance when an area of fractured rock is encountered.

In all investigations of this type range is the decisive question. Both theory[4] and practice confirm that the maximum radar range in granite is about 50-150 m depending on the frequency and the type of reflector. In sedimentary rock the range is reduced because of the increased attenuation caused by water in the pores.

CROSSHOLE MEASUREMENTS

In the RAMAC system the transmitter and receiver are entirely independent units. They can thus be used in different boreholes or with one antenna at the ground. Such measurements are routinely performed to measure the wave velocity in the rock. Reflections observed in this new configuration will give additional information about the orientation of the fracture zones and have proved useful though the result are rather complicated to interpret.

Tomographic techniques can also be applied to crosshole radar measurements. The attenuation or the speed of the radar pulse must then be accurately determined for very many rays between the boreholes. The data can be inverted if the quality is sufficiently high and will provide the attenuation or the wave velocity at all points between the boreholes. These results are

extremely interesting because they provide a quantitative picture of the quality of the rock. Unique pictures have been obtained in this way of the structure and degree of fracturing within the fracture zones. Tomography has at times contributed decisively to the interpretation at complicated sites.

Figure 3 shows a tomogram based on the attenuation of radar waves. Increased attenuation correlates closely with the position of the fracture zones determined by reflection methods (marked by capital letters) and geophysical logging. The varying thickness of the zones is a real effect which can be observed in different cross-sections of the same volume. Details of a fracture zone can thus be investigated by tomography and the analysis will provide values of the electric parameters which are directly related to the porosity of the rock.

The tunnel also appears as a strongly attenuating object in the tomogram in Figure 3. Actually the tunnel does not absorb energy, but by scattering energy away from the pulse it will have the same effect on the pulse as an absorbing object. On the other hand the propagation time of the pulse is hardly affected by the tunnel which consequently is only seen with difficulty in velocity tomograms. The tunnel appears elongated in the tomogram since it intersects the plane spanned by the boreholes at a very oblique angle.

PRACTICAL INVESTIGATIONS OF TUNNELS

The RAMAC system has been used in practice both to locate tunnels and to investigate sites prior to tunnelling. Some recent measurements will be described briefly.

Site investigations were performed during construction of a waste water tunnel called the Saltsjö tunnel under central Stockholm. Before excavation two boreholes were drilled from the surface at 60° inclination and reflection and tomographic measurements were performed during two days.

The rock turned out to be heavily attenuating but it was still possible to calculate tomograms based on attenuation and wave velocity. Such a tomogram is shown in Figure 4. The position of

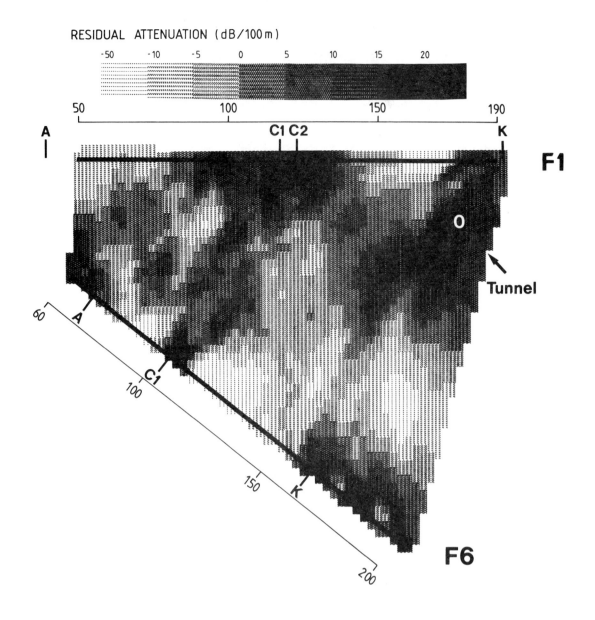

RESIDUAL ATTENUATION (dB/100m)

Fig.3 Tomogram based on wave attenuation between two boreholes in Stripa. Fracure zones and a tunnel appear as attenuating areas. The white ring marks the known position of the tunnel.

some major fracture zones can be predicted already from these tomograms. The results were then extended by taking into account the reflection measurements, which can detect much weaker fractures.

The resulting model is indicated in Figure 4. It was compared with observations when the tunnel reached the investigated area and the radar model seems to agree well with the observed fracture pattern as far as can be determined from the tunnel.

Since there are only two boreholes available an ambiguity will occur because no measurements can resolve a calculated model from the corresponding model mirrored in the borehole plane. Such ambiguities can often be removed by careful planning of the experiments.

Usually there are fewer boreholes available for measurements than would be desirable so it is valuable to extend the measurements whenever possible by using alternative configurations, e g by placing one antenna at the ground or in a

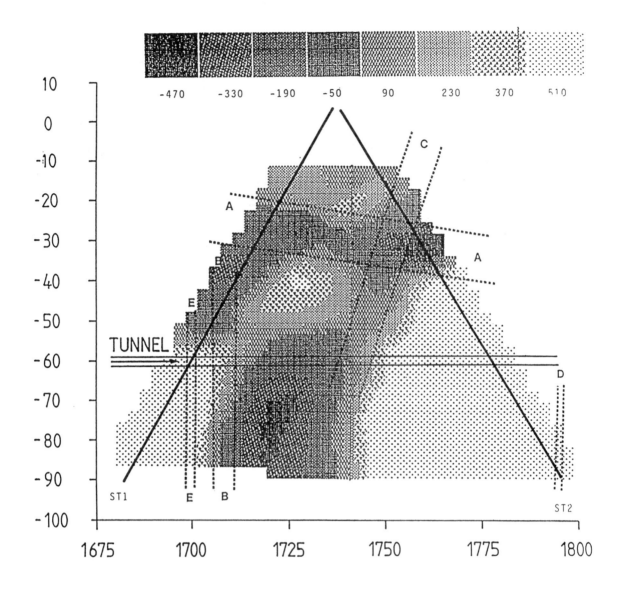

Fig.4 Tomogram calculated between two boreholes prior to
construction of a waste water tunnel under Stockholm.

tunnel. The latter case applies in Figure 5 from measurements at the Grimsel Test Site in Switzerland performed in cooperation with Nagra to prepare for a new project designed to predict rock conditions ahead of a tunnel face.

One antenna was moved in the tunnel while the other was fixed in a borehole as shown in the schematic picture in Figure 5. The reflection measurement was quite successful and shows in particular a very prominent reflection from a lamprophyric dyke intersecting the tunnel.

An interesting feature seen in Figure 5 are weak waves which apparently reach the antenna

before the main pulse. The reason for this behaviour is that the wave velocity in the rock is only about 40% of the velocity in air. Pulses partly propagating in the tunnels can therefore arrive before the "direct" wave but they will be weakened and heavily distorted.

Measurements from tunnels are often complicated by radar waves propagating along the tunnel. From a practical point of view such measurements are however important, e g in tomographic work where it may be necessary to add measurements from tunnels to extend the ray coverage. Antennas designed to simplify

ANTENNA POSITION IN TUNNEL

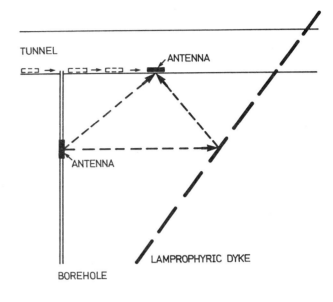

DIRECT
PULSE

REFLECTED
PULSE

PROPAGATION TIME

TUNNEL

ANTENNA

ANTENNA

BOREHOLE

LAMPROPHYRIC DYKE

Fig.5 Reflection measurement from the Grimsel Test Site performed
between tunnel and borehole according to the schematic figure.
The measurements were interrupted when passing another tunnel.

measurements in tunnels are presently under
development.

A particularly complicated situation occured
during recent measurements in a salt mine in
Canada performed to locate a dangerous inflow of
water. The salt which is located in a single
layer will hardly attenuate the radar waves at
all but the surrounding sedimentary rock is
highly attenuating. The radar pulse is thus
confined to the salt layer but the reflections

from the dense net of excavation tunnels made
the interpretation complicated. Measurements
were mainly performed between oblique
boreholes. After excluding reflections due to
known objects one could observe a reflection
coming from the roof in a place where the rock
appeared to be faulted. Later investigations in
the mine revealed a water inflow near this
point.

CONCLUSIONS

The RAMAC borehole radar has been developed into a versatile system which can be used to investigate a site in detail prior to construction using several configurations and modes of investigation. Numerical techniques have been developed to handle the data analysis efficiently. Practical tests have been performed at many different sites. Radar measurements can also be used to locate tunnels and even boreholes in rock.

ACKNOWLEDGEMENT

The borehole radar system was developed within the Crosshole Programme of the International Stripa Project. We are grateful to SKB and the personnel at Stripa for excellent conditions during this work. We are also indebted to the International Minerals & Chemical Corporation and Nagra for permission to present radar results. Dr G. Sattel and Dr P. Blümling from Nagra took active part in the Grimsel measurements.

References

1. Olsson O., Forslund O., Lundmark L., Sandberg E. and Falk L. The design of a borehole radar system for detection of fracture zones. Proceedings 2nd NEA/Stripa Project Symposium, Stockholm, 1985, p. 172-189.

2. Olsson O., Falk L., Sandberg E., Carlsten S. and Magnusson K.-Å. Results from borehole radar reflection measurements. Proceedings 2nd NEA/Stripa Project Symposium, Stockholm, 1985, p. 190-202.

3. Olsson O., Falk L., Forslund O., Lundmark L.and Sandberg E. Crosshole investigations - Results from borehole radar investigations.Stripa Project, IR-87-11, Stockholm, 1987.

4. Cook J. C. Radar transparencies of mine and tunnel rocks. Geophysics, vol. 40, 1975, p.865-886.

Evaluating and predicting ground settlements caused by tunnelling in London Clay

M. P. O'Reilly M.E., Ph.D., C.Eng., M.I.C.E., M.I.H.T.
Transport and Road Research Laboratory, Crowthorne, Berkshire, United Kingdom

SYNOPSIS

A method for estimating the amount of the ground settlements caused by tunnelling through London Clay is developed. Four elements are involved; (i) a relation between bulk strength and depth for the London Clay, (ii) the effect of the geometry of the tunnel heading on stability, (iii) the relations between load factor and ground loss determined from an extensive series of tests on model tunnels in a geotechnical centrifuge and (iv) an existing relation between the width of the settlement trough and depth to tunnel axis.

The values predicted using the method are compared with comprehensive settlement data from six lengths of tunnel driven through London Clay at depths to axis of 3.4 to 29.3m and with excavated diameters of 1.52 to 4.15m Good agreement between measured and predicted values was achieved on the assumption that there are two modes of deformation/failure above tunnels depending on their depth below ground surface; overall the predicted values of relative ground loss and settlement are lower than the measured values by 21 and 16 per cent respectively.

INTRODUCTION

It has been shown that the normal Gaussian distribution curve provides a good approximation of the shape of the settlement of the ground surface above a tunnel[1] so that the settlement, S, at a transverse distance, y, from the centreline of the tunnel is given by the expression:

$$S = S_{max} \exp (-y^2 / 2 i^2) \quad \ldots \quad \ldots \quad \ldots \quad (1)$$

where i is the horizontal distance from the tunnel centre line to the point of inflection on the settlement trough and S_{max} is the maximum value of S over the centreline of tunnel ie at y = 0. It follows that the volume of the settlement trough, V, per unit length of tunnel is given by:

$$V = \sqrt{2\pi} \; i \; S_{max} \simeq 2.5 \; i \; S_{max} \quad \ldots \quad (2)$$

Thus if any two of V, i and S_{max} can be estimated tunnellers are in a position to make predictions of the extent and magnitude of the ground settlements which are likely to be caused by their tunnelling operations.

However, although the lateral extent of the settlement trough at the ground surface, defined by i, can be predicted with reasonable success using semi-empirical relations derived from field observations[2,3] there is as yet no straight forward method for estimating either V or S_{max}. Current settlement predictions are therefore based on "guesstimates" of groundloss, V, obtained from case histroy records and experience[4].

This paper, using data drawn from several sources, adopts a load factor approach, which takes account of support conditions around the tunnel face, to quantify tunnel stability. Relations between load factor and ground loss are then used to give predictions of ground settlement which are shown to be in reasonable to good agreement with field measurements on actual tunnels driven in London Clay.

THE BULK STRENGTH OF LONDON CLAY

Skempton[5] stated that "London Clay is an unusually constant geological material at least within the region of the city and its suburbs" and produced the relation, shown dotted on Fig. 1, between average undrained shear strength and depth when the London Clay extended to the ground surface: he also provided a modification to this basic relation at shallower depths when the London Clay was overlaid by terrace gravels. The shear strength determinations on which these relations were based were made in the triaxial apparatus on 1½ in (38 mm) diameter specimens cut from 4 in (102 mm) diameter "undisturbed" borehole samples[6].

The London Clay is heavily fissured and it has been shown that average undrained shear strengths based on the results of tests on 38 mm diameter specimens are considerably higher than those obtained from insitu bearing tests carried out using large plates[7,8,9,10,11]. The position can be summed-up by quoting Marsland[12] who stated that "comparison of the results of the laboratory and insitu tests indicate that the lower values measured on small specimens in the laboratory were more representative of the large-scale strength of the clay than the average values of such tests".

Examination of the above references suggests that a representative value of the coefficient of variation for the results of shear strength determinations on 38 mm diameter specimens would be about 25 per cent. For such a coefficient of variation the full line in Fig. 1, which reduces by 50 per cent the shear strengths given by Skempton[5], would represent a relation between undrained shear strength and depth below which some 2 per cent of shear

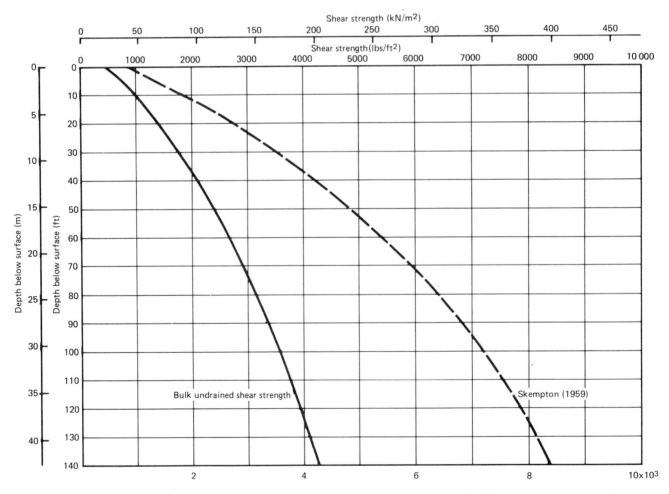

Fig. 1 Relations between undrained shear strength and depth for London Clay

232

strength values obtained by testing 38 mm diameter specimens would be expected to lie. This relation is, therefore, put forward as a reasonable undrained shear strength/depth relation for a large mass of London Clay. Support for the view that this is a reasonable estimate of the order of magnitude of the bulk strength of the London Clay is provided by the back-analysis of the short-term slip failure at Bradwell by Skempton and La Rochelle[13] where they showed that "the shear strength mobilised along the slip surface amounted to about 55 per cent of the strength as measured in conventional undrained triaxial tests".

STABILITY OF TUNNEL HEADINGS

The stability number, N, was defined by Broms and Bennermark[14] as:

$$N = (\sigma_Z - \sigma_T)/Cu \quad \ldots \quad \ldots \quad \ldots \quad \ldots \quad (3)$$

where, σ_Z is the overburden pressure given by the product of the unit weight of soil, γ, and the depth to tunnel axis, Z.

σ_T is any temporary support pressure such as compressed air applied within the tunnel and Cu is the undrained shear strength of the soil.

On the basis of their laboratory model tests and analysis of considerable field data, Broms and Bennermark[14] concluded that face instability occurred in the shorterm* when the stability number exceeded 6.

More recently a programme of centrifuge model tests has been undertaken as part of the extensive research studies of tunnels carried out at Cambridge University for the Transport and Road Research Laboratory[15]. These have shown that the geometry of the tunnel heading (Fig. 2) and in particular the length, P, of unsupported tunnel behind the face have a considerable influence on the stability number at collapse, N_{tc}[16, 17]. The relations between P/D, C/D and N_{tc} obtained from tests in the centrifuge of model tunnel headings in kaolin are shown in Figs 3 and 4; in these tests the undrained shear strength was 26 kN/m² and did not

---

*In stiff clays such as London Clay the clay softens on excavation and the shear strength reduces with time.

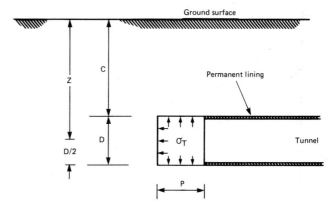

Fig. 2 Geometry of tunnel heading

vary with depth. These figures show that maintaining support as close to the face as possible increases the stability of the tunnelling works so that a tunnel with the lining right up to the face is about twice as stable as one where the lining begins some four diameters or so behind the face.

LOAD FACTOR AND RELATIVE GROUND LOSS

The limitation of stability numbers is that their critical value depends on the support arrangements in the vicinity of the tunnel face ie the geometry of the tunnel heading. It can be overcome by the use of a load factor defined as the ratio N/N_{tc}, where N is the stability number under working conditions N_{tc} is the stability number at collapse given by Figs 3 and 4.

Relative ground loss, $\nu \ell$, (usually expressed as a percentage) is the ratio of the volume of the settlement trough at the ground surface, V_s, to the volume of tunnel excavation, V_{exc}. In the research at Cambridge University both Mair[16] and Seneviratne[18] produced relations from model tests in plain strain between relative ground loss and load factor; these relations[19] are shown in Fig 5.

PREDICTIONS OF GROUND LOSS DUE TO TUNNELLING IN LONDON CLAY

Reasonably comprehensive data[20,21,22,23,24] are available on the geometry of the tunnel heading and the settlements caused by driving six sections of tunnel in free air ($\sigma_T = 0$)

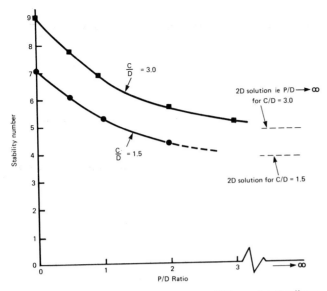

Fig. 3 Influence of heading geometry on stability number at collapse from model tests in the centrifuge (Mair 1979)

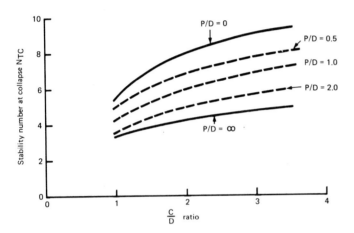

Fig. 4 Influence of heading geometry on stability number at collapse from model tests in the centrifuge (after Kimura and Mair 1981)

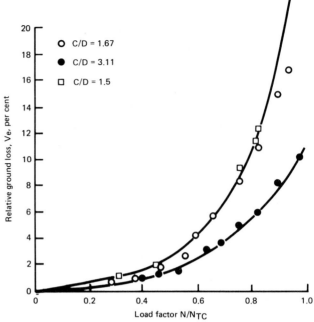

Fig. 5 Relation between relative ground loss and load factor from plain strain model tests (after Mair, Gunn and O'Reilly 1981)

through natural London Clay*. Excavation was by hand through five of the sections while a 1.52 m diameter tunnelling machine with a scheduled length of 4.27 m and a rear hood 0.71 m long was used for location 7 at Sutton[20]. Shields with lengths between 3.25 and 3.48m[23, 24] were used at Regents Park and Green Park while the tunnels at King's Cross and Location 5 at Sutton were driven without a shield[20, 21].

---

*Data from the deep location at Sutton[20] have not been used here because that section of tunnel was overlain by a considerable depth of fill material.

Surface settlements were measured on lines of levelling stations or studs and the settlements of these were determined by precise levelling with reference to a number of temporary bench marks located nearby but well away from the influence of the tunnelling operations using an invar staff and automatic level having an integral parallel plate micrometer.

Details of the geometry of the tunnel heading and the settlements are given in Table 1 together with values of σ Z and N_{tc} for each section of tunnel. For higher values of the C/D ratio, the appropriate value of N_{tc} was obtained by adding an adjustment factor to the value of N_{tc} for C/D = 3 given in Fig. 3. This adjustment factor was obtained from the expression:

Adjustment factor = $2\ln(C/D+1)-2.77$ ... (4)

This expression plotted in Fig.6 assumes that the extension of the relations between P/D and N_{tc} given in Fig. 4 to higher C/D values have the same shape as the curve given by the formula $N_{tc} = 2 + 2\ln(C/D + 1)$ the lower bound solution for a heading in plane strain[25].

234

TABLE 1.   Details of settlement measurements on tunnels in London Clay

Location	Sutton[20]		King's Cross[21]	Regent's Park[22]		Green Park[23]
	Location 5	Location 7		High Tunnel	Low Tunnel	
Depth to tunnel axis, Z m	3.4	4.9	14.06	20	34	29.3
Excavated tunnel diameter,D,m	1.78	1.52	4.13	4.15	4.15	4.15
Cover to crown of tunnel excavation, C, m	2.51	4.14	12.00	17.93	31.93	27.23
C/D ratio	1.4	2.7	2.9	4.3	7.7	6.6
Length of unsupported tunnel behind face, P, m	0.7	4.98	0.7	3.25 - 3.48[24]		3.35
P/D ratio	0.39	3.3	0.17	0.81 avg.		0.81
Overburden pressure, $\sigma_Z' = \gamma Z$, at axis kN/m²	66.6	96.0	275.6	392.0	666.4	574.3
Stability number at collapse N_{tc} from Fig. 3 and equation 4	6.2	4.9	8.6	7.7	8.7	8.4
Measured proportionate ground loss per cent	1.1	2.9	0.6	1.3	1.4	1.4
Measured surface settlement over tunnel centreline, S_{max} mm	3.6 to 5.7 (4.1 avg.)	5.6	4	7	5	6.2

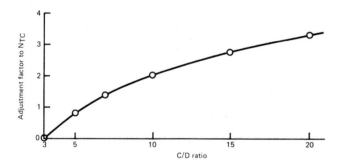

Fig. 6 Adjustment factor to stability numbers at C/D = 3 given in Fig. 4 for increased C/D ratios

It is not immediately obvious what value of bulk undrained shear strength, Cu, should be adopted in the calculation of N.   After some trial calculations it was decided to obtain the load factors, N/N_{tc} given in Table 2 using values of N based on using either (i) the bulk Cu value at the level of the highest point of the tunnel excavation: this value is considered to be the average value of mass shear strength over a zone extending one tunnel diameter above and below the tunnel crown or (ii) the average bulk Cu value over the depth between the ground surface and the axis of the tunnel excavation. The values of bulk undrained shear strength in cases (i) and (ii) respectively, would be appropriate for failure/deformation mechanisms around a tunnel which are similar to those postulated by Broms and Bennermark[14]; these are

shown in Fig. 7 for openings in vertical walls (i) at depths to the axis of the opening greater than four diameters and (ii) for openings nearer the ground surface respectively
    Having determined load factors for both shear strength conditions at each of the six locations values of ground loss, vℓ, were then read for each load factor from Fig. 5.   The upper curve for a C/D ratio of approximately 1.5 was used for the shallower location at Sutton, an interpolated value for the second location at Sutton and the lower curve C/D = 3 approx) on Fig. 5 was used for the tunnels at the other four locations.

COMPARISON OF ACTUAL AND PREDICTED SETTLEMENTS
The actual and predicted ground losses for the situations considered are shown at the foot of Table 2.   Use of the average bulk Cu value over the depth to the tunnel axis - case (ii) above - gives good agreement for the shallower section of tunnel at Sutton and fair agreement for the deeper one, but overestimates by a factor of between two and three, the ground losses over the tunnels at the remaining four locations.   On the other hand the use of the bulk shear strength at the top of the tunnel excavation gives reasonable agreement for the shallower tunnel at Sutton, but underestimates by a factor of over three the ground loss at

235

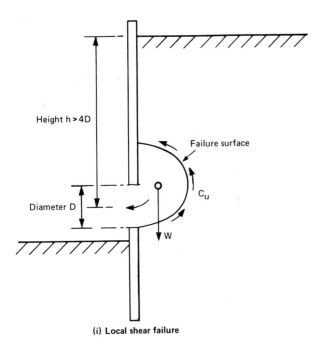

(i) Local shear failure

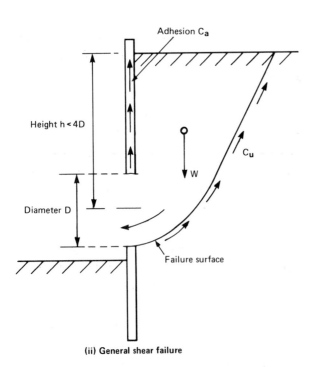

(ii) General shear failure

Fig. 7 Failure mechanisms for a hole in a vertical wall
(Broms and Bennermark 1967)

ters to the axis of the opening postulated theoretically by Broms and Bennermark[14] for a hole in a vertical wall.

The possibility of lower than average bulk shear strength of the London Clay providing an alternative explanation of the ground losses at Sutton was considered and eliminated. The shear strength data obtained from unconfined compression tests on forty 38 mm diameter specimens obtained from two boreholes are shown in Fig. 8 together with the results of similar tests on twelve specimens obtained by hammering U38 tubes horizontally into the tunnel face: also shown is the relation between bulk shear strength and depth taken from Fig. 1. Of the 52 results only five lie below the bulk strength/depth relations. According to Skempton and

the deeper tunnel there. Thus to obtain the best agreement with actual ground losses involves the postulation of different deformation and failure modes for tunnels shallower than and deeper than a C/D ratio lying somewhere between the deeper C/D ratio of 2.7 at Sutton and the value of 2.9 at King's Cross. This compares with a C/D of 3.5 ie four diame-

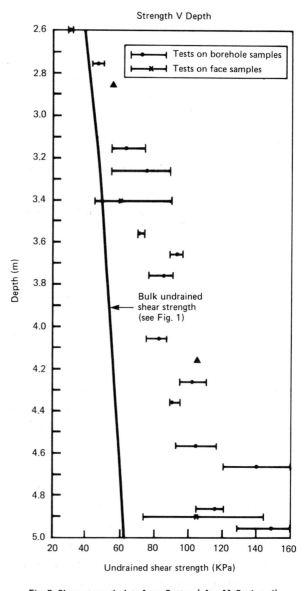

Fig. 8 Shear strength data from Sutton (after McCaul et al)

236

TABLE 2. Actual and predicted ground losses

Location	Sutton				King's Cross		Regent's Park				Green Park	
	Location 5		Location 7				High Tunnel		Low Tunnel			
Mass shear strength from Fig. 1												
At ground surface kN/m²	←				20.1							→
At tunnel excav. crown kN/m²	40.7		52.7		99.6		126.9		173.4		160.5	
At tunnel axis kN/m²	47.9		55.1		111.1		136.5		180.7		167.6	
	(i)*	(ii)*	(i)	(ii)	(i)	(ii)	(i)	(ii)	(i)	(ii)	(i)	(ii)
Relevant Cu value kN/m²	40.7	34.0	52.7	37.6	99.6	65.6	126.9	78.3	173.4	100.4	160.5	93.9
$N = \gamma Z$ /Relevant Cu	1.6	2.0	1.8	2.6	2.8	4.2	3.1	5.0	3.8	6.6	3.6	6.1
Load factor N/N_{tc}	0.26	0.32	0.37	0.53	0.33	0.49	0.40	0.65	0.44	0.76	0.43	0.73
Predicted ground loss from Fig.5	+ 0.9	+ 1.2	x 0.9	x 2.0	o 0.6	o 1.5	o 0.9	o 3.0	o 1.1	o 4.6	o 1.1	o 4.2/6.9
Actual relative ground loss per cent	1.1		2.9		0.6		1.3		1.4		1.4 /8.7	
Difference: Actual minus predicted relative ground loss per cent	0.2	-0.1	2.0	0.9	0	-0.9	0.4	-1.7	0.3	-3.2	0.3	-2.8

*See page 4 for definition

\+ Value for C/D = 1.5 Curve from Fig. 5

x Interpolated value for C/D = 2.7 from Fig. 5

o Value for C/D = 3.0 Curve from Fig. 5

Henkel[6] unconfined compression tests tend to give values of measured strength about 20 per cent too low and if the low results are increased by this amount they would all lie above the shear strength/depth relation.

Once it is accepted that there are two modes of deformation/failure above tunnels the agreement between measured and predicted ground losses in Table 2 is very good. At Sutton. where the two sections of tunnel were shallow, the best agreement is obtained using the average bulk shear strength between tunnel axis and the ground surface; at the other locations, where the sections of tunnel were deeper, the best agreement is obtained using the bulk shear strength at the top of the tunnel excavation. The indications from the present analysis are that the change-over depth for ground deformation behaviour above a tunnel heading occurs at a C/D ratio of about 2.8.

Having established a method of predicting values of relative ground loss with reasonable accuracy, estimates of settlements can be made using the value of i, the distance from the tunnel centre line to the point of inflection in the settlement trough, determined by O'Reilly and New[2] for cohesive soils. They found values of i in metres could be successfully calculated from the relation:

$$i = 0.43 Z + 1.1 \quad \ldots \quad \ldots \quad \ldots \quad \ldots \quad (5)$$

where Z is the depth to tunnel axis in metres

Using the relevant values of relative ground loss predicted in Table 2, together with calculated values of i obtained from equation (5), predicted settlements have been obtained using equation (2). These are compared to the measured settlements at each location in Table 3. The agreement between measured and predicted settlements is good, with a maximum difference of 2 mm.

Although these are data only from six situations it is worthwhile mentioning the range of values covered; depth to tunnel axis varied from 3.4 to 34 m, excavated tunnel diameter varied from 1.52 to 4.15 m, the length of unsupported heading behind the tunnel face varied from 0.7 to 5 m so that the range of C/D and P/D ratios covered are 1.4 to 7.7 and 0.17 to 3.3 respectively. The actual ground losses are equal to or greater than the predicted values at five of the six locations studied, similarly, four of the six values of actual settlement exceed the predicted values. This is as would be expected since it can be argued that the ground loss values determined in centrifuge model tests should represent the minimum

TABLE 3. Actual and predicted maximum settlements at the ground surface

Location	Sutton		King's Cross	Regent's Park		Green Park
	Location 5	Location 7		High Tunnel	Low Tunnel	
Relevant predicted ground loss loss from Table 2 per cent	1.2	2.0	0.6	0.9	1.1	1.1
Calculated i(m) using equation 5	2.6	3.2	7.1	9.7	15.7	13.7
Predicted surface settlement above tunnel centreline using equation 2 (mm)	4.6	4.5	4.5	5.0	3.8	4.3/26.7
Actual surface settlement above tunnel centreline (mm)	3.6 to 5.7 (avg. 4.1)	5.6	4	7	5	6.2/31.9
Difference: Actual minus predicted surface settlement above tunnel centreline (mm)	-1.0 to +1.1 (avg. -0.5)	1.1	-0.5	2.0	1.2	1.9

values and do not include any allowance for imperfections, inherent or otherwise, in the construction process. Only at King's Cross and the shallower tunnel at Sutton are the predicted values of ground loss equal to or greater than the actual values. Predicted settlement at King's Cross exceeds the actual value while at the shallower tunnel at Sutton where the settlements measured at seven closely spaced points along the tunnel centreline varied between 3.6 and 5.7 mm the prediction lay neatly in the middle of the measured results. Overall, the predicted values of relative ground loss are 21 per cent lower than the measured values and predicted settlements are 16 per cent lower. Indeed the agreement may well be better than this given the measurements at Sutton[20] and earlier at Warrington in cohesionless soils[28] which showed that the magnitude of settlement of the ground surface along the tunnel centreline can vary quite appreciably over short distances without any apparent change in ground conditions.

CONCLUSIONS
Given the good agreement between measured and predicted values at the six situations considered, it is clear that the method put forward in this paper provides a good means of predicting ground losses and the magnitude and extent of settlements caused by tunnelling through London Clay; the method may well prove to be applicable to other soil conditions. The greatest uncertainty was in characterising the strength of a mass of London Clay. Luckily this material is relatively uniform over large areas and it was found that the bulk shear strength/depth relation in Fig. 1 which is defined by the lower bound results obtained in triaxial tests on 38 mm diameter specimens obtained from boreholes gave good results. This argument is of course circular and it could equally well be contended that the construction of a tunnel is just another large scale deformation test involving very large volumes of ground which has provided a relation between shear strength and depth very similar to that derived from large plate-bearing tests and back analysis of a massive slope failure in the field[7,8,9,10,11,13].

Be that as it may the method adopted to characterise the bulk undrained shear strength of London Clay and to recognise the role of fissuring were straightforward and rational. Indeed the distinction between intact and bulk or mass strength is well established in rock mechanics where the difference can be tenfold or more[27,28] although it has not been recognised to anything like the same extent in soil mechanics.

The above approach also helps to reconcile the divergent views expressed on the questions of stability numbers and settlements. For tunnelling in London Clay Ward[29] has suggested that to limit ground movements the stability number needs to be restricted to 1 or 2 rather than the values of 5 or 6 suggested by Peck[1] and Broms and Bennermark[14]. If, however, the stability number is assessed using the bulk shear strength of London Clay, rather than the strength obtained on small, 38 mm diameter, borehole samples, the limiting values suggested by Ward would be doubled to 2 to 4.

The empirical relations between $C/_D$, $P/_D$ and N_{tc} in Figs 3 and 4 were obtained from two- and three-dimensional model tests in the centrifuge and would, therefore, be expected to be representative of conditions around real tunnels only if there were no imperfections in the tunnelling process. The data, however, are limited to a maximum C/D ratio of 3.5 and while a constant shear strength distribution with depth could have advantages experimentally, it is not clear how a more realistic strength gradient increasing with depth would affect the results. On the other hand the relations between relative ground loss and load factor in Fig. 5 were obtained from two-dimensional model tunnels although they have in this paper been applied in essentially three-dimensional situations. That they have worked is indeed somewhat surprising but then Atkinson and Potts[30] in their investigations on model tunnels in cohesionless soil found that their upper and lower bound calculations seemed applicable to both three-dimensional and plane strain situations. Further centrifuge testing of model tunnels to extend the relations in Figs 3 and 4 to higher C/D ratios and to explore more fully the relations between relative ground loss and load factor in three-dimensional situations would certainly appear to be well worthwhile.

Lastly, it must be emphasised that the settlements considered here occur immediately the tunnel is driven and in the weeks immediately following that event. Long-term settlement due to consolidation of the ground surrounding the tunnel can also occur and can be particularly severe in normally or near normally consolidated soils[5,31]. Although long term distortions due to consolidation resulting from tunnel construction are likely to have occurred in London Clay their magnitude would be expected to have been low and to have been of much less significance than settlement occurring immediately after the tunnel was driven.

ACKNOWLEDGEMENT

The work described in this paper forms part of the programme of the Transport and Road Research Laboratory and this paper is published by permission of the Director. Any views expressed in this paper are not necessarily those of the Department of Transport. Extracts from the text may be reproduced, except for commerical purposes provided the source is acknowledged.
Crown Copyright.

References

1. Peck R.B. Deep excavations and tunnelling in soft ground. Proceedings of the Seventh International Conference on Soil Mechanics and Foundation Engineering, Mexico, 1969, State of the art volume, (Sociedad Mexicana de Mecanica de Suelos), p 225-290.

2. O'Reilly M.P. and New B.M. Settlements above tunnels in the United Kingdom - their magnitude and prediction. Proceedings Tunnelling '82 Symposium (London Institution of Mining and Metallurgy 1982), p 173-181.

3. Cater R.W and Shirlaw J.N. Settlements due to tunnelling in Hong Kong. Tunnels and Tunnelling, 17 (10) 1985, p 25-28.

4. Attewell P.B., Yeates J. and Selby A.R. Soil movements induced by tunnelling and their effects on pipelines and structures (Blackie, London 1986).

5. Skempton A.W. Cast in-situ bored piles in London Clay. Geotechnique, 9(4), 1959, p 153-173.

6. Skempton A.W. and Henkel D.J. Tests on London Clay from deep borings at Paddington, Victoria and the South Bank. Proceedings of the fourth International Conference on Soil Mechanics and Foundation Engineering, London, England, Vol. 1, 1957, p 100-106.

7. Ward W.H., Marsland A. and Samuels S.G. Properties of the London Clay at the Ashford Common shaft: in-situ and undrained strength tests. Geotechnique, 15(4) 1965, p 321-344.

8. Burland J.B., Butler F.G. and Dunican P. The behaviour and design of large diameter bored piles in stiff clay. Proceedings of Symposium on Large Bored Piles, Institution of Civil Engineers, London, 1966, p 51-69.

9. Hooper J.A. and Butler F.G. Some numerical results concerning the shear strength of London Clay. Geotechnique, 16 (4), 1966, p 282-304.

10. Marsland A. Large in-situ tests to measure the properties of stiff fissured clays. Building Research Establishment Current Paper CP 1/73, 1973.

11. Marsland A. In-situ plate tests in lined and unlined boreholes in highly fissured London Clay. Building Research Establishment Current Paper CP 5/73, 1973.

12. Marsland A. The shear strength of stiff fissured clays. In stress-strain behaviour of soils, Proceedings of the Roscoe Memorial Symposium, Cambridge University, March 1971, p 59-68. Edited by Parry R.H.G. (Foulis and Company Limited, Oxford, 1972).

13. Skempton A.W. and La Rochelle P. The Bradwell slip: a short-term failure in London Clay. Geotechnique, 15(3), 1965, p 221-242.

14. Broms B.B. and Bennermark H. Stability of clay at vertical openings. Journal of the Soil Mechanics and Foundations Division, American Society of Civil Engineers. 93, SMI, 1967, p 71-94.

15. O'Reilly M.P. Murray R.T. and Symons I.F. Centrifuge modelling in the TRRL research programme on ground engineering. Proceedings on the application of centrifuge modelling to geotechnical design symposium, Manchester, April 1984, (Balkema, Rotterdam, 1985) p 423-435

16. Mair R.J. Centrifugal modelling of tunnel construction in soft clay. Ph.D. thesis, Cambridge University 1979.

17. Kimura T. and Mair R.J. Centrifugal testing of model tunnels in soft clay. Proceedings of the tenth International Conference on Soil Mechanics and Foundation Engineering, Stockholm (Rotterdam: Balkema), Volume 1,1981 p 319-322.

18. Seneviratne H.N. Deformations and pore-pressure dissipation around shallow tunnels in soft clay. Ph.D. thesis, Cambridge University 1979.

19. Mair R.J. Gunn M.J. and O'Reilly M.P. Ground Movements around shallow tunnels in soft clay. Proceedings of the tenth International Conference on Soil Mechanics and Foundation Engineering, Stockholm, (Rotterdam: Balkema), Volume 1, 1981, p 323-328.

20. McCaul C. O'Reilly M.P. and Crabb G.I. Settlements over a small diameter tunnel driven by hand and machine in London Clay. Municipal Engineer, Volume 3, 1986, December, p 311-322.

21. West G. Heath W.G. and McCaul C. Measurement of the effects of tunnelling at York Way, London. Ground Engineering, 14 (5) 1981, p 45-53.

22. Barratt D.A. and Tyler R.G. Measurements of ground movements and lining behaviour on the London Underground at Regents Park. Transport and Road Research Laboratory Report LR 684 1975.

23. Attewell P.B. and Farmer I.W. Ground settlement above shield driven tunnels in clay. Tunnels and Tunnelling 7 (1) 1975 p 58-62.

24. Clark J.A.M. Aspects of mechanical shield tunnelling and comparison with hand shield tunnelling. Proceedings Institution of Civil Engineers. Paper 7270S The Victoria Line, Supplementary Volume 1969.

25. Davis E.H. Gunn M.J. Mair R.J. and Seneviratne H.N. The stability of shallow tunnels and underground openings in coehsive material. Geotechnique, 30 (4) 1980 p 397-416.

26. O'Reilly M.P. Ryley M.D. Barratt D.A. and Johnson P.E. Comparison of settlements resulting from three methods of tunnelling in loose cohesionless soil. In Ground Movement and Structures: Proceedings of the second international conference, Cardiff, 1980 Geddes J.D. ed editor (London: Pentech Press 1981) p 359-376.

27. Hobbs N.B. Factors affecting the prediction of settlement of structures on rock: with particular reference to the Chalk and Trias. In Settlement of Structures: conference organsied by the British Geotechnical Society, Cambridge, (London: Pentech Press, 1975) p 579-596.

28. Brady B.H.G. and Brown E.T. Rock Mechanics for Underground Mining, p 527. George Allen and Unwin, London 1985.

29. Ward W.H. Discussion Fourth Main Session
Proceedings seventh international conference
on Soil Mechanics and Foundation Engineering,
Mexico, Volume 3, 1969, p 320-325.
30. Atkinson J.H. and Potts D.M. Stability
of a shallow circular tunnel in cohesionless
soil. Geotechnique, 27(2), 1977, p 203-215.
31. Glossop N.H. and O'Reilly M.P. Settlement caused by tunnelling through soft marine
clay. Tunnels and Tunnelling (9) October
1982 p 13-16

A1 (M) Hatfield tunnel

M. J. Palmer C.Eng., M.I.Struct.E., M.I.H.T.
Hertfordshire County Council, Hatfield, Hertfordshire, United Kingdom
J. F. L. Lowndes T.D., C.Eng., B.Sc.(Eng.), F.I.Mech.E., F.C.I.B.S.E., F.H.K.I.E.
Mott, Hay & Anderson, Croydon, Surrey, United Kingdom

SYNOPSIS

The paper traces the origins of the Hatfield
Tunnel. It describes the reasons for its
adoption and examines the alternative solutions
considered for its construction.
The geological characteristics of the ground
are described and the problems resulting
from the legacy left from the ice age are
outlined together with the methods employed to
overcome these difficulties. Particular
reference is made to the need to permanently
dewater the site.
The unique concept to use the completed tunnel
structure as the basis for a major urban
re-development programme are described.
The very special problems associated with
building the U.K's longest motorway tunnel
beside and on the alignment of one of Europe's
busiest roads are outlined.
The complex electrical and mechanical services
necessitated by the Department of Transport's
requirement for a fully automated control system
for this unmanned tunnel are described.
Particular reference is made to the lighting,
ventilation and power distribution systems
together with traffic monitoring, CCTV,
emergency telephone and fire fighting systems.
Finally, the authors draw conclusions regarding
possible lessons to be learnt from the project.

Historical Background

Motorway traffic speeds through Hatfield today
with drivers probably unaware that above and
around them the town can now go about its daily
business with comparative ease.

Aerial View of A1(M) Hatfield Tunnel
Looking North

This was not always the case and until the last
length of A1 through Hertfordshire was finally
improved to motorway standard and opened to
traffic on 10 December 1986 travellers journey-
ing on this important north-south route could
expect to meet frequent and long delays.
The situation for local residents was little
better with their day to day routes constantly
choked with traffic and their general environment polluted with noise and fumes. The area
was generally becoming run down with little or
no chance of attracting the urban renewal so
urgently needed. It was with this background
that efforts were made in the early seventies
to devise a solution which would under one
overall comprehensive scheme resolve the con-
flict between traffic and environment in a
positive and creative manner.

243

The problem facing the design teams had its
origins in the 1920 – 30's, a period marked by
uncontrolled development.

With more and more cars coming into general use
a new road was created, the A555 Barnet By Pass
along a line which was later to be destined as
the A1. Development soon followed the new road
and by the early 1930's a new airfield had been
developed adjacent and to the west of the road,
whilst to the east Hatfield developed in a
jumble of industrial estates, petrol stations,
hotels, shops and housing including blocks of
flats.

It was not until 1954 that a conscious effort
was made to divert traffic out of Hatfield old
town and the Barnet By Pass was re-classified
as A1. By this time, however, conditions on A1
were becoming unacceptable and in 1959 a decision
was taken to improve the twelve miles of A1
between "The Block" at Welwyn and South Mimms.
Various routes, some diverting radically to the
east and west of the existing route were studied
together with alternatives designed to improve
the existing road. These studies culminated in
1962 with a decision by the Minister of Transport
that the improvements of A1 should be undertaken
as a series of on-line improvements designed
such that they could ultimately be converted
into a continuous motorway, a decision which has
been reconsidered and reaffirmed at various times
since the original decision. The mid-sixties saw
the completion of on-line schemes both to the
north and south of Hatfield leaving only the
section through Hatfield itself to be resolved.

The chosen option

Publication in 1972 of the Urban Motorways
Committee report on "New Road in Towns" led to
review of the scheme with the result that three
on-line and two westerly off-line by pass
alternatives were identified. This period
coincided with the introduction of public
participation in the preparation of trunk road
schemes and public opinion on the alternatives
proposed was sought in 1974.

Topographically the area is reasonably level
therefore gradient was to present no difficulty.
Horizontal alignment for the off-line solutions
would require a massive westerly loop to take
the route around the existing airfield, by now
the major employment centre in the area, before
re-joining the previously improved lengths of A1.
These westerly routes were extremely wasteful of
good agricultural land and were environmentally
intrusive. The most attractive alignment from
the highway point of view was clearly on-line.
Environmentally however, the route was potentially disastrous with up to 22 commercial
premises and 200 dwelling units needing to be
demolished and existing property both residential and commercial being exposed to
environmental pollution on a vast scale.
A surface route providing for six lanes of
new motorway plus four lanes of local road
occupying the existing route together with
whole-scale demolition to the east were
dismissed immediately on environmental
grounds. Alternatives which provided a
degree of screening for the neighbouring
properties not directly affected by the
proposal were then considered. However,
the most practical solution whereby the
new motorway was hidden by artificial
mounding would need further land acquisition and was therefore even more
damaging. Thus the only alternative was
to hide the route in a retained cutting.
This would increase construction costs but
would be less land hungry.
The problem of the local road still remained
and the retained cut solution was not
environmentally attractive. The need to
cater for the local road led to consideration being given to a double deck system
but this, whilst providing the required
road capacity at minimum land-take, showed
no advantage over construction costs and
would be difficult to construct. It was
realized therefore, that if a broader view
were taken there was a unique opportunity to
overcome the conflicting demands of highway,
environment and local needs under one comprehensive plan. This led to the section
passing nearest the town being placed in
tunnel with the existing road staying to
form the local road after opening the main
scheme. Thus it was possible to create a
redevelopment area of 25 acres (10 hectares)

of land on the western side of Hatfield within half mile of the existing town centre.

Traffic

At the feasibility stage the route covered by the scheme was already showing signs of severe congestion with inevitable delays occurring particularly at peak hours. In addition to the north-south movement along A1 the route also forms an important junction with the east-west A414 route connecting east coast areas with the motorway network and western routes. The A414 also shares a common line with A1 through the main corridor passing in front of the British Aerospace factories.

From studies of traffic patterns taken during the early 70s it was predicted that by the year 2001 with and without the scheme the heaviest loaded section of the route would have 53,000 vehicles per day and 69,000 vehicles per day respectively. The actual traffic flows in 1980 were found to be around 57,000 per day of which 18% were heavy vehicles. A feature of the scheme was an undertaking that traffic would not be subjected to additional delays as a result of the roadworks, therefore much thought was put into the design to ensure that the project was constructionally feasible. The primary diversions necessary were included within the design as the suggested means of carrying out the works.

General conditions

The geological structure of the area shows the underlying rock to be chalk. This is found approximately 20 metres below existing ground level with the upper layers of chalk being soft and weathered before the harder more blocky chalk is encountered.

Early glacial action covered the chalk with a thin layer of gravels before capping the area with a thick layer of impervious boulder clay. It is the presence of this clay which is responsible for the most significant problem to be overcome, that of water.

Trapped within the chalk is significant quantities of water forming part of the London artesian basin whilst above, the clay has provided a natural basin for the collection of ground water draining from the surrounding

area. Later glacial action filled in this upper basin with mixed gravel silts and alluvium up to 15m thick. The permeable nature of this material has maintained the ponding effect such that a perched water table has been formed approximately 6 metres below existing ground level and more significantly 2 metres above the proposed tunnel section road surface.

Ground Water

The problem created by the perched water table could have been resolved by constructing the tunnel and approaches within a watertight box suitably designed to resist uplift. Although technically feasible such a solution would be prohibitively expensive. Borehole and pumping tests showed the upper glacial gravels to vary considerably and permeability coefficients ranging from 3×10^{-3} to 7×10^{-5} metres/sec were encountered. During the feasibility study stage alternative methods of dealing with water were investigated and consideration given to use of a vertical system draining the upper water through the boulder clay and into the lower glacial gravels and chalk. Site trials based on such a system using both lined and unlined bores were carried out. However, the trials revealed unexpected problems mainly relating to air entrapment in the fill and movement of fines from the upper gravels into the gravel column comprising the borehole fill which drastically restricted the drainage effect. The use of steel liners did not solve these problems and further problems related to collapse or unjointing of the perforated lining tubes during the pull back of the temporary outer steel lining tubes occurred. It was found that hydrogeological conditions could produce high pressure on the borehole lining tubes immediately above and below the boulder clay and although high specification liner tubes could in part overcome these problems there remained reservations regarding longer term maintenance liabilities if such a solution were to be adopted. This together with a risk that chemical and bacteriological encrustation could occur due to the differing chemical composition of the two water tables, lead eventually to the

adoption of a french drain system to deal with
the permanent lowering of ground water.
The system adopted consists of a grid of filter
drains formed by two longitudinal drains approximately 3.5m below finished carriageway level
with cross drains at 30m intervals. The choice
of filter medium is carefully selected to be
compatible with adjacent soil characteristics
in order that silt migration is avoided and
the status quo maintained. Water intercepted
by filter dains discharges to a pump chamber
behind the east abutment of the tunnel at
the southern substation. Water is then pumped
to high level and falls to a separate sump
located at Roehyde from where it is discharged
via pumps to a balancing pond of 1200 cu metres
capacity and thence into a local brook,
Ellenbrook. The discharge is limited to a
maximum rate of 75 litres/sec to avoid scour
and inundation of the existing water courses.
Surface water is catered for by a separate
positive drainage system which in the tunnel
and to the south also discharges via a common
route using the sumps described previously.
Water from the northern approach to the
tunnel is collected via a further sump
located adjacent to the northern portal of
the tunnel. The water is discharged via
pumps to a gravity pipe system which trans-
ports the discharge 1,600 metres to an outfall in the River Lee. The outfall is
controlled by reducing pipe diameter to 375mm
at the outfall which will cause surcharging of
the drainage system upstream under pump
operating conditions. The flow in these
circumstances is balanced by the provision
of storage within the system itself achieved by
adopting a piggy back twin 750mm diameter pipe
system between the pumping sump and the outfall.
The drainage design makes provision for preventing pollution of water courses by oil or other
chemicals which may be spilt on the highway.
Within the tunnel a valve operated separated
chamber can be brought into action to intercept contaminated surface water before it
reaches the discharge pumps. This water can
then be disposed to the foul sewer if appropriate or held within the chamber to be
removed by tanker if the pollutant is of a

nature requiring special disposal. The main
outfall points at Ellenbrook and River Lee
are protected by oil traps and penstocks.

Hatfield Tunnel design options

The tunnel provides unrestricted access to all
categories of authorised motorway traffic and
at 1,150m in length it is the longest of its
kind in Europe. It was to be built on or was
alongside one of the busiest traffic routes.
Whilst much of the tunnel was situated to the
east of the existing route it was impossible
to avoid crossing the A1 at the northern
extremity of the tunnel. If traffic chaos
were to be avoided the method of dealing with
this crossing of the existing A1 was crucial
to the viability of the scheme. This factor,
together with the need to afford the Electrical
and Mechanical Contractor controlled access to
the works associated with the tunnel demanded
that the construction of the tunnel structure
be split into predetermined phases. An optimum
of three main sections were identified.
Section 1 would require the construction of
all the tunnel structure from the southern
portal to a point near St Albans Road West,
approximately 242 metres. The northernmost
lengths of this section needed an early
completion in order to allow the lengthy
operation of diverting statutory undertaker's
services out of the existing St Albans Road
and over the tunnel lid.
Completion of these diversions were vital before
continuing the tunnel northwards. A timescale of
52 weeks from start of contract was decided upon
in order that the electrical contractor could
have sufficient structure available to commence
installation. Coincident with this section,
Section 2 of the tunnel was designed to commence
from the northern portal and extend southwards
approximately 472 metres. Built into this
section was a requirement to construct a section
of tunnel in isolation to enable the diversion
of southbound A1 to take place so releasing the
section of new tunnel located underneath the
existing trunk road. A time scale of 66
weeks was allowed for this section. The final
section Section 3, then comprised the remaining
centre portion of the tunnel and was programmed
to be complete 84 weeks from the start of the

contract. In each case the M & E contractor would follow the Civils Contractor at each sectional completion and receive occupation for a given period before handing each section back to the Civils Contractor to enable final motorway finishing to be completed.

Various forms of tunnel construction were considered all based on a common cut and cover approach. In total four wall options were considered these being:

a) Insitu reinforced concrete inner and outer walls forming a portal frame with an insitu roof connecting the three walls.

b) Insitu reinforced concrete free standing inner and outer walls supporting an insitu roof simply supported on bearings.

c) Diaphragm outer walls with a central wall made up of bored piles 3.0m apart.

d) Sheet pile outer walls with a bored pile central wall.

For the insitu portal solution the bulk earthworks would be carried out in the conventional manner whereas with the other alternatives the excavation could be carried out after the tunnel roof had been constructed, albeit at a higher excavation cost.

The solution for dealing with the roof construction similarly offered alternatives as follows:

a) Insitu reinforced concrete cast monolithically with the insitu walls.

b) Insitu reinforced concrete but supported on bearings.

c) Precast concrete 'M' beams with a composite concrete top slab set on bearings placed on a capping beam running the length of the diaphragm or sheet piled walls.

The favoured solution was the insitu reinforced concrete portal.

In addition to cost this option offered a number of distinct advantages particularly in view of the ultimate aim to redevelop over the tunnel lid. The need for expensive cladding which in turn would give rise to future maintenance problems was avoided and the cast finish would represent the finished product. The difficulties of producing a satisfactory junction between the roof slab and the walls incorporating bearings and sophisticated

bearing shelf drainage did not apply in this case. Whilst in the longer term the use of beams for the roof would have inevitably led to leakage problems and presented difficulties when it came to the replacement of bearings. The solid roof was also less susceptible to the transmission of traffic vibrations into any buildings placed above, and would be more resilient to fire damage resulting from an incident within the tunnel itself. The ease in which the insitu option would be adaptable for ducting to take the mechanical and electrical services and the lack of specialist techniques needed for the construction process all added to the advantages whilst finally the performance of the structure could be more confidently predicted which would be important in satisfying future development clients.

The Revelopment Package

The early initiatives lay with the Hertfordshire County Council who as Agent Authority for the Highway scheme, were keen to produce a scheme which would enhance the environment whilst satisfying the Highway objectives and those of the District Council who recognised the urgent need to revitalize the infrastructure of the area but who could not hope to mobilize the enormous financial resources which would be necessary to embark on wholescale demolition and dispossession of existing businesses which was so obviously needed. Close working relationships were established between the two Authorities and in turn with the Department of Transport who needed to be convinced that the large investment was worthwhile. The District Council gave full vent to their imaginative ideas for the future shape of Hatfield and were given the opportunity to take part in the statutory consultation process being undertaken for the Highway scheme.

Following a joint Public Inquiry the Secretaries of State for the Environment and Transport decided to proceed with the project. The shape of the site being long and thin gave the District Council a number of difficulties but at the southern end of the site there was a considerable wedge of

adjacent land either side of the highway
which could be usefully developed.
However, this section of road was to be in
open cut and lidding this section could not
be justified on engineering or environmental
grounds. The County and District Councils,
keen to see the full potential realized for
the site expressed their full commitment to
the project by contributing, together with
the Department of Transport, one third of the
cost each of increasing the length of the
tunnel by 190m to include this southern
portion. The need for the Department of
Transport to have access to the tunnel roof
at all times for future maintenance also
presented the redevelopment team problems and
threatened the viability of the project at one
stage. Any building situated directly on the
tunnel itself would be at risk from being pulled
down to give access to the tunnel lid and
insurance would be difficult if not impossible.
It was therefore accepted that the lid would
need to be accessible at all times, and the
redevelopers would need to devise a means of
overcoming this difficulty. The financial
burden was still too great for the District
Council to undertake alone and they sought a
development partner from the private sector.
This process proved fairly lengthy and it was
not until 12 June 1984 that the District
Council selected the Carroll Group of
Companies as their partner, some three
months after the start of the motorway
contract. Rather than allow the problems
of access to the tunnel lid to restrict the
scale of the development the Carroll Group
proposed a bold futuristic solution which
featured buildings spanning the tunnel lid
or for smaller buildings allocated the
ground floor for car parking. In this way
the tunnel lid would always have ready access
should the need arise.
The underlying theme for the redevelopment
is leisure with the focus of the development
being a 230,000 sq ft glass covered shopping
area situated over the southern section of the
tunnel containing a variety of leisure
orientated retail units. Included in this
mall will be an ice skating rink, restaurant,

Proposed Development
on the Tunnel Lid

exhibition and activity areas. Elsewhere on
the site will be a cinema complex, an hotel,
offices and residential housing. The scale
of the proposed development, although
receiving widespread public and political
support, caused concern to neighbouring
retailers and Councils who were also embark-
ing on new developments of their own. This
concern manifested itself into objection to
the detailed planning application and
resulted in a further Public Inquiry following
which the Secretary of State gave his condition-
al consent on 20 March 1986. The conditions
related to "Tenant mix Agreements" which were
made binding on the developers through landlord
control exercised by the District Council, and
this offered protection for both local
businesses and developments further afield.
The legal basis for the joint venture has
similarly proved complex. The essential
ingredient is an agreement for Welwyn
Hatfield District Council to purchase from
the Secretary of State surplus highway
acquired land clear of the tunnel and lease
land above the tunnel lid to enable the
redevelopment to proceed. The lease is
subject to restrictions namely on loading
and as previously described maintenance
access rights so protecting the integrity
of the tunnel structure. Engineering
aspects of the scheme have been dealt with
again under a process of joint venture with
all parties contributing to the final designs.

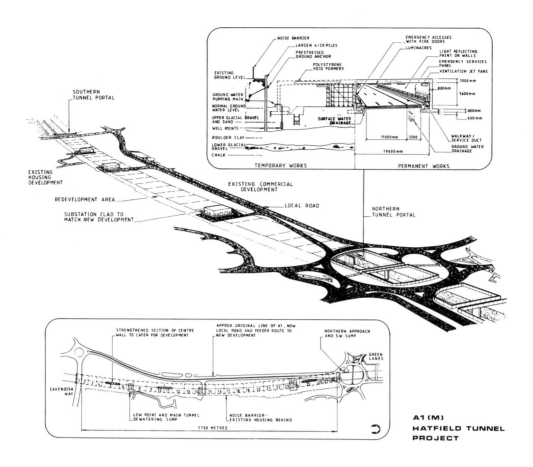

A1 (M)
HATFIELD TUNNEL
PROJECT

Tunnel construction

Undoubtedly the focus of attention on the
scheme was the construction of the tunnel,
but this was only part of the overall project
and in all 5 kilometres of new motorway together with 21 associated structures including
two major grade separated junctions also had
to be built. The construction programme for
the tunnel was therefore inextricably linked
to the remainder of the works notably by the
requirements to use excavated material from
the tunnel site in order to construct embankments required elsewhere, and the need to
develop and integrate traffic management
systems. The enormity of the traffic
management role can be judged by the fact
that during the course of construction
close on 60 major traffic diversions were
required in order to integrate the new
motorway in and around the travelling public.
This was all achieved without causing any worse
disruption than already existed. Before any
diversion phase could be implemented a complicated series of meetings involving designers,

contractor and police were necessary in order to
be convinced that the proposal would work, the
resulting chaos in the event of error would have
enormous practical and political repercussions.
To help keep local inhabitants informed of the
multitude of changes a high profile publicity
exercise was maintained from site with
regular information bulletins and public
relation features issued.

Clearly the constraints imposed by the close
proximity of the existing A1 on the west and
occupied residential property on the east of
the tunnel site were to influence greatly
both the design and programming of the tunnel
construction. Equally significant were the
problems presented by other key factors
occurring along the length of the tunnel.
Of these the presence of a redundant railway
bridge carrying a major local road serving
Hatfield laying across the line of the
southern portal, the presence of major
pedestrian routes severing the line of the
tunnel at St Albans Road West and near the
northern portal each leading directly from

the town into the British Aerospace (BAe)
factories brought the need for constantly
changing diversions and temporary works
with the resulting interruption of a
continuous construction cycle for the
tunnel.

Wherever possible demolition of existing
property and the diversion of Public
Utility Services was carried out prior
to the main Civil Engineering work but the
presence of services in routes crossing the
tunnel could not be dealt with until the
appropriate section of tunnel had been built.
The complexity of services in the vicinity of
St Albans Road West required particular
attention and if the overall programme was to
be met it was necessary to commence Section 1 of
the tunnel construction sequence at its northern
extremity such that bay 9 was required only 24
weeks after the start of the works in order to
give the Service Companies an opportunity to
complete their work. Simply finishing the
tunnel structure was not sufficient and to
overcome the problem of maintaining an
isolated section of backfill to carry the
service diversion up to the tunnel, a
geotextile reinforced earth wall was used
to minimize the effect on adjacent construction activities and also prevent
eccentric load patterns being imposed on the
tunnel walls.

Just north of this point a further service
crossing was removed prior to the main works
starting by driving a compressed air tunnel
through the waterlogged gravels below the
level of the new motorway tunnel in order to
relocate a trunk sewer.

Construction of Section 1, the southern
portion of Section 2 as far as bay 22 and
Section 3 could all proceed with minimal
effect on A1 traffic. However, the
remaining sections of the tunnel all lay
under the heavily trafficked A1 and extensive
traffic diversions were necessary. Con-
structional problems were further complicated
at this northern end of the tunnel by the
need to keep open pedestrian routes. Consequently before work on the tunnel could
commence new subways were needed across each

leg of the existing Green Lanes roundabout
which in the final layout would be maintained
broadly in its original form but with the
tunnel approaches passing through the area
occupied by the centre island. Precast
segmental construction was specified to ease
construction and for speed, with various
temporary routes established to maintain
serviceability of the roundabout before the
subways could be commissioned and the major
task of moving the traffic clear of the tunnel
site put in hand.

Northbound traffic using A1 was catered for by
simply shifting the existing route to the west
so that it was just clear of the tunnel
excavation. Southbound traffic, however,
needed a more drastic switch. In this
instance approx 400m of new carriageway was
constructed on the extreme eastern boundary of
the site before taking the new route across the
completed tunnel at bay 20-22 to rejoin the
existing line. It was then possible to close
the southern leg of the original roundabout at
Green Lanes at the point where it was to cross
bay 29 and re-create the junction at the tunnel
roof cross-over point. This changed the
existing circular roundabout into an elongated
roundabout up to 400m long and known on site
as the "longabout". It maintained all the
previous turning movements, albeit with a
slight lengthening of the distance to be
travelled. In practice this proved to allow
more ordered peak hour queuing capacity and
the junction performed well particularly in
respect of the need to keep good lines of
access in and out of the British Aerospace
factories.

The creation of a similar "longabout" was
to be used in a later phase for the
construction of the approach ramps when the
northern leg of the Green Lanes roundabout
was moved 400 metres north, making use of a
temporary route for northbound traffic down
onto the completed section of northbound
motorway.

The extraordinary measures necessary to
cater for the A1 traffic had not made any
allowance for the logistical problems which
still faced the Contractor if the project

250

were to be built within the specified time-scale. Unrestricted access into and out of the site from A1 was not permitted and all movements had to be via purpose made access points where all vehicles leaving the site could pass over wheel cleaners. Clearly good access was essential in ensuring all trades were adequately served if progress were to be maintained. Site movements were restricted to the narrow strips of undisturbed ground between the three parallel lines of tunnel foundation. This created conflicts in demands for space required by uninterrupted waggon access for excavation and concreting operations compared with the equally vital needs of the wall shuttering gangs for storage and large cranage.

Over approximately two thirds of the tunnel length it was impractical to batten back the excavation. Therefore temporary sheet piling comprising 14m long Larssen 420 and 4A sheets were chosen to support the sides of the excavation with a height of support varying from 7m - 10½m. The presence of the boulder clay presented practical difficulties in achieving a simple cantilever support and the sheets were propped by 16m long 60 T tensioned ground anchors spaced at 3m centres and drilled at 70° into the granular strata. Although the ground anchors were disposable the sheet piling and twin channel wallings were designed to be re-usable as work progressed. The close proximity of occupied property, residential property within 10 metres on the eastern boundary and the design offices of BAe within 25m to the west, required stringent noise control parameters and a 12 hour leq of 75 dBA with a peak of 85 dBA during normal working hours was specified, measured 1m from adjacent windows fronting the site. The specification also required the use of a recognised noise reduction system for all piling operations. The 'Hush' system was used for the majority of driving operations occasionally augmented by a Vibrodrive method. All subsequent withdrawals were made using a vibration method. Once the sheet piling had been installed it was possible to commence

bulk excavation.

Of the 900,000m³ of excavation required throughout the contract approx 410,000m³ including temporary working space was generated within the tunnel site. Bulk excavation was carried out exlusively using 360° hydraulic excavators and transported by road-going eight-wheel tipper trucks. These unmodified vehicles were capable of operating both on and off site due to the predominantly granular nature of the ground. The pre-dictions of material types to be encountered derived from the various pre-contract soil survey reports were largely upheld. Although there were some significant changes in quantity, predicted classifications of the various strata encountered held no unpleasant surprises and no major difficulties were experienced. Commercially useable gravels were predicted and approximately 130,000m³ was found on site. These were stockpiled and later blended with material imported from off-site and used for capping layer or granular fill to structures. Surplus and unsuitable material was con-veniently disposed of at a nearby refuse tip which was nearing the end of its life. The presence of the high water table necessitated the bulk excavation to be carried out in two stages with initial cut reducing the ground level to a point just below walling level. Early attempts by the Contractor to reduce the water in local areas by means of large diameter Armco pipes sunk vertically proved ineffective and this was followed by an attempt to install a continuous machine-laid mole drain along the line of the excavation. Again this system was unsuccessful with the laying machine finding it all but impossible to install an intact pipe. The system finally adopted was to install a system of disposable well points. The main system comprised two lines situated each side of the bulk excavation along the approx-imate centre line of the abutment bases. The wells were spaced at 1.5m centres and comprised 60mm diameter polythene tubes with coconut matting filter heads sunk vertically into the granular stratum to a depth of approx 6m.

Associated header pipe and dewatering pumps completed the installation. Drawn off water was pumped to a temporary outfall via a series of open ditches and temporary culverts. To reduce the noise nuisance to a minimum, 3" submersible electric pumps were used from an early stage. Dewatering was carried out progressively in stages to suit the sectional construction programme. As water was lowered in each area the permanent system would gradually take over with water temporarily outfalling to permanent manholes from where it was lifted into the temporary outfall header pipe and ditch system. In this manner the permanent system took over progressively from the disposable system such that by the time the main tunnel construction was under-way the excavation was being kept dry by the permanent design system for the area then under construction. This method proved highly successful.

The full scale of the redevelopment proposals and its implications for the design only became apparent after work for the motorway had already started on site. The original design had foreseen the possible need to cater for incidental concentrations of load and a system making use of a hardened section of centre wall was included in the original design. This was to prove useful in forming the basis for the provision of three such strengthened areas, one in each section of the tunnel so that the developers could realize the full potential offered by the site.

At the chosen points the centre wall was re-designed to act as a shear wall trans-ferring both the tunnel load and concen-trated loads from the future development to a pile cap containing 85 no 700mm diameter piles each capable of taking a load of 273 tonne. To cater for such loading levels it was necessary to design each pile to found in the stronger strata provided by the chalk. This required a design length of 19 metres and a need to deal with both the upper and lower water tables. To overcome these problems and the potential for bore collapse through the granular layers

all pipes were bored within a full depth pre-driven steel casing. The subsequent concreting operation was carried out using a traditional tremie-pipe.

The uncomplicated design concept for the main fabric of the tunnel favoured conventional shutters or a continuously moving simple shutter. The Contractor elected to opt for the former system. Each section of the tunnel was split into panels ranging from 1.5m to 8.6m in length with a constant height of 7.2m to make up the 21 metres nominal pour lengths chosen. The shutter comprised 19mm paper faced plywood with 225 x 75mm backing timbers supported by twin super slim soldiers at 1.5m centres and 25mm diameter ties at 2.8m vertical centres. The heavy robust shutters enabled the Contractor to achieve a high turn round rate and rapid concrete placement. Various open-ings, recesses and cabling trunk ways were detailed to be cast into the walls and special shutter unit plants were made to cater for these. Movement joints were formed every 42 metres.

The falsework to support the tunnel soffit was based on Cuplock system scaffolding which proved quick and easy to handle to meet the strict construction schedules. Primary and secondary bearers receiving the ply deck were unusually of aluminium beams, 5m access open-ings were provided through the falsework to serve as general site access and to facilitate the forward movement of stripped falsework materials for subsequent re-erection. The central 12m of each roof span was voided with 600mm diameter polystyrene voids at 814mm centres. Whereas the introduction of these voids provided valuable weight and cost economics on a structure of this size, their use was not without some difficulty. The buoyancy provided by the polystyrene imposed considerable uplift during concreting which was initially resisted by Cordeck straps and fixings. However, the uplift effect during concreting was still sufficient to induce unacceptable rippling within the ply sheet which was reflected in the finished surface of the early roof pours. To overcome this problem additional longer bolts and mini-timber soldiers were placed under the secondary support members to provide adequate load distribution.

The statistics associated with the tunnel structure give a good impression of the logistical problem which faced the Contractor. The volume of concrete required by the tunnel alone was 82,000 cu.m of 30/20 quality and this was placed in just 49 working weeks. The environmental constraints limiting noise levels prevented concreting operations proceeding through the night and to keep to programme complete bays were cast as single pours demanding outputs in the region of 120 cu.metre per hour. To achieve a reliable source of concrete supply an on site batching facility was installed capable of producing 80 cu.metres of concrete per hour. For large pours supplies were augmented by a local Readymix plant having a similar capability to the site facility. At the working face all concrete was pumped into position. In general deck pours were a two pump operation and in all 47 separate pours were needed ranging from 230 cu metres to 1520 cu.metres. Concrete production on site peaked at 2900 cu.metres in a single week. The enormous volumes of traffic this generated together with concurrent earthmoving operations all requiring access meant that mobility around the site was vital and the maintenance of adequate servicing facilities for the various trades was a delicate compromise. Initially the Contractor had considered using tower cranes and travelling gantries positioned clear of the main excavation but such ideas were dismissed as being inflexible and of limited capability. The close proximity of the BAe airfield with its operational height restrictions also effectively rules out this option. The Contractor relied, therefore, on large 110 tonne crawler mounted cranes equipped with 180ft jibs to provide the majority of on site lift capability. Access was eased as the roof construction got into full swing when it was possible to locate one crane astride the centre wall, positioned such that it could

lift over a complete deck section undergoing curing process to service the next adjacent bay. On completion of the outer carcass of the tunnel the outer faces of the structure were waterproofed using emulsion for the walls and Bituthene and Servideck for the roof before installing back-of-abutment drainage using Filtram, a geotextile drainage system, and finally backfilling with granular material. Inside, the Contractor was at this stage able to commence construction of the elevated walkways which were to serve as trunking for the electrical services and also as public access in the event of breakdown once the motorway was in service.

The completion of structural work was promptly followed by the carriageway gangs. The foundation of the new motorway were laid directly onto existing granular material without the need for capping layer and the fabric of the road was made up of 300mm of type 1 subbase, 125mm of HRA roadbase laid in a single layer followed by two layers of DBM upper roadbase to give a total thickness of 205mm before the final surfacing of 40mm HRA wearing course. This final layer was not laid until after the bulk of the electrical installation had been carried out to reduce the risk of damage to the completed motorway surface.

Monitoring Systems

As work progressed, in addition to the usual regime of material quality testing it was necessary to maintain more specialist checks unique to this project. Of particular interest were the effects of the dewatering. During the design stage, concern had been expressed from interested parties bordering the site as to the risk of settlement resulting from the dewatering. Consequently a series of piezometers were installed radiating from the site. These were monitored regularly both prior to and during construction so that an accurate draw down profile could be kept to compare with the design expectations. The results vindicated the original predictions and full draw down of 3.85m was achieved at the site of the tunnel with a draw down below original water level of 2.13 metres occurring adjacent

to the tunnel wall rapidly diminishing to
1.5m 50m from the tunnel, 0.5m 100 metres
from the tunnel and with no measurable
difference 1km from the tunnel.

The close proximity of the British Aerospace
factory gave rise to concerns expressed by
BAe regarding the effects on their sophisticated metal milling machines of movements
caused by pile driving, ground water lowering
or even excavation. Although accurate predictions at the design stage were difficult
it was anticipated that a maximum of 25mm
immediately adjacent to the tunnel could be
expected diminishing to zero 30m away. In
order to monitor the affects on the factory
a programme of precise levelling was devised
with the Building Research Station who would
independently assess the results and report
to interested parties. To date the movements
detected have been less than 1mm and it would
be reasonable to assume that the tunnel construction has had no affect on the machine
facilities at the factory.

Electrical and Mechanical Services

The establishment of two separate contracts
and the appointment of two Engineers for the
civil engineering and for the Services work
did, in spite of initial apprehensions, work
remarkably well. It allowed each Engineer
to have equal status over his own speciality
and removed layers of management, with their
latent inherent misunderstandings, which
would have existed had the Services work been
a sub-contract to the main Contractor.

The appointment of Mott, Hay and Anderson,
Electrical and Mechanical Division as the
E and M Consultant allowed the development
work and experience they had obtained on
two similar tunnels on the M25 to be incorporated in the Hatfield project.

The pre-selection, by competitive tender
and placing of contracts for specialised
E and M equipment - luminaires, fans and
computer systems before the appointment of
the Services contractor ensured that the
designer's requirements for these vital
components were fully understood and met
by the successful suppliers. This procedure also ensured that the competing

tenderers for the E and M Services contract
used the same price basis for these items.
Tender drawings and specifications issued
for the Services work outlined the scheme
in considerable detail. Quantities, locations,
ratings, method of installation of equipment,
circuiting, cable sizing and routing were
defined in the documents but the tenderers
were permitted their choice of suppliers for
all items except those pre-selected. The
Services contractor prepared working drawings
for the installation work based on his selection of equipment.

Lighting and Ventilation

The Electrical and Mechanical Services provided
were designed to allow the safe passage of
motorway traffic through the tunnel at the
maximum permitted speed of 70 mph. The
systems are fully automatic permitting
unmanned operation. Attention has been
given to the maintenance regime required in a
vehicular tunnel both in the quality of the
equipment installed (IP65 being the ingress
protection code generally used within the
tunnel) and also in the provisions made for
the lighting, ventilation and control systems
to cope with contraflow working required when
one bore is closed for maintenance.

The sidewalk ducts adjacent to the hard
shoulder in each bore are used for cable
routes and fire mains. Emergency distribution panels (E.D.P's) are sited above the duct
at approximately 40 metre intervals. The 60

E.D.P's house electrical distribution equipment for tunnel lighting and emergency telephone and fire fighting facilities. The central walkway duct (adjacent to the outer lane) is used to accommodate the electrical services and panels for the ventilation system. Lighting is a primary provision; the system is automatically switched in six stages using photometers to respond to the external luminance. There are 5220 luminaires in the tunnel, fluorescent lamps being used for the basic lighting through the tunnel supplemented by low pressure sodium lamps for stages 3 - 6 in the threshold and exit zones. The minimum lighting is at night when Stage 1 provides two continuous lines of fluorescent luminaires through the length of each bore using one lamp of each twin lamp luminaire. Stage 2 lighting (the minimum daylight condition) is achieved by using both tubes in the continuous row of fluorescent fittings. Stage 6 lighting, which is used with the brightest external conditions, utilizes nine rows of luminaires in the threshold zone (205 metres long six rows in the two transition zone (105 m each), four rows in the exit zone (65 metres long) and uses both lamps of the two rows of luminaires in the interior zone (665 metres long). The intermediate stages 2 - 5 use combinations of the luminaires provided. Every tenth luminaire in the two basic lines of lighting is fed through uninterrupted power supplies systems to provide 'emergency' lighting in the event of a total power failure. Each bore of the tunnel is longitudinally ventilated by 52 jet fans. The fans are fed in pairs from control panels mounted on the central walkway with one fan of each pair being over the central walkway and the second above the outside wall walkway. The fans are automatically controlled in each bore by three air-monitoring systems which assess the level of carbon monoxide in the air and check the visibility. The fans in each bore are switched in four groups to give zero, quarter, half, three quarter or full ventilation in response to the prevailing conditions. The fans are reversible for use in 'contra flow' traffic conditions. Each fan is rated at 20 kW and develops a

thrust of 600N.

The three sumps for ground and storm water each incorporate ultrasonic water level sensors to facilitate automatic working of the pumping system. Each sump is provided with an oil skimmer pump to remove floating hydrocarbons from the water surface. There are eleven main pump sets provided ranging from 22kW rating to 85kW rating. Fire fighting hose reels in the E.D.P's are fed from a fire main which has its own pumping system in the northern sub-station.

Automatic control facilities are provided by a computor based system comprising:

A dual computer based in-station in the mid-point sub-station.

Data out-stations in the four sub-stations.

Three air monitoring and visibility monitors in each bore.

Photometer out-station at the portals.

Terminals at mid-point sub-station, South Mimms depot and at the police HQ at Welwyn Garden City.

The system monitors pollution in the tunnel atmosphere, water levels in the sumps, portal and threshold luminance and the state of plant (fans, lighting equipment, pumps and switchgear) and automatically controls the facilities. If necessary lighting and ventilation may be controlled from the South Mimms Maintenance Depot.

The electrical load of the tunnel represents a connected load of 4 - 8 MW and a probable maximum demand of 3.25 MW. There are two 11kV intakes at the north and south sub-stations with the mid-point sub-station fed from each of the primary intakes. A fourth sub-station at Roehyde provides for the pumping load. Stand-by diesel engine alternators are installed in the northern sub-station and at Roehyde, each unit being rated at 750kVA, to assure the pumping systems and other essential services in the event of a total power failure from the public supply.

Lessons to be learnt

The Hatfield project offers a useful blueprint for the future but it should not be seen as a plea for tunnels in every town. It must be accepted that 'easy option' road improvements are now largely completed and if the demand for high quality roads is to be met without total disregard for the environment it is necessary to consider modern projects on a much broader basis. Hatfield has shown what can be achieved if a comprehensive concept is considered from the beginning rather than leave individual interests to pursue their own narrower goals.

Having the Statutory Authorities as the design leaders would appear to offer the best catalyst to enable a comprehensive scheme to be evolved but the comparative late involvement of the private sector developer has led to many difficult problems needing to be tackled late in the cycle. If the full potential offered by such schemes is to be fully realized it cannot be over emphasized that the earlier the various parties are brought together the better. The scale of the scheme has been such as to put under the spotlight a number of other important facets from which lessons can be drawn. Without doubt good communications and first rate working relationships with all participants is a vital prerequisite to the successful conclusion of such complex projects. Such conditions do not just happen, and all staff must be encouraged to work at it and at all costs prevent personal vendettas developing.

Traffic management measures were an essential feature of the scheme. The highway authority and the designers had given significant undertaking during the scheme preparation and as such wished to exercise strong control on site. It seems reasonable that the Engineer should maintain the initiative on this aspect thereby allowing the Contractor to concentrate on progress and logistical problems. The advice from the Police proved invaluable but caution is necessary to balance carefully that which is necessary for real safety since implications can be enormous. Traffic management at Hatfield was expensive but traffic did keep moving relatively freely and private and political comment has been very favourable which tends to suggest that the public are prepared to pay a premium to ease their burden whilst such schemes are constructed.

The use of high profile public relations posture assisted enormously in educating the local inhabitants and travelling public of the vast and constantly changing traffic management measures. Full opportunity was taken to use the scheme as a shop window on the profession for local bodies, schools and foreign visitors. Although this can be time consuming when there are so many demands on time, the benefits appear worthwhile. It is surprising that despite roadworks being common place the average concept of the scale of work involved is very limited. The extensive use of information bulletins and general openness with the public is to be recommended for such projects.

ACKNOWLEDGEMENTS

The views expressed in this paper are those of the Authors and do not necessarily constitute the views of the Authority which they represent.

The Authors are grateful to the following for their permission to publish this paper:
Mr D A Holland, The acting Chief Highway Engineer, Department of Transport.
Mr M F Hardy OBE, The County Surveyor Hertfordshire County Council.
The Directors of Mott Hay & Anderson.

Contract Data:
Client: Secretary of State for Transport
Scheme Design: Civil Engineering - Hertfordshire County Council
                                       - Highways Department

                   Tunnel Electrical and Mechanical Works - Mott Hay & Anderson
                                               - Electrical & Mechanical Services
Contractors: Civil Engineering - Tarmac National Construction
                   Electrical & Mechanical Services - W H Smith and Company
                                       - Electrical Engineers Limited

Computer-aided drilling for tunnelling accuracy and economy

T. Puhakka M.Sc.
Tampella, Ltd., Tamrock, Tampere, Finland

SYNOPSIS

The paper reviews new standards of accuracy, speed and economy achieved with computerized drill jumbos and also highlights the possible dangers of excessive automation.

In tunnel excavation projects using drill-and-blast techniques, drilling is no longer the bottleneck in the excavation cycle since modern hydraulic drill jumbos are already sufficiently powerful and reliable. Similarly, the most economical result is not achieved by maximizing penetration rate as drill steel and bit wear must be kept within economical limits.

The recent introduction of computerized drill rigs is having a considerable effect on overall drill cycle performance and excavation costs.

The main benefits of computerization in tunnelling are:

(i)   Longer rounds. Consistently greater accuracy in collaring the holes at the face and in achieving the correct hole bottoms allows overbreak to be converted into longer round length for the same volume.

(ii)   Increased pull. Accurate drilling ensures that the 20-30 cm usually left unblasted at the end of the hole remains constant, even with 8-9 metre round lengths.

(iii) Optimization of the drill pattern. The "extra" holes normally drilled to ensure effective pull are unnecessary. The number and location of drill holes are optimized.

(iv)   Avoidance of human error. Computerization allows all rounds to be drilled in the optimum way.

Fully "Robotic" drilling is as impractical as expecting computers to design drill rigs. In computerized tunnelling, the operator's role will continue to be vital to control the quality of excavation. He is also needed to adjust drilling parameters as the tunnel progresses, and to analyze the effect of individual parameters on the whole excavation process. This may be called CAD - "COMPUTER AIDED DRILLING".

COMPUTERIZED DRILLING

The development of mechanized drilling rigs
started after the hand-held drilling (Fig. 1,
curve I) in the early 60s with pneumatic
drilling jumbos (Fig. 1, curve II). The
introduction of hydraulic drilling in the
1970's increased not only the efficiency of
drilling, but also improved the environment
of the drill operator (Fig. 1, curve III).
Significantly better performance together
with better economical results were achieved.

During the following ten years the further
development of hydraulic drilling rigs has
made drill rigs not only more efficient but
also more reliable, and this has resulted in
greater overall economy in drilling. The
total economic aspect has become more
important in tunnel excavation.

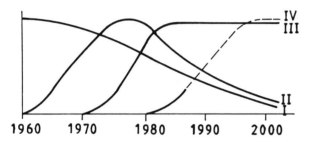

Fig. 1 Development of drilling rigs.

The computerized Tamrock "Datamatic" utilizes
mechanically and hydraulically proven
technology to achieve an automated drilling
sequence (Fig. 1, curve IV).

Through automation a better quality in
drilling may be obtained. Before discussing
the advantages of computerized drilling over
traditional methods, a brief description of
how the "Datamatic" operates is appropriate.

COMPUTERIZATION

The "Datamatic" has an Electronic Control
Unit (ECU) which controls all the functions
of the drilling rig. This is equipped with a
printed circuit board based on microprocessor
technology and containing a memory of
drilling patterns, constants and boom models.
The positions of the feeds and rock drills,
including all joints of the booms, are
controlled ten times a second.

The positions of the joints of the booms,
feeds and the drill rig's carrier are
measured with 16-bit accuracy through sensors
placed in the components. The servo-valves
controlled by the ECU direct the correct oil
flow to the correct places. The boom
cylinders, sensors, servo-valves and boom
microprocessor all operate in a so-called
closed-loop control.

Fig. 2 Electronic control unit (ECU) and
        sensors

INPUT DATA

The total drilling pattern is planned with a
desk computer using special planning
programmes. All the necessary input
information is given to the program in
three-dimensional form starting from the
set-up level, an imaginary curved surface
placed on a certain point from the actual
rock face.

The input information includes the following
data:

- position, direction and depth of each
  hole
- boom rotation angle for each hole
- drilling sequence of holes
- position and direction of the reference
  line, the laser beam.

The program with input information is stored
on a cassette and is transferred to the
electronic control unit (ECU) by the operator.

NAVIGATION

The navigation of the drilling rig is done
after transferring the given drilling pattern
information into the ECU. One feed is set
parallel with the tunnel's reference line,
the laser beam, and the navigation button is
pressed. After this the electronic control
unit calculates the position of the rig in
the tunnel (x,y,z coordinates) and
recalculates the drilling pattern according
to the drilling rig's position.

OPERATIONAL INFORMATION

The drilling rig is equipped with an
operator's cabin where the control panel,
desk computer and visual display unit (VDU)
are situated. Drilling progress can be
monitored continuously on the VDU where the
drilling pattern is shown. The function of
the sensors and values of the constants can
also be shown on the VDU.

Separate symbols are used to mark the
different stages in the drilling of each hole
(drilled out, being drilled, next to be
drilled, planned). The drill cut is shown
separately enlarged. The long-range
penetration rate is also recorded and shown
as a curve over the last 40 metres.

Fig. 3   Datamatic HS 205 D

OPERATIONAL LEVELS

The "Datamatic" can be operated in three
different modes: the automatic mode or the
two alternatives of manual over-ride
operations, one of which is the manipulator
mode and the other is the direct control
mode. The mode of operation can be selected
individually for each drilling boom by means
of push buttons on the control panel. The
design of the control system makes it easy to
choose between the different modes, and the
system is set back to the automatic mode
again by a push button.

Automatic mode: After navigation is
completed the control system moves the boom
to the programmed position to drill a hole
according to the preprogrammed drilling plan.
After setting the feed against the rock the
whole drilling cycle proceeds automatically.

The operator can follow the penetration
rates, directions of the chain feeds in
relation to the reference line, and the
drilling of holes on the VDU.

Manipulator mode: In the manipulator mode
precise manual control of the boom and chain
feed is very easy since the movements are
performed by 3-axis joy-sticks, although they
are still controlled by the microprocessor.

Direct control mode: In the direct control
mode the operator can operate every cylinder
of the boom separately and the microprocessor
is not used.

Other special functions such as correction
alignment compensator, adjustment of
collaring and automatic double flushing are
also included in the "Datamatic".

QUALITY TUNNELLING

Accurate profile

In drill-and-blast techniques accurate hole
alignment is one of the most critical factors
affecting the quality of the tunnel
dimensions.

In manual drilling the operator's skills play
an important role. However, certain aspects
- no matter how well carried out - lead to
poor hole tolerances, and difficulties in
charging and in achieving an accurate tunnel
profile.

When drilling a 25-30 m^2 heading, poor hole
alignment can lead to overbreak of 15-20 % in
horizontal tunnels. In curved and inclined
tunnels the overbreak can be considerably
more. Manual drilling in ramps and curves
typically gives rise to both overbreak and
underbreak (which produces an undersized
tunnel).

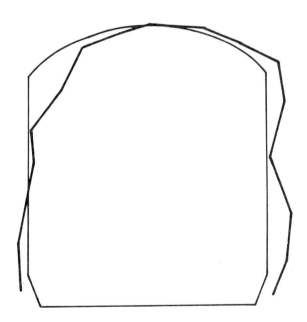

Fig. 4 Typical profile with manual
        drilling - both over- and under-break
        (test mine)

In computerized drilling, consistent accuracy
and quality controlled hole alignment is
ensured with the aid of a computer controlled
three dimensional drilling pattern and
computerized hole spotting. Computerized
drilling allows collaring of holes to be
adjusted beforehand to the minimum.

Even if the start position of the hole has
been moved (in the jumbo's manipulator mode)
the direction of the hole can be changed by
the correction function for the hole to meet
the programmed hole bottom.

During test drilling in the Tamrock test
mine, several rounds were drilled with the
"Datamatic" using all three operational
levels. The drift size in the tests was
5.0 x 4.0 m (W x H) and the hole length used
was 5.1 m. The rock type in the test area was
granodiorite with an average uniaxial
compressive strength of 155 MPa. The results
from Tamrock's test mine proved that with
computerized drilling in the automatic mode,
overbreak is reduced to 8-10 % in a given
size of tunnel.

The "Datamatic" HS 315 U was used for
drilling in the Dokka hydropower project in
Norway 1986. The rock type on the project was
strongly layered mixed migmatite and
migmatite gneiss. According to the profile
measurements, underbreak was reduced to
2.1 %, ie. only half that of manual drilling.

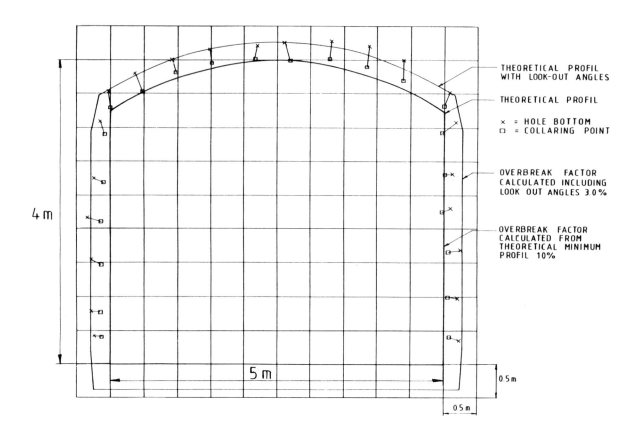

Fig. 5 Accurate tunnel profile with computerized drilling (test mine)

The reduction of overbreak from 20 % down to 8 % in a 5 x 5 m^2 tunnel means savings of about 3 m^2 (solid)/tunnel metre.

LONGER ROUNDS

Tests made in Finland in a 5 x 5 m^2 size tunnel situated in granite showed that rounds as long as 8-9 m can be succesfully blasted when the drilling is done with high accuracy. At the same time, the unblasted hole length at the hole bottom remains around 20 cm as for shorter rounds.

With accurate computerized drilling excessive overbreak may be converted to longer rounds, and this makes drilling time more productive. The reduced overbreak also leads to savings in blasting, loading and shotcreting. The overall better quality results in less rock support work.

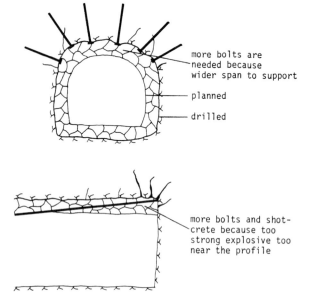

Fig. 6 The effect of poor hole alignment on reinforcement costs (manual drilling).

262

OPTIMIZED DRILLING PATTERN

In manual drilling, the lay-out of the
drilling pattern is dependent upon the
operator's skills and experience. The
accurate design of the drill cut and hole
alignment as well as the burden and spacing
of the contour holes play an important role
especially when excavating long rounds.

Due to the accurate alignment of the holes in
computer-controlled drilling, no extra holes
are needed and also the charging and blasting
of the holes are more certain to achieve the
desired pull.

Through the long-range penetration rate
monitored on the VDU the presence of bad
joints or cracks in the rock can be observed.

By monitoring profile and pull the optimized
drilling pattern can be used and the desired
fragmentation of the rock for mucking and
further processing is achieved.

FAST TUNNELLING

The computerized drilling rig is navigated
onto the tunnel's coordinates with a laser
beam. Thus the jumbo needs only one
reference line for precise positioning of the
desired drilling pattern and to calculate the
fastest routes for moving the boom from hole
to hole.

Compared to manual drilling, as much as 20 %
in total drilling time can be saved using
automated drilling techniques. Yet an
automated drilling rig with as many as three
booms can still comfortably be controlled by
one operator.

OPERATOR'S ROLE

Despite the many automated functions in
computerized drilling rigs, the need for the
operator's presence cannot be underestimated.
Automated drilling should in this sense be
called computer aided drilling - CAD - and
acts a tool for handling continuous routine
operations and for avoiding human errors.

The operator's function is to do what
computers and automation cannot do -
analyze, interpret and define the effect of
the individual parameters on the total
excavation cycle, an exceedingly important
role in monitoring drilling performance. Thus
there is an obvious need for an experienced
operator capable of evaluating the changing
conditions in excavation.

CONCLUSIONS

The need for economical tunnelling has
emphasized the importance of optimizating the
whole drilling cycle. The drill and blast
method can be made more competitive by using
computerized drilling compared with
traditional methods or with full-face tunnel
boring. The computer-aided drilling system
is based on high speed tunnelling techniques
that with an automated quality controlled
drilling sequence consistently produce the
most accurate final tunnel profile possible.

The Dosco CTM5 tunnelling machine

G. Richardson B.Eng., C.Eng., F.I.Min.E.
M. J. Gollick
Dosco Overseas Engineering, Ltd., Newark, Nottinghamshire, United Kingdom

SYNOPSIS

The application of circular tunnels in deep mines has been under review by British Coal for a number of years. Recently several new drivage systems have been evaluated and considerable knowledge of roadway stability and machine characteristics has been gained. Based on this experience British Coal released a specification for a machine capable of driving a 5-m diameter tunnel to be used in the new Selby coalfield.

To comply with the specification a total mining system was to be designed and built by Dosco to cut, load out and support the circular tunnel. This system is known as the CTM5 machine, and uses the boom in shield principle, greatly modified for use in deep mines. This type of arrangement has many advantages over existing circular tunnelling machines because of its short overall length and relatively low cost. This makes the CTM5 suitable for shorter length circular drivages than had previously been viable.

The CTM5 has been designed to set permanent steel supports 1.9 metres from the excavated face. This has required the production of a short shield, for immediate roof support, which incorporates a support erection system. The shield has also been designed in two pieces to accommodate limited strata convergence. Coupled to the lower half of the shield is a discharge conveyor. The shield and conveyor are pushed forward from a mainframe which is stelled to the roadway sides. The cutting boom is slide mounted and fixed inside the mainframe.

As the CTM5 was a new concept in roadway drivage, Dosco carried out a full series of underground trials on each component system of the machine and these were carried out at Middleton Limestone Mine. These operational trials are discussed in the paper along with the machine's potential. At the time of writing the paper the underground installation at Selby had been delayed and results were not available.

INTRODUCTION

Dosco has for many years been involved in both Mining and Civil Engineering tunnelling operations covering a broad range of applications, both in the U.K. and overseas.

The first circular tunnelling machine was produced in 1973 and consisted of a roadheader boom in a shield. These machines were used by Civil Contractors in shallow tunnels which required, by virtue of their intended purpose, a segmental type lining. The cutting boom was based on the MKIIA Roadheader, utilising 48kw, and tunnel diameter ranged from 2.0 to 5.2 metres. More recently, the basic tunnelling machine has developed into a larger, heavier duty unit, able to excavate harder rock (up to 120 MPa) and suitable in tunnels 4.5 to

7.0 metres diameter. The machine specification has generally been uprated and is currently based on the MkIII Heavy Duty Roadheader cutting boom with up to 250kw capacity.

A particular aspect of civil tunnelling, unlike mining, is the normal requirement for the supply of a complete 'Tunnel Package'. This package is specifically designed around equipment and mining conditions with a view to obtaining maximum system output. Experience in this type of supply has enabled Dosco to produce modern equipment with such up-to-date features as laser control, profile guidance, fully mechanised erectors and integrated supply and debris clearance routes.

British Coal has extensive circular tunnelling experience both with Tunnel Boring and Shielded Boom type machines with the benefits and associated problems well defined. The ideal design requirement for a machine in the Selby coalfield obviously reflected this experience, but also sought to include other valuable knowledge already to hand from the Selby North Spine Roadway, where a Robbins Tunnel Boring Machine has been in use for a number of years.

Dosco undertook to meet the parameters and ultimately produced a machine based broadly on civil engineering experience, but extensively modified to suit deep mine conditions.

Design Parameters

(i)   To overcome, as practically as possible, the possibility of the shield becoming trapped.

(ii)   To similarly overcome the very long prop free front associated with typical tunnelling shields erecting supports at the rear. (The prop free front is the distance from the exposed face to the last permanent support).

(iii)   To enable fully circular steel supports to be erected, (using standard in-web fish plates), at either 1.0 or 0.5 metre centres.

(iv)   To provide a machine suitable in a range of tunnel diameters, accepting that certain componentry would need to be changed.

(v)   To provide a relatively low cost machine.

(vi)   To provide access to the face.

(vii)   To enable rapid movement from site to site in view of the relatively short lengths of drivage.

Against this general background, the CTM5 Tunnelling Machine was designed and produced and subsequently tested at Middleton Limestone Mine, prior to its intended installation at Wistow Mine in the Selby Complex.

To further complement the machine a back-up system consisting of a semi-rigid conveyor receiving section, with its own advancer unit, crusher and plough device, specialised support trestles and support moving system, all designed to achieve optimum machine performance, is under consideration by British Coal.

FUNCTION AND MAIN FEATURES

The machine is designed for the rapid excavation of circular roadways at depth, which requires supporting on steel rings. Tunnel diameters may vary between 4.5 and 7.0 metres and are achievable by changing certain componentry around the basic cutting unit. Construction is heavy duty and as such will cope with all coal measure strata within the normal confines associated with the boom cutter principle.

Main Design Features

*   Capable of high rates of advance.
*   Able to excavate hard rock.
*   Shield (canopy) yields under load.
*   Short shield length allows permanent supports to be set within 1.9 metres of the face.
*   Permanent support erection is carried out within a supported zone.
*   Cutting, loading and support operation is largely concurrent.

266

* There is no conventional track type running gear.
* There is no conventional debris gathering system.
* Dust suppression is fully integrated.

Machine Description

In general terms, it is a combination of both roadheader and shielded type equipment and comprises of the following major items: yielding shield, cutting unit, primary scraper conveyor, ring erector, support and gripper frame, hydraulic powerpack, dust suppression system and secondary 'back-up system', as shown in Figure 1.

Its very short length also provides good steering characteristics, both for accurate line and change of grade.

At the rear of the shield at crown position, four slots extend approximately 40 degrees either side of centre line to hold mesh panels which, when retrieved during the ring build operation, give immediate roof cover to exposed ground.

Full face cutting is achieved from a single central position, utilising a heavy duty two-speed cutting boom fitted with a scrolled head, all mounted onto a sliding pedestal. Head speed change is achieved through a twin speed

DOSCO CTM5 TUNNELLING MACHINE

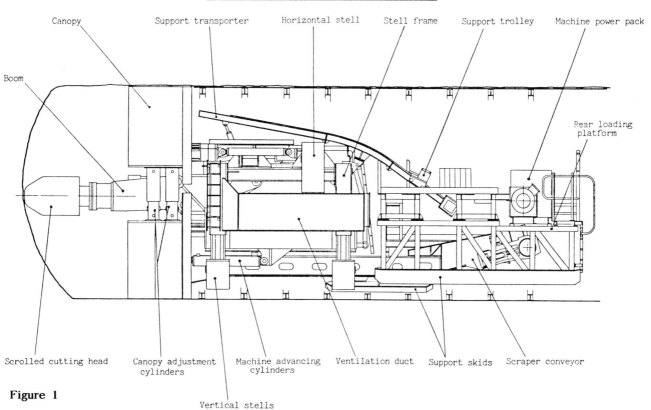

Figure 1

Probably the most important feature is the yielding shield, which can reduce or increase by up to 150 millimetres over nominal diameter, depending on the situation. This built-in flexibility allows some convergence to be accommodated and extra height to be cut with support where necessary. The shield is much shorter than the conventional type, and at only 1.3 metres allows support setting within 1.9 metres of the face.

cutter motor which maintains the torque value in either case. The actual cutting operation is manually controlled by pilot operated joysticks with final periphery profiling subject to electronic control. A Visual Display Unit provides the boom 'x' and 'y' co-ordinates in relation to the required tunnel diameter. Mounted in the shield invert is a scraper conveyor which extends the machine's full length and discharges onto a secondary belt conveyor.

267

Cut debris loads either by its natural progress down the workpile, or by the action of the scrolled cutting head. As supports are not set at the face (in front of the shield), it is not necessary to fully load-out forward, this being achieved by the crowding action of the shield during the advancing cycle.

Cutting and supporting is designed to work concurrently, the system being to assemble the ring on the erector during the cutting operation with setting during the shield advance sequence. Actual support is a five-section ring, (152mm x 127mm), connected by Standard Four bolt in-web fish plates and a six-bolt friction clamp at the crown position. Conveying of ring sections from the rear loading platform is via a mechanical trolley with little manual effort required until loading the erector. Ring rotation and expansion to roadway is fully mechanised, leaving strutting and bolt tightening as the only manual operation. Controls for ring building are located in two positions, on the rear loading platform to control the movement of ring sections forward, and at the erector to control the actual build operation. The controls have a built-in safety system.

Advance of the machine is effected from a skid mounted gripper frame, fixed around the cutting unit and connected to the shield by four large hydraulic rams. During advance the gripper frame expands against the roadway, allowing the cutting unit to move, and subsequent contraction of the gripper allows its own forward movement to a position where cutting can restart. As the cutting unit is actually supported by the gripper frame, not the base frame and conveyor, vibration and stress loading normally experienced during excavation is minimal, and subsequently not experienced by the main machine.

Integral dust suppression equipment consists of a 0.6 metre diameter duct, left side positioned, passing front to rear and connected via a flexible coupling to an exhaust system. Discharge may be either right or left of machine

centreline depending on tunnel layout. Complementing this are two Coanda air tubes situated at positions such to force dust away from operators towards the exhaust duct opening.

On the right of the machine is the operator platform which contains the machine controls grouped accordingly for easy use and access. There is a laser target within easy view of the operator for machine alignment.

A powerpack is mounted on the rear loading platform, unlike the electrical panels which are positioned outbye on trestles above the back-up system. The rear loading platform is also skid mounted and automatically advances in line as the machine takes up a new position.

Back-Up System

The back-up system is independent to the machine and consists of a semi-rigid conveyor receiving section, which extends back from the machine for 50 metres. Its structure is designed to sit and slide in the curved invert and is consequently trapped and guided to maintain its line. At the inbye end is the 'advancer' unit which, when in operation, grips floor to roof, allowing the conveyor to be pushed forward. The whole system works in conjunction with a 100 metres loop storage facility, which automatically releases the conveyor belt.

A 750 millimetres wide bridge belt conveyor, with a designed overlap of 5 metres, feeds from the machine to the receiving section, and at its discharge is a rotary crusher which sizes material down to -100 millimetres. The use of the crusher is two-fold; to prevent outbye transfer points becoming blocked, and to provide suitably sized debris for the invert fill. Should the crusher fail or be unnecessary then it can easily be disconnected and pulled clear.

Above the receiving section are several support trestles which carry the ancillaries including the transformer and dust filter unit. At its outbye end is a plough device for invert filling with separate control.

Supports and materials are conveyed to site
conventionally and off-loaded at the invert fill
position. From here they are transferred by
powered monorail to the loading platform at the
machine rear.

Operating Procedure

Machine advance involves six main operations and
is shown in Figures 2 to 7, which explain in
full detail.

UNDERGROUND TRIALS

Test Site

In view of several new concepts it was felt
necessary to install and test a machine in a
suitable underground location prior to
installing in the production environment at
Selby.

The main purpose of the trial was to test
compatibility of the system and develop the
design concept when necessary to a satisfactory
conclusion. Therefore a site which would allow
advancing, steering and ring erection operations
with a minimal amount of cutting was required.

This requirement was fulfilled at Middleton
Mine, situated near Matlock in Derbyshire, which
currently produces around 400,000 tons per annum
from a conventional drill and blast operation.
The limestone is typically very hard and
generally considered unsuitable for economic
excavation by roadheader. (Strength tests
undertaken by Dosco indicated the limestone to
be 90-130 MPa).

A partially excavated, level site, previously
developed to a length of 25 metres and
'D' shaped, became available in early 1986, and
whilst not the correct profile, was subsequently
adopted as the test site. The profile was such
that only minimal side trimming, along with the
removal of approximately 1 metre from the
invert, was necessary to allow passage of the
machine up to the face position.

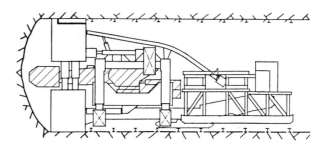

Figure 2
Machine in start position. Horizontal and
vertical stells extended, shown X. Roadway
fully supported at rear of shield.

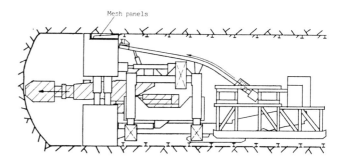

Figure 3
Cutting boom sumps forward removing strata upto
the required depth. Mesh panels are loaded in
to the canopy slots and are attached to previous
panels. Ring assembly starts.

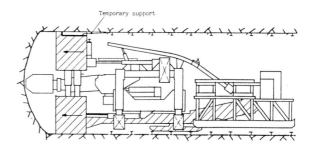

Figure 4
Shield advanced into newly exposed ground. Mesh
panels extend from canopy slots giving temporary
cover to crown area.

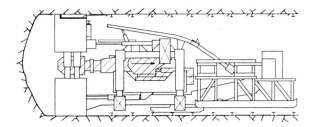

Figure 5

Cutting boom retracted, ring positioned, strutting commences.

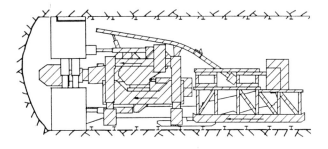

Figure 6

Stells retracted. Cutting boom, gripper frame and rear support frame advanced. Ring erection completed.

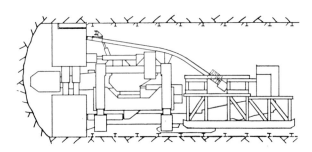

Figure 7

Advance cycle complete, operation ready to restart.

Actual build conditions at the site were good, taking place in a large junction with suitable height, overhead crane, power, ventilation and tool shop facilities. Assembly of the machine took approximately four weeks utilising a four man team on a single shift basis.

Testing and trial of the machine involved the following major functions, each investigated and developed where necessary.

Advancing/Steering

(i)   Initial progress of the machine (from the launch position) proved difficult, as the shield top section actually tilted forward about 20 degrees from vertical, digging into the ground and restricting movement. The problem was attributed to the lack of control of the shield top which, unlike the bottom half, did not have hydraulic advancing cylinders. Two additional cylinders were fitted, one in each top quadrant, which resolved the problem.

(ii)   Steering of the machine also improved dramatically from the above modification. The advance cylinders, which are located at either end by swivel bearings, work either individually or in pairs to give the necessary line and grade adjustment.

(iii)   The limestone, which in the main is self-supporting, could not duplicate typical mining conditions and therefore, other than testing the raising and lowering techniques, little could be done to simulate canopy roof control.

(iv)   During machine advance it was possible to get out of sequence with support and machine positioning, which occasionally caused the vertical stell pads to foul on the invert ring sections. The problem stemmed from the ability to over and under advance the 1 metre increment specified for the trial. A simple visual indicator relating machine to ring set position was introduced, enabling the operator to be fully aware of the exact machine position.

Cutting/Loading

The cutting rate in the limestone was approximately 10-12 m3/hour reducing to 6-7 m3/hour when loading was taken into account. The boom did have an underslung spade device which could be lowered to pull debris onto the conveyor, however in practice it was slow and cumbersome.

In order to improve the overall cutting and loading rate three major modifications were

270

undertaken:-

(i)   The scraper conveyor return roller was repositioned 450 millimetres further forward at the most practical position on the shield leading edge.

(ii)   The cutting head was replaced by a scrolled type which extended further backwards, about 60%, improving the loading relationship with the conveyor.

(iii) The underslung boom spade device was removed.

These aspects considerably improved the overall cycle time showing that, unlike the original situation where cutting had to stop to allow debris to be cleared, cutting and loading was now a continuous operation.

A further feature which improved the cutting operation was the control afforded by the ZED Electronic Profile Guidance System. A Visual Display Unit enables the operator to be fully aware of the head position with regard to tunnel periphery at all times. The system obviously allows an accurate profile to be cut and also ensures that the invert area normally covered in debris is clear of obstructions prior to shield advance.

Support Erection

Support erection involves six main operations, (refer to Figures 8 to 13, which give full details of a build sequence).

RING ERECTION SEQUENCE

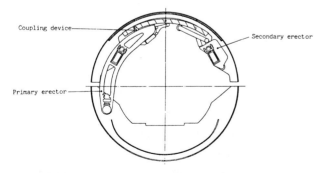

Figure 8

First section placed and located on erector by coupling device.

No major problems were experienced with the support assembly equipment, however several general modifications were necessary to improve the overall build operation:

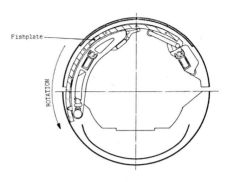

Figure 9

First section rotated allowing attachment of second section.

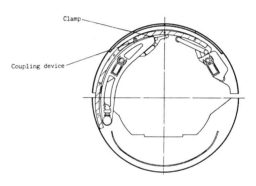

Figure 10

Sections one and two secured by means of a clamp. The coupler is unlocked and relocated on the second section.

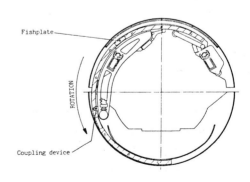

Figure 11

Clamp released. First and second sections rotated allowing attachment of third section.

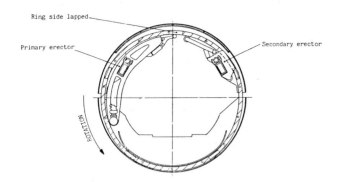

Figure 12

Assembly operation repeats until all five sections are on the erector. Necessary misalignment of sections one and five is achieved by the secondary erector.

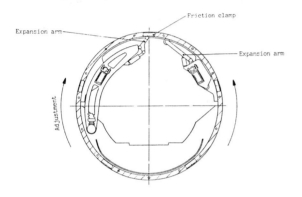

Figure 13

Ring adjusted for correct position. Final expansion achieved by hydraulic arms prior to fitting friction clamp.

(i)   The rear support platform was modified to enable ring sections to be stored in such a manner that they could be placed directly on the erector trolley with little man effort.

(ii)   Following many ring building exercises it became apparent that the loose fitting of fish plates prior to loading ring sections in the erector reduced cycle time and smoothed the build operation. The best complete build time achieved during the trial was 35 minutes. (Figure 14 shows a detailed activity chart).

(iii)   A complete ring building exercise including strutting involves 67 bolting and unbolting operations. To maintain a quick assembly time these functions must be achieved efficiently, therefore the use of an air or hydraulic impact hammer is highly recommended.

(iv)   Initial strut design was 3 per ring section, i.e. 15 in total, but of these it was found only 7 could be set during the ring build operation. The remaining 8 could only be inserted behind the machine due to a foul condition with the stell pads. Reducing strut density from 3 to 2 and altering their location on the section removed the problem and allowed all 10 struts to be fully inserted at build time, (see Figures 15 and 16).

(v)   The constant advancing and drawing back of the shield, which would not normally happen in its correct application but was necessary for the test programme, caused the ring guide plate situated at the shield invert to flatten, and affected both the speed and ease with which the ring could be assembled. This aspect, although unlikely to happen in a coal mine application, was considered at length and resulted in a redesign both to improve the strength, but more importantly to make the unit detachable for easy replacement.

Machine Hydraulics

Initial design and layout is based on previous circular machine experience, although in this particular case the powerpack assembly was skid mounted as a separate item and towed at the rear of the machine. In operation, although the system worked well, several points were highlighted for improvement and were subsequently modified as follows:-

(i)   All major circuits including boom operation, machine advance and side stelling were modified to a pilot operated system.

(ii) Changing to pilot operation improved hose runs, control layout and general accessibility.

(iii) Joystick operation on the boom improved operator technique, both for cutting, loading and profiling.

(iv) Repositioning the powerpack onto the rear support frame removed the lengthy and susceptible hose runs.

Important Trial Results

(i) Excavating and supporting can largely be achieved simultaneously, although an overlap may occur depending on strata type and ease with which it is cut and loaded. The obvious benefit from this aspect is increased machine utilisation.

CTM5 RING ERECTION ACTIVITY CHART
RESULTS BASED ON MIDDLETON MINE EXPERIENCE

Figure 14

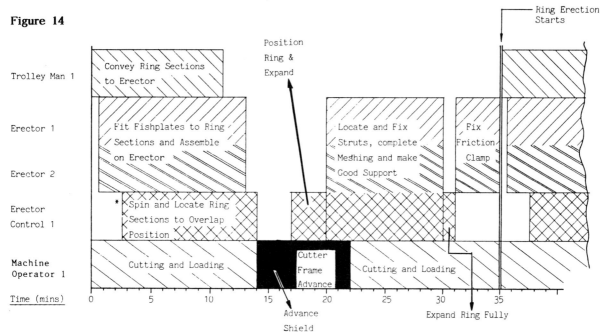

Ring erection is a basic 4 man operation working in conjunction with the machine operator

NOTE: Above sequence assumes cutting and loading complete at end of *"Spin and Locate" operation. In actual application this may not be so, it depends on strata type and ease at which it is cut and loaded.

CONCLUSIONS TO DATE

Although modications (mainly mechanical) were necessary to improve certain sections of equipment, the actual operating procedure for excavating and supporting in a circular profile worked very well, confirming the overall machine concept.

As previously stated, Middleton Mine is not a coal mine and therefore total compatibility to a mining environment could not be tested. However, based on both the trial results and our general mining experience, it is our view that the machine is now ready to commence in its intended application.

(ii) Circular arches, (five sections), can be erected much quicker, safer and with considerably less effort than the equivalent 'D' shaped arch in a conventional development.

(iii) A short length shield is extremely controllable, allowing both advance and retraction should it become necessary.

(iv) Rigid machine positioning allows hard rock to be excavated.

(v) Dust suppression is efficient from a fully integrated system.

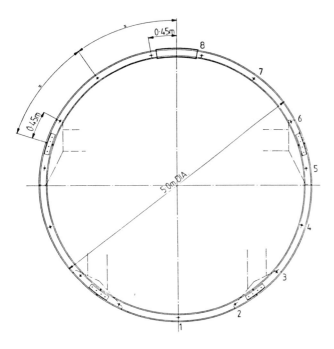

ORIGINAL STRUT POSITIONS

Figure 15

Strut 1 difficult to set (beneath machine body).
Struts 2, 3, 5 and 6 cannot be set due to stell
pads.

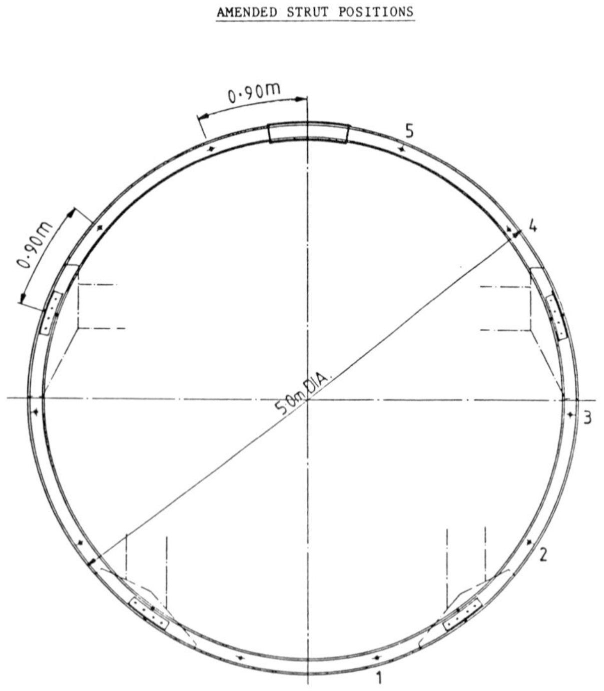

AMENDED STRUT POSITIONS

Figure 16

Struts repositioned to allow full insertion
during arch erection process.

FUTURE DEVELOPMENTS

It is fully appreciated that mining conditions
do vary considerably and that the CTM5 in
current form may not fully suit a particular
application. Problems due to depth, faulting,
water, etcetera, may dictate a machine capable
of erecting a segmental type support or a
conventional arch, or indeed a mixture of both.
In order to fully meet these requirements
derivatives of the CTM5 capable of meeting the
above criteria are currently under development.

The CTM5 has been modified in line with
experience at Middleton Mine and will be
installed in the Wistow Mine at the Selby
Complex. At the time of preparing this paper
the underground installation had been delayed.

274

Development of roadheading equipment for tunnelling by NATM

A. Sandtner Dipl. Ing.
Underground Mining and Tunnelling Division, VOEST-Alpine AG, Zeltweg, Austria
K. H. Gehring Dipl. Ing., Dr. mont.
Montanuniversität Leoben, Austria, and Underground Mining and Tunnelling Division, VOEST-Alpine AG, Zeltweg, Austria

SYNOPSIS

From its development soon after the Second World War, the New Austrian Tunnelling Method (NATM) became popular as a proven and economical method for tunnelling under a variety of rock and other environmental conditions and at many project types and locations. Although a basic principle of NATM required smooth mechanical excavation, it has been practised in most cases by drill and blast excavation. This method is better able to cope with the task of a multiple-step sequence of excavation and rock support, mainly with regard to very variable rock conditions. Several attempts at mechanization or adaption of existing mechanical excavation systems have been undertaken. The use of a specialized tunnel excavator with a revolving backhoe was found to be a good solution for urban soft ground tunnelling. Excavation by roadheaders has also proved successful under certain limiting conditions.[5]

The aim of this paper will be to describe and discuss steps in the development of a new roadheader-based system which is designed to meet the specific demands of the NATM over a wide range of operational conditions, and to present the first results of operations.

TUNNELLING BY NATM

It is not intended to describe in this paper the principles and the possible operational sequences of NATM-tunnelling in detail, for these are well known to everybody familiar with tunneling. Much literature is available about these items.[1, 2, 3, 4, 6]

Only those points and aspects will be selected, which directly concern and influence the subject of mechanization.

Briefly, NATM constitutes a method where the surrounding rock or soil formations of a tunnel are integrated into an overall support structure. The surrounding rock itself forms a part of the support structure thus reducing the amount on artificial support.

To achieve this effect, the following main principles must be observed:

(a) The geomechanical behaviour of the surrounding rock must be taken into consideration.

(b) Adverse states of stress and excessive deformation must be avoided by applying the appropriate means of rock protection or support in time.

(c) The supporting effect can be achieved by the creation of a ring-like bearing structure, e.g. by closing the invert of the tunnel.

275

(d) Rock protection and support should be optimized according to the admissible deformations.

(e) To preserve the bearing capacity of the surrounding rock, excavation should be performed as cautiously as possible.

(f) Dimensioning and timely placing of the support should be optimized by appropriate checking of rock deformation. (e.g. by convergence control)

All measures of tunnelling will have to cope with the above demands. The appropriate sequence of excavation and rock protection is of great importance.

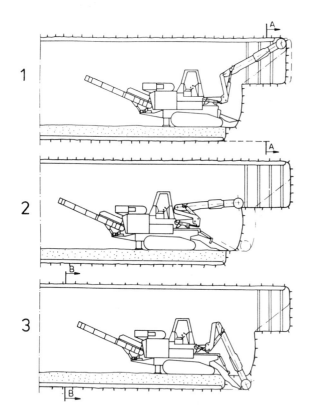

Fig. 1 Excavation with short advanced roof section.

As an example of the operational sequence, Fig. 1 shows the individual steps for tunnelling in soil or poor to moderate rock. The first step advances the top heading over a certain length and this is followed by placing a thin support shell, consisting of steel arches, wire mesh and shotcrete.

Under difficult rock conditions (for example when heavily fissured) or in soil, this first step is preceded by driving means for advanced roof protection, such as steel piles of steel rods If necessary wedge-shaped temporary supporting rock bodies can be recessed. (Fig. 2).

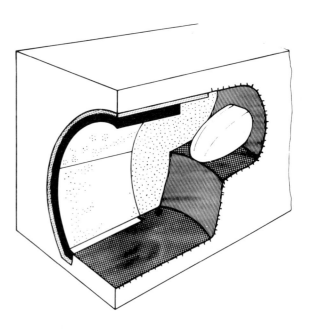

Fig. 2 Configuration of advanced roof section with supporting wedge.

The next step is the excavation of the bench, and this is followed by protection work. Afterwards the floor arch is excavated (if necessary) and then shotcrete is placed, reinforced with wire mesh and steel arches if necessary. The invert ring is closed and the next advance can be started.

Problems with mechanization

It will be seen from the foregoing,

276

that the individual steps of excavation concern only a small volume and also that the rock surface to be protected - during each step is restricted. Also the actual period for each individual step is comparatively short.

The length of one single advance can be sharply restricted due to the encountered conditions and this process calls for extremely flexible equipment. On the other hand the excavation time alone will not exceed approximately 20-30 % of the total time of a cycle, leading to low rates of equipment utilization. The investment costs for tunnelling machines are far higher than for drilling equipment and, low utilization can be a crucial point when the tunneling machine is solely used for excavation.

Another factor is the restricted space for the individual operations, which calls for a high flexibility for the individual functions.

REQUIREMENTS FOR MECHANIZED TUNNELLING

Based on the principles of NATM and the obstacles mentioned above a catalogue of requirements on a mechanical tunnelling system will have to cover the following:

(a) The system must be able to excavate all the above listed individual stages and intermediate stages, and be able to cope when these stages must be changed due to project conditions.
(b) Mucking out must be possible from any position where material is excavated.
(c) To increase the degree of utilization of the system, it should be possible to include also equipment and functions for rock support. The necessary power supply should come from the machine.

(d) To increase utilization another method is to work alternatively at two tunnel faces, e.g. in twin tube tunnels. This must be enabled by tramming independently from cables and with a high tramming speed.
(e) To facilitate transport on the site, tramming should be possible independent from electric power.
(f) To repay the high investment costs on more than one project, the system or machine must be able to be operated within a wide range of cross sections and rock conditions.
(g) The individual components or assembly groups of the machinery must be restricted in weight and dimension to be lowered into small shafts or passed through airlocks. Restricted dimensions are also required for road or rail transport.
(h) To achieve good working conditions all functions, which cause increased load onto the floor, should be performed without moving the main machine to avoid floor damage. This concerns mainly the functions for excavation and mucking.

This list is by no means complete and it has to be considered that some conditions will call for certain alterations.

A SYSTEM FOR MECHANIZATION OF NATM

The basic considerations cover a wide field. The demand of the market for tunnelling equipment had to be studied to find a range of data. On the one hand the need for tunnels is growing and on the other hand the profits of mechanization are also acknowledged.

The basic demands can be stated according to Table 1. These data have been fixed in accordance with reknown Austrian construction and consulting companies.

Rock conditions:	soil
	rock up to 60 MPa
Cross-section:	30-65 m²
Weight of machine:	max. 60 t
Performance of	
excavation (at 30 MPa):	40 bank m³/h
Loading capacity:	100 m³/h
Range of excavation	
advanced roof section:	4 m
floor arch	0,8-1 m
	(below track level)
height	7 m
width	7 m

Table 1: Basic data for a mechanized
NATM-System

Other features cover:

The possibility of integration for
rock supporting devices, direct loading
to railbound or trackless haulage equipment, additional outlets for power supply for job site equipment, e.g. welding
equipment.

These features would cover a wide
range of traffic tunnels (single- and
double-track subway tunnels, single
track railway tunnels, small road tunnels) and tunnels for water power stations (e.g. diversion tunnels).

Also the operation with a long advanced roof section in larger cross sections should be possible.

Due to the fact that traffic tunnels,
especially for railbound traffic, show a
markedly increasing importance worldwide, the above range can be judged as a
good first step for such systems.

When considering all these facts, it
was found that a roadheader-based system
would suit best, both for the range in
cross section and for the rock conditions planned to be excavated. Also the
machine can be used as a carrier for
peripheral equipment. To meet the other

demands, it became evident that the versatility of individual functions of a
standard-type roadheader needed considerable improvements.

THE AMT 70

The Alpine Miner Tunneller AMT 70 was
developed for NATM. It is based to some
extent on well proven components of
VOEST-ALPINE's ALPINE MINER series, but
several functions have been altered or
even changed by new solutions to meet
all the requirements of NATM. The specific outlay has been tailored to meet
the needs of underground operation in
tunnels.

Fig. 3 shows an arrangement drawing
with all important assembly groups.

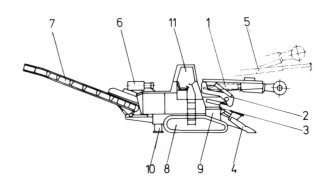

1	Cutter Boom	8	Crawler Track
2	Wing	9	Frame
3	Turret	10	Rear Support
4	Loading Apron	11	Driver's Cabin
5	Telescopic Scraper Arm	12	Electrical Equipment
6	Chain Conveyor	13	Hydraulic Equipment
7	Swivel Belt Conveyor	14	Lubrication System

Fig. 3 The AMT 70 assembly groups

Fig. 4 gives an idea of the appearance
of the AMT 70. While the central body of
the machine (frame, turret, conveyors)
can be judged to be quite similar to
standard roadheaders, mainly the cutter
boom and the loading system show new
ways to solve the problems. These solu-

Fig. 4 AMT 70, front view

tions will now be looked at in more detail. First a summary of the most important technical data will be presented in Tables 2, 3, and 4 and Fig. 5.

Overall length:	17,000	mm
Width of apron:	3,800	mm
Width over crawler tracks:	2,870	mm
Height:	3,260	mm
Ground clearance:	430	mm
Width of crawler tracks:	700	mm
	alt. 800 or 900	mm

Table 2 Main dimensions of AMT 70

Electric equipment:	1000 V / 50 Hz	
	(other voltages available)	
Total installed classic power:	335	kW
Cutter motor:	175	kW
Hydraulic power pack motor:	75	kW
Chain conveyor motors:	2x37	kW
Motor for swivel belt conveyor:	11	kW
additional outlets for	220 V/380 V	
Diesel engine:	110	kW
Crawler motor		
electric-hydraulic:	2x30	kW
diesel-hydraulic:	2x55	kW
Working pressure of		
hydraulic system:	150-260	bar

Table 3 Powering and power supply

Cutting speed:	3.4, 4.0, 4.8 m/s
Conveying speed	
chain conveyor:	1.1 m/s
swivel belt conveyor:	1.5 m/s
Tramming speed	
electro-hydraulic:	6.75-18.9 m/min
diesel-hydraulic:	13.0-36.8 m/min
Conveying capacity:	200 m³/h

Table 4: Important operational data

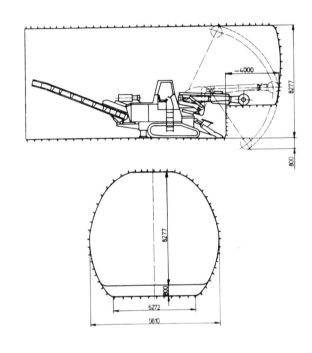

Fig. 5 Range of cutting of the AMT 70

The range of cutting is demonstrated in Fig. 5

Excavation

To achieve advanced cutting in the roof section as well as undercutting below track level, it was necessary to find a new kinematic system for the horizontal and vertical movement of the cutter boom (Fig. 6).

Fig. 6 Kinematic system of cutter boom

The main part is a so-called "wing", which allows a wide range of operation for the cutter boom, but also operation - for instance during bench cutting - with a retracted wing. (Fig. 7) This kinematic system allows a very exact and sensitive control of the boom's longitudinal movement for sumping-in or for cutting a face, which is flat in every direction.

Fig. 7 Cutter boom position for bench cutting

Even the cutting of an inclined bench, which has been found suitable for certain conditions, can be effected without moving the machine during cutting. This provides the best geomechanical condi-

tions which are of great importance, mainly in unstable rock conditions. A rack and pinion-drive integrated into the turret provides the lateral movement. The racks, situated on both sides of the turret, are fully enclosed and driven by two hydraulic pistons each. This system provides a constant slewing speed of the cutter head (in contrary to slewing cylinders).

A drum type cutterhead was choosen, as this type shows greater versatility regarding different and changing rock conditions. Also the lateral forces required for cutting are much lower than with a spiral type head, which should result in better stability over the long lever arm of the cutting boom in an extended position.

Loading

The removal of the excavated material was another important task for the system. The solution is in two steps, the principal being to pick up excavated material at any point in front of the machine and to provide an almost clean surface for the final and for intermediate shotcrete layers if necessary.

The first step was to improve the versatility of the loading apron. Based on the standard loading system with lobster type gathering arms it was found necessary to increase the range of loading. Therefore the whole loading assembly and the conveyor are placed on a sledge. (Fig. 8)

They can be shifted via a hydraulic cylinder to 1.300 mm forwards and 650 mm backwards from the zero position. Additionally the loading table can be tilted upwards to 430 mm and downwards to 800 mm related to the track level. This enables the gathering arms to pick up most of the muck from the floor arch and

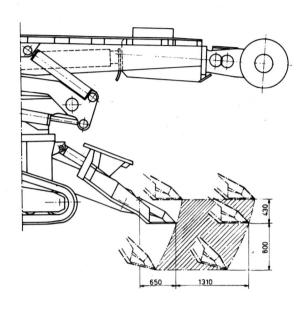

Fig. 8 Range of movement of loading assembly

provides increased loading performance
by pushing the apron into the excavated
muck.

For the large range of excavation
expecially in the advanced roof section
this loading device would not be sufficient. To muck out also these areas, a
telescopic scraper boom has been integrated into the cutter boom. With an
extended length of 3,400 mm and the ability to be turned horizontally and vertically to some extent, it is able to
reach the most remote areas to collect
the excavated material there. When cutting the floor arch the loading process
can be assisted by using this scraper
arm. The scraper blade also provides
clean surfaces.

Travelling

Although travelling is not a vital function in a tunneling system, some attention has been paid to find a solution
best suited for the demands of tunnelling. The crawler assembly itself is
standard for construction machinery, but
new for roadheaders is the possibility
to travel independently from electric
power by a diesel-hydraulic system which
can drive the crawler motors. To increase the manoeuvrability of the machine, the cheeks of the loading apron
can be folded upwards to enable passing
through narrow adits and cross-cuts.
Pedal control of all crawler motions
assists in close control of the boom
under extreme conditions.

The AMT 70 can cut gradients up to
+/- 12 degrees, the limiting inclination
for travelling is +/- 20 degrees. In a
6,5-m wide tunnel the machine can pass
around rectangular deviations into a
5,5-m wide tunnel with an inner radius
of 2 m. (Fig. 9)

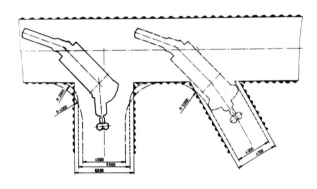

Fig. 9 Viable deviations of the AMT 70

Other Features

Other features comprise a drivers cabin,
which can be shifted sidewards hydraulically by 950 mm and forwards by 1,200 mm
for to improve the field of vision for
the driver, a central lubrication system
for interval lubrication (for important
greasing points, like the disk bearing
of the turret, the loader gears, the
shafts of the chain conveyor) and also
for manual lubrication. The long swivel

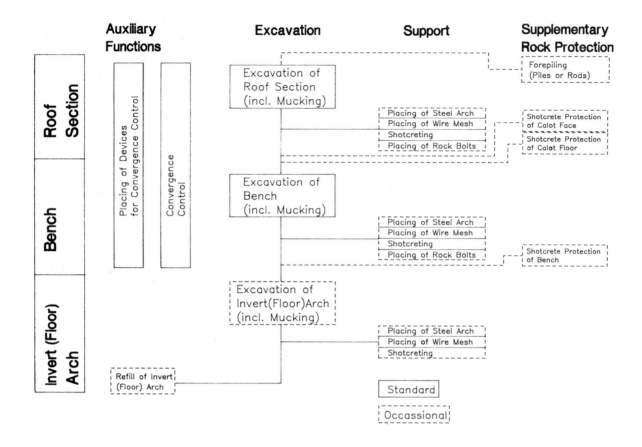

Auxiliary Functions	Excavation	Support	Supplementary Rock Protection

Fig. 10 Operational steps of the NATM

belt conveyor allows for loading into even really large dumpers.

Peripheral Functions

Besides the actual functions of a road-header specialized for NATM-conform methods of excavation, the AMT 70 can be equipped with additional equipment to form an integrating system. This mainly concerns all functions of rock support. Here the AMT 70 can act as a carrier and as a power supplier for such devices. Fig. 10 indicates the main peripheral functions, which integrate functions of the NATM.

Arch lifting can be mechanized by a very simply designed arch lifting device. This device is mounted tiltably to the cutter boom and is locked in a rear position during cutting. Afterwards

it is tilted forwards and allows placing the roof segments of the steel arches.

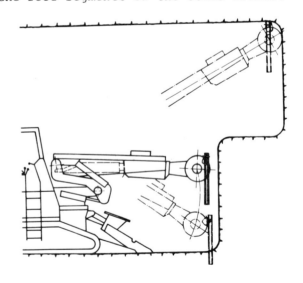

Fig. 11 Placing of steel arches

By using the cutter boom kinematic the arch can now be lifted forwards into the calot (Fig. 11) and fixed there.

282

Pile Driving and Rock Bolting

Steel piles can serve as an advanced support to protect the tunnel's crown during excavation in soft, unstable ground. Such piles are driven into the soil by hydraulic jack hammers (pile drivers). To overcome the high reaction forces from hydraulic pile driving, a pile driving device can be mounted on a supporting platform on top of the AMT 70. (Fig. 12).

This consists of a longitudinally shiftable sliding track equipped with a telescopic arm, which can be swivelled vertically or horizontally. This arm carries the actual driving boom, which is equipped with a hydraulic hammer including advance drive. This can be adjusted in every required direction to drive the steel piles or steel rods into the soil. During cutting operations the pile driving device is drawn back into a parking position.

Fig. 12 Pile driving device on AMT 70

Whereas the pile driver is designed for tunnelling in soft ground conditions, a drill boom similar to the boom described above can be attached for drilling bolt holes in every necessary direction. Driving of the rock bolting unit is effected - in the same way as of the pile driver - via the AMT 70's own hydraulic circuit.

Placing of Shotcrete

Theoretically the placing of shotcrete can be solved in the same way as pile driving or rock bolting by using a shotcrete robot, whose nozzle is mounted to a telescopic boom. Whether this method will become truly economical in the future will to a high degree depend on the developement of earlier setting mixtures, based on wet shotcrete. For alternative conventional manual spraying of shotcrete, the AMT 70 can be equipped with a working platform, which can also be used when placing the reinforcement mats.

SYSTEM FUNCTIONS AND NATM

This section will give an indication as to what extent the individual steps which are required for tunnelling according to NATM can be mechanized by the AMT 70 and its components. This check will be in 6 groups:

(a) tunnels in soil, cross section below 40 m²
(b) tunnels in soil, cross section 40-60 m²
(c) tunnels in soil, cross section more then 60 m² (long advanced top heading)
(d) tunnels in rock, cross section below 40 m²
(e) tunnels in rock, cross section 40-60 m²
(f) tunnels in rock, cross section more then 60 m² (long advanced top heading)

Fig. 13 illustrates the requirements. It will be seen that the system is able to cope with most of the individual steps over a wide range of project conditions.

Operational steps which can be mechanized by the system comprise, depending

283

	Soil Cross Section						Rock (Ucs ~ 40 MPa) Cross Section					
	< 40 m2		40–60 m2		> 60 m2		< 40 m2		40–60 m2		> 60 m2	
Excavating of Roof Section (incl.Mucking)	9,0 %	◉	9,0 %	◉	8,0 %	◉	10,5 %	◉	11,0 %	◉	12,0 %	◉
Placing of Roof Arch	4,5 %	◐	4,5 %	◐	5,5 %	◐	4,5 %	◐	5,0 %	◐	5,5 %	◐
Placing of Wire Mesh in Roof Section	6,5 %	○	6,0 %	○	6,5 %	○	5,5 %	○	5,5 %	○	5,5 %	○
Shotcreting in Roof Section	13,0 %	◐	12,0 %	◐	12,0 %	◐	10,5 %	◐	11,0 %	◐	12,0 %	◐
Excavating of Bench (incl.Mucking)	9,0 %	◉	9,0 %	◉	9,5 %	◉	10,0 %	◉	11,0 %	◉	11,0 %	◉
Placing of Steel Arches (lateral)	6,5 %	○	5,0 %	○	4,0 %	○	4,0 %	○	3,0 %	○	2,5 %	○
Placing of Wire Mesh (lateral)	4,5 %	○	3,5 %	○	3,0 %	○	4,0 %	○	3,5 %	○	3,0 %	○
Shotcreting of Side Walls	13,0 %	◐	12,5 %	◐	12,0 %	◐	11,0 %	◐	10,0 %	◐	9,0 %	◐
Excavating of Floor Arch (incl.Mucking)	4,5 %	◉	5,5 %	◉	6,0 %	◉	7,5 %	◉	8,0 %	◉	8,5 %	◉
Placing of Floor Segment (Steel Arch)	6,5 %	○	7,0 %	○	7,0 %	○	6,0 %	○	6,5 %	○	6,5 %	○
Concreting of Floor Arch	6,5 %	○	7,0 %	○	7,0 %	○	6,5 %	○	6,5 %	○	7,0 %	○
Refill of Floor Arch	4,0 %	○	4,5 %	○	4,5 %	○	4,0 %	○	4,0 %	○	3,5 %	○
Driving of Steel Piles	12,5 %	○	14,0 %	○	15,0 %	○						
Placing of Rock Bolts							16,0 %	◐	15,0 %	◐	14,0 %	◐
Percentage of Operation Time with AMT 70 – System	66,4 %		67,0 %		56,0 %		70,0 %		71,0 %		58,0 %	
	First Column: Approx. percentage of overall time of one cycle of Advance						Second Column: ◉ Basic function ◐ Already existing, or planned additional function ○ Not plannned for integration					

Fig. 13. Covering of operational steps of the NATM by the AMT 70-system

on the groups above, approx. 55-70 % of the overall time, either today or by developments in the future. The problem of bolting in smaller cross sections is still unsolved. Solutions for shotcreting (without placing of wiremesh) exist already and their integration into the system will depend on the actual demand. Other steps, like placing the arch segments for the bench and floo, and concreting the floor, are of minor interest due to the low demand in time and low requirement on physical exertion. This leads to the conclusion, that in practice, when considering system availability and rest time for the crew, a degree of utilization of the whole system between 45 and 60 % should be achievable.

As an example on the basis of a rock tunnel with 60 m² cross section and comparing the roadheader with the competitive system drill- and blast-heading, the comparison will look as follows. The following main project data are assumed:

- Unaxial compressive strength: 20 MPa
- Rock quality: moderate
- Length of single advance: 2 m
- Cross section
    roof section: 20 m²
    bench: 35 m²
    floor arch: 5 m²

Rock support consists of the following elements:
(a) Steel arch, 5 segments (without floor segment), 1 arch / unit m
(b) Rock bolts, length 4 m, 22 bolts /

284

unit m of tunnel (roof section:
10 bolts, bench: 6 bolts every side)

(c) Shotcrete 20 cm, reinforced with
2 layers of wire mesh

(d) Floor concrete 20 cm (1 layer of
wire mesh)

The equipment comprises:

(a) for drill and blast-heading
   1 drilling-jumbo with 2 drill rigs
   and basket
   1 30-t excavator
   1 wheel loader
   1 shotcrete machine
   3 dumpers

Drill and Blast—Heading

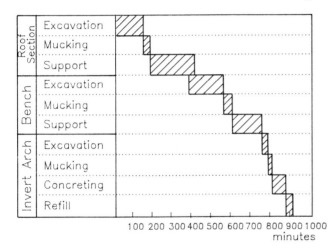

Lead time is included into the respective time values

Fig. 14 Comparison of time demand between drill- and blast heading and heading with AMT 70

(b) for mechanical excavation
   1 AMT 70 equipped with rock bolting
   device and arch lifting device
   1 wheel loader
   1 shotcrete machine
   3 dumpers

The relevant working cycles can be read
off Fig. 14. It is evident therefrom
that by application of the fully mechanized system approximately 20 % of the
time can get saved.

APPLICATION AT KARAWANKEN-TUNNEL

The Karawanken-Tunnel, which is under
construction at this time, forms an important link between Austria and Yugoslavia. After completion it will provide
an easy road connection between Carin-
thia in Austria and Slovenia in Yugoslavia.

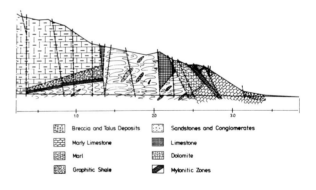

Fig. 15 Karawanken-Tunnel, Lot South, geological section

The tunnel is a two-lane road-tunnel
with a length of approximately 8,5 km.
It passes through old Paläozoic and Mesozoic layers, mainly limestone, dolomite and sandstone. These strata, which
can be found in the northern and central
part of the tunnel, can be judged as
stable over almost their entire extent.
But in the southern part the rock

Heading with AMT 70

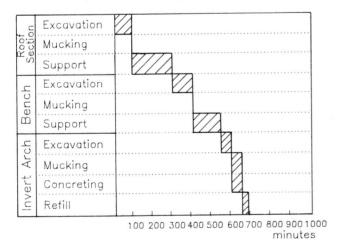

conditions are much worse. As may be seen from the geological section (Fig. 15), two main critical areas have to be passed through. One is formed by highly waterbearing brecciated talus deposits, the second by black graphitic shales.

a horizontal sliding plane and are partly heavily factured and friable. Block-like intercalations of sandstone cause additional difficulties. These two zones were planned for mechanical excavation.

Due to the large cross section of about 100 m², the tunnel is driven with a long advanced roof section of 53 m². Tunnelling is performed by NATM. A typical cross sections can be seen in Fig. 16.

For this project, the AMT 70 was used only for excavation, due to the fact that the large cross section enabled very flexible operation by single units.

These can be travelled from roof section to bench section and viceversa and their utilization will be satisfactory. Fig. 17 shows the sequence of excavation in the roof section. The unstable ground demands a more or less continuous support of the face by a "supporting wedge" and the large cross section needs a change of the position of the AMT 70 during excavation. The drawing shows the sequence of excavation which allows the best control of rock conditions in roof and face. It can be seen that one single

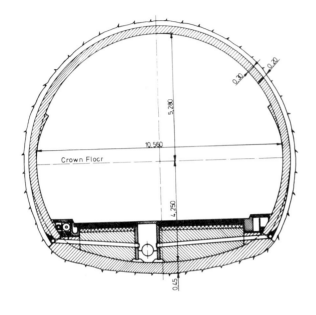

Fig. 16 Karawanken-Tunnel, typical cross
      section

These shales are situated in or close to

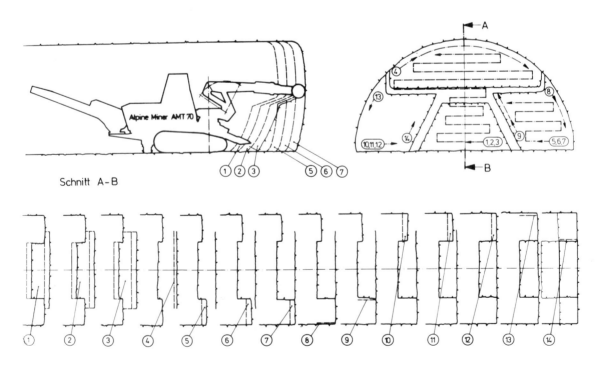

Schnitt A-B

Fig. 17. Excavation sequence with AMT 70 in roof section

advance of approx. 1,5 m from one position is performed in three steps, every advance starting with cutting the support wedge and afterwards the rest of the profile. After achieving an advance of 1.5 m, a separate step "profiling" takes place.

Alternatively the AMT 70 was also used for bench excavation. Meanwhile rock support (steel arch, rock bolts, reinforced shotcrete) took place in the roof section. Fig. 18 shows the AMT 70 during bench excavation, which was undertaken by dividing the whole excavation cycle into three steps with three single advances each, right bench, left bench and central bench.

Fig. 18. AMT 70 during bench excavation

Results of Operation

The main operational data are summarized in Table 5. These data are based on the results of a sequence of 9 working days in the talus deposits, where the AMT 70 was operated exclusively in the roof section under most difficult rock conditions (friable, instable strata and high water inflow).

Cross section total	101 m²
Rock protection / unit m of tunnel	
shotcrete (25 cm)	4,2 m³
shotcrete for face protection	0,5 m³
protective wire mesh	53 kg
steel arch (TH 27)	610 kg
steel lagging	773 kg
concrete for floor arch	3,6 m³
Total advance	27 m
Excavated volume	1.431 bank m³
Overall working time	216 h
Utilization of AMT 70	18,7 %
Cutting performance	36,2 bank m²/h
Pick consumption	0,021 picks/bank m³

Table 5: Data for AMT 70 operation in the roof section

It will be seen from Table 5, that the performance of the AMT 70 was satisfactory, mainly when considering the required multiple-step excavation cycle. Also the difficult geometry of excavation was no hindrance in achieving this value. The low degree of utilisation reflects the extremly high expenditure necessary due to the rock conditions. The extent of rock support can also be seen from Table 5. By using the AMT 70 alternately in the roof section and in the bench, this figure could be considerably increased to more than 30 %.

Conclusions and Further Steps

The main conclusions of this trial ope-

287

287

ration can be summarized as follows:

(a) cutter motor power should be increased to increase performance in harder rock strata

(b) conveyor motor power and conveyor width should be increased to cope with peak amounts of muck.

(c) increasing the range of the swivel belt conveyor appeared necessary

Further steps will now include these improvements for the next machines. One important step, which could not be checked during this operation, was the performance of the overall system. This will be the task for a further trial operation.

SUMMARY

It was the aim of this paper to present a newly designed system to mechanize tunnelling performed by NATM.

By studying the individual steps of the development and trial operation it was demonstrated that the functions "excavation" and "mucking" could be solved satisfactorely. Improvements will be focussed to improve details of the design and to increase power. Not proven up to now is the task of creating an integrated system covering all the individual functions of NATM tunnelling. These additional functions can be principally performed by already existing solutions which have been proven under other circumstances, and the equipment therefore can be attached to the ALPINE MINER AMT 70 as described. This step should not be a difficult technical problem.

Whether the full performance of the whole system - as described above - will be achieved, is at this time not mainly a question of existing technical solutions. It relates to the actual demands of a tunnel project where the specific demands require the equipping of the AMT 70 with the mentioned "peripheral" devices, as described.

References

1. Golser J. and Müller P.J. and Schramm J.M. The NATM, a Special Tunnelling Conception and its Application in poor Rock. Proceedings Geotech-80, Volume 1, 335-345

2. Müller L. Der Felsbau, Band 3, Tunnelbau. Ferdinand Enke Verlag, Stuttgart 1978

3. Rabeewicz L.v. Bemessung von Hohlraumbauten. Die "Neue Österreichische Bauweise" und ihr Einfluß auf Gebirgsdruckwirkungen und Dimensionierung. Rock Mechanics and Engineering Geology 1963, 224-243

4. Rabcewicz L.v. The New Austrian Tunnelling Method. Water Power, November, December 1964, January 1965.

5. Reuter G. Teilschnittmaschinen beim Tunnelvortrieb nach der "Neuen Österreichischen Tunnelbaumethode". Bergbau 9/1980, 505-511

6. N.N. The New Austrian Tunnelling Method. Schriftenreihe der Österreichischen Forschungsgesellschaft für das Straßenwesen, Heft 74, Wien 1980.

Slurry shield tunnelling for Mexico City

J. M. Schmitter B.Sc., C.Eng.
M. V. López Portillo B.Sc., C.Eng.
J. C. Orozco B.Sc., C.Eng.
Solum, S.A. de C.V., Mexico

SYNOPSIS

The article presents the complete 5.3 km sewer tunnel project called "Semiprofundo Iztapalapa", excavated with a 4000 mm O.D. slurry shield, at 12 m below ground level, in 28 months. Six shafts were used for the construction, all of them were sunk as caissons with the aid of flotation. To improve the ground conditions, pressure grout was applied at the begining and ending of each drive between shafts.

Primary lining was formed by precast bolted concrete segments, five pieces plus key per ring, and the final lining was cast in place reinforced concrete.

The behaviour of tunnel lining and surrounding ground showed only small movements despite the soft clayey soil in which the tunnel was excavated.

A comment is made about future uses of the system for the next tunnel projects in Mexico City.

INTRODUCTION

Tunnels and cities have a close relationship, as occurs in Mexico City.

Situated on the bottom of an old lake dewatered by the urbanization, the city has a continuous need to spread out its sewers, subway lines, utilities, etc. in its "difficult" subsoil that has called the attention of many experts in soil mechanics around the world.

The tunnel era started in the nineteen sixties, by using open face shields, sometimes with grilles or with face jacks, to dig small sewers. Compressed air was used to avoid extrusion of the clayey face.

Regional subsidence of the city caused by water pumped out for water supply, made it necessary for the main drainage system to become "Deep" to avoid disruptions and slope reversal of conduits.

One of the latest sewer projects for the city is the "Semiprofundo Iztapalapa", planned, designed and built under the guidance of the authorities of the city, "Dirección General de Construcción y Operación Hidráulica" DGCOH (General Direction of Hydraulics, Construction and Operation), as part of the Master Drainage Plan of Mexico City[1].

The project, now in operation, was built to serve as a link between a man-made regulation lagoon and a covered river (Fig. 1). Total length of tunnel is 5340m, with an internal finished diameter of 3.2m; a pumping station is used to raise the water from the tunnel to the covered river; in the future there will be a branch of the Deep Drainage System, 10 to 15m below the Semiprofundo Iztapalapa to remove the need for pumping.

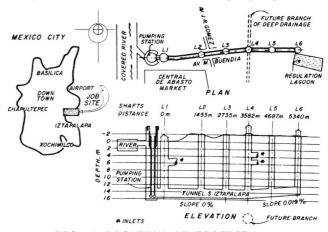

FIG. 1 LOCATION OF PROJECT.

The slurry shield technique was successfully applied for the first time in Mexico in this project, as described by -- Schmitter, Orozco and Camacho[2], after a careful analysis and study of the available tunnelling tools around the world that were suitable for the Mexico City clayey subsoil.

This paper shows the main features of

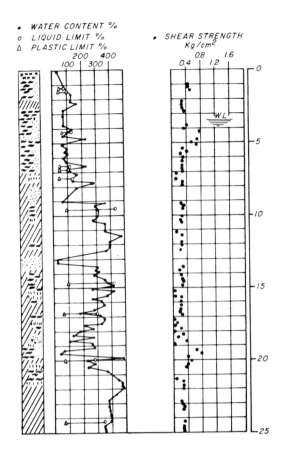

● WATER CONTENT %
○ LIQUID LIMIT %
△ PLASTIC LIMIT %

SYMBOLOGY

FILL SAND
SILT FOSSILS
CLAY VOLCANIC GLASS

FIG. 2 BORING LOG.

the construction and some data on the behaviour of the tunnel and its surrounding ground.

CONSTRUCTION FEATURES

Excavated soil.

Highly compressible clay is the predominant soil excavated by the machine. The natural water content of the clay varied between 300 and 400%, the shear strength, as measured with a torvane, is 0.23 to 0.40 kg/cm² and its bulk density is 1.15 times heavier than that of water.

Lenses of sand, 0.5m thick, are present in the clay excavated by the shield. A typical boring log is shown in Fig. 2.

Access Shafts.

As shown in Fig. 1, six shafts from L1 to L6 were used for the project. These were built as caissons using the flotation principle to sink the shaft in a reservoir filled with bentonite mud to avoid bottom failure of the soft soil.

The construction procedure as developed by Cravioto J. and Villarreal A[3]. includes the following activities, Fig. 3.

a) Excavation of a circumferential trench, 0.6m wide, 21m deep and with an external diameter of 14m; which is stabilized with bentonite mud and a heavy concrete collar at ground level.

b) Excavation of central core and simultaneous filling with bentonite mud to avoid bottom failure or collapse of the clay sides. As a result a 14m diameter cylindrical reservoir, 21 m deep and full

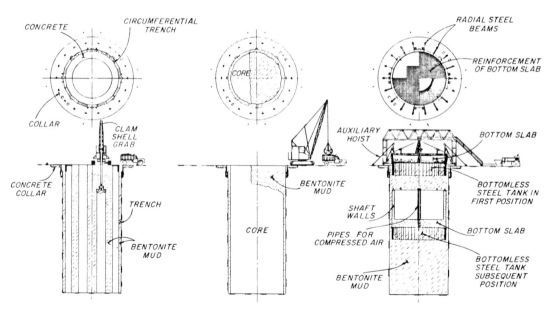

FIG. 3 SHAFT SINKING

290

of bentonite mud is formed.

c) Placement on top of the reservoir, of a bottomless cylindrical floating tank made of steel plate, of 13m diameter and 3m height. This tank is temporarily supported on the concrete collar, by means of several radial steel beams.

d) Pouring of the concrete for bottom slab and a small portion of the walls of shaft, on top of the floating tank.

e) Applying compressed air, the floating tank is forced upwards until a balance between the weight of the concrete and the displaced mud is obtained. The radial steel beams become free and the tank is allowed to sink under control to a depth where the newly formed section of the concrete wall is supported again on

the radial steel beams.

f) The process is repeated again and again, adding new portions of the concrete wall and balancing the floating forces acting on the shaft under construction, until bottom slab reaches its final depth.

g) Finally, the bentonite mud, which remained during the sinking process between the shaft walls and the inside of the floating tank, is displaced by means of a heavy grout made with cement mortar.

Ground treatment

To avoid instability of the soil while cutting the concrete wall of the shaft to launch the shield or to receive it in the next shaft, ground treatment based on pressure grout was carried out at each shaft (Fig. 4).

The pressure grout was applied through pipes with holes, covered with sleeves, placed in the subsoil.

Shaft seal

The slurry shield, once in the ground, has enough sealing effect between soil and machine to sustain the design pressure at face, but in the first meters a shaft seal must be placed to solve the problem.

Slurry shield

The specially designed slurry shield used in this project was manufactured by Okumura Corp. of Japan, with a 4.000m O.D. and 6.300m length, as shown in Fig.5.

It was recommended for this machine that the total weight divided by the displaced volume should be equivalent to the bulk density of the excavated soil to avoid

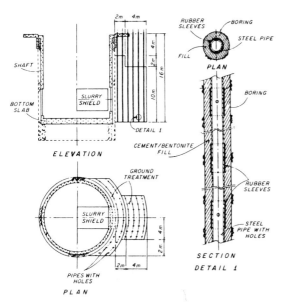

FIG. 4 GROUND TREATMENT.

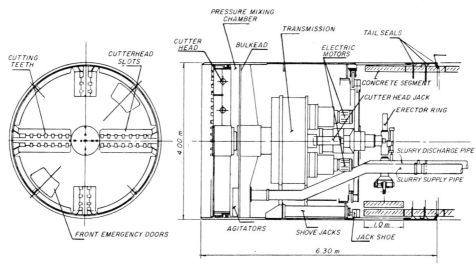

FRONT VIEW   LONGITUDINAL SECTION

FIG. 5 SLURRY SHIELD.

the tendency either to sink or to float.

The combined action of a cutterhead that can support both face and slurry pressure offered extra safety provisions. The bentonite slurry used in the system was formed from the natural excavated clay, which is bentonitic, and water from the municipal treatment plant, which were mixed in surface ponds near the access shafts. The applied pressure at face was 0.7 kg/cm^2 and was selected after Broms and Bennermark[4] formula for extrusion of soft clays.

Disposal of muck

The benefit of a bentonitic natural soil, with high water content is partially countered by the difficulty of an easy separation of the water from the soil.

Fortunately it was possible to dispose of the excavated soil plus light slurry, in the form of a heavy slurry, by means of pipe trucks and dump trucks.

The pumping system was capable of handling a supply slurry to the face with a bulk density of 1.04 and a discharge slurry from the face with a bulk density of 1.10.

Concrete lining

The primary lining was formed by bolted sealed concrete segments, 1.000m wide, 0.175m thick, six pieces per ring, with an external diameter of 3.850m as shown in Fig. 6.

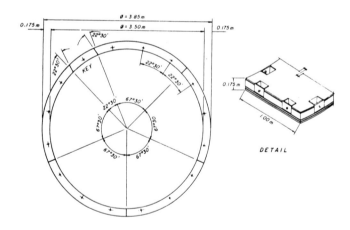

FIG. 6 PRIMARY LINING.

The placing of contact grout in the void between the concrete segments and the natural soil was carried out during shoving. Bentonite, cement and sand were mixed with water in a grout plant located at the shaft. A travelling container car was used to transport the grout.

Final lining was formed by cast in place reinforced concrete, 0.150m thick, which

provided an internal finished diameter of 3.200m for the conduit.

Driving and lining program.

The driving and lining program for the complete project, as prepared by López Portillo[5], is shown in Fig. 7.

This includes excavation with erection of the primary lining and concreting of the final lining for the 5340 meters.

The standing times at each shaft include change of installations, machine overhauling, and in some cases waiting for orders.

Gross average advance rate for excavation and primary lining including standing times at shafts was 6.24m/day.

Net average advance rate excluding standing times at shafts was 8.32 m/day.

Daily average per working day was 10.12m

Maximum advances for excavation and primary lining were:

        18m per day
        89m per week
       360m per month

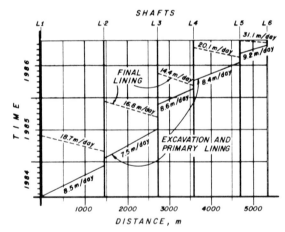

FIG. 7 DRIVING AND LINING PROGRAM

Maximum advances for final lining were:

        42m per day
       295m per week
      1019m per month

Settlement

The movements induced at the surface during tunnelling were levelled against bench marks, showing an average settlement of 12mm, with maximum of 25 mm.

Fig. 8 shows a typical settlement diagram, with some uplift at edges. Fig. 9 shows a time settlement diagram for a typical surface point, with some interesting recuperation of settlement with time.

red at the bottom of the inclinometer casing.

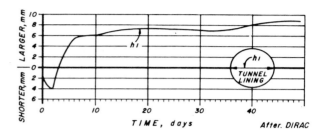

FIG. 10 CHANGES IN HORIZONTAL DIAMETER

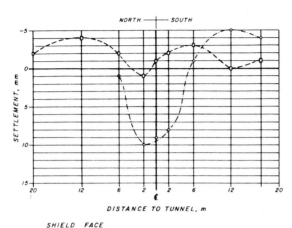

SHIELD FACE
o——o——o AT SECTION
o——o——o ONE MONTHS AFTER

FIG. 8 SETTLEMENT DIAGRAM

The guidance and topografic survey assisted by laser allowed the arrival of the shield at the shafts with average deviations of 26mm in line and 83 mm in grade.

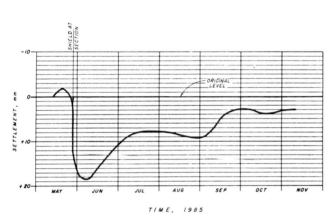

FIG. 9 SETTLEMENT-TIME DIAGRAM

The internal horizontal diameter of primary lining was measured by DIRAC[6] over a time period and typical results are plotted in Fig. 10. First there is a reduction of about 4mm while the tail seals pass over the ring, then an enlargement that reaches 6mm in six days and finally a tendency to stabilization with deformations of less than 0.07mm/day.

The surrounding soil shows displacements caused by shield advance, as measured with an inclinometer, Fig. 11.

In this instrumentation, the inclinometer casing was placed before the tunnel excavation, on the projected centre line, with the lowest point of casing located 30cm above the crown of the shield. Displacements of as much as 10mm were measured

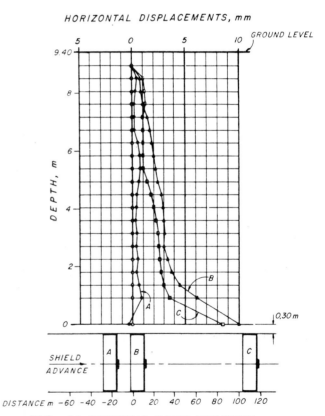

FIG. 11 EXTERNAL DISPLACEMENTS.

CONCLUSIONS

The continuous growth of Mexico City with almost 14 million inhabitants, is responsible for the need for new tunnels, some of them "deep" at around 30m below ground level.

The soft clay which forms the main component of the subsoil, with high ground

water levels, is a difficult material to tunnel in. If improperly excavated it can cause very high settlements on the surface of almost 500mm, and diametral deformations of primary lining of the order of 350mm as described by Schmitter and Moreno.[7]

The use of the slurry shield technique brings a new horizon to the tunnelling that the city needs, with almost twice the speed of construction and drastic decrease of settlement on the surface and in the deformation of primary lining. The continuous pressure on the face while it is being excavated and the simultaneous grouting of the annular space, between lining and soil, make a perfect combination to avoid excesive settlements.

The well known system of compressed air with open face shield, was practically limited to a maximum pressure of 1.5 kg/cm^2 for human and economical reasons, because of the high altitude of Mexico City, which is almost 2240m over sea level. The slurry shield does not have that limitation.

The Semiprofundo Iztapalapa project (Fig. 12) was to some extent the final stage of an experimental study that was started back in 1978 when engineers from DGCOH were looking for a tunnelling machine that could work in the sensitive, very soft clays of the city.

FIG. 12 SEMIPROFUNDO IZTAPALAPA

It is interesting to note that the bentonitic clayey subsoil of the city does not need any additional material to form the slurry for circulation other than water.

The soft condition of the soil permits fast and easy excavation, but disposal is a more serious problem, since at present there is no treatment plant, just a sedimentation pond.

At present, the DGCOH with the new experience, has put to work two additional

tunnelling machines of the same type but with an O.D. of 6.240m, on drainage projects, in Mexico City with excelent results, to avoid future flooding problems of southern and eastern zones.

Future tunnelling works for subway or deep drainage are being considered using similar machines. The relatively high initial cost for the equipment is compensated by the speed of construction, thus lowering the actual price of the tunnel.

References

1. DDF, DGCOH, El sistema hidráulico del Distrito Federal. Un servicio público en transición, DDF, 1982.

2. Schmitter M.J., Orozco C.J. and Camacho O.P. Slurry Shield at Mexico City Clay. Underground Structures in Urban Areas, ITA, Tunnel City 1985, - Prague, Sept. 1985.

3. Cravioto J. and Villarreal A. Recent Experience in the Construction of - Tunnels and Shafts in the City of Mexico, Constructora Estrella, S. A., México 1966.

4. Broms, B. and Bennermark, L. Stability of Clay at Vertical Openings J. Soil Mech. and found. Div. Proc. ASCE 93 1967 SMI: 71 - 94.

5. López Portillo V. M. Procedimiento constructivo del colector Semiprofundo Iztapalapa mediante la utilización de un escudo de frente cerrado, presurizado con lodos, AMITOS, 1987.

6. DIRAC, S.A. de C.V. Informes de la instrumentación del colector Semiprofundo Iztapalapa, presentados a la Dirección General de Construcción y Operación Hidráulica, 1986.

7. Schmitter M.J. and Moreno F.A. Tunel con deformaciones excesivas, Seventh Panamerican Conference on Soil Mechanics and Foundation Engineering, Panam 83, Canadian Geotechnical Society 1983.

LIST OF CAPTIONS

FIG. 1   LOCATION OF PROJECT
FIG. 2   BORING LOG
FIG. 3   SHAFT SINKING
FIG. 4   GROUND TREATMENT
FIG. 5   SLURRY SHIELD
FIG. 6   PRIMAY LINING
FIG. 7   DRIVING AND LINING PROGRAM
FIG. 8   SETTLEMENT DIAGRAM
FIG. 9   SETTLEMENT-TIME DIAGRAM
FIG.10   CHANGES IN HORIZONTAL DIAMETER
FIG.11   EXTERNAL DISPLACEMENTS
FIG.12   SEMIPROFUNDO IZTAPALAPA

Ground movements and settlements caused by tunnelling for the Singapore Mass Rapid Transit System

J. N. Shirlaw B.Sc., C.Eng., M.I.C.E., M.H.K.I.E., F.G.S.
S. Doran B.Sc., C.Eng., M.I.C.E.
Mass Rapid Transport Corporation, Singapore

SYNOPSIS

Analysis of the settlements over the bored tunnels of the Singapore Mass Rapid Transit System has, so far, been concerned mainly with 3 topics. These are: a comparison of the effects of different tunnelling methods in similar ground; the extent and magnitude of consolidation settlements; and the effects of tunnel/tunnel interaction. It was found that the New Austrian Tunnelling Method produced generally lower and more consistent settlements than shield tunnelling in stiff boulder clay. In the soft clays and sands of the Kallang deposit the immediate settlement over open shields with compressed air were similar to those over Earth Pressure Balance Shields. Consolidation settlements in the often highly compressible Singapore soils could be large, but the use of compressed air and well sealed lining helped reduce such settlements. The high shove pressures used with the Earth Pressure Balance Shields generated high pore pressures. Dissipation of these pore pressures caused consolidation settlements that followed an error-function curve distribution. Tunnel/tunnel interaction was found in both the stiff boulder clays and the soft marine clays, but the effect was generally small. The use of the BAT probe to monitor pore pressures around tunnels and the effects of the various modes of settlement on adjacent structures are also discussed.

INTRODUCTION

It is a basic requirement of tunnelling that the construction should not cause undue damage to any surrounding or overlying structure or services. In order to satisfy this criterion it is necessary to be able to predict both the ground movements associated with various tunnelling methods and the tolerance of the surrounding structures. Although some notable work has been done using both centrifuge modelling and finite element methods for parametric studies of tunnel effects, much can still be learnt from back-analysis of field measurement.

The construction of the Singapore Mass Rapid Transit System has included 11.2 route kilometres formed by twin bored tunnels. Internal diameter of the tunnels varied from 5.23m to 5.4m. The tunnelling contracts and the superficial geology are shown in Figure 1.

Settlement monitoring over the tunnels has been carried out by placing arrays of markers at right angles to the tunnels. The arrays are placed at 15 to 25m intervals and consisted of 4 to 13 markers each. As a rough estimate, some 2500 settlement points were installed just to monitor ground movements over the tunnels. This figure does not include the settlement points installed on buildings, or to monitor the effects of cut-and-cover station excavation. With each settlement point being monitored generally between 30 and 100 times the total number of readings taken was well over 100,000.

A summary of all the available data would be impossible in the limited space available here. However, analysis of the results has concentrated on certain specific areas of interest. These are:-

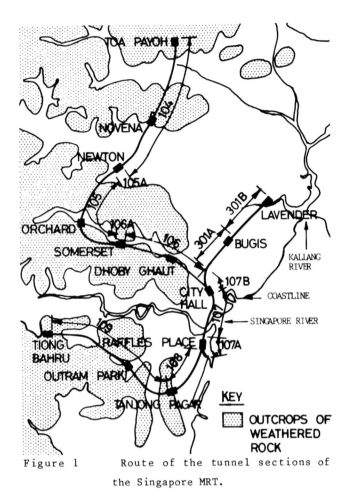

Figure 1   Route of the tunnel sections of
the Singapore MRT.

a) A comparison of different tunnelling methods
   in similar geological strata.
b) The relative magnitude and extent of
   settlements caused by changes in pore
   pressures, i.e. consolidation.
c) The problem of tunnel-tunnel interaction.
Before summarising the findings on these topics,
a quick resume of the engineering properties of
the Singapore soils will be given.

Engineering Geology
The area shown in Figure 1 included five
different major geological units: The Kallang,
Jurong and Old Alluvium formations, Bukit Timah
Granite and the Singapore Boulder Bed. These
units are described in greater detail below, and
some typical engineering properties as used in
design are shown in Table 1.

a)   Kallang Formation (K)
     The Kallang Formation (Singapore PWD)
     includes most of the recent holocene and
     late pleistocene deposits. It is of
     importance both because of its extent, Tan

and Lee[2] estimated that 25% of Singapore
was covered by Kallang formation, and its
nature. The soft clays and permeable sands
of the formation pose many of the most
interesting geotechnical problems in
Singapore. The formation can be subdivided
into four major sub-groups of different
engineering properties.

ai)   Marine Clay (M)
The most important of the sub-groups is the
marine clay, which consists of an upper and
a lower member. The upper member is
generally close to normally consolidated,
while the lower member is slightly
overconsolidated. The plasticity index of
the clay is in the range of 30 to 80, and
the Cu/p' ratio varies from 0.25 to 0.32.
This means that shear strengths generally
vary in the range 15 to 70kpa with depth.
It has a sensitivity on average of about 4.
The maximum depth to the base of the lower
marine clay found under Singapore is 40m.

The marine clay is compressible, with an
average Cc of 0.85. Large consolidation
settlements are often noted around
sheetpiled excavation due to this high
compressibility.

aii)   Estuarine Clay (E)
Inland the soft clays become much more
organic and are generally described as
Estuarine. The organic content is very
variable, and this results in an extremely
variable water content, from 20% to 700%.
The shear strength of the clay is often
very low, below 10kpa, and it is highly
compressible. Cc values of over 5 have
been recorded, although 1 to 2 is more
common.

aiii) Fluvial Clay (F2)
In between the upper and lower members, and
sometimes below the lower member, a thin
(2-5m) layer of stiffer, dessicated clay is
often found. The shear strength of this
layer, generally 60 to 100kpa, is
sufficient to make it important as a
significant restraint for sheetpiles.

TABLE 1

Soil Type	Bulk Density (Mg/m^3)	Undrained Shear Strength (kpa)	Drained Friction Angle	PI	Cc	Cv m^2/yr	K cm/sec
Marine Clay (M)	1.5 - 1.7	15 to 70	22°	30-80	0.85	2	$10^{-9} - 10^{-7}$
Fluvial Clay (F2)	1.7 - 2.0	50 to 100	22°	10-50	0.20	10	$10^{-8} - 10^{-5}$
Estuarine Clay (E)	1.1 - 1.6	5 to 50	5°	10-120	1-5	10	$10^{-9} - 10^{-5}$
Fluvial Sand (F1)	1.7 - 1.9	-	30°-35°	-	-	-	$10^{-5} - 10^{-1}$
Old Alluvium (O)	2.0 - 2.2	50 to 300	35°	10-50	-	25	$10^{-8} - 10^{-4}$
Weathered Granite (G4)	1.7 - 1.9	35 to 100	30°	10-50	0.1	40	$10^{-8} - 10^{-5}$

aiv) Fluvial Sand (F1)

Associated with the fluvial clay, or in the body of the marine clay, occur lenses of fluvial sand. The nature of the sand in these lenses varies greatly, from poorly to well graded. The permeability of the sand lenses is several orders greater than that of the surrounding clays.

b) Jurong Formation (S)

The Jurong formation comprises interlayed sedimentary rocks including sandstone, mudstone and siltstone. The formation is variably weathered. The weathering grade used in Singapore are slightly different from those recommended by the Geological Society of London[3]. As applied to the Jurong formation they are:-

S1 Fresh and slightly weathered rock.
S2 Moderately and highly weathered rock.
S3 Completely weathered rock.

c) Old Alluvium (O)

The old alluvium consists of semi-lithified sands and overconsolidated clays of middle-pleistocene age.

d) Bukit Timah Granite (G)

Bukit Timah Granite is used as a broad classification for a suite of granitic rocks including granodiorites and micro-granites. Granite, in its strictest sense, is not common in Singapore.

The weathering products of the Bukit Timah granite are commonly classified as G1, G2 and G4, as for the sedimentary rocks of the Jurong Formation. Because the parent rocks are mostly fine grained the G4 is a silty clay or clayey silt, very different from the weathered granite found in Hong Kong. The transition from G4 to G1 is often fairly abrupt.

e) Singapore Boulder Bed (S3)

Underneath much of the Central Business District of Singapore is a material often called the 'Singapore Boulder Bed' Pitts[4].

It does not outcrop anywhere, and so is not shown in Figure 1. Near the Singapore River, however, it comes very close to the surface, particularly in the area of Raffles Place Station, and it was encountered in a significant proportion of the tunnels constructed under contracts 106, 107B, 107A and 108.

The bed consists of sandstone boulders in a matrix of stiff, consolidated clays. The boulders are often very large, up to $200m^3$, and very strong, with unconfined compressive strengths in the range 50 to 180Mpa.

Selection of Tunnelling Methods

Methods of tunnelling had to be flexible enough to cope with ground conditions that, on most contracts, varied from very hard sandstones to soft marine clays. The bulk of the bored tunnelling work was therefore carried out with Greathead type shield machines. These were equipped either with a road header or back-actor buckets for excavation. In the case of Contract 108 the shield was designed so that the roadheader was removed after a section in S1/S2, to be replaced by a backactor in the Kallang deposit. Face rams, breasting plates, and extendable decks and hoods were also generally provided. Compressed air, jet grouting, chemical grouting and lime piles were used to aid face stability in unstable ground.

On two contracts the contractors used fully mechanised tunnel boring machines. On C105 a Hitachi-Zosen drum-digger was used to drive 3 tunnels in G4 and Kallang Deposit. On C301B two earth pressure balance machines were used to drive 760m between Lavender and Bugis Stations. These drives were almost entirely in Kallang deposits, with Old Alluvium occassionally occurring below axis level (Elias and Mizuno[5]).

The New Austrian Tunnelling Method was adopted for short lengths of tunnel on three contracts, C104, 105 and 107A as shown in Table 2.

Precast concrete linings were used on all the shield drives, both semi- and fully mechanical, except the C105 drives with the Drum digger. This machine erected a temporary lining of circular steel ribs and timber lagging. Once

TABLE 2

Contract	Geological Unit Tunnelled	Method of Tunnelling	Additional Measures
C104	G4	NATM then shield	C.A.
	S1/S2	NATM	
	K	Shield	C.A. + chemical grouting in F1
C105	G4	Drum Digger (3 drives) NATM then shield (1 drive)	C.A.
	K	Drum Digger	C.A.
C106	S3 & S4	Shield	
	K	Shield	Jet Grouting
C107	S4	Shield	
	K	Shield	C.A. + chemical & jet grout-
C107A	S3	NATM	
	K	NATM	Chemical grouting in F1
C107B	S3/S4	Hand drive/ shield	
C108	S3	Shield	C.A.
	K	Shield	C.A. + Jet grouting
C109	S1/S2/S4	Shield	C.A.
C301A	S3/S4	Shield	C.A.
	K	Shield	C.A. + chemical grouting in F1
C301B	K	EPBM	

the drive was complete and the compressed air removed, a permanent lining was cast in-situ. In the NATM tunnels a permanent lining was constructed after the completion of the temporary lining of shotcrete, mesh and light ribs.

Due to the highly compressible nature of some of the overlying soils, particularly the estuarine and marine clays, a stringent water-tightness specification was required for the tunnels. An average maximum flow of $5ml/m^2/hour$ and a local maximum of $10ml/m^2/hour$ over a 10m section was specified (Copsey and Doran[6]). For the P.C.C. rings all the contractors, who were responsible for detailed design, proposed to use sealing material located in grooves near the rear face of the segments as the primary defence against water ingress. The materials used on Phase 1 (Contracts 104 to 109) varied considerably, including Bitumastic Strips, neoprene gaskets and composite neoprene and bitumastic strips. Not one of these proved fully effective. To meet the specifications additional measures including back-grouting, caulking and water activated polyeurethane foams were adopted.

On Contract 301 a water expansive gasket of a proprietary brand 'hydrotite' was used. This proved extremely effective in producing an extremely dry tunnel immediately on construction.

MONITORING AND METHODS OF ANALYSIS
Only a very generalised requirement for monitoring over tunnels was given in the specification. As the detailed design was carried out by the contractors the result was that the type and layout of monitoring varied considerably from contract to contract. The only aspect reasonably common to all contracts were surface and building settlement points. Surface settlement points were installed in arrays at right angles over the tunnels, with the arrays typically every 15 to 25m along the alignment. The arrays varied from 5 points, extending only 5m on either side of the tunnels, to 13 points extending up to 30m from the centre line. All buildings close to the line of the tunnels were also monitored for settlement.

Generally relatively little use was made of piezometers, extensometers or inclinometers for routine monitoring. These instruments were typically only used for intensive monitoring at points of particular interest. Examples of the more intensive monitoring including a study of four tunnel interaction (described in Lo et al[7]), the effects of NATM tunnels passing under the corner of an underground carpark (described below) and the lateral and vertical movements resulting from the C301 Earth Pressure Balance Shields.

Surface settlement readings generally had to be interpreted in isolation due to the absence of other instrumentation. It was known that settlement was generally due to three basic causes: ground loss at the face and tailskin, consolidation and tunnel/tunnel interaction. Each of these basic causes appeared to give a distinct pattern which could be picked out from the data:-

a) Ground (or immediate) loss
This settlement occurs as the face is driven under the settlement point, and the transverse array has the form of an error function curve (Schmidt[8], Peck[9]).

b) Consolidation
This settlement is often associated with the removal of compressed air from a tunnel (Glossop and Farmer[10]). Hurrell[11] has suggested that the resulting trough is a double error function curve and is in proportion to the amount of ground loss. Fitzpatrick, Kulhawy and O'Rourke[12], however, have shown from computer studies that anistropy can have a major influence on the width of any resulting settlement trough. Cater et al[13] have given examples which show that consolidation settlements are not related to the magnitude of ground loss settlements, and that they can be asymmetrical in asymmetrical geology.

Glossop and O'Reilly[14] have shown that the settlement on decompression of compressed air tunnels follows a straight line when plotted against time on a logarithmic scale.

By plotting transverse troughs at different periods, and by plotting settlement against log time it was generally possible to separate out immediate and consolidation settlements with a reasonable degree of certainty, as will be shown below.

c) Tunnel/Tunnel Interaction

All the MRT bored tunnels are in pairs, either northbound and southbound on Phase 1 or westbound and eastbound on Phase 2A. The two Phases join at City Hall and Raffles Place Stations, where passengers will interchange. On C107 four running tunnels were driven between these two stations.

The presence of the first tunnel can have a significant effect on the settlement caused by the driving of a second tunnel. This has been pointed out by Schmidt[8]. The trough of settlement over a second tunnel can be asymetrical, leaning towards the first tunnel.

Prediction of settlements due to tunnelling

The prediction of settlement over tunnels is of great importance in urban areas. However the methods of prediction currently used are generally very coarse, so that predicted and actual settlements can vary by an order of magnitude in exceptional cases. The best available methods relate to tunnelling in clays. It has been shown by various authors that the settlement ratio, the area of the settlement trough to area of the tunnel face, can be related to the stability number, N, as defined by Broms and Bennermark[15]. Even then the proposed design lines vary quite cnsiderably, such that for a given stability number the settlement can vary by a factor of at least 3 depending on whose proposed relationship is adopted. A sample of such design curves is given in Figure 6.

Parametric studies have been carried out by many authors using either finite element analysis or laboratory centrifuges. Unfortunately finite element analyses are frequently carried out as plane strain problems with little real appreciation of the process of tunnelling. More appropriate 3 dimensional models are now being used (Fujimori et al[16], Baudendistel[17]), and appear to be yielding interesting results. Laboratory centrifuge models published to date have also not modelled the full process of tunnelling, but have still provided a valuable guide on the relationship between factors such as unsupported length and settlement.

Very little has been published on how the settlement is affected by different tunnelling methods. It is rare to have the opportunity to study different methods in similar ground in the field. Because most numerical and laboratory methods simplify the process of excavation they tend to yield the same answer irrespective of the method of tunnelling.

Predictive methods for consolidation settlement during and after tunnelling are rare in the literature. One notable exception is Hurrell.

The Singapore MRT included different methods of tunnelling in similar ground, and tunnellling in or under soils that are very prone to consolidation. The major purpose of this paper is therefore to shed some further light on these aspects.

THE EFFECT OF DIFFERENT TUNNELLING METHODS

Two detailed studies of different tunnelling methods is marine clay and in the Singapore boulder bed have already been published by the current authors (Shirlaw, Doran and Benjamin[18], Shirlaw and Copsey[19]). The findings are summarised below:-

Tunnelling in Kallang Formation

Four methods of tunnelling in the predominantly soft clays of the Kallang formation were studied by Shirlaw and Copsey[19]. These were:-

C104 & C301A	Greathead type shields with compressed air.
C105	Drum-digger with compressed air.
C108	Greathead type shields with jet grouting and compressed air.
C301B	Earth pressure balance shields.

On contracts 108 and 105 it was concluded that the settlement was so dominated by consolidation that little detailed information on immediate settlements could be obtained. Two general conclusions were reached. One was that overall settlements over the C108 tunnels were reduced by the jet grouting. The reduction, up to 60mm, could be related to the virtual elimination of ground loss settlements by the presence of a 1.5m thick annulus of cement grout around the tunnel. However, this beneficial effect has to be considered together with the large heave, up to 400mm, experienced during jet grouting (Berry et al[20]).

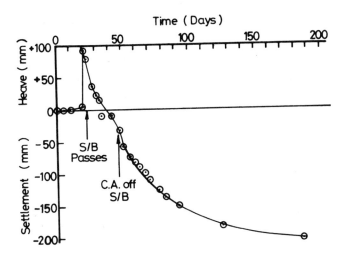

Figure 2   Development of settlement with time over the southbound Orchard to Newton tunnel, driven by drum-digger.

The development of settlement with time over the C105 drum-digger is shown in Figure 2. The machine was operated in soft clays as a type of EPBS. The operator tried to balance the rate of extraction of spoil against the rate of shoving. However, the machine did not have the sophisticated pressure sensors and other measuring devices available on a true EPBS. The result was often, as shown in Figure 2, a large initial heave. Once the compressed air was removed large consolidation settlements occurred. This will be discussed below.

A direct comparison of settlements over tunnels driven with Greathead shields in compressed air, on C104 and C301A, could be made with the EPBS tunnels on C301B. It was found that the ground loss settlement developed over a period of between 1 to 3 weeks. When the troughs for this period were plotted, as in Figures 3 and 4, the results were close to the

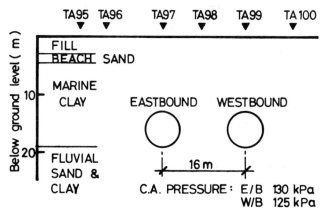

Figure 3a   Settlement array TA95 to 100 over C301A C.A. Tunnels.

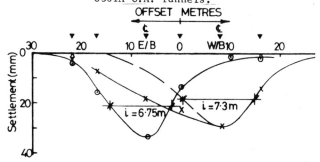

⊙ Measured settlement due to E/B passing
x Measured settlement due to W/B passing

Figure 3B   Settlement troughs developed up to 14 days after each shield passes, TA95 to 100.

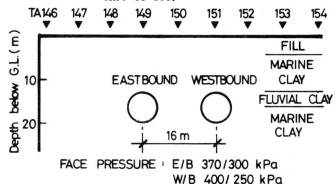

Figure 4a   Settlement array TA146 to 154 over C301B EPBS Tunnels.

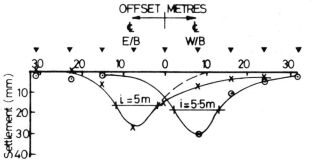

⊙ Measured settlement due to E/B passing
x Measured settlement due to W/B passing

Figure 4b   Settlement troughs developed up to 14 days after each shield passes, TA146 to 154.

301

typical error function curve. For both cases there was a definite 'lean' of the trough due to a second tunnel towards the first tunnel. After this effect had been removed, as shown, the settlement ratio for each type of tunnel was calculated. The results are shown as a histogram in Figure 5. It can be seen that the immediate, ground loss, settlements over the two cases was remarkably similar, with most cases being under 3%.

It was found that while the magnitude of the ground loss was similar, the troughs over the EPBS tunnels were noticeably narrower. 'i' values represented about 0.375 x depth to axis (Z), compared with the approximately 0.5Z found for the compressed air tunnels.

The settlement values over the EPBS tunnels was only achieved by using very high pressures during the shove, typically 1.2 to 1.4 times the total overburden pressure. Originally a pressure closer to the estimated ko value had been used, but it was found that settlements over the first tunnel were then much higher than expected. Using the higher shove pressures resulted in smaller settlements, 30 to 40mm typically, and little measurable heave ahead of the shield.

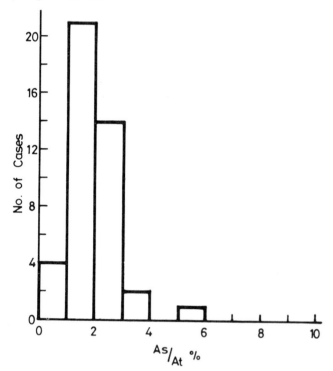

Figure 5a   Histogram of immediate ('ground loss') settlement over C301B EPBS Tunnels.

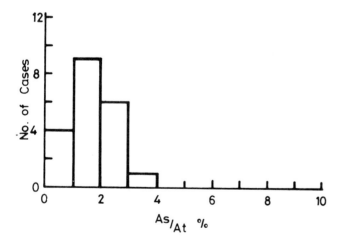

Figure 5b   Histogram of immediate settlement over C301A Tunnels.

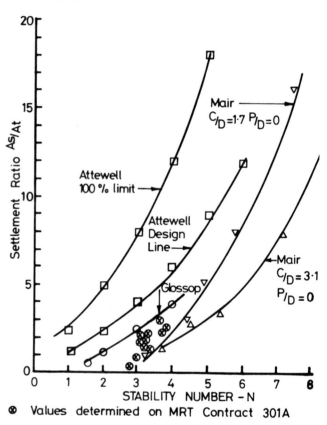

Figure 6   Relationship between N and $^{As}/A_T$ derived by various authors.

To compare the achieved results with various possible predictive curves the settlement ratios from the C301A tunnels has been plotted against stability number in Figure 6. For calculating the stability number, N, the following equation has been used:-

$$N = \frac{\sigma_{vo} - P_T}{C_v}$$

C_v, the shear strength of the marine clay, as measured by the field vane test has been used without correcting for plasticity index. Correction factors, as suggested by Bjerrum[21], are commonly used in Singapore for embankments and deep excavations, but it is questionable whether they should be used for tunnels.

It can be seen from Figure 6 that the line proposed by Glossop gives a good upper boundary for the field values. The curves derived from centrifuge work published by Mair[21] provides a good lower bound. The centrifuge derived curves represented in Figure 6 are those assuming full crown support at all times. The field measured values, where crown support is temporarily lacking before the ring is grouted, are thus expected to be higher. The significant difference between the measured values and the design line proposed by Attewell[23] can probably be related to 3 factors:-

a) The very high degree of workmanship and supervision applied in Singapore due to tunnels being in an urban area. Rings were invariably grouted as soon as they left the tailskin in soft ground. Attewell notes that this was rarely the case in the examples studied by him.

b) The size of the tunnels. There appears to be some indication that smaller tunnels produce higher settlement ratios.

c) The rigorous exclusion of consolidation settlements in this analysis.

The stability number for the EPBS was negative, because of the very high face pressures used. The reason why the immediate settlement over the EPBS tunnels was similar to that over the compressed air tunnels, despite the marked difference in pressure, can be explained by the observe ground behaviour behind the shield. Clay around the compressed air tunnels maintained a void so that a solid skin of grout could be achieved. In the EPBS tunnels the unsupported clay dropped straight onto the rings as soon as the shield was shoved.

Although the rings were still grouted this grout tended to form bulbs and fractures in the ground and not to flow around the ring. Confirmation of this behaviour was obtained when a segment was taken cut for cross-passage construction and the grout behaviour could be clearly seen.

The high slurry pressures used generated outward ground movement, as recorded by Elias and Mizuno[5]. They measured a heave of 6mm ahead of the shield, and lateral movements of up to 4mm. This outward movement must have partly compensated for the inward movement at the tail skin. This behaviour was similar to that recorded by Clough Finno and Sweeney[24] with a similar machine in San Francisco.

Tunnels in 'Singapore Boulder Bed'

Two methods were used to drive tunnels through the S3. On contracts 108, 107B and 106 shields were used, generally without compressed air. The boulders encountered posed formidable problems to excavation. The shields were sometimes in virtually a full face of 150Mpa sandstone, which greatly restricted progress.

On contract 107A, the contractor had initially proposed to use shields to drive two 170m tunnels to link Raffles Place Station with future cut-and-cover tunnels under the Telok Ayer Basin. However, programming problems and the difficulties experienced with boulders elsewhere in the S3 led the contractor to put forward an alternative proposal, to drive the tunnels using the NATM. The alignment of the two tunnels was extremely close, with, in places, barely 2.5m between the tunnels' extrados. The tunnels also had to pass under the corner of an underground carpark, as shown in Figure 7. Settlements were consequently a major concern in assessing the revised method.

By the time the revised method of working was proposed there was already evidence of significant settlements over shields in S3. Cater et al had shown that in Hong Kong settlements over shield driven tunnels in ground containing large boulders were up to four times as large as over NATM tunnels in similar ground. The proposed method was therefore accepted, subject to intensive monitoring of ground movements so that the assumptions could be checked before the carpark was reached.

303

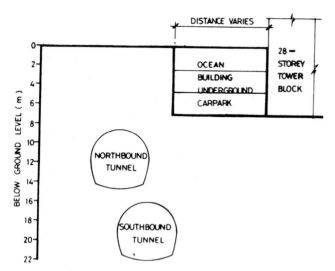

Figure 7   Section of C107A tunnels passing underneath Ocean Building Carpark.

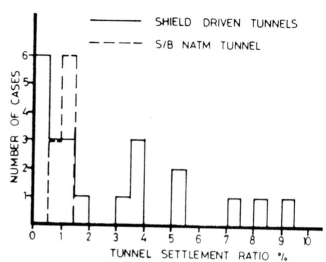

Figure 8   Histogram of tunnel settlement ratio, comparing shield driven and NATM tunnels in Singapore 'Boulder Bed'.

The lower, southbound tunnel was driven first and the permanent lining cast before driving the upper, northbound, tunnel. Settlement monitoring over the southbound showed typical settlement curves which could be approximated as error functions. 'i' values were of the order of 0.5Z. Settlement over the northbound was both larger and had the same trough width as the deeper southbound tunnel. The unusual settlement behaviour over the northbound was considered to be mainly due to tunnel/tunnel interaction by Shirlaw, Doran and Benjamin. This aspect will be discussed in greater detail below. Because of the interaction, and because the northbound was generally very close to the upper surface of the S3, the settlements over the northbound were considered atypical.

The settlements over the southbound only were plotted as settlement ratio on a histogram as shown in Figure 8. All the results fall into a narrow band between 0.5% and 1.5%. When the results of shield driven tunnels are added to the histogram it can be seen that these are much more varied, with settlement ratios as high as 9.5%. Because of the high strength of the S3 matrix the stability number of both the NATM and shield tunnels, although in free air, must have been less than 3, and probably down below 2. In view of these values, the settlement ratios of up to 10% must be considered highly unusual. It seems probable that the cause was the overbreak inevitably produced when removing hard rock by explosives, chemical splitting or percussion.

The shield tunnellers were somewhat cautious in grouting this overbreak because of the danger of grout moving forward into voids over the shield and building up on the skin. The shotcrete used for the NATM tunnel provided quick support directly onto the ground irrespective of the excavated profile.

CONSOLIDATION SETTLEMENTS

Reviewing the settlements over all the MRT tunnels it is apparent that some of the largest settlements, in places over 300mm, have occurred not over the very soft ground sections, but where the face was in rock or weathered rock. The primary cause for this appears to have been consolidation due to seepage into the tunnels. In no case were really major, uncontrolled, flows of ground water allowed, but even relatively minor flows quickly generated significant, and widespread, settlement. One example, from C105, is shown in Figure 9. The drum digger was excavating through G4 when it encountered a fractured, water-bearing dyke. The drum-digger face was closed off and the drive halted to allow compressed air to be applied. While the shield was halted significant settlements developed up to 200m beyond the face, as shown in Figure 9. The shield was 5m below the G4 surface, but overlying the G4 was up to 5m of highly compressible 'E' deposits. It can be seen that

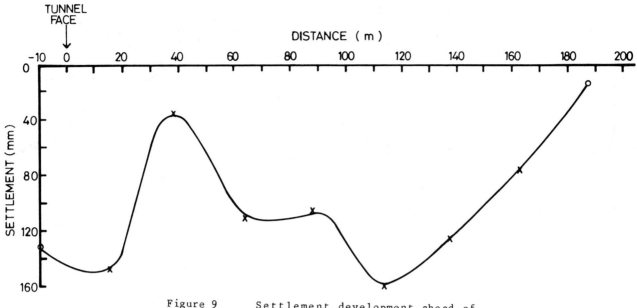

TUNNEL
FACE

Figure 9   Settlement development ahead of
the tunnel face after 2 week pause
in construction, C105.

the extent and magnitude of the settlements was
far greater than the immediate, ground loss,
settlements experienced in softer ground and
described above. Although the presence of the
water-bearing dyke may be considered an atypical
event, settlements of similar magnitude and
extent were recorded over shattered S1 rocks
when tunnelled in free air. These examples
highlight the sensitivity of the Singapore clays
to dewatering.

In the Kallang formation the face had to be
stabilised to allow safe tunnelling, and the
compressed air or other methods used also tended
to prevent water ingress at the tunnel face.

Settlement when the compressed air was
removed showed that there was still some
consolidation over these tunnels, so a study was
carried out to quantify the effect, and seek
ways to reduce it. The same tunnelling methods
studied for the ground loss settlements in the
Kallang formation were reviewed for
consolidation settlements.

A line of settlement points on C104 near
Newton Circus was of interest because of the
relatively high settlements, nearly 100mm,
recorded there. This line, the 'G' line, is
shown in Figure 10. It was found that if the
settlement was broken down into 5 periods, as
shown in Figure 10, then there were quite
clearly two ground loss periods of about 2
weeks, when the tunnels passed underneath. The

other 3 periods showed very flat settlement
profiles consistent with consolidation. The
overall magnitude of the total consolidation
settlements was about the same as the total
ground loss settlements. When plotted on
against logarithmic time, Figure 11, it can be
seen that the consolidation phases show up as
straight lines after each tunnel passes.
Interestingly, the final removal of the
compressed air had apparently little effect.
This is probably because the tunnels were on an
upgrade approaching Newton Station, and the
compressed air was already significantly reduced
by the time the final decompression took place.
Leakage into the tunnels just beyond the 'G'
line was initially higher than the specification.
Another major factor was the sand lens in the
marine clay. Air pressures were set well above
the level of this sand lens, and it ran water
during tunnelling.

A similar settlement/log time curve over the
C301 compressed air tunnels shows a markedly
different picture, Figure 12. When the air was
removed from the eastbound tunnel there was no
measurable effect. However, after the
construction and removal of air from the
parallel westbound tunnel a significant
consolidation phase did commence. The lack of
consolidation settlement after 'air-off' on the
eastbound tunnel and the development of
significant consolidation settlements after

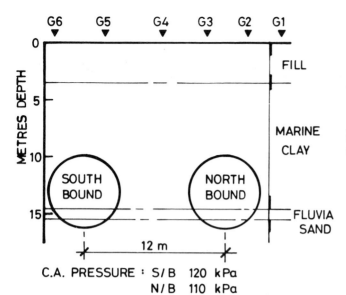

C.A. PRESSURE : S/B   120 kPa
N/B   110 kPa

Figure 10a   Settlement array G1 to G6 over
C104 C.A. tunnels.

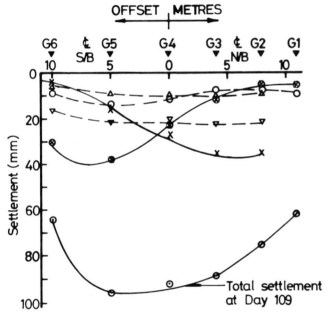

a) S/B passed Day 7 ⊗   Day 1-9
b)   O   Day 9-24
c) N/B passed Day 28 x   Day 24-32
d)   △   Day 32-46
e) Air off Day 46-64 ▽   Day 46-109

Figure 10b   Breakdown of the development of
settlement at array G1 to G6 at
various periods.

'air-off' on the westbound tunnel was consistent over the 300m of tunnel in this area. The development of the consolidation settlement is still at an early stage and there is not yet enough data to make any absolute conclusions.

The C105 drum-digger tunnels provide the antithesis of the C301 tunnels. The temporary

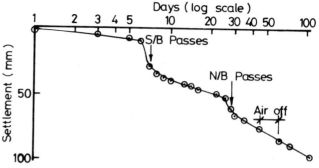

Figure 11   Settlement/log time at point G5.

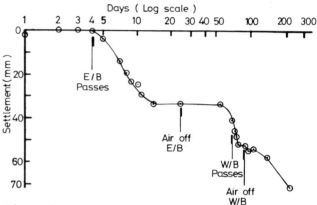

Figure 12   Settlement/log time at point TA150
over C301A C.A. tunnels.

lining of timber boards could not be properly water proofed, despite the use of a polythene sheet and grouting behind the boards. As shown in Figure 2, consolidation settlements of over 100mm rapidly followed the decompression of one tunnel. The characteristic, widespread, consolidation settlement can be seen in the lateral array Figure 13. The settlement after both the S/B and N/B tunnels had been driven, predominantly consolidation, exceeded 350mm in places.

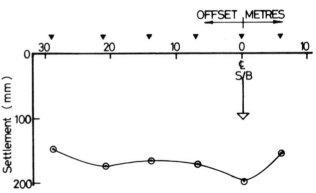

Figure 13   Lateral settlement trough produced
170 days after passage of S/B
tunnel, C105 Orchard to Newton.

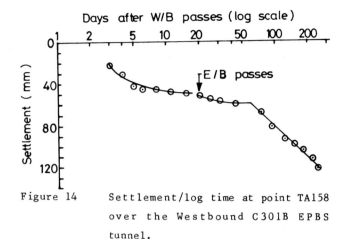

Figure 14   Settlement/log time at point TA158 over the Westbound C301B EPBS tunnel.

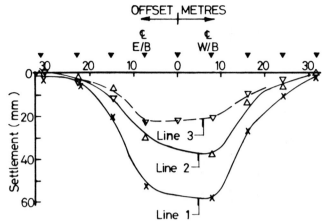

x – Line 1 total settlement to 24·4·87
△ – Line 2 settlement to 2 weeks after E/B passes 2·1·87
▽ – Line 3 settlement 2·1·87 to 24·4·87

Figure 15a   Troughs showing the development of settlement up to 4 months after the EPBS tunnels passed array TA148-154.

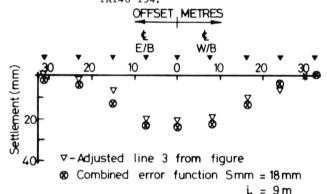

▽ – Adjusted line 3 from figure
⊗ Combined error function Smm = 18mm
                                    i = 9 m

Figure 15b   Demonstration that the consolidation settlements over the EPBS tunnels follow the form of an 'error function' curve.

Settlements over the C301 earth pressure balance shields, when plotted against a logarithmic scale, Figure 14 show a rather different development compared with the compressed air tunnels. The settlement virtually stabilized after the passage of each shield. But then, as shown in Figure 14, a sharp drop occurred some 3 to 5 weeks after the second drive had passed under the point. The particular point given as an example here was the most dramatic, with the longest pause before the onset of consolidation settlements and the fastest rate of consolidation settlement. However, the general trend shown was typical of all the points plotted.

The general shape of the consolidation settlements over the earth pressure balance shields did not follows the wide-spread, flat shape experienced over the compressed air tunnels. If the consolidation is abstracted from the immediate settlements then it takes the shape of a combined error function curve, one over each tunnel, with a width 'i' equal to $z/2$. This is shown in Figure 15.

In the six to eight months following completion of the tunnels the consolidation settlements measured between 18 and 81mm. With an earth pressure balance shield detailed face records cannot be kept, but by comparison with adjacent boreholes there appeared to be an association between the stiff, fluvial clays in the crown and low settlements; and between softer marine clay in the crown and the higher settlements.

Because the consolidation settlements were of error-function form their magnitude can be expressed as a settlement ratio, $A_S/A_T\%$. If the settlement ratio due to ground loss and due to consolidation 6 months after completion of the tunnel (the last available figure) are added, then the histogram of A_S/A_T changes quite radically, as shown in Figure 16. If the current settlement trend continues then a maximum A_S/A_T of 13% is likely 2 years after tunnel driving.

Although the data is not yet complete, it appears that the total settlements over the EPBS driven tunnels will probably slightly exceed that over the CA driven tunnels. This is despite the EPBS drives being in marginally better ground, with a fairly persistent Fluvial

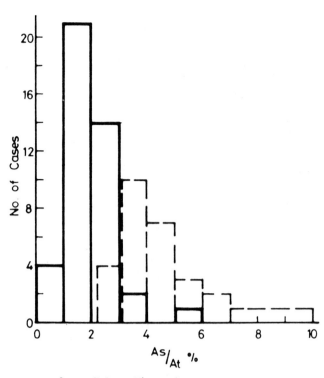

——— Immediate settlement
— — — Settlement up to August 1987

Figure 16   Histogram showing the difference
             between the settlement ratio over
             the EPBS tunnels due to immediate
             settlement and due to total
             settlement 6 months after the
             tunnels were completed.

Clay layer in the crown. The total settlement
trough for the EPBS drives is narrower and
steeper.

On Phase 1 it had been established that large
settlements over the tunnels was almost
invariably associated primarily with
consolidation rather than ground loss. To study
the causes further a limited programme of
monitoring using the BAT ground water sampling
probe (Torstensson and Petsonk[25]) was carried
out on C301. Because of the information yielded
by this exercise, it will be described in some
detail.

Porewater pressure measurements from within the
tunnels

At four locations along the westbound tunnel
from City Hall to Bugis, probes were jacked out
through the axis-level grout plugs. The tips
were located about 1m beyond the tunnel
extrados, at locations where the marine clay was
known to extend at least 1.2m below axis. The
probes were generally installed in the last ring

built as soon as it had cleared the tailskin and
been grouted. The initial reading was generally
taken between 4 and 12 hours after the probe tip
was installed. Depending on rate of progress
this typically represented a delay of between 36
and 56 hours between the excavation of the face
corresponding to the tip position and the
initial reading.

The pattern of porewater pressure before,
during and after the decompression of the W/B
tunnel are shown in Figure 17. The compressed
air pressure, which was routinely set to balance
the estimated hydrostatic water table at crown,
is also shown. This air pressure provided face
stability numbers of 3 to 4, using the shear
strength/depth profile measured at the nearby
Bugis Station. Face measurements of shear
strength using a push-in vane were lower than
the Bugis results, and indicated stability
numbers of 4 to 5.

It can be seen from Figure 17 that the
passage of the shield caused very little
disturbance to the pore water pressures in the
clay. During the period that compressed air was
maintained in the tunnel pore water pressures
fluctuated around the estimated hydrostatic
level. As the air was removed there appears to
have been some reduction in pore water pressures
at all points, but the pressure recovered except
at ring 720 where the pressure continued to fall
with a total drop of some 5m. The long term
drop at R720 is almost certainly because of its
location, only 6m short of Bugis Station. The
period after 'air-off' in the tunnel coincided
with the final excavation of Bugis, and pore
pressure drops of up to 6.5m were recorded
elsewhere around the station. Probe 520 was
installed into the central pillar between the
two tunnels (the remaining probes were installed
in the opposite direction) and recorded a
significant increase in pore pressure over
hydrostatic. This may reflect the increasing
load in the central pillar as the support of the
compressed air was lost. Probe 647 was almost
exactly under the settlement array TA92 to 100,
and does show a small, temporary, drop
consistent with the small consolidation
settlement measured at the array. An initial
assessment of the consolidation settlements
indicates that there was a delay of about a

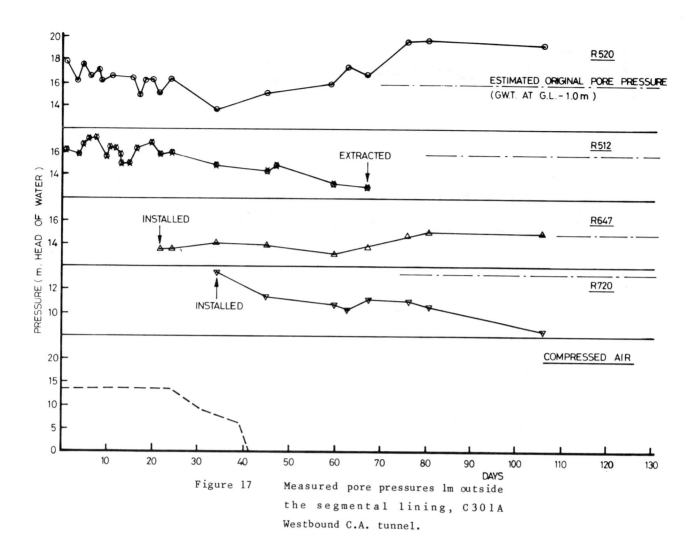

Figure 17   Measured pore pressures 1m outside
the segmental lining, C301A
Westbound C.A. tunnel.

month before the full trend developed. This
would be consistent with the start of the decay
of the excess pore pressures measured at 520.

A single probe was installed just behind the
shield in the eastbound EPBS tunnel, at ring 665.
The depth from ground to axis level was about
18m, with an estimated insitu total stress of
300kpa and water pressure of 165kpa. The
average pressure during the shoving of the
shield was 350kpa, with an 'at rest' pressure
during ring building of 250kpa.

The probe at ring 665 showed a pore pressure
of 256kpa some 6 hours after excavation. The
high excess pore pressure, 90kpa over the
hydrostatic is clearly related to the high face
pressures during shoving. Unfortunately
insufficient sealing thread was used to
waterproof the probe tube at Ring 665 and the
tube was observed to be acting as a local drain
in the soil. As a result pore water pressures
around the probe tip reduced rapidly and after
eight days no reading could be obtained. So it

was not possible to accurately monitor the decay
of the excess pore pressures with time. Some
six months after the installation of the probe
at R665, one of the probes from the compressed
air tunnels was recovered and re-installed at
R657 in the EPBS eastbound tunnel. The readings
taken on the probe were 161kpa, approximately
hydrostatic. This does not quite tally with the
settlement readings, which indicate continuing
settlement at this time. The decay of the high
excess pore pressures measured around the EPBS
tunnel and the consolidation settlements
measured over those tunnels are quite clearly
cause and effect. This behaviour has been
predicted by Finno and Clough[26]. The high pore
pressures measures are initially probably a very
localised feature. The delay in the onset of
consolidation possibly reflects a phase when the
pore pressures are rearranging rather than
dissipating. Once the pore pressures have been
rearranged into a uniform hydraulic gradient
away from the tunnels, then consolidation

309

Original ground level

Settlement

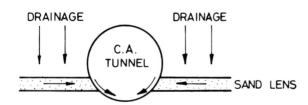

DRAINAGE   DRAINAGE

C.A.
TUNNEL

SAND LENS

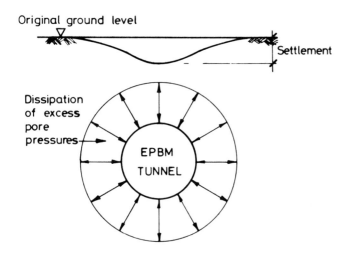

Original ground level

Settlement

Dissipation
of excess
pore
pressures

EPBM
TUNNEL

Figure 18   Explanation of difference in
              development of consolidation
              settlements over C.A. and EPBS
              tunnels.

settlement starts.

The difference between the relatively flat consolidation settlements experienced at Newton Circus and the 'error function' shape consolidation settlements over the EPBS tunnels is explained in Figure 18. The seepage of water into the tunnels from the sand layer caused widespread settlements because of the difference in permeability between the sand and the overlying marine clay. Over the EPBS tunnels the radial dissipation of the raised pore pressures caused a settlement trough similar to that over the radial movement of ground towards an unsupported face.

Initial results over the C301 C.A. tunnels show a trough of error function shape, but with wider dimensions than the initial, ground loss troughs. The shape appears to be similar to that recorded by Hurrell over C.A. tunnels.

TUNNEL/TUNNEL INTERACTION

The theoretical interaction of the four tunnels driven in close proximity under the Singapore Padang has been the subject of papers by Lo et al[7] and Lo et al[27]. Unfortunately the field measurement of these effects was severely constrained by the jet and chemical grouting required to allow one of the tunnels to be driven through a full face of poorly graded beach sand.

Tunnel/tunnel interaction was clearly identifiable from the monitoring carried out on the C107A NATM tunnels already described in some detail above. The interaction could be seen in the unusually wide settlement trough produced by the second tunnel. The magnitude of the settlements over the second tunnel was also generally two or three times as high as over the first tunnel, although a significant proportion of the difference was almost certainly due to the upper tunnel being at, or close, to the upper S3 interface. The interaction can also be clearly identified in measured inclinometer data, shown in Figure 19. While the lower tunnel caused only a horizontal movement from crown to invert level, the driving of the upper

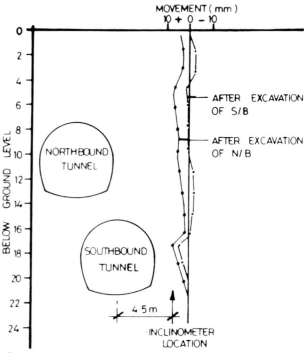

MOVEMENT (mm)
10 + 0 − 10

AFTER EXCAVATION
OF S/B

AFTER EXCAVATION
OF N/B

NORTHBOUND
TUNNEL

SOUTHBOUND
TUNNEL

4·5m

INCLINOMETER
LOCATION

Figure 19   Deflection measured by
              inclinometer positioned just
              before the Ocean Building Carpark,
              C107A.

tunnel generated a horizontal movement right down to the invert of the lower tunnel.

The immediate settlement troughs on C301 for both the compressed air and the EPBS tunnels, shown above, both show a characteristic asymetry of the second trough in the direction of the first tunnel. In the EPBS drives this asymetry could be due to the onset of consolidation over the first tunnel. In the compressed air tunnels, however, the movement over the first tunnel can only be due to the passage of the second tunnel. The magnitude of the interaction settlement is small, some 10 to 15mm. It seems probable that this degree of movement is purely due to the increased overburden pressure on the first tunnel causing the lining to deflect slightly. The clousre of any radial joints built with the ends of the segments not fully square could account for much of the movement.

While the identification of tunnel/tunnel interaction is extremely interesting, the effects, within the general context of the settlements over MRT tunnels, were relatively minor. The geometry of the two tunnels in Figure 7 in overconsolidated clay, is probably as extreme as most engineers would like to get. Nevertheless the settlement solely attributable to the interaction, maybe 20 to 30mm, is relatively minor compared with the magnitude of settlement experienced elsewhere due to other cuases, particularly consolidation. If the authors are correct in ascribing the interaction settlement on C301 to movement in the segmental lining caused by an increase in pressure on the lining, then it is probable that this settlement would have occurred slowly in the long term even if the second tunnel had not been driven. Peck[9] has recorded that in the long term the load on tunnels tends to reflect the full overburden pressure. The second tunnel may therefore only have been precipitating the inevitable.

PERFORMANCE OF ADJACENT STRUCTURES
The pattern of ground settlements over tunnels is of interest primarily because is reveals the basic movements that affect nearby structures. However, structures may not follow exactly the ground movements caused by tunnelling. The foundations and the rigidity of the structure itself can significantly affect the response of a structure to underlying ground movements.

Structures adjacent to the tunnels ranged from modern highrise structures, to one hundred year old masonry shop houses in poor condition. The tolerance and response of various classes of structure to both ground loss and dewatering settlement that occurred when tunnelling in the Kallang formation is discussed in this section.

Typical Foundation Techniques
Shallow flexible raft foundations have traditionally been employed for the construction of the two and three storey masonry shop houses that were adjacent to long lengths of the MRT route and commonly fell within the zone of influence of the tunnels.

These structures generally consisted of long terraces founded at ground level, i.e. without a basement, on a flexible, light reinforced or mass concrete raft. The soft clays under these rafts was invariably improved by driving 100mm diameter, 2.4m long timber piles cut from the local Bakau hardwood at close centres (typically 250-300mm) into the soft clays. The short length of these piles meant that they were rarely able to penetrate to a firmer layer; their effect being one primarily of soil improvement by increasing the shear strength of the soil mass beneath the structure.

Where the line of the terrace ran parallel to the direction ot drive, which was normally the case as routes followed street alignments, it was generally found that the short sharp ground loss profile had reduced to a low magnitude at the distance of the building frontages and little damage was occassioned as a result.

However where the line of tunnels ran obliquely or normal to the line of the terraces the structures became exposed to the full curvature effects of the ground loss profile. The low flexibility of the foundation meant that the structure had little ability to do other than follow the new ground surface profile and extensive shear cracking occurred in masonry walls and plaster finishes emanating from joints of weakness such as doors and windows.

Conversely the performance of structures founded on Bakau pile foundations in all cases performed well when subjected to the wide flat settlement trough induced by consolidation settlement as both structure and services settled together at a uniform rate with little differential settlement.

Piled Foundations that extended through the soft surficial Kallang deposits to either the Bukit Timah or Jurong formations have been employed for most of the more modern and larger structures such as multi-storey office and housing developments, road bridges and flyovers. The most commonly used type has been driven pre-cast piling.

In virtually all cases the bearing or socket length of the piles was at or below the invert level of the tunnels and hence outside the zone of influence of the tunnels. Despite tunnelling in extremely close proximity (within 2m) to the pile shafts of several of these structures no discernable damage due to ground losses occurred.

Conversely consolidation settlement of the Kallang formation caused both increased load on the piles due to negative skin friction and differential settlement of the ground surface in relation to the rigid piled structures.

In only one case did the increased negative skin friction load on a pile lead to failure of a pile and this occurred in a precast driven pile that was supporting a block of flats located approximately 25m from the line of the nearest tunnel. Damage due to consolidation settlement around piled structures was generally dictated by the form of construction used to form the ground floor slab and the manner in which services were connected.

In cases where the ground floor slab was cast as a slab on ground separation occurred between the base slab and building columns. Walls separated at either ground floor or first floor level and were subject to extensive shear cracking.

In cases where the ground floor slab was formed as a suspended slab from a pile cap beam, the structure remained undamaged and a void formed under the slab. However services such as gas, water, electricity and sewerage were subject to severe local strains at the point that they left the soil and entered the building.

Where services were not cast integrally or suspended from the ground floor slab, problems occurred, particularly with inflexible drainage connections under the slab.

In conclusion it should be remembered that when making an estimate of the likely damage effects that settlement will cause to adjacent structures it should be remembered that engineering estimates based on allowable limits of slope or differential settlement implicitly assume that the building under consideration is in a serviceable condition, that normal factors of safety have been employed in the design of the foundation and structure by a competent engineer and that the construction of the building had been carried out to a good standard.

It has been the experience in Singapore that in virtually all cases of concern the buildings have either been in a poor state of repair or that settlements, differential movements or vibrations, within normally acceptable limits, have revealed defects in either the design or workmanship which has contributed to abnormally high damage to the structure.

It is a sobering thought to most engineers who have been involved with the Singapore MRT that the route of the proposed Phase II tunnels pass within a short distance of the site of the Hotel New World. This was a 13 storey reinforced frame structure supported on precast driven piles, designed by a registered professional engineer, which was constructed approximately 15 years ago and had undergone extensive recent renovations. The outward appearance, together with previous experience of this class of structure, would indicate that no undue distress would have been caused by tunnelling in close proximity to it: however the structure contained such gross design and construction defects Thean et al[28] that it collapsed of its own accord in 1986 with the loss of 37 lives.

CONCLUSIONS

The major conclusions drawn from the observations made above are:-

a)   The settlement over tunnels can be split

into three broad categories: Immediate (or 'ground loss'), consolidation and interaction.

b) The magnitude of 'ground loss' settlement can be significantly affected by the method of tunnelling. For free air tunnelling in a stiff boulder clay the NATM method produced generally less settlement than shield driven tunnels.

c) Consolidation settlements were often significantly greater than 'ground loss' settlements in Singapore.

d) The magnitude of consolidation settlements over tunnels in the soft clays and sands of the Kallang formation appeared to be partly related to the initial water tightness of the lining system used. The use of 'hydrotite' water expansive seals on concrete segments significantly reduced consolidation settlements.

e) Earth pressure balance shields driven using a high face pressure minimised immediate settlement, but at the cost of long term consolidation.

f) At least two, and possibly three, different types of trough resulted from consolidation settlements. Leakage at the tunnel face or at the rings resulted in a very wide, flat trough. Raised pore pressures generated by high face pressures caused a narrow trough. An intermediate trough was measured over well sealed C.A. tunnels.

g) Tunnel/tunnel interaction was found due to driving twin tunnels both in stiff boulder clay and in soft marine clay. The effect was, however, generally relatively minor.

h) The two main causes of settlement, 'ground loss' and consolidation had often very different effects on adjacent buildings.

i) The sharp 'ground loss' profile had little effect on rows of shop houses parallel to the tunnels. More noticeable effects were found where the tunnels were driven obliquely or normal to the line of shop houses on rafts.

j) Consolidation generally had little effect on structures founded on short 'bakau' piles. Buildings piled down to firmer strata were often more prone to minor

damage including the separation of unpiled floor slabs from piled structure and dislocation of services.

k) The BAT porewater probe provided useful information about porewater behaviour close to the lining at a low cost.

Acknowledgements

Figures 1, 2, 3, 4, 5, 6, 10, 11, 12, 13, 14, 15 and 16 have been taken, with minor amendments and updating, from the paper by Shirlaw and Copsey[19].

Figures 7, 8 and 19 have been taken from the paper by Shirlaw, Doran and Benjamin[18].

References

1. Singapore Public Works Department 'Geology of the Republic of Singapore' publ. Singapore PWD 1976.

2. Tan S B and Lee K W 'Engineering Geology of the marine member of the Kallang Formation of Singapore' Intl. Symp. on Soft Clay, Bangkok 1977 pp75-88.

3. Geological Society Engineering Group Working Party Report 'The logging of rock cores for engineering purposes' Q.J. Eng. Geol., 3(1) 1970 pp1-25.

4. Pitts J 'A review of geology and engineering geology in Singapore' Q.J. Eng. Geol., 17, 1984, pp93-101.

5. Elias V and Mizuno 'Tunnelling with earth pressure balance shield'. 5th Seminar, Case histories in soft clays, NTI, Singapore 1987 (In print).

6. Copsey J P and Doran S R 'Singapore Mass Rapid Transit System - design of precast concrete segmental tunnel linings'. Proc. Singapore Mass Rapid Transit Conf. 1987 pp225-239.

7. Lo K W, Lee S L, Makino H, Chang L K, Leung C F and Miharc T 'Tunnels in close proximity' Proc. Singapore Mass Rapid Transit Conf. 1987 pp283-299.

8. Schmidt B Prediction of Settlements due to tunnelling in soil: three case histories. RETC Proc. 1974.

9. Peck R B   Deep Excavations and tunnelling in soft ground. <u>Proc. 7th Int. Conf. on Soil Mechs. and Found. Engrg.</u> Mexico City 1969.

10. Glossop N H and Farmer I W   Settlement associated with the removal of compressed air pressure during tunnelling in alluvial clay' <u>Geotechnique</u> 29 No 1, 67-72, 1979.

11. Hurrell M R   "The empirical prediction of long term surface settlements above shield-driven tunnels in soil'. <u>Proc. of 3rd Int. Conf. 'Ground Movements and Structures'</u> UWIST Vol. 3 publ. Pentech press 1985 pp161-172.

12. Fitzpatrick L, Kulhawy F H and O'Rourke T D   'Flow patterns around tunnels and their use in evaluating construction problems'. <u>Soft Ground Tunnelling</u> Ed. Resindiz and Romo, publ. A A Balkema, Rotterdam 1981.

13. Cater R W, Shirlaw J N, Sullivan C A and Chan W T   'Tunnels constructed for the Hong Kong Mass Transit Railway' <u>Hong Kong Engineer</u> October 1984 pp37-43.

14. Glossop N H and O'Reilly M P   'Settlement caused by tunnelling through soft marine clay' <u>Tunnels and Tunnelling</u> October 1982 pp13-16.

15. Broms B B and Bennermark H   'Stability of Clay at vertical openings' J. Soil Mech. Found. Div., ASGE, 93(1) pp71-94.

16. Fujimori T, Uchiyama C, Kurimi H and Takasaki H   'Use of NATM in soft ground near Tokyo, Japan' <u>Proc. 4th Intl. Symposium Tunnelling '85 Brighton,</u> publ. IMM 1985 pp93-103.

17. Baudendistel M   'Significance of unsupported span in tunnelling' <u>Proc. 4th Intl. Symposium Tunnelling '85 Brighton,</u> publ. IMM 1985 pp103-109.

18. Shirlaw J N, Doran S and Benjamin B   'A case study of two tunnels driven in the Singapore 'Boulder Bed' and in grouted coral sands'. <u>Proc. 23rd Annual Conf. of Eng. Group of Geol. Soc.</u> University of Nottingham 1987 (In print).

19. Shirlaw J N and Copsey J P   'Settlements over tunnels in Singapore Marine Clay' <u>Proc. 5th Intl. Seminar, case histories in soft clays</u> NTI, Singapore 1987 (In print).

20. Berry G L, Shirlaw J N, Hayata K and Tan S H   'A Review of the Grouting Methods utilised for Bored Tunnelling with emphasis on the Jet Grouting methods' <u>Proc. Singapore Mass Rapid Transit Conference</u> 1987 pp207-214.

21. Bjerrum L   'Problems of soil mechanics and construction on soft clays'. <u>Proc. 8th ICSMFE, Moscow</u> 1973 pp111-159.

22. Mair R J   'Geotechnical aspects of soft Ground Tunnelling' <u>Proc. Int. Seminar on Constr. Problems in Soft Soils</u> NTI Singapore 1983.

23. Attewell P B, Yeates J and Selby A R   'Soil Movements induced by tunnelling and their effects on pipelines and structures', publ. Blackie, 1985.

24. Clough G W, Sweeney B P and Finno R J   'Measured soil response to EPB Shield Tunnelling' <u>ASCE Jour. of Geot. Eng. Vol. 109 No. 2</u> February 1983.

25. Torstensson B A and Petsonk A   'A device for in-situ measurement of hydraulic conductivity'. Proc. 4th Int. Geot. Seminar, Field Instrumentation and In-situ Measurement, NTI Singapore 1986 pp157-162.

26. Finno R J and Clough G W   'Evaluation of soil response to EPB Shield Tunnelling' <u>ASCE Jour. of Geot. Eng. Vol. 111, No. 2,</u> Feb. 1985 pp155-173.

27. Lo K W, Chang L K, Leung C F, Lee S L, Makino H and Tajima H   'Field Instrumentation of a Multiple Tunnel Interaction Problem' <u>Proc. 8th Reg. Conf. on Soil Mech. and Found. Eng.</u> Vol. 1 Kyoto 1987 pp305-309.

28. Thean L P, Vijiaratnam A, Lee S L and Broms B B   'Report of the Inquiry into the Collapse of the Hotel New World' publ. Singapore National Printers Ltd., 1987.

Use of finite-element modelling to assess factors affecting circular tunnel ring performance *in situ*

B. G. D. Smart B.Sc., Ph.D., C.Eng., M.I.Min.E.
P. W. H. Olden B.Sc., M.Sc., A.C.G.I.
Department of Mineral Resources Engineering, University of Strathclyde, Glasgow, Scotland, United Kingdom

SYNOPSIS

Observations of the excessive ring deformation which occurred in a coal-mine tunnel suggested that an apparent down-rating of the support system could be due to the following causes:-

(i)   Lack of radial confinement at the shoulders of the ring, due to weathering of weak strata.

(ii) Systematic installation of the rings with the top two segments leaning away from the face.

While the best long-term solution to both causes is to apply shotcrete to corrugated mesh panels located within the flanges of the rings, this may only be applied some distance back from the face after significant deformation has occurred.

A solution to the problems induced by the misalignment of ring segments which can however be applied at the face is to increase the shear strength of the inter-ring strutting system and an appropriate strut has been designed and tested.

The paper, therefore, is a specific example of how a combination of in situ observations and appropriate numerical modelling facility can be used to enhance the performance of a support system.

INTRODUCTION

Recent experience with the application of five-segment full-circle 152mm x 127mm RSJ's with 16 inter-ring struts (Figure 1) in a coal-mine tunnel suggested that there is a discrepancy between the apparent strength of the support assembly as determined by full-scale laboratory tests and that exhibited when the support system was installed underground. The tunnel diameter was 5.732m and the rings were set ultimately at .75m spacing.

Accepting that the discrepancy arose because of differences between test and in situ conditions, observations of the excessive ring deformation which occurred (figure 1) suggested the following principal differences existed over several hundred metres of tunnel length:-

(i)   Lack of radial confinement at the shoulders of the ring due to weathering of weak roof strata with an associated application of load to the crown of the ring, compared to the degrees of confinement simulated in the laboratory test.

The in situ condition arose because a series of faults displaced the anticipated sandstone and siltstone host rocks, placing the tunnel at least partially within mudstones and other weaker rock types. Disturbed ground in the proximity of the faults also contributed to asymmetrical loading of the rings.

(ii) Systematic installation of the rings with the top two segments leaning away from the face relative to the bottom three segments, compared to a "perfectly" aligned ring tested in the laboratory.

The operational problem appeared to be caused by the method used to erect the rings and possibly also interaction between the rings and the bearing pads of the full face tunnelling machine during machine advance. In order to investigate the influence of the observed differences between laboratory and in situ conditions on the support system performance, a number of finite element models

315

FIGURE 1. DEFORMATION OF RINGS

were constructed as described below.

FINITE ELEMENT MODELLING
ANSYS[1] is a comprehensive finite element
analysis program applied extensively worldwide
in the field of mechanical engineering to
solve structural, electro mechanical and
heat transfer problems. It was used to construct
the series of models which examined the significance of the observed differences between
the in situ and laboratory test conditions.
Previous experience had been gained with
ANSYS[2] in gateroad support system modelling.

The models were developed in three stages:-

Model 1 was a two-dimensional model with
half of the axi-symmetric ring being formed
from 12 regular beam elements, radial confinement
of the ring being provided by non-linear springs
as shown in figure 2. The springs were built
into the model in such a way that they could

be switched on or off, depending on the loading
configuration being examined. The weathering
and dead-weight loading of the upper weaker
strata was represented by switching off the
elements around the upper part of the ring
and applying a distributed dead-weight loading
along the crown of the ring.

Model 2 was a more detailed two dimensional
model using 20 beam elements to represent one
half of the axi-symmetric ring, including the
joints between ring segments. Radial confinement
was provided as in model 1.

While the two-dimensional models 1 and 2
enabled the effect of variation in confinement
on perfectly-set ring yield loads to be examined,
a three-dimensional model was required in order
to examine the effect of ring installation with
the top two segments systematically misaligned.
Hence model 3 was constructed, an "infinitely
long" assembly of rings and struts produced
by coupling displacements at the strut ends.

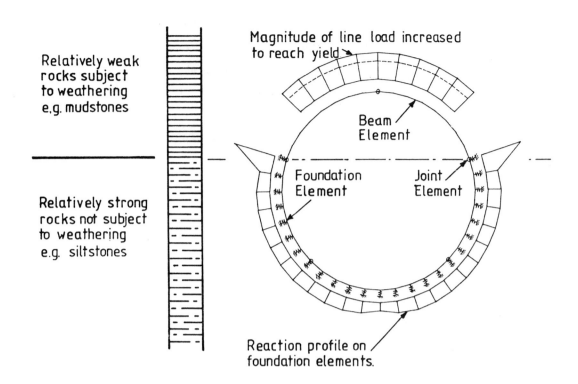

Relatively weak rocks subject to weathering e.g. mudstones

Relatively strong rocks not subject to weathering e.g. siltstones

Magnitude of line load increased to reach yield

Beam Element

Foundation Element

Joint Element

Reaction profile on foundation elements.

FIGURE 2. TWO-DIMENSIONAL FINITE ELEMENT MODEL OF RING INTERACTING WITH HOST ROCK

The fixity of the struts was taken to be rigid at one end and pinned at the other. This is a semi-fixed condition representing moderately good assembly of the ring and struts. The effect of ring segment misalignment was examined by running model 3 with a perfectly aligned ring and then with the ring crown displaced by 150mm and 300mm relative to the invert.

The element types used in these models were selected as follows from the ANSYS element library:

STIF24 - a three-dimensional plastic beam used to represent ring "I" section beam. STIF39 - non-linear force-deflection element used to represent the confinement and ring joints.

STIF20 - a three-dimensional plastic pipe used to represent the struts.

Results

All the finite element models were non-linear and required an iterative solution. An increment of distributed load was applied across the crown of the ring and the model allowed to converge to a stable solution. The resulting displacements were then examined and the model restarted with an additional load increment. Thus a load-deflection

graph could be produced for any point on the model structure. The load-deflection curves obtained in this manner for all the models run are presented in figure 3.

Model 1 was run with two configurations. Initially the laboratory test condition was simulated by providing complete radial confinement. Subsequently weathering of the strata around the shoulders was modelled by removing confinement in that region. Load-deflection curves for both configurations are shown in figure 3, while the typical distorted shape of the second "weathered" configuration is shown in figure 4. Examination of figure 3 shows that the yield load of the model structure is reduced by at least a factor of 2.75 when weathering on the ring shoulder is simulated.

In an attempt to improve the yield load of the model, the material specified for ring manufacture was upgraded from 43A to 50B mild steel. The result, evident in figure 3, was to take the reduction actor for yield loads down from 2.75 to 2, compared to the fully confined model.

The effect of preloading the model by applying an in-line expanding force to the crown point joint was also examined. This

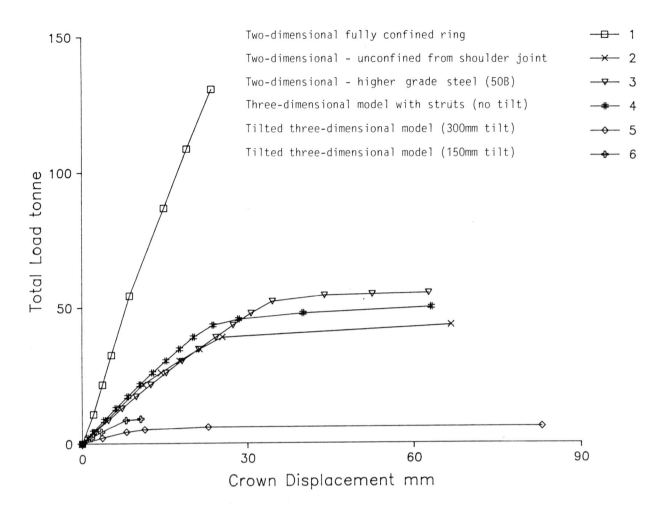

Two-dimensional fully confined ring ⊟ 1
Two-dimensional - unconfined from shoulder joint ✕ 2
Two-dimensional - higher grade steel (50B) ▽ 3
Three-dimensional model with struts (no tilt) ✳ 4
Tilted three-dimensional model (300mm tilt) ◇ 5
Tilted three-dimensional model (150mm tilt) ⊞ 6

FIGURE 3.   LOAD/DISPLACEMENT RESULTS FOR RING MODELS

had the effect of stiffening the ring initially, but subsequently softened the model slightly. The overall effect was insignificant compared to that of removing confinement.

The effect of incorporating inter-segment joints into the model caused small rotations to occur about the joints. This model shows a yield load reduction factor of 3.33 compared to the fully confined model.

The effect of arch segment misalignment was examined by running model 3 with a perfectly aligned arch, then with crown to invert displacements of 150mm and 300mm, all with weathering at the shoulder. The load-deflection curves are shown in figure 3. The perfectly aligned three-dimensional model compares favourably with the earlier two-dimensional model, but it is immediately apparent that the misalignment drastically reduces the yield load.   150mm misalignment causes a reduction by a factor of at least 11, while 300mm misalignment causes a reduction by a factor of at least 22.

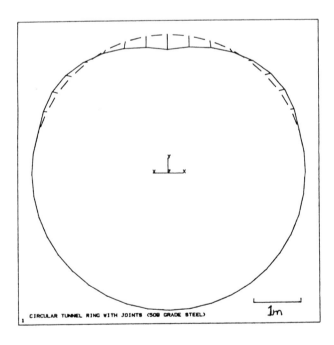

CIRCULAR TUNNEL RING WITH JOINTS (50B GRADE STEEL)

FIGURE 4.   DISTORTED SHAPE OF 50B GRADE STEEL RING LOADED TO SIMULATE "WEATHERED" CONDITIONS AS IN FIGURE 2. (LOAD/DISPLACEMENT CURVE IS GRAPH 3 IN FIGURE 3)

The 150mm misalignment case was taken to be representative of the actual installation, and having noted that this structure began to yield within the struts as opposed to the ring shoulders in the perfectly aligned models, the effect of increasing the strength of the struts was examined. The strut wall thickness was increased from 4.5mm to 10mm, the result being shown again in figure 3. This improved the yield strength of the structure bringing the reduction factor down from 11 to 7.5.

Conclusions from Modelling

These results suggest the following order of decreasing significance for the various factors which influence the in situ behaviour of the support system.

1st - Systematic ring segment misalignment and toppling action of the rings.

2nd - Weathering of the strata around the ring shoulder.

3rd - Type of steel within range 43A - 50B.

Accepting that operational problems made it difficult to set perfectly aligned rings, attention was devoted to improving the anti-toppling characteristics of the strutting system and preventing weathering of weaker strata.

PROPOSED SOLUTION TO THE PROBLEM OF SUPPORT SYSTEM INSTABILITY

The Solution

Because of restrictions on manning levels at the face of the tunnel and the need to maintain unimpaired advance rates, a two-stage solution was proposed for enhancing the support system stability.

Initially, at the face, due care should be taken to set the ring segments in proper alignment and the anti-toppling or shear strengths of the existing so-called "heavy duty" tubular struts should be improved.

Secondly, as close to the face as possible, it was proposed that corrugated mesh be installed within the flanges of the rings and covered with shotcrete, creating a highly stable reinforced concrete lining which would preclude further toppling and weathering. An analysis of the strutting effects of in-web shotcrete panels suggests enhancements by factors of 20 on simple compression and 40 in anti-toppling reaction,

relative to the existing heavy duty tubular strutting system. The corrugated mesh and shotcrete were existing product but the improved strut required development.

Strut Development

Two sets of tests were performed on each of
(i) A conventional heavy duty tubular strut
(ii) The above strut reinforced as shown in figure 5.

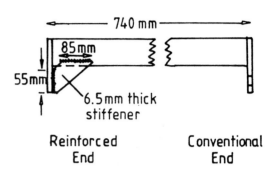

FIGURE 5. COMPARISON OF CONVENTIONAL AND MODIFIED HEAVY DUTY TUBULAR STRUT

The tests were not British Coal standards[3], but were instead designed to examine the struts' ability to prevent arches toppling in a systematic manner.

The loading arrangement for Test 1 and the results obtained are shown in figure 6. This applied an identical bending moment to each end of the struts.

It can be seen that for the conventional strut, strut strength in bending depends on the orientation of the end lugs relative to the bending force. When the strut is loaded with the end lugs pointing toward the bending force, the strut is very weak, the end lugs alone deforming to allow the RSJ's to come together. This is referred to later as the "weaker configuration".

Testing of the reinforced struts in a similar manner showed that the effect of reinforcement is to modify the weaker configuration, deformation of the tube determining the ultimate strut strength irrespective of end lug orientation.

When arches topple, one end of a conventional strut is loaded in the stronger configuration while the other is unavoidably loaded in the

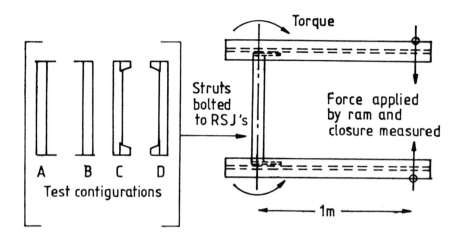

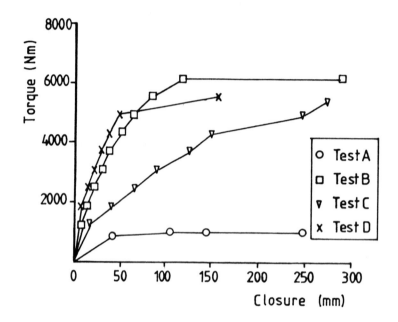

FIGURE 6. BENDING TEST PERFORMED ON STRUTS

weaker configuration, as shown in figure 7.
Test 1 indicated that the reinforced struts
would increase the resistance of the support
assembly to toppling. In order to examine
this deduction, the test rig shown in figure 8
was constructed. The results of that test
are also shown in figure 8, and these confirm
that use of the reinforced strut enhances the
resistance of the support assembly to toppling
almost doubling it at large deformations.

Conclusions Regarding Proposed Solution

Comparatively simple modifications have been
proposed to the existing "heavy duty" tubular
strut, effectively doubling the resistance
developed by that strut to the toppling of
rings. The modified strut will however be

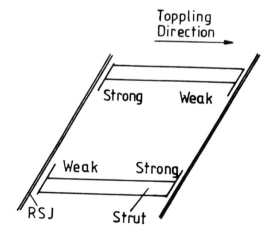

FIGURE 7. EFFECT OF STRUT ORIENTA-
TION ON TOPPLING RESISTANCE

320

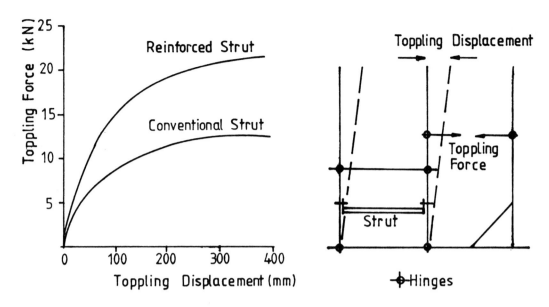

FIGURE 8. TOPPLING TEST PERFORMED ON STRUTS

marginally more difficult to install, requiring
a socket spanner to be used instead of a ring
spanner, and will of course be more expensive.
The resulting likely enhancement in support
system performance in the geological conditions
described far outweights these disadvantages,
the use of improved strutting being more cost
effective than, for example, changing the ring
segments from 43A to 50B grade steel and retaining conventional struts. Subsequent installation
of currugated mesh and shotcrete within the
flange ring would not only prevent weathering
of the weaker strata, but it is estimated further
reinforce the support systems resistance to
toppling and distortion along the circumference
of the roadway by creating high shear-stiffness
panels between rings.

GENERAL CONCLUSIONS AND RECOMMENDATIONS
General Conclusions

Comparatively simple finite element models
have been used to demonstrate the influence
of geological and operational factors on
full-circle strutted RSJ support system
performance.

A method of improving that performance
has been proposed, utilizing a combination
of struts with improved resistance to ring
toppling installed at the face, and in-flange
corrugated mesh and shotcrete placed as
near to the face as possible.

Recommendations

The further application of finite element
modelling to the design of full-circle support
systems should be pursued. In particular,
the combination of RSJ's, corrugated mesh
and shotcrete should be more rigorously
examined in a range of geological conditions,
eg. conditions giving rise to floor heave
as well as those described in this paper.

The concept of a strut with improved
resistance to ring or arch toppling should
be considered in a more general context.
Conventional "heavy duty" tubular struts
are "stiff" with regard to bending, compression and tension, but not with regard
to resisting arch toppling. Any site using
RSJ's which show a tendency to deform systematically along the tunnel should benefit
from application of the improved strut.

References

1. DeSalvo, G.J., and Swanson, J.A., ANSYS
Users Manual, Vols I and II for version
4.1, Swanson Analysis Systems Inc., March 1983.
2. Smart, B.G.D., and Olden, P.W.H.,
Application of the ANSYS program to Coal
Mine Support Design, ANSYS Conference Proceedings, Swanson Analysis Systems Inc., 1987.
3. British Coal Specifications 547: 1985
Struts of the types requiring modifications
to arches and 683: 1982 Struts of the types

321

not requiring modifications to arches.

Acknowledgements

The authors gratefully acknowledge the research
funding provided by British Coal and the
ECSC, and the interest shown by the Area
and Headquarters Technical Department Staff
of British Coal.

Use of tunnel deformation monitoring for excavation control in weak bedded rock—Isangoyana Rail tunnel, Zululand

C. R. Speers
Hawkins, Hawkins and Osborn, Rivonia, South Africa
J. C. Sharp B.Sc., A.R.S.M., D.I.C., Ph.D., C.Eng., M.I.M.M.
Geo-Engineering, Jersey, Channel Islands

SYNOPSIS

The excavation of the iSangoyana rail tunnel, 2,4km long with an overall cross section of 70m^2 has recently been completed. The tunnel was excavated using conventional large scale drill and blast techniques through weak, bedded sandstones/siltstones and carbonaceous shales with a near-horizontal bedding.

Excavation support comprised resin anchored and resin grouted tensioned reinforcement in conjunction with shotcrete which was mesh reinforced in the poorer rock zones. A 250mm thick unreinforced concrete lining was placed some 8-14 months after excavation when all significant movements had ceased.

Rock instrumentation comprising 19 convergence stations and 5 extensometer arrays was installed immediately after excavation to check the stabilisation characteristics of the tunnel cross section under varying geological, stress and rock support conditions. From the observations carried out, it was possible to distinguish between areas of adequate support (small controlled movements) and areas where support was initially inadequate leading to excessive inelastic deformations accompanied by bed separation and requiring subsequent heavier support to be installed. Using the performance data obtained, it was found generally possible to optimise the degree of support required thus permitting maximum advance rates to be achieved.

The high standard of tunnel monitoring allowed both a close control of the excavation and support process and the identification of areas where remedial measures were necessary in the form of grouting behind the final lining. In comparison with precedent experience in such rock types,[1] the tunnel excavation and support was carried out with comparatively few problems as a result of the control information provided by routine performance monitoring.

INTRODUCTION

The Coal Line Improvements project was undertaken between 1979 and 1988 to upgrade the existing single track railway line between the coalfields of the Eastern Transvaal and Richards Bay harbour. The line is used for the export of coal via Richards Bay to Europe, Australia and Japan. Part of the upgrading involved the construction of a 2,4km long double track tunnel at iSangoyana, some 70km north west of Richards Bay.

The tunnel is straight with respect to horizontal alignment and has a bearing of 132 degrees with an upward gradient of 1 in 160 towards Richards Bay. The finished and lined tunnel profile, as shown in <u>Fig. 1</u>, is D-shaped with a radius of 5,060m and vertical sidewalls of 2,272m height. The finished tunnel area is approximately 60m^2 .

The tunnel was driven using drill and blast methods through near-horizontal, weak, bedded and moisture-sensitive sandstones, siltstones and carbonaceous shales, which have been intruded by dolerite sills and dykes.

Previous tunnelling projects in similar rock types in South Africa (for example, the Drakensberg Tailrace, Main Access and Headrace

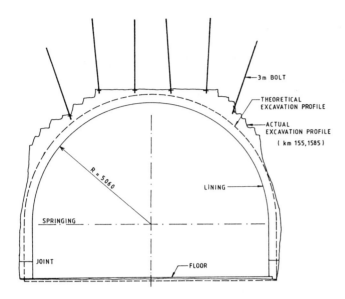

Fig. 1 Typical Cross Section showing Excavation
and Final Lining Profiles

tunnels; and the Orange-Fish tunnel) showed
that the iSangoyana tunnel required to be
finally lined with either a concrete or
shotcrete lining in order to prevent long-term
deterioration of the excavated periphery due to
drying out of the rock. It was further
required that the lining be capable of
performing as a structure carrying long-term
rock loading thus reducing any such reliance on
the primary support.

Because of the nature of the rock, primary
support comprising rockbolts and shotcrete was
required immediately following excavation
without undue rock loosening occurring.

As part of the overall control process
relating to the checking of the adequacy of the
support measures installed, tunnel deformation
monitoring was undertaken. This paper
describes the monitoring procedures used and
based upon performance evaluation relates the
level of installed support to the prevailing
geological conditions.

GEOLOGY
The geological longitudinal section of the
tunnel is shown in Fig. 2. The rocks belong to
the Pietermaritzburg Formation of the Ecca
Group, Karoo Sequence. At the tunnel site, the
formation consists of an unfolded and
unmetamorphosed sequence of four relatively

thin, lithologically similar units, namely
carbonaceous shale, sandstone/siltstone,
interlaminated siltstone/shale and interbedded
sandstone/siltstone/shale. This sequence has
been tilted at up to 5 degrees towards the
coast as a result of the Gondwanaland
continental movements.

At the tunnel site the sedimentary sequence
is capped by sandstone belonging to the Vryheid
Formation of the Ecca Group. At this point the
tunnel attains its maximum cover of 173m.
Denudation has taken place on the Vryheid side
of the tunnel where the cover is as low as 15m
and as a result, the rock at tunnel level is
weathered over the first 200m.

A number of minor north-south striking
normal faults are present, the most significant
being one at the centre of the tunnel where the
displacement was some 3-4m. The sedimentary
rocks have been intruded by a number of post-
Karoo dolerite dykes up to 4m thick and sills
up to 10m thick.

The occurrence of jointing is related
directly to the rock type. In the stronger
sandstones and siltstone there is generally
only one north-south striking joint set,
whereas in the weaker shales generally two sets
(north-south and east-west) are present and up
to four sets are found in the proximity of
intrusions. In unweathered rocks the joint
aperture is generally closed to very narrow
with mica and chlorite filling. In the
weathered rock, the joints are generally
infilled with clay with typical thicknesses in
the range 5-20mm.

Although most of the tunnel is below the
water table, seepage was minimal owing to the
impermeable nature of the sedimentary strata
and was generally confined to the dyke zones.

The predominant structural feature affecting
tunnelling was the bedding of the sedimentary
rocks, the spacing of which ranges from close
in the shales to medium/wide in the
sandstone/siltstone horizons. The bedding is
very weak in shear and tension due to the
presence of mica, chlorite, clay or
carbonaceous fillings.

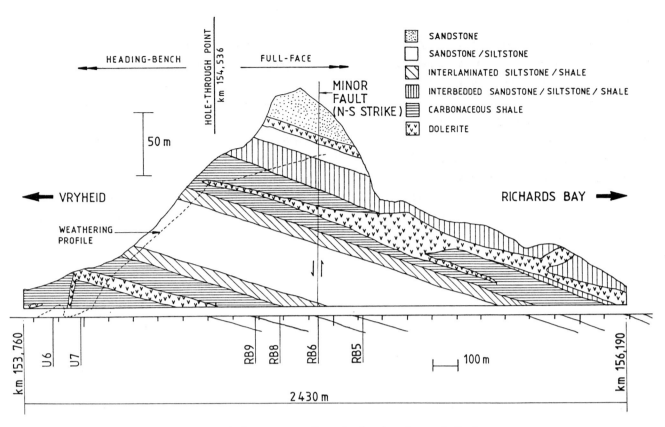

Fig. 2 Longitudinal Section through Isangoyana Tunnel showing General Geology

Site investigations comprised air-photo interpretation, surface geological mapping, seismic refraction and magnetometer surveys over the portal areas (4400m survey length), core logging from ten NX-size (54mm) diamond drilled boreholes (772m total), water packer testing of selected holes, and laboratory testing of rock core. The rock core was tested mechanically to determine uniaxial compressive strength, Young's modulus, Poisson's ratio, and Duncan free swell values and typical results are given on Table 1.

Mineralogical studies were undertaken of both the macro and microfabrics.

Table 1   Rock Material Properties

Rock Type	Uniaxial compressive strength (MPa)	Young's modulus (GPa)	Poisson's ratio	Duncan free swell (strain)
Carbonaceous shale	63 – 98	15	0.15	0,0169
Sandstone/siltstone	113 – 123	21	0,17	0,0037
Interlaminated siltstone/shale	92 – 125	18	0,16	0,0055
Interbedded sandstone/siltstone/ shale	81 – 105	14	0,10	–
Dolerite	126	100	0,26	–

Note: Owing to drying effects the uniaxial compressive strengths given above for the fine grained rocks may be significantly greater than the strengths at natural moisture content.

TUNNEL DESIGN

The selection and timing of primary support installation were based on the expected behaviour of the tunnel cross section in weak bedded rock under varying degrees of cover.

For tunnel excavations in weak, near horizontally bedded rocks, the prominent failure modes are related to shear overstress along bedding partings leading to fall out of the rock particularly from the haunches of arched tunnel sections. If such effects are not adequately controlled, failure of the tunnel crown may occur through bed separation and strata buckling mechanisms[1,2]

In order to control such effects and to mitigate against the adverse shape effect of the arched profile, rock reinforcement was placed immediately behind the advancing tunnel face. The pattern and length of rockbolts were derived initially from precedent experience in similar tunnels with appropriate variations for geology and depth of cover. To provide optimum benefit from the rock reinforcement, particularly in relation to the near surface zone around the tunnel periphery, tensioned reinforcement was specified based on precedent observations in such rock types[3].

Careful attention was given to blasting patterns and blasthole drilling accuracy in order to both minimise damage to the excavation periphery and to provide a sound substrata for rock reinforcement and shotcrete lining.

In the moisture sensitive siltstones and shales through which the tunnel passes, drying out of the rock and resulting microfissuring can lead to a significant reduction in the strength of the rock mass and ultimately disaggregation and spalling. In order to inhibit the adverse effects of these drying processes, the excavation periphery was shotcreted immediately after excavation with mesh reinforcement being provided in the more critical sections of the tunnel.

EFFECT OF CONSTRUCTION STRATEGY ON SUPPORT INSTALLATION

The contractor's excavation programme called for the simultaneous excavation of the tunnel from both ends using a full-face advance from the Richards Bay portal and a heading-bench advance from the Vryheid side. No lining was placed until hole-through had been achieved.

Owing to the need to advance as quickly as possible the Contractor placed priority on minimising the rock support in relation to the geological conditions encountered. With this approach it was necessary to systematically check the adequacy of the support installed particularly where changing rock conditions were encountered. As a result, the following control programmes were established:
- Rockbolt pull-out and shotcrete strength tests at the commencement of tunnelling and when changes occurred in rock conditions, rockbolt diameters or shotcrete mix.
- Analysis of drilling/blasting patterns together with measurements of drillhole lengths and perimeter blasthole barrels.
- Close supervision of bolt installation and timing of tensioning.
- Monitoring of tunnel sections to measure the deformation and stabilisation characteristics of the excavation.

For tunnel performance monitoring, both tunnel convergence and extensometer observations were carried out. For routine monitoring operations immediately behind the advancing face, high quality convergence monitoring was adopted in order to minimise interference with tunnelling operations. Where significant initial convergence was recorded, extensometer arrays were installed to determine in detail the deformation characteristics of the excavation periphery.

CONVERGENCE MONITORING

The arrays generally comprised five pins as shown in Fig. 3, placed within 2m of the tunnel face, being recessed into the rock to prevent blast damage. The pins were approximately 1,2m long and consisted of a stainless steel ring attached to a length of rebar which was debonded for 0,9m from the excavation periphery. The pin was installed in a percussion drilled hole using fast-setting polyester resin. Convergence was measured using a Sinco tape extensometer which has a

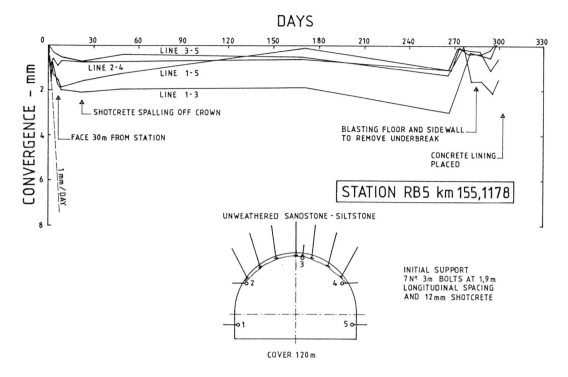

Fig. 3 Convergence Monitoring Results for Station RB5 - Adequate initial support

claimed accuracy of ±0,01-0,02mm and an actual working resolution of some 0,5mm for the line lengths adopted.

Nineteen stations were installed at intervals varying between 20m in the weathered low cover rock at the Ulundi end to 300m in the unweathered sandstone/siltstone on the Richards Bay side. Three pins were placed in the heading advance and the other two pins after removal of the bench.

Six sets of results which indicate the range of behaviour observed are given in Figs. 3-8. Three of the graphs show early stabilisation with small movements of the order of 3-10mm as a result of the correct support having been placed at the face, whilst others show that an inadequate level of initial support led to relatively large inelastic movements of the order of 20-40mm, and required additional support to be placed at a later stage.

The deformation characteristics observed are described in detail below.

CONVERGENCE ARRAY
RB5 (Figure 3)
The observed behaviour shows an almost completely elastic response of the

sandstone/siltstone strata within three tunnel diameters (30m). No bed separation or rock loosening has occurred.

CONVERGENCE ARRAY
RB6 (Figure 4)
The results show the inelastic response of a 17m wide fault zone in interlaminated siltstone/shale which was inadequately supported with bolts which were too short and too widely spaced to inhibit progressive deformation at depth. Strata separation has occurred along micaceous bedding. Additional later bolting improved stabilisation but ongoing progressive deformation and rock loosening are evident. The resultant long term rock load on the concrete lining is estimated to be equivalent to some 4m of loosened rock.

At this location it was also found that where the initial bolting is too short it is generally pointless trying to stabilise the excavation with shotcrete even if this is applied in significant thicknesses. (Optimum stabilisation in such rock types can only be achieved through the installation of longer length bolts, the exact length being dependent on both the excavation geometry and the delay

327

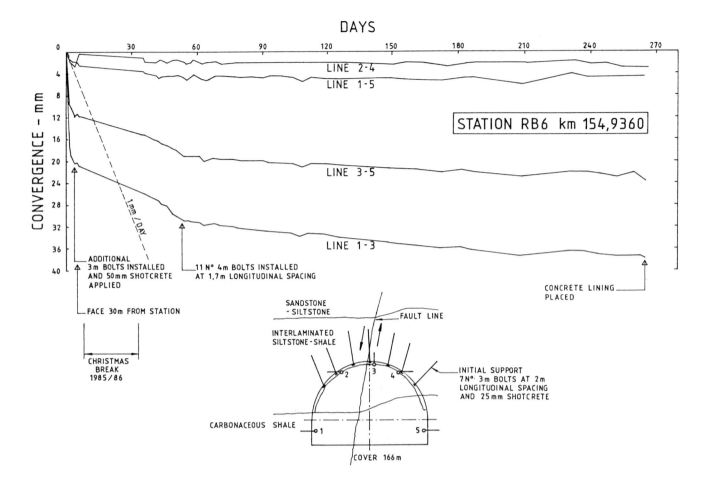

Fig. 4   Convergence Monitoring Results for Station RB6 -   Inadequate initial support and partially successful remedial support

in time incurred prior to the second bolting stage).

Fig. 4 also shows that for the rock conditions encountered, the initial support is insufficient if the initial rate of movement on all the lines in the crown/haunch areas of the excavation exceeded 1mm per day. The initial rate of movement was determined after three rounds of advance and permitted an early decision to increase rock support as necessary.

CONVERGENCE ARRAY
RB8 (Figure 5)
These observations show the characteristic response of interlaminated siltstone/shale influenced by weak bedding partings (10mm clay seams) with horizontal shear displacement of sidewalls evident. The bolting is sufficient to limit loosening of the crown profile to about 1m depth, however, the haunch bolting is

inadequate to prevent loosening of rock in this zone.

CONVERGENCE ARRAY
RB9 (Figure 6)
The data show the response of blocky, jointed carbonaceous shale with pronounced subvertical jointing and subhorizontal clay seams (shears) above the crown. The initial bolting was inadequate for the tunnel size and rock conditions and allowed a significant degree of progressive loosening to take place around the tunnel/periphery and beyond the reinforcement zone.

The long term loading on the concrete lining will be influenced by such progressive loosening around the tunnel periphery. From the data obtained, an influence zone of rock above the crown of some 4-5m in extent was derived.

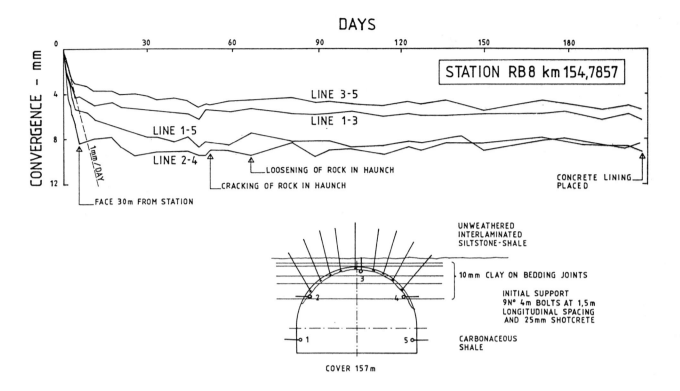

Fig. 5 Convergence Monitoring Results for Station RB8 - Adequate crown initial support but inadequate haunch support

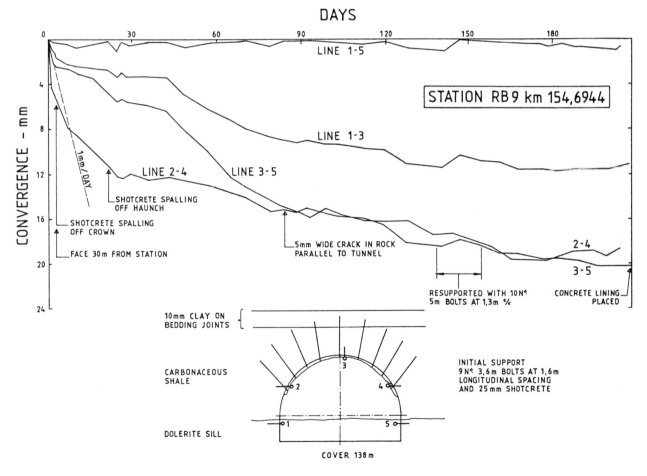

Fig. 6 Convergence Monitoring Results for Station RB9 - Inadequate initial support and successful remedial support

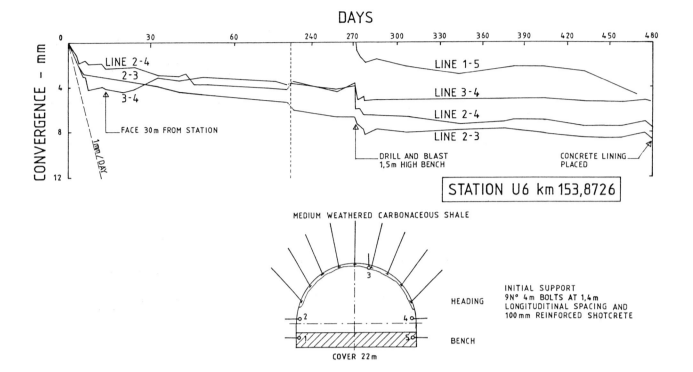

DAYS

Fig. 7 Convergence Monitoring Results for Station U6 - Adequate initial support for both heading and bench advances

CONVERGENCE ARRAY
U6 (Figure 7)

A generally elastic response of weathered, low cover carbonaceous shale was observed with very limited bed separation. The inferred horizontal stress is similar to the vertical stress. Nominal additional convergence due to bench excavation is also evident.

CONVERGENCE ARRAY
U7 (Figure 8)

This shows only a partial inelastic response of unweathered carbonaceous shale due to the heading development but pronounced profile disturbance due to invert removal. Ongoing creep of the sidewalls is evident and the inferred horizontal stress is greater than the vertical.

The potential long term lining loading is equivalent to a loosened zone of some 2-3m of rock above the crown.

EXTENSOMETER MONITORING

The behaviour of the rock mass around the tunnel periphery was determined at selected zones of significant displacement by means of extensometer arrays.

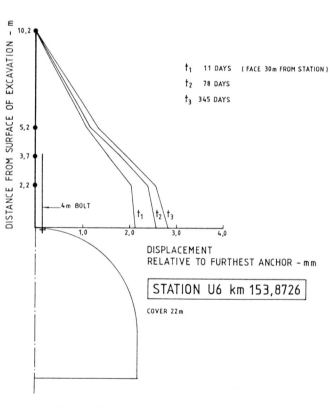

Fig. 9 Typical Extensometer Response

330

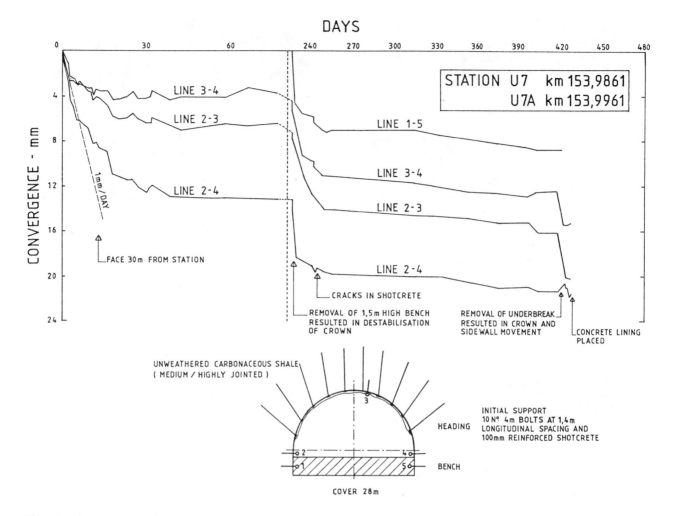

Fig. 8 Convergence Monitoring Results for Station U7 - Adequate initial support for heading advance
but inadequate for bench excavation

A typical relative movement–depth relationship (at station U6) is shown in Fig. 9. The deformation patterns obtained indicate that the rock mass is behaving in an essentially elastic manner except for some ongoing creep in the near-surface rock.

ASSESSMENT OF MONITORING CONTROL MEASURES

The monitoring control showed that the installed support at the face was generally adequate to limit rock loosening and to provide safe tunnelling conditions. However, in certain zones excessive loosening due to inadequate initial support was evident and stabilisation was only achieved by later, heavier support.

The use of well engineered and carefully controlled support measures ensured a rapid tunnelling advance rate with the hole-through of the 2,4km long tunnel being completed in thirteen months with final bench removal at the Vryheid side taking another two months. In terms of support used, some 11 400 rockbolts and 37 800m^2 shotcrete (mainly unreinforced) were used. The effectiveness of the bolting and shotcreting coupled with controlled blasting measures was confirmed by the monitoring programme.

From an assessment of the monitoring records, the potential long term loadings, onto the concrete lining were estimated to be equivalent to a loosened zone of some 0–1m of rock over 60 percent of the tunnel, 2–3m over 31 percent, 4–5m over 7 percent and in excess of 5m over 2 percent of the tunnel.

331

Plate 1   View of Excavated Cross Section at hole through location

CONCLUSIONS

The successful excavation and support of the iSangoyana tunnel serves to indicate that uncertainties and risks associated with driving large span tunnels in weak, bedded rock can be greatly reduced by establishing a tight control of the excavation/support process.

Wherever tunnelling conditions are critical, deformation monitoring forms an important part of the control process and permits efficient rock support usage commensurate with safe and rapid advance.

ACKNOWLEDGEMENTS

The permission of the South African Transport Services and the primary consulting engineers, Robertson and Hitchins, to publish the paper is greatly appreciated. The particular assistance of Mr. W. Martin in the monitoring is gratefully acknowledged. The co-operation and active involvement of the Contractor, a joint venture of Clifford Harris and Marti A.G., in the monitoring measures is also acknowledged.

REFERENCES

1. Sharp, J.C., L.A. Endersbee and T.W. Mellors, Design and observed performance of permanent cavern excavations in weak, bedded strata. Proc. Design and Performance of Underground Excavations ISRM, Cambridge, U.K. 1984.
2. Obert, L., and W.L. Duvall, Rock Mechanics and the Design of Structures in Rock, John Wiley and Sons, New York, 1967.
3. Sharp, J.C., R.J. Pine, D. Moy and R.J. Byrne, The use of a trial enlargement for the underground cavern design of the Drakensberg pumped storage scheme, 4th Congress Int Soc Rock Mech, Montreux 1979.

Use of underground mining and tunnelling techniques for *in-situ* oil recovery

H. G. Stephenson B.Sc., C.Eng., F.I.M.E., P.Eng.
Norwest Resource Consultants Ltd., Norwest Mine Services, Ltd., Calgary, Alberta, Canada
R. W. Luhning B.E.(Chem.Eng.)
In Situ Operations, Alberta Oil Sands Technology and Research Authority, Alberta, Canada

SYNOPSIS
It is the authors' opinion that underground mining technology, particularly the specialized techniques of shaft sinking and tunnelling, may be applied to increase the world's recoverable oil reserves by making accessible for exploitation oil considered non-recoverable by "conventional" recovery methods.

For example the "Shaft and Tunnel Access Concept" (SATAC) utilizes tunnels located in or close to the pay zone to provide access for drilling equipment and personnel. Semi-horizontal wells drilled from the tunnel into the reservoir permit the application of gravity drainage and/or in situ processes. Appreciably higher recoveries of the oil in place are expected compared to in situ processes applied through surface wells.

Timely development of mine assisted techniques such as SATAC is necessary to ensure that an anticipated shortfall in the world's output of conventionally obtained oil can be replaced by oil obtained from vast heavy oil and bitumen resources presently subject to very limited exploitation.

Exploitation of these "non-conventional" resources will be essential to avoid increasing dependence on Middle East sources unless additional "conventional" oil deposits can be located and developed.

In order to test the Shaft and Tunnel Access Concept an Underground Test Facility has been constructed to provide access to one of the world's most abundant but difficult reservoirs, the Athabasca Oil Sands in Alberta, Canada. From tunnels below the reservoir horizontal wells have been drilled into the pay zone and steam will be applied to mobilize and drain the bitumen.

The concept is likely to have wide application in difficult oil reservoirs and the paper describes in some detail the construction of the Underground Test Facility.

THE WORLD OIL SITUATION
Before discussing the use of underground mining and tunnelling techniques in oil reservoirs, it is important to examine briefly the extent to which Europe and North America are dependent on Middle East oil. Comments by Gall in an article in Forbes magazine [1] illustrate the problem. Mr. Gall points out that world oil production peaked at 10.45 M m^3 (65.7 million barrels) daily in 1979. Under the pressure of high prices consumption, and therefore production, had fallen to 8.9 M m^3 (56 million barrels) by 1983. Regardless of price, however, oil is being consumed faster than it is being discovered. We are, as Mr. Gall says in his article, "living off stored wealth". Oil consumption is expected to continue at an annual rate 25% higher than the rate at which oil is discovered.

Mr. Gall quotes from a discussion with Mr. J.P. Riva, a petroleum geologist and author of "World Petroleum Resources and Reserves". Mr. Riva believes the world can continue to produce oil at current levels for another 30 to 40 years though, during that period, the geographical distribution of production will change rapidly. In 1985 for example, the Middle East produced 1.63 M m³ (10.3 million barrels) daily, or 19% of the world's oil. Since the Middle East has 57% of all proven reserves of conventional oil we can expect that by the year 2005 the Middle East will be producing approximately 4.13 M m³ (26 million barrels) daily, or 50% of the world's oil, and by 2020 it will be producing 75%. By then however the capacity of Middle East oil fields will be so strained that world production of conventional oil will rapidly begin to fall.

This illustrates the strategic problems which can arise for the developed nations of the free world as a consequence of an increasing dependence on Middle East oil, especially when the problems of transporting oil through such sensitive regions as the Straits of Hormuz are considered.

THE CANADIAN OIL SITUATION

At the end of 1985 it was estimated that the remaining established reserves of conventional oil in Canada totalled 1,260 M m³ (7.9 billion barrels).[2] Given the current rate of consumption, without new discoveries, conventional oil reserves would meet Canadian needs only until the year 2000. It is clear that the problems facing Canada are similar to, though more extreme than, those facing the world at large. Fortunately Canada has vast reserves of non-conventional oil in the oil sands and heavy oil fields. It is these resources, the role which underground mining technology is likely to have in their development, and the potential for application of this technology world wide, which is the main thrust of this paper.

OIL SANDS OF ALBERTA

Imagine a deposit of oil bearing sand averaging

20 m in thickness, containing from 8-15% by weight of bitumen, and occupying an area the size of Scotland, almost 70,000 km². These are the Alberta Oil Sands. The total reserves are estimated to be approximately 266,400 M m³ (1.67 trillion barrels),[3] over 200 times the reserves of conventional oil in Canada and approximately four times the reserves of conventional oil in all of the Middle East oil fields combined!

The resource is vast. Unfortunately, the problems of producing this oil at an acceptable rate of recovery and with attractive economics are formidable.

The oil sands vary in depth from surface outcrops to beds covered by more than 800 m of overburden. The direct use of surface mining techniques to recover the shallow oil sands has led to the construction of two of the largest surface mines in the world. Their present combined capacity of 30,000 m³ (190,000 barrels) of synthetic crude per day requires the two mining operations to mine 380,000 tonnes of oil sands daily. (It is interesting to compare the size of these two oil sands mines with the coal industry in Great Britain which produces, from all its underground and surface mines, approximately the same tonnage of mineral.) The largest of these mines is presently being considered for a 50% expansion. The total cost of this mining equipment is expected to be somewhere between 600 and 800 million dollars. (Norwest Mine Services, as part of the Norswego joint venture with two other companies, is presently responsible for producing the specifications for the additional mining equipment for this 50% expansion.)

Of the total reserve of hydrocarbons in the oil sands of Alberta only 5,200 M m³ (1.95%) of this resource is generally considered recoverable by surface mining and alternative methods of recovering oil from the remainder must be developed. Consequently, a large number of pilot projects have been implemented which utilize various in situ recovery systems to produce oil using wells drilled from the surface. Generally speaking, the in situ systems require the use of steam to heat the bitumen, causing it to flow and creating conditions in which the oil can be pumped to the surface. However, these in-situ projects have, with a few exceptions, resulted in high costs and low recovery of the oil in place. It is not expected that, except in very exceptional cases, the recovery of the resource by this method will exceed 20% of the oil in place; even achieving 10% has proven impossible for many of these pilots.

THE SHAFT AND TUNNEL ACCESS CONCEPT

As early as the mid-1970's it became apparent that alternative methods had to be developed if Canada was to benefit from the oil sands reserves. In 1975 the Alberta Government set up the Alberta Oil Sands Technology and Research Authority (AOSTRA) with initial funding of 100 million dollars and with the primary responsibility of developing the technology to establish alternative commercial methods of exploiting the hydrocarbon reserves of the oil sands. Naturally the bulk of this effort was directed towards in situ methods applied through wells drilled from the surface. We will refer to this as the "Surface Access Concept", or SAC. However amongst the many proposals received by AOSTRA were several which utilized shafts and tunnels to gain access to the reservoirs. This is known as the Shaft and Tunnel Access Concept (SATAC).

The SATAC concept involves the construction of vertical shafts from the surface, and the development of tunnels in oil sands or in strata above or below the reservoir. This network of tunnels would then utilized to provide access for drilling equipment, pipelines, and personnel to apply in situ methods, not from the surface wells, but through semi-horizontal wells drilled from tunnels very close to the reservoir. The horizontal wells would be utilized for both the injection of steam and the production of bitumen from the oil sands.

The basic SATAC and SAC concepts are illustrated in Figure 1.

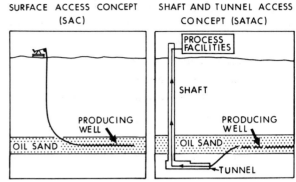

Figure 1 In Situ Operations Through Horizontal Well;

The concept does not utilize mining techniques to extract oil sand from the beds for processing. Stephenson [4] has expressed the view that it is extremely unlikely that bulk underground mining of the sands and transportation to a processing plant could be economically viable in the foreseeable future.

During the period 1976 to 1981 various studies of the concept were completed. Each of the studies carried out on the SATAC concept recognized the potential for a significantly higher recovery of bitumen in place using underground access. However, in each case, the validity of the conclusions reached were dependant on data derived from purely conceptual studies. This highlighted the need for more factual data to allow increased confidence in technical and economic projections. It was clear that, until a pilot project was constructed, little concrete information would become available to improve the credibility of the economics calculated for the project.

The potential of the oil sands, the promise of higher recovery using the SATAC approach and the urgent need for hard data led AOSTRA to give very serious consideration to the construction of an underground test facility to resolve the many uncertainties which remained.

THE SATAC CONCEPT - SOME QUESTIONS

Some of the uncertainties in applying the SATAC

concept have been listed by Carrigy and Stephenson [5].

Major Mining Related Uncertainties

. The preferred horizon for tunnel construction and the type of support and/or lining needed.

. The effect of various geological/geotechnical parameters on construction of shafts and tunnels.

. The difficulty involved in protecting the tunnels and shafts against steam pressures and thermal stresses.

. The rate of gas emission from strata surrounding the oil sands, and the extent of mine ventilation problems.

. Costs for the development of shafts and tunnels.

Major Process Related Uncertainties

. The spacing, length and alignment of injection and/or production wells for optimum recovery of bitumen.

. The quantity and pressure of steam required for optimum bitumen recovery.

. How the use of horizontal wells from tunnels compares with in situ operations from surface accessed wells.

. The complexity of drilling, completing and servicing horizontal wells from tunnels.

. Determination of reservoir characteristics which favour in situ operations using horizontal wells.

. The protection of underground personnel and facilities against well "blow out", particularly if high pressure steam is involved.

THE NEED FOR AN UNDERGROUND TEST FACILITY

Clearly if the SATAC concept was to be examined further, the next steps were

. to determine the technical and economic feasibility of accessing the reserve area by underground methods.

. to construct an Underground Test Facility, referred to from this point on as the U.T.F.

. to carry out pilot tests of in situ processes from the tunnels of the U.T.F.

The facility would provide a valuable research opportunity and could be utilized to evaluate alternative in situ recovery processes. If the concept was shown to be technically feasible and viable, the U.T.F. could subsequently form part of a commercial operation.

In December 1982, AOSTRA retained Norwest Resource Consultants Ltd. (Norwest), a Canadian company based in Calgary, Alberta, to prepare development proposals for the access phase of U.T.F.

The assignment undertaken by Norwest was to be site specific and related to an area with adequate reserves to sustain a pilot plant operation. Norwest was required to:

. collect geotechnical data on the site conditions

. design the access phase of the facility

. prepare requests for proposals for construction of the access phase

. provide detailed capital cost estimates

The next section of this paper describes the planning and engineering of the access phase of the U.T.F. A paper by Stephenson, Owen and Turner [6] provides additional details.

PLANNING THE FACILITY

A decision was taken that the U.T.F. would be designed and constructed in two stages.

Stage I, the access stage, included two vertical shafts and a network of tunnels of sufficient length to house the infrastructure necessary for the development of the facility.

Stage II was to be a phased operation as follows:

. Phase A; Would include tunnels, and supporting infrastructure, to allow a pre-pilot trial of the drilling and process operations

- Phase B; Dependent upon the results obtained in Phase A, a full pilot operation would be developed.

Site Selection

A site was selected forty-four kilometers northwest of Ft. McMurray (Fig. 2). The site had the following characteristics:

- Overburden: 91.4 m thick,
- Payzone: 19.6 m average thickness,
- Bitumen in the payzone: 13.76% average by weight,
- Reserves: 50 M m^3 (325 million barrels) of bitumen in place.

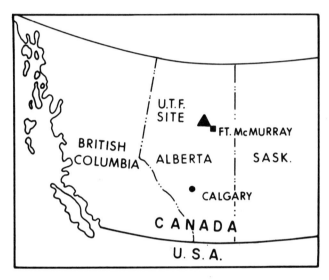

Figure 2 Site Location For Underground Test Facility

Design of the Access Phase

The initial step in designing the access phase was to decide whether one or two shafts were required and to determine the shaft diameter(s). In order to arrive at this decision, the duty of the shaft system was specified as follows.

Ventilation

The shaft system was to be capable of circulating enough fresh air to dilute methane and any hydrogen sulfide emissions which might be encountered, taking into account the possible increase in gas emissions resulting from a heated oil reservoir. The design air quantity was also required to provide cooling of the tunnels during a limited thermal pilot operation.

Materials Handling

It was decided that a skip cage combination capable of hoisting 100 tonnes of waste per hour from tunnels would be sufficient.

Equipment Transportation

The shaft system would require the capacity to transport tunnelling and drilling equipment, broken down as necessary, to the shaft bottom. The system was to be capable of handling pipes of suitable lengths for underground pipelines transporting steam and product.

Access to Tunnelling Horizon

A shaft depth of 213 m was selected, with an inset at 183 m providing access to the main tunnelling horizon in limestone.

Selection of Shaft Configuration

In addition to the parameters mentioned above, other factors which were taken into account in selecting the shaft configuration included:

- the security and safety of personnel working in the U.T.F.;
- the proportionately high cost of shaft construction, particularly for a pilot-scale facility;
- the comparative technical advantages of the methods of shaft construction considered; namely "blind shaft boring" and "freezing and excavating".

It was concluded that the underground test facility required two 3.0 m shafts.

Selection of Shaft Construction Method

Shaft sinking had not previously been successfully carried out through the oil sands or the strata above them. Geotechnical investigations had shown that the properties of the strata through which the shafts were to be sunk would determine the shaft construction method. The strata consisted, in descending order, of soft, weak, clayey, and silty deposits, the oil sands themselves, and the Devonian limestone below the reservoir. Characteristics of the strata which caused most concern included:

. the presence of swelling clays and very weak materials in the formations above the oil sands;

. the slabbing of oil sand when a free face is exposed, believed to be caused by exsolution of gas and evidenced by failure in open pits and in a short trial shaft sunk many years previously.

Only two methods of construction were considered worthy of serious consideration. These were:

. Blind shaft drilling
. Freezing and excavating

Detailed examination of these two systems was completed and blind shaft drilling was chosen. This method is similar to the drilling of vertical oil wells except that the bit assembly and drill pipe are much larger and the drilling rig is utilized, not only to drill the shaft, but also to place the steel liner. Drilling mud is utilized to support the walls of the shaft and to carry cuttings to the surface. In this particular case, the mud pressure was expected to minimize exsolution of gas from the oil sand and prevent sloughing of the shaft wall. A further advantage was that no personnel would be in the shaft during construction and lining operations.

Shaft Liner and Equipment

The design for the two shafts is shown in Figure 3.

Both shafts were to be equipped with a steel liner having an internal diameter of 3.03 m and capable of withstanding full hydrostatic head and ground swelling pressures at a safety factor of 2.5. The liner was to be constructed from steel plate. Each liner section was 13.5 m long; up to 9 t in weight, equipped with stiffener rings and grouting pipes on the outside, and equipment rings welded on the

inside. The thickness of steel plate utilized ranged from 16 to 20 mm. Inspection ports were provided to allow testing for gas or noxious fluids prior to break out from the shaft wall.

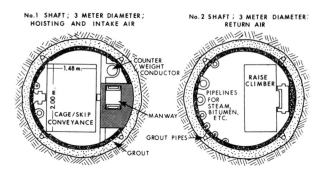

Figure 3 Plan View of Shafts Showing Equipment Disposition and Ventilation Duty

No. 1 shaft was to be utilized for intake ventilating air and would be equipped with a skip cage and counterweight with the skip cage running on wooden guides. This shaft would also be equipped with a staged ladderway for emergency egress.

No. 2 shaft was designated the return air shaft and would accommodate all pipelines for steam, bitumen, etc. This shaft would be equipped with an A.B. 500 Universal Hoist providing emergency access via a cage mounted on a vertical rack.

Main Hoist

An electrically-powered single-drum hoist and a head frame were to be installed at No. 1 shaft to handle the skip cage. The hoist would be powered by a 250 hp electric motor and capable of manual, semi-automatic and automatic operation.

Surface Layout

The Underground Test Facility was designed as a self-contained unit capable of being expanded from a Pre-pilot Trial through Pilot Process to Commercial operation.

The Surface Facilities comprise:

. A water supply system and treatment unit
. Fire fighting facilities

- Diesel generators for emergency power supply
- A workshop/warehouse complex and mine dry building
- Air compressors
- An administration building

A Conspec computer unit was included to provide status indication on all major items of surface equipment and was interfaced with an MSA tube bundle underground environmental monitoring unit so providing overall site monitoring. The unit had capability to accommodate the subsequent Drilling and Production elements of the Facility.

Underground Layout

The layout of the underground tunnels was planned in detail to the Phase "A", Pre-pilot stage, a total of 980 m of drivage. Figure 4 shows the tunnel network and support services which include air, water and electricity, equipment assembly station, rock handling facilities, pumping capability and a refuge chamber for use in case of emergency. The roadway configuration was designed to permit a full assessment to be made of the effect of the inherent joint structure on roadway formation and stability. The layout provided for the first wells to be drilled directly over a test tunnel to determine the impact on the roadway of steam based in situ operations in a reservoir above.

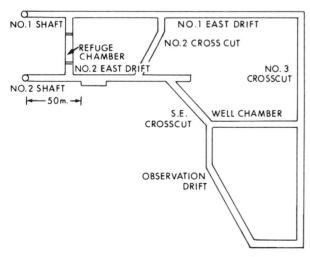

Figure 4 Layout of Access Stage of Underground Test Facility

A tunnel horizon was selected in the Devonian Limestone at a horizon 13 m below the base of the reservoir.

This horizon was selected to provide, in this first ever attempt to apply the SATAC system, the safest possible horizon for personnel and equipment. A tunnel could have been constructed in any of three horizons, the shale above the reservoir, the oil sands, or the limestone below. However, there were serious doubts whether the tunnel could be maintained in safe condition in either the shale or the oil sand, once steam was applied to the reservoir.

The expected configuration of the drill required a tunnel cross-section 5 m wide and 4 m high. Geotechnical studies indicated that roof support would require full-column contact bolts on a standard 1.5 m grid. Bolt length was generally 2.1 m supplemented with 3 m bolts at intersections. As an additional precaution, the Well Chamber, Shaft Stations and Key Access Roads were to be shotcreted to eliminate the potential for weathering. Standard Drill-and-Blast techniques were chosen for the initial tunnel works.

CONSTRUCTION OF THE ACCESS STAGE

The engineering and capital costing of the Access Stage was finished in January 1984. In June of 1984, AOSTRA made the decision to go ahead with construction of the Access Phase, to commence design of the drilling equipment, and to engineer the Pilot Phase.

Norwest was retained to act as Project Manager and Owner's Representatives on site. The Harrison/Saturn joint venture was selected as General Contractor and they in turn selected the Simmons/Santa Fe joint venture to construct and line the two shafts.

Construction of Shafts

The rig selected to drill the shafts was Regent Drilling Rig No. 14 shown in Figure 5. This was a conventional deep hole oilfield rig, depth rated to 6100 m, and with a 500 t hook

Figure 5 Blind Shaft Boring Drilling Rig

Figure 6 Downhole Assembly (Approximately 250 Tonnes)

load capacity. The rig was modified to accept a 1.25 m drive table and a 35 cm diameter dual wall drill pipe. In addition structural modifications were made to allow pickup, suspension and lowering of liners within the rig framework. The mast was a self erecting design, 43.28 m high.

Patterson [7] describes how a number of large diameter drill bits were considered for this project. It was finally decided to use a Drilco flat bottomed bit design incorporating 16 cutters. The drill bit assembly weighed 250 t and is shown in Figure 6.

No. 2 shaft was drilled first since verticality was less critical on this shaft and, if any problems arose, the experience gained could be applied to the No. 1 shaft. The shaft was spudded on February 4th, 1985 with drilling of the first shaft forecast to require 60 days.

The blind shaft drilling operation began very slowly due to difficulties experienced in a highly plastic clay zone near the surface. This caused problems with clay balling on the bit and difficulty in circulating cuttings and drilling mud. As the operation progressed, and modifications were made to the mud circulation system, the penetration rate improved and, on day 30, the bit reached the base of the oil sands and entered the limestone. Soon afterwards the drilling bit was changed, having drilled for 606.75 hours, a new world record. Some problems were encountered in the clay beds in the upper Devonian Limestone but these were gradually overcome and the shaft was completed on day 55, 5 days ahead of schedule. The average rate of penetration was 3.8 m/d.

During shaft drilling regular checks were made on verticality and the deflection was never found to exceed 0.2 degrees from vertical.

Verticality was controlled largely by the distribution of drill string weight within the shaft and the use of centralizers. Soon after entering the limestone the total suspended weight was over 240 t, of which only half was utilized to provide pressure on the bit. The remainder acted as a plumb bob to keep the bit and drill string on line.

Patterson [7] describes how the liner was installed and grouted.

On April 3, 1985, the first section of liner was lowered into the hole . The liner was floated into place by filling the interior with fresh water.

The liner joints were welded and inspected using an automatic ultrasonic scanning system. Defects requiring repair were ground out, rewelded and reinspected. The last section of liner was welded and lowered into place April 16, 1985.

It is interesting to note that during installation it was possible to rotate the 140 t liner by hand while it was hanging from the blocks.

The fact that the liner hung free was an indication of the effectiveness of the mud system in maintaining hole stability and of the high standard of shaft alignment.

The liner was grouted in place using over 1000 t of cement, placed in 6 stages over a period of 6 days.

Drilling of No. 1 shaft began in April and the shafts, pit bottom, and support facilities were completed in May 1986. Figure 7 shows the headframe of the U.T.F.

Tunnel Construction

Before breakout from the shafts, probe holes were drilled through the inspection ports in the shaft liner to determine if flammable or noxious gasses or water were present. No problems were encountered, a section of the

liner was cut out and for the first time ever tunnelling began to provide access to the Athabasca oil sands. Figure 8 is the first

Figure 7 The Headframe of the U.T.F.

Figure 8 The First Photograph Taken Underground in Deep Oil Sands. Norwest Personnel at the Bottom of No. 2 Shaft are Herb Young, Senior Mining Engineer (Left) Gerry Stephenson, President (Centre) and Howard Owen. Project Manager (Right)

photograph ever taken underground in the deep oil sands. Figure 9 shows the completed tunnel

341

carrying the bitumen and steam pipe lines and Figure 10 shows the pit bottom of No. 2 shaft.

Figure 9 A Completed Tunnel, Steam, Bitumen and other Pipelines are Suspended Near the Roof

Figure 10 The No. 2 Shaft Bottom

THE UNDERGROUND DRILL RIG

A prototype drill rig has been constructed to drill the wells from the tunnel. The rig, shown in Figure 11, has been designed to both drill and complete the wells, installing special casing to permit steam injection and bitumen production. The rig is an electro-hydraulic, self propelled, track mounted unit designed to operate in the confined space of the tunnel and in the type of atmosphere normally encountered in a coal mine. The rig has a maximum thrust of 100 t and is capable of

drilling 222 mm horizontal holes to a depth of 600 m. Equipment is provided to survey the hole and modify the direction of the drill bit. All drilling is done through a blow out preventer connected to a 40 m long, 244 mm diameter casing cemented in position.

Figure 11 The Prototype Drilling Rig in the Well Chamber

THE PROCESS

The first in situ process to be applied at the U.T.F. has been described by Edmunds [8].

Wells have been drilled in pairs with the producer well near the base of the reservoir and the injector about 5 m above it. Three pairs of wells have been drilled 24 m apart with an effective completed length of 60 m in the reservoir. Steam will be injected into both wells initially and communication is expected between the wells after 50 to 100 days.

Numerical simulation has indicated that a steam chamber will form in the cold, immobile oil sand. As steam is injected it travels to the edge of the chamber heating the undepleted sand at the boundary of the chamber. The bitumen is mobilized and drains to the production hole with the condensed steam. Numerical modelling has indicated that, for the base case performance forecast described by Haston [9], a recovery of 50% of the oil in place can be predicted after four years of in situ process operations.

GEOTECHNICAL MONITORING

The application of steam to the reservoir at 1500 kPa and 200°C may have some impact on the tunnel in the limestone approximately 15 m below the wells.

The effect on the tunnel cannot be predicted with accuracy and a geotechnical program has been developed with the primary purpose of monitoring the effect of steam on the reservoir and the adjacent strata. The program consists of a series of vertical observation wells drilled from the surface and temperature, steam and movement probes located in bore holes in the tunnels and shafts.

SAFETY

Many elements of the U.T.F. are unusual, perhaps even unique. The shafts were the first ever successfully constructed through the oil sands. The tunnels are the first ever constructed at depth adjacent to the oil sands. The drilling rig and wellhead equipment has been built especially for the SATAC concept. The application of the in situ process from underground tunnels will be the first ever attempted in oil sands and very few examples exist of this concept being applied in any type of reservoir.

This poses an unusually difficult problem in determining the hazards which may exist underground, in mitigating those hazards, and in dealing with emergencies if they do occur.

Environmental and Process Monitoring

Data from the monitoring system is fed to, and displayed in, a surface control room.

Critical data includes analysis of air samples for CH_4, CO, H_2S and O_2 as well as information on the status of the process steam and product systems. Emergency shut down buttons and high and low level alarms are strategically located. A video system has been installed to monitor each well head. Figure 12 shows the monitoring system and sampling and video camera locations.

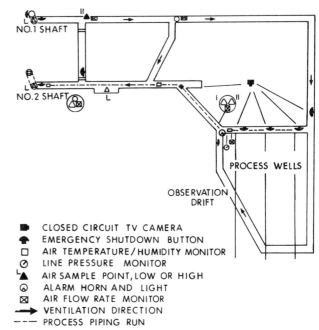

CLOSED CIRCUIT TV CAMERA
EMERGENCY SHUTDOWN BUTTON
AIR TEMPERATURE/HUMIDITY MONITOR
LINE PRESSURE MONITOR
AIR SAMPLE POINT, LOW OR HIGH
ALARM HORN AND LIGHT
AIR FLOW RATE MONITOR
VENTILATION DIRECTION
PROCESS PIPING RUN

From: AOSTRA U.T.F. In Situ Bitumen Recovery, J.A. Haston, et al

Figure 12 Monitoring and Control System for the In Situ Process

Management and Codes of Practice

Norwest Mine Services Ltd. have been appointed by AOSTRA as Mine Operations Contractor charged with responsibility for worksite safety and security.

Given the unique nature of the operation and the multi-disciplined elements involved, it was decided that Facility operations would be covered by Codes of Practice supplemented by Operational Procedures. The Codes establish the parameters to maintain a safe healthy working environment while the Procedures instruct workers on job operation in this environment.

The first stage in the process is to complete a hazard analysis and develop Codes to respond to the perceived hazards.

Prior to the commencement of Phase A tunnelling, twelve Codes of Practice were agreed with the Government Agencies involved and Operational Procedures were developed to match the Codes. Working to the Codes and Procedures, the tunnels were completed without accident or incident.

The Drilling Codes and Procedures were in place

prior to February 1987 and at the time of writing, work is in progress on establishing Process Codes.

An essential element in safety is training of workers and training modules have been developed for both on-site staff and visitors.

PRESENT STATUS

At the time of writing all six wells have been completed and steam injection is expected to begin in early November, 1987. Figure 13 shows an isometric view of the U.T.F. including the shafts, tunnels and the wells for the first attempt at steam injection.

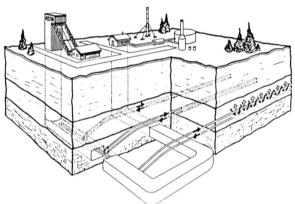

From: An Underground Road To A Wellhead, J.C. Suggett, June 1987

Figure 13 Underground Test Facility

ECONOMICS

The cost of the U.T.F. to date has been slightly over fifty million dollars. This includes a 36 km road, two shafts, 1 km of tunnel, underground and surface facilities, an underground drill and six wells. This investment in a pilot project reflects the importance of the oil sands in Canada's energy supply scenario and the enthusiasm in Alberta for the SATAC concept.

An economic analysis of a base case commercial operation has been described by Haston [9]. This study was based on an operation producing 1600 m³/d using three shafts, 15 km of tunnel and 400 wells. The capital cost was almost $200 million and annual operating costs were

$30 million. Economic analysis showed that, at a 10% discount factor, the project would deliver bitumen at a supply price of $11/m³ (or $18.70/bbl). (All costs in this section are quoted as mid 1985 Canadian dollars.)

Figure 14 provides some indication of the appearance of a commercial operation.

Figure 14 An Artist's Conception of a Commercial SATAC Operation

CONCLUSIONS

The author believes that completion of the U.T.F. shafts and tunnels has clearly demonstrated the ability of mining and tunnelling engineers to provide access to oil reservoirs suitable for application of in situ processes using horizontal wells. If the in situ process is equally successful in producing bitumen at a reasonable price, and recovering a percentage of the oil reserve significantly higher than that experienced using surface wells, the potential of the SATAC concept will have been confirmed in one of the world's most difficult but abundant oil reservoirs. The opportunity to utilize this technology in heavy oil and in partially depleted conventional oil reservoirs will be apparent, with significant benefits to countries with indigenous reserves. The opportunity will then exist for the tunnelling and mining industries to develop and exploit their capabilities and technology on a large scale, in a completely new field. There is, almost certainly, both light and oil at the end of the tunnel!

References

1. Gall N. "We Are Living Off Our Capital" Forbes Magazine; September 22nd, 1986, 62-66.

2. B.P. Statistical Review of World Energy, June 1987.

3. Alberta's Reserves of Crude Oil, Oil Sands, Gas, Natural Gas Liquids and Sulphur. Energy Resource Conservation Board St. 86-18.

4. Stephenson, H.G. An Evaluation of The Underground Approach to Oil Sand Development. AOSTRA Seminar on Underground Excavation in Oil Sands; May 19th, 1978.

5. Carrigy, M.A. and Stephenson, H.G. Progress Report On the Construction of An Underground Test Facility. Third International Conference on Heavy Crude and Oil Sands; Long Beach; California, July 1985.

6. Stephenson, H.G., Owen, H.D., and Turner, L.R. The AOSTRA Underground Test Facility - An Update. CIM A.G.M. Vancouver, April, 1985.

7. Patterson, M.A., Cuthbert L.G. and Tremble D. Blind Boring Through Oil Sands - A Trail Blazer. CIM A.G.M. Vancouver, April 1985.

8. Edmunds, N.R. The Use of Gravity Drainage Processes In The U.T.F. AOSTRA Conference on Advances In Petroleum Recovery and Upgrading Technology; Edmonton, June 2 - 3rd 1987.

9. Haston, J.A. AOSTRA U/G Test Facility: Second Generation Technology for In Situ Bitumen Recovery. Centennial Convention Canadian Eng., May 1987.

Problems associated with tunnelling operations in the construction of the Warsaw underground

Jan Szyndler M.Sc.
Mining Construction Company, Katowice, Poland
Jan Mateja
Mining Construction Company, Katowice, Poland
Kazimierz Rułka Prof., Dr., Eng.
Central Mining Institute, Katowice, Poland

ABSTRACT

An underground railway was included in the development programme for the capital city of Warsaw as early as 1927. For various reasons the project was commenced only in 1983.

Considering underground lines in the plans and selection of respective sites, especially when reconstructing Warsaw after World War II allowed shallow design of line I, i.e. placing rail head at the depth of 9-15.5 m. mainly by opencast method. However, the 23.1 km long line I includes a section of 6.2 km requiring employment of mining (underground) methods. Main difficulties ere caused by significant variability of Quarternary and Tertiary formations and their considerable water content. Principal hazards are:
- watered dust and fine sands.
- water lenses occurring inside impermeable layers,
- fluxing of Tertiary formations and high susceptibility to quicksand phenomena,
- occurrence of post-glacial blocks.

The performed survey and detailed ground analysis pointed to non-mechanised shields as the best method for tunnelling operations in variable hydrogeological conditions.

The paper presents technological and organization solutions of the project,
experience gained after driving approx. 2.0 km of the tunnel as well as recommendations for tunnelling further sections of the line.

1. INTRODUCTION

The No. I line of the Warsaw underground railway is being constructed principally by excavation from the surface. Only one section, of length of about 6 km, is being excavated by an underground method. The driving of tunnels on the No. I line of the Warsaw metro was entrusted to the Mining Work Enterprise of the Mining Construction Company in Katowice.

The Mining Construction Company - GBG - is a multi-plant firm employing about 30,000 people. Its potential, both in personnel and equipment, places it among the largest world organizations specializing in the field of mining construction.

The Mining Construction Company currently comprises over a dozen plants, most of which are enterprises executing mining work while the remainder are specialist technical facilities plants.

The Mining Construction Company has its own Research and Development Establishment "BUDOKOP".

During the post-war period the GBG plants have participated in the execution of:

347

- 22 new mines,
- 125 extraction levels,
- modernization and redevelopment of the majority of the Polish coal mines and certain salt mines.

In order to implement these projects the personnel from our plants have:
- sunk 385 new shafts with a joint total length of more than 150 km,
- deepened existing shafts and sunk inter-level shafts with a joint total length of 86 km,
- driven many million meters of roadways in the mines,
- excavated chamber workings with a joint total cubic capacity of more than 33 million cubic metres,
- drilled bore holes of various kinds with a total length of 364.700 m.

Apart from its operations in the construction and redevelopment of Polish mining facilities, the GBG plants have taken an active part in the export of Polish know-how, services and technical achievements, constructing facilities of many kinds and implementing mining construction services in such countries as: Bulgaria, Chile, the People's Republic of China, GDR, FRG, France, Hungary, Italy, Yugoslavia, Turkey and USSR.

As well as projects with a strictly mining profile the personnel of certain of the plants in GBG have taken an active part in the building of the underground sections of hydrotechnical facilities, rescuing ancient monuments of our natural culture and carrying out repairs to railway tunnels.

In this paper some of the technical aspects of work involved in the excavation of the No. I line of the Warsaw metro by the underground method are described and also the experience gained here by the personnel of the Mining Work Enterprise in Mysłowice.

2. CHARACTERISTIC FEATURES OF THE CONSTRUCTION PROJECT

2.1. History of the building of the Warsaw Metro [1]

By the year 1919 the Warsaw communications system was already seriously overloaded. Nevertheless, the first efforts towards the building of an underground railway date from 1927 when a project for two routes was developed and approved. Unfortunately, the metropolitan authorities were not in a position to finance this investment from their own resources. Propositions put forward by several foreign consortia who were interested in undertaking this project were considered by the City Council but were ultimately rejected as not sufficiently advantageous. In 1938 the original plan for the metro route was modified. The new line was to have a length of 45 km, of which 15 km were to run underground, while the construction was to be implemented in stages and was envisaged as lasting 35 years. The outbreak of war put an end to all thoughts of realizing this conception.

A new conception for a deep underground railway was developed at the beginning of the nineteen fifties. Building work was commenced, based on broad cooperation with the Soviet Union, and envisaged large scale contributions from Polish industry.
After the execution of 757 m of shafts, 778 m length of experimental roadways, 1256 m length of track tunnels and about 8 thousand m^3 of installation rooms, work on the building of the metro was suspended and only an experimental section was completed.
However, design studies were continued to develop the most advantageous conception for the Warsaw metro, based on the experience already gained.

In 1971 the economic and technical criteria were developed for the first line of a shallow lying metro on the route Młociny - Natolin.

The building of the first line of the
Warsaw metro, currently under way, was
decided by a decree issued by the
Council of Ministers No. 266/82 in
December 1982, authorizing the construction of the first line of a rapid underground railway. The building of the No. I
line of the Warsaw metro was begun on
April 15th, 1983.

2.2. Siting and characteristics of the route of the No. I metro line

From the very earliest days of development, the north-south route was
considered to be of the greatest
importance for the Warsaw metro.
For this reason when developing town
planning schemes for new districts or
in the rebuilding of older districts
of Warsaw ravaged during the war, suitable space was reserved for the building
of the future metro. This made it possible to plan the No. I line of the metro
as a shallow line, excavated principally
from the surface. The project envisages
a total length of route of about 23.1 km
(Fig. 1).
The central part of this route, running
through the centre of the city, was
planned as an underground excavation
not disturbing the ground surface.
The metro line is designed as a system
of two tunnels of diameter 5.5 /5.2 m
situated at a distance of about 8.5 m
from each other and having a mean depth
below the surface of the rail head of
9 - 15.5 m. Inclination of the rails
is 3^0-7^0, while deviations from the
straight line run of the tunnels are
faired with arcs of radius of the order
of 300 - 3000 m.

2.3. Hydrogeological conditions

The concept of building a shallow lying
metro found justification in the   the
more favourable ground and water conditions met with at that level than that
for a deep railway.

$\textbf{\textit{::::::::}}$ —opencast method
$\textbf{\rule{1cm}{2pt}}$ —full face tunnelling

Fig. 1. Warsaw tube; line No. I

In the vicinity of the metro the ground
is formed of large basic stratigraphic
units:
- Tertiary formations - Pliocene
- Quaternary formations - Pleistocene,
  Holocene.

The Pliocene formations are deposited
in strata consisting of about 60 % clays
and dusty clays and about 40 % of dusty
and dusty-arenaceus sediments and also
fine-grained sands.
Thickness of sediments in the particular
sedimentation cycles varies from about
1.0 up to more than a dozen metres.

The basal strata of the quaternary is
represented locally by preglacial
sediments. These sediments are formed
of fine and coarse-grained sands as well
as gravels, while at the top of these
formations are dusty sands, dusts and
clays. Above the preglacial sediments
or directly on the Pliocene are

found Central Polish glaciation sediments. They are represented principally by moraine clays with single boulders of various sizes.

All these sediments exhibit numerous disturbances and irregularities. Ground waters influence the excavation of tunnels; they appear both in the Tertiary and the Quaternary sediments.

In the Pliocene sediments the ground water does not occur as a continuous layer but appears in the interbedding of the arenaceous and arenaceous-dusty clays and cracked clays. The water-bearing soils exhibit a low filtration coefficient and easily form running sands or quick sands. These waters become stabilized at a depth of 6-8 metres.

In the Quaternary sediments two levels of soil waters are distinguished:
- surface level,
- basal level

The surface level of ground waters is formed by water-bearing strata exhibiting in general a small discharge and are only weakly recharged with water.

Fluctuations in the water table range from 0.8 - 2.0 m.
The basal level of the ground waters is formed by waters occurring in the strata of the fluvioglacial and marginal sands. These strata form large reservoirs of underground waters having a thickness of from a few up to some tens of metres. These strata exhibit high discharge and are well replenished. In these strata the water table is stabilized at a depth of from 8 - 15.0 metres.

2.4. Choice of excavation method

These hydrogeological conditions as described here do not favour the driving of tunnels by the underground method. The major obstacle is the broadly varied deposition of the Quaternary and Tertiary and also their high degree of water-bearing (Fig. 2). The principal hazards to be found here are:
- highly water-bearing dusty and fine-grained sands,
- water lenticles located in the interior of non-permeable strata,

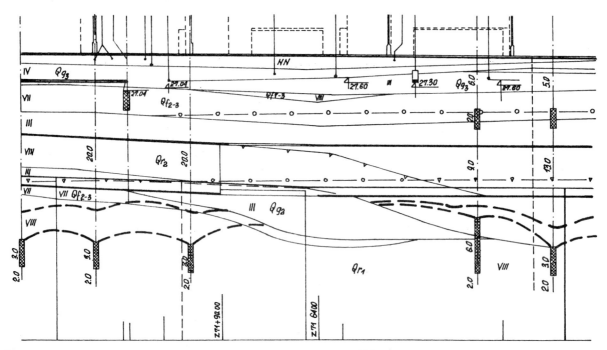

Fig. 2. B-8 track tunnel longitudinal profile, NN - uncontrolled embankment, II - sandy clays, IV - clayey sand, VII - fine sand, VIII - medium and coarse sand.

- water-borne displacement of the Tertiary formations and their high susceptibility to the occurrence of running sands,
- the occurrence of post-glacial boulders.

These specified water hazards have been investigated in detail over certain sectors of the metro route, while over the remaining sectors intensive studies are being conducted to enable precise determination of these hazards.

In these circumstances it was decided to drive the tunnels by the underground method using a tunnelling shield. Choice of a suitable shield construction to suit the described conditions was preceded by a detailed analysis of shield types used in West European countries, in Czechoslovakia and in the USSR. As a result of this analysis it was concluded that the best solution would be to use a non-mechanized shield, recognizing this shield type as the most suitable for the varying ground and water conditions met with in the Warsaw metro terrain.

Ultimately a Soviet non-mechanized Sz Cz N - 1S type tunnelling shield was chosen (Fig. 3).

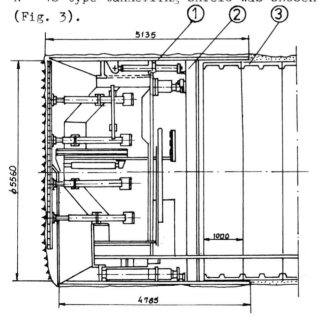

① - shield
② - stop collar
③ - tunnel support

Fig. 3. SzCzN - 1S non-mechanized shield

2.5. Technology for tunnel driving using a shield

Driving of tunnels using a shield involves a certain cycle of operations in which the following phases may be distinguished:
- erection of equipment and preparatory development of the building site,
- draining of the ground by means of depression wells,
- constructing the installation shaft,
- installing and starting up the tunnelling shield,
- driving of the tunnel with systematic advance draining of the ground,
- constructing the dismantling shaft,
- dismantling the shield and transporting it to the next section of the track.

Shafts are executed successively along the projected route of the metro track. In general they form part of the station excavations having dimensions 23 x 13 metres. In this case the shaft lining is formed of a so-called "Berlin wall". In order to speed up the commencement of draining of the next successive section by the shield method - prior to the ultimate implementation of the station excavation - two shafts are sunk of circular section and diameter 10 m with a temporary brick walling lining.

The actual driving of the tunnel by the shield method (Fig. 4) is implemented in a continuous work three-shift organization. Every cycle of work at the excavation face involves the following operations:
- forward shift of the shield through the ground over a distance of 0.2 - 1.0 m, depending on ground stability,
- manual working of the face in segments from top to bottom with successive securing of the exposed face with temporary timber support,
- loading of the gotten by an overhead loader to the mine type cars,
- installation of tunnel lining, either tubbing or made from prefabricated

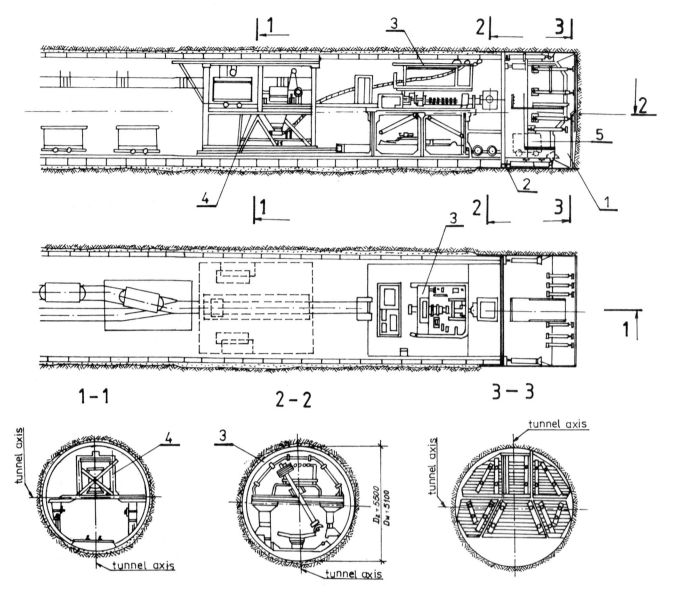

Fig. 4 Full face tunnelling system   1 – SzCzN – 1S shield, 2 – packing ring, 3 – control, 4 – cementation bridge, 5 – overhead loader (tunnel axis).

reinforced concrete elements, according to ground hydrogeological conditions, – injection filling of cavities.

Applying this method as described, up to October 20th, 1987, about 3000 m of track tunnel for the Warsaw metro have been driven, reaching a mean advance rate of about 2 m per day.

3. SOME INTERESTING TECHNICAL AND ORGANIZATIONAL METHODS EMPLOYED

In the tunnel driving the method of tunnel ground drainage by means of depression wells was applied as standard.

These wells have a diameter of 508 mm, a depth of 11–22 metres under ground surface level and were set out originally on both sides of the track tunnels at a distance of 5.5 metres from tunnel axis and at intervals of from 20 to 40 metres.

Well construction comprises a 356 mm diameter sub-filter pipe, a main filter of diameter 356 mm, a perforated filter covered with a No. 10 gauze mesh and an over-filter pipe of diameter 356 mm.

Each well is equipped with a deep-well pump with a delivery of 3 – 4 m^3/hour. Effectiveness of ground drainage effected in this way is controlled in piezometric bore-holes. In difficult hydrogeological conditions the under-pressure method is also used, utilizing a type IgE-81 well-point installation.

This scheme for ground draining method proved to be insufficient in many cases. Undrained sandy formations of quicksand type and also numerous postglacial boulders of large dimensions were responsible for the situation occurring in the early stages of the excavations when ground subsidence of unacceptable dimensions was found and even craters where quicksands had flowed off.

Reducing the interval between the depression wells to only 10 m over certain sections was also insufficient to give satisfactory draining of the ground, i.e. to a degree such as to ensure no further quicksand flow off. In this situation the method of ground stabilisation from the surface by injection was introduced.[2] Two methods of performing the injection process were tried out:

- the classical method, where the injected agent exerts a thrust on the walls of the injection bore-hole with constant pressure or with constant discharge (absorption),

- the stream-pressure method, where use is made of the hydraulic effect of breaking down the bore-hole walls by means of a stream of injection agent of considerable energy, so that this agent also penetrates by mixing with the ground material. Excess agent not absorbed by the ground flows back via the bore-hole to the surface.

The method chosen for application depends on the properties of the ground. One or multi-component chemical solutions in the classical injection method penetrate grounds with a filtration coefficient of up to 1.10^{-7} m/s (100 ± 0.01 darcy). In non-cohesive soils with a homogeneous grain size consist, e.g. fine grained sands and dusty sands, the classical

method is more suitable for pumping the injection agent, since practical experience has shown that in a homogeneous soil it is possible with this method to achieve a cylindrical shaped piece of ground of radius 1 metre with modified properties.

In soils of argillaceous structure and in very clayey sands it is more suitable to use pressure-stream injection, particularly in strata of quicksand type whose specific characteristics are due to the molecular type structure of the ground skeleton filled with water and water vapour. The introduction of surface active agents into the injection liquid and also the high-energy stream action make it possible to change and consolidate the quicksand structure.

A radius of penetration of the injection agent of 0.75 m has been achieved in quicksands and up to 0.3 m in hard plastic clays.

Denser siting of the depression wells together with the introduction of chemical injection gave a considerable degree of improvement in the stability of the ground ahead of the shield, but these measures were not sufficient to eliminate entirely the hazard of sudden appearance of quicksand type soils at the tunnel working face, particularly under the roof. Only due to very careful shield operation, particularly the construction of temporary lining at the face and maintaining always in readiness the classical means for combating the effects of quicksand break-in (hay) was it possible to overcome these difficulties. In the further sections of tunnel excavation it was possible to maintain ground surface subsidence within acceptable limits.

Figure 5 shows the arrangement of depression wells siting and also gives measured values of ground subsidence on the example of section B8 of the tunnel route.

During the course of tunnel drivage various modifications were made to the

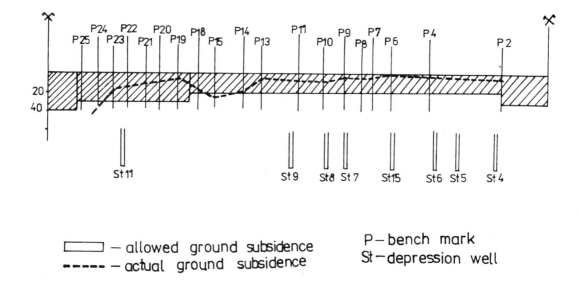

Fig. 5. Ground subsidence and location of depression wells.

shield. An additional roof projection of length 35 cm was built on and the temporary lining cylinders were withdrawn, allowing an increased web and to quicken bringing down of the soil under roof protection.

After complex analysis of the problems involved in the construction of the Warsaw metro the mining authorities decided, among other things, that the scope and nature of the underground work to be undertaken, in particular the application of mining methods for its implementation in conditions of occurrence of mining hazards and also hazards for the city buildings and facilities at the surface, made it essential to observe particularly rigorous technical and organisational protection regulations in carrying out this work. For this reason it was decreed that work on the building of the metro should be subject to the appropriate regulations laid down in the mining code and should be under the special supervision of the official mining authorities.

4. CONCLUSIONS

The advances currently achieved in the construction of the Warsaw metro by the underground method, the efficiency of execution of this work and the results of the control checks made by the mining offices and the investment authorities provide a basis for concluding that the decision to apply this technology for excavation of the tunnel in the ground conditions met with along the route of the Warsaw metro and also the organisational decisions represent a guarantee of the successful implementation of this important investment project.

Despite the initial difficulties encountered, the personnel from the Mining Work Enterprise in Mysłowice managed in a short time to master the technology of tunnel drivage using a shield, achieving a very satisfactory advance of the order of 50 - 60 m/month.

In the moraine clays advance is limited at the moment by the manual method of winning the cohesive ground.

354

Consideration is being given to the
feasibility of partial mechanisation of
winning by means of a cutting tool that
could be rapidly dismantled.

5. SOURCE MATERIAL

1) Gąsior S., Pękacki H., Paszcza H.:
Driving of tunnels for the No. I. line of
the Warsaw metro by the underground
method using a tunnelling shield.
Materials from the Symposium: Construction of the Warsaw metro tunnels by the
underground method using a shield.
April 1986.

2) Kubański A.: Technical and organisational conditions governing the use of
injection operations. Materials from the
Symposium: Construction of the Warsaw
metro tunnels by the underground method
using a shield. April 1986.

Comparison of calculated and measured displacements on cut-and-cover tunnels

A. Tisa Civ. Eng.
K. Kovari Dr., Prof.
Swiss Federal Institute of Technology Zurich,
Department of Rock Engineering and Tunnelling, Zurich, Switzerland

SYNOPSIS

A computation model for cut-and-cover
tunnel is presented. It takes the lateral
backfill into consideration as part of
the structure. The high-precision deformation measurements carried out on a series of tunnels with different geometries
and backfill conditions have provided
validation for the computation procedure.

INTRODUCTION

Reduction of pollution and preservation
of the landscape are becoming increasingly important. Consequently tunnels
for road and railroad construction are
nowadays frequently being built by the
cut - and - cover construction method,
whereby the concrete vault is laterally
backfilled and finally covered over in
accordance with the principles of landscape design or of making use of the
ground surface.

The thickness of the tunnel lining, its

reinforcement and the stiffness of the
lateral backfill are the most important
factors that influence construction costs
and, to a certain extent, the duration of
construction for a given geometry and
cover height. The safe and economic
planning and design of such structures
has to be based on a clear understanding
of the mutual effect on one another of
the three structural elements - concrete
lining, undisturbed ground and backfill.
This interactive effect is further complicated because the lateral backfill is
placed in a series of lifts each of which
initially acts as a load and then serves
as part of the structure. When the compaction work on a given section of backfill is completed, it resists outward
displacements of the arch, and mobilises
support reactions.

To gain further insight into this mechanism, high-precision deformation measurements were carried out on several
structures. The results of these observations have led to the development of a
computation procedure which not only adequately explains the measurements but
also provides a design method for cut-
and-cover tunnels.

357

MEASUREMENT PROGRAM AND MEASURING INSTRUMENTS

The measurement program consists essentially of determining the deflection curve of the tunnel lining, which is supplemented by levelling of the abutments and by measurement of their rotations. The deflection line is obtained by Invar-Wire measurements with the "Distometer" precision instrument. In the kinematic system of reference (Fig. 1) with abutment A considered as immovable and a horizontally free abutment B, the displacements u_i, v_i of the points of measurement and the displacement vectors resulting therefrom can be calculated from the change in length of the sides of the triangles [1].

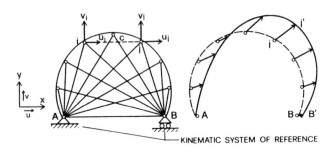

Fig. 1   Determination of the complete deflection of a tunnel lining by a mesh of individual convergence measurements.

Since the precision of a Distometer measurement is better that 0.05 mm. when the measured distance is 10 m., the displacement vectors can be determined very precisely even in the case of an intersection at a very small angle. The measuring line C shown in Fig. 1, being a redundant measurement, provides a check on the accuracy, since the difference be-

tween the horizontal displacement components $(u_j - u_i)$ should agree with the directly measured change in the length of the line C. Such agreement is actually achieved in the field with an accuracy of better than 0.25 mm. If the vertical abutment movements (v_A, v_B) obtained from levelling are taken into consideration, then the differential displacements in the vertical direction can be derived. The evaluation of the comprehensive measurement data obtained, for example, in a twin tube at a single cross-section with 25 measured lengths is carried out with the help of the evaluation programm "INVAR" [2]. This also provides a clear graphical representation of the results of the measurements.

RESULTS OF FIELD MEASUREMENTS

The interaction between tunnel lining and lateral backfill will now be demonstrated on the basis of three selected examples. These are the Zurzach Bypass on Cantonal Highway NK 131, the Maria Zell Tunnel on National Highway N2 in Canton Lucerne, and the Brünnen Tunnel on National Highway N1 for the Bypass of the city of Berne, all in Switzerland. A glance at Figures 2 to 4 shows that completely different tunnel forms and widths are being dealt with.

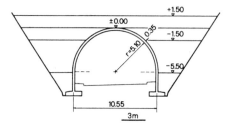

Fig. 2   Zurzach Tunnel: cross-section with backfilling stages

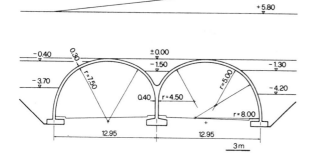

Fig. 3   Maria Zell Tunnel: cross-section
with backfilling stages

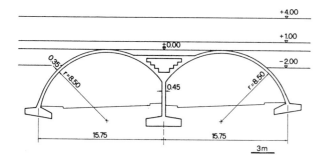

Fig. 4   Brünnen Tunnel: cross-section
with backfilling stages

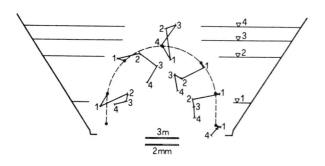

Fig. 5   Zurzach Tunnel: displacement
vectors shown as a sequence of
vectorial components

In Fig. 5, the displacement paths of the
measuring points on a tunnel cross- section (Zurzach Bypass) are shown for the
backfill stages indicated. One feature
peculiar to this project is the backfilling with concrete rubble 2.40 m thick for
construction reasons. Since the left
abutment (A) is considered to be immovable, only the differential settlement

$(V_B - V_A)$ was taken into consideration in
the case of the vertical displacement
components.

In Fig. 6, the displacement vectors resulting from backfilling up to the crown
of the arch are shown at two different
cross - sections of the Maria Zell
Tunnel [3]. In this case the levelling was
taken into consideration under the
assumption that the centre abutment was
immovable in the vertical direction. The
side abutments thus show only the
differential settlements with respect to
the latter. The displacements at the two
cross-sections exhibit remarkable
agreement. The tendency to asymmetrical
behaviour is a result of the non-uniform
(asymmetrical) backfilling procedure.

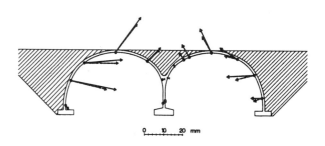

Fig. 6   Maria Zell Tunnel: arch deformations at sections M_1 and M_2 due
to backfilling up to the crown

In Fig. 7, the displacement vectors are
again shown only for the stage of backfilling up to the crown; here the results
from three different sections of measurement of the Brünnen Tunnel[3] are depicted·
In contrast to the Maria Zell Tunnel,
rather large differential settlements of
the side abutments (in relation to the
centre abutment) are evident on account
of the larger span and the variable char-
acter of the subsoil. In this structure,
as previously, the result of the measurement were consistently reproducible from
one cross-section to the next.

359

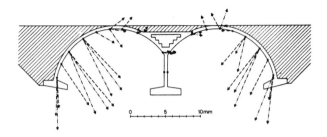

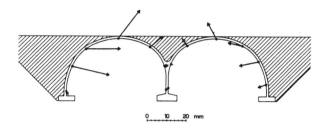

Fig. 7 Brünnen Tunnel: arch deformation
at sections M_1,M_2 and M_3 due to
backfilling up to crown

What general conclusions can be drawn
from Figures 5, 6 and 7 with regard to
the behaviour of the structure ? The
lateral backfill obviously places a load
on the lining horizontally and vertically
in such a way that the sides of the arch
are displaced inwards and the crown upwards. The tunnel lining at the stage of
backfilling up to the crown is thus in a
"prestressed state" that is statically
favourable with regard to the subsequent
placement of the covering fill.

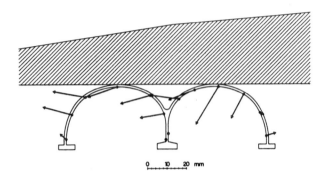

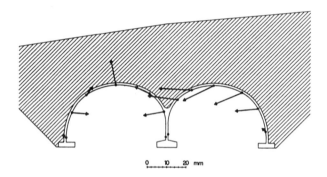

Fig. 8 shows how such further fill acts
on the strucure. Here the arch displacements of the Maria Zell Tunnel as a result of the placing of a cover 5.40 m
thick are depicted. The arch deforms in
an outward direction at the sides and inwards at the crown, depending on the
stiffness of the lateral backfill and the
amount of the displacements, support reactions are mobilised. In Fig. 8b, only
the differential settlements due to the
cover are shown. As can be seen from
Fig. 8b, a cover this thick is not quite
capable of compensating for the "prestressing" mentioned above. If no further material is deposited, then the intermediate phase shown in Fig. 8a is responsible for the greatest stresses to
which the arch is subjected.

Fig. 8   Maria Zell Tunnel: a) Displacement of the vault caused by
backfilling up to crown; b) Displacement caused by the load of
the cover only (hatched area);
c) Total deformations of the
vault

The preceding considerations suffice to
show that the stiffness of the laterally
backfilled material does not warrant
great attention, as is commonly assumed.
It becomes a governing consideration only
when the cover height is very large and
in such a case the development of a natural supporting structure within the cover
fill itself must be taken into account.

THE COMPUTATION MODEL

The comprehensive observational data from several rather large tunnel-construction projects with various cross-sectional shapes and each with 4 to 5 backfilling stages that even take place asymmetrically have made it possible to set up a calculation model that is capable of describing satisfactorily the wide variety of phenomena [3]. The calculation model (Fig. 9) consists of a slab that simulates the already placed backfill soil <2>, and it contains a beam structure embedded in the latter for the tunnel vault. The material properties are assumed to be fully elastic, with moduli of elasticity corresponding to the stiffness of the soils and of the vault concrete.

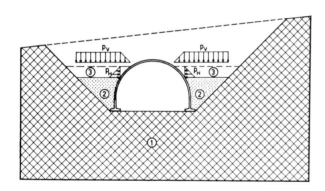

Fig. 9   Interaction between tunnel arch and soil: <1> subsoil, <2> compacted backfill, <3> placement of last layer of backfill

The boundaries of the slab are chosen in such a way that differential settlements and abutment rotations can be taken into consideration according to the prevailing conditions. The load in vertical direction is the weight P_V of the layer of fill last introduced <3>, and in horizontal direction the earth pressure P_H caused by same. The calculation proceeds step by step, starting from the first backfill stage, in which it appears initially only as a load quantity. The calculated deformation quantities and internal forces are stored. In the next step of the calculation, this first backfill stage already constitutes an integral part of the slab. The next step of the calculation is then carried out with new load increments. The results of this new calculation step are added to the previous ones. The calculation proceeds in this manner until the last layer of fill has been considered. One feature peculiar to the calculation model is that it has at its disposal a "model memory" so that it can fully take into account an asymmetrical filling procedure which nonetheless leads to a symmetrical final state. In such a case, the resulting deformations are assymetrical as is shown by the field measurements and the calculations. The determination of the soil-pressure coefficient for the horizontal loading P_H poses a special problem. Soil-mechanics considerations and back-calculation from the measured displacements show that it makes sense to carry out all calculations with the coefficient of earth pressure at rest and with the coefficient of active earth pressure. In this manner the uncertainty inherent to the matter lies between these limits. The calculation model described herein differs in essential aspects from that proposed for flexible steel pipes embedded in the earth [4].

COMPARISON OF THE MEASUREMENTS WITH THE COMPUTATIONS

An example for the comparison between measured and calculated displacements is shown in Fig. 10 and 11, and refers to the Zurzach tunnel. The calculations were carried out with values for the modulus of elasticity of 100000 kN/m² for the compacted backfill, 25000 kN/m² for the backfill layer being placed, and g = 2,1*10⁷ kN/m² for the vault concrete; a Poisson's ratio ν = 0.3 and the angle of internal friction φ = 32° were used. The density of the soil was assumed to be g = 20 kN/m³. In Fig. 10 a pronounced asymmetry can be noted, particularly in the horizontal displacements. This results from the above-mentioned asymmetrical backfilling stages which are often unavoidable. This asymmetry in the deformation diagram is, however, still readily visible even in Fig. 11. The calculation model described here was applied using the "RHEOSTAUB" program for the design of a series of tunnel-construction projects, and the validity of the results was checked by systematic measurement of deformations during the construction.

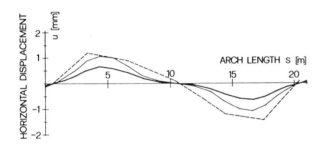

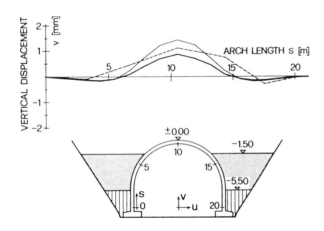

Fig. 10   Zurzach Tunnel: displacement
          components **u** and **v** of the arch;
          backfill to depth -1.50 m below
          crown of arch
          Measurements: ━ ━ ━ ━
          Computations:
              active earth pressure ━━━━
              earth pressure at rest ━━━━

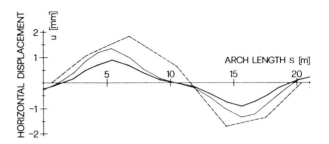

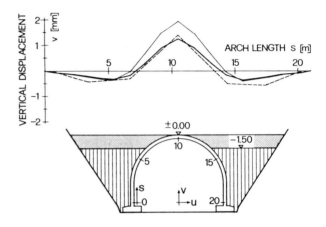

Fig. 11   Zurzach Tunnel: displacement
          components **u** and **v** of the arch
          for backfill to level of crown
          Measurements:
          Computations: ━ ━ ━ ━
              active earth pressure ━━━━
              earth pressure at rest ━━━━

REFERENCES:

1. Kovari K. and Amstad C. Decision Making and Field Measurements in Tunnelling 25th OYO Anniversary Lecture Meeting Tokyo, 1979.
2. Tisa A. Handbuch zur Benützung des Programms "INVAR". Institut für Bauplanung und Baubetrieb- Fels und Untertagbau,-ETH Zurich, 1987.
3. Kovari K. and Tisa A. Computational Models for Cut-and Cover Tunnels Based on Field Measurements in Geomechanics. 4th Int. Conf. on Numerical Methods in Geomechanics, Edmonton, 1982.
4. Klöppel K. and Glock D. Theoretische und experimentelle Untersuchungen zu den Traglastproblemen biegeweicher, in die Erde eingebetteter Rohre. Veröffentlichung des Institutes für Statik und Stahlbau der TH Darmstadt, Heft 10, 1970.

Application of recently developed grouting procedures for tunnelling in the Milan urban area

R. Tornaghi
B. Bosco
B. De Paoli
RODIO S.p.A., Casalmaiocco (Milano), Italy

SYNOPSIS

The "cut and cover" method predominantly used in the fifties for the construction of Line 1 could no more be applied for the extension of the Milan Underground Railway network in the central urban area, involving more and more problems related to the treatment of cohesionless alluvial soil, partly to be excavated under the water table.

The often complex design features and strict specifications about potential pollution led to the application of recently developed techniques such as sub-horizontal jet-grouting, and the use of quite new types of suspensions and chemical solutions for permeation grouting.

Main design features and ground improvement criteria are briefly outlined with reference to the works in progress within the lots awarded to specialist contractor Rodio Co.

More detailed information is given on the first large scale application of a new type of fine grained cement grout with special additives enhancing permeation and minimizing the hydrofracturing effects involved by other suspensions. The performance is emphasized in terms of ground surface movements continuously monitored during injection and tunnelling stages.

INTRODUCTION

The network of Milan Metro system presently consists of two operating lines (1-2) which cover an overall length of 53 km (mainly underground) with 63 stations.

Under construction are, besides suburban extensions of lines 1-2:

- line 3, crossing the city center in north-south direction on an underground route of 11 km with 15 stations
- the Railway Connecting Line (Passante Ferroviario), linking some existing stations which receive traffic from southeast and north-west regions; this line will be 20 km long (9 km underground) with 9 stations (4 underground).

The construction of the first line, started more than 30 years ago, was carried out by a "cut and cover" downward procedure involving the first large scale application of the slurry trenching technique (developed in the early fifties in Italy) to create lateral ground support.

This so called "Milan method" could no more be applied extensively for the subsequent lines, owing to the layout and depth of underground structures. In order to reduce or avoid traffic disruption and to solve the problems related to interference with public utilities, safety of buildings and groundwater, more flexible procedures have been applied that are mainly based on soil improvement by grouting from the surface or totally underground ahead of the excavation face.

The latter procedure, widely used for line 3 and railway connecting line under construction, consists of the following steps:

- excavation of adit shafts at about 500 m intervals, with square or circular retaining structures formed by concrete diaphragm panels or jet-grouted columns
- boring of 3 m dia. pilot drifts by shield equipment or excavation after soil consolidation by sub-horizontal conventional grouting or jetgrouting ahead of the working face (fig. 1)

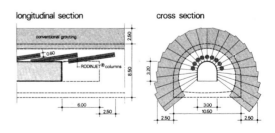

fig. 1 Metro Line 3: soil treatment for drift (subhorizontal Rodinjet) and for main bore (radial conventional grouting from drift)

- radial treatment by conventional grouting from the drifts in order to create an arch of consolidated soil around the planned main bore

- underground arch excavation by common earth moving equipment, with minimum protection of steel ribs and reinforced shorcrete
- soil grouting downwards, beneath water table
- underground excavation of the invert and construction of the permanent concrete lining.

During the construction of Line 2 in the seventies, soil improvement was carried out by permeation grouting with the combined use of cement-clay or cement-bentonite suspensions and chemical silicate solution with organic reagent.

Afterwards stricter specifications about potential pollution prevented the use of any organic product.

When the construction of Line 3 started some years ago, since no inorganic reagent added to sodium silicate was adequate for effective strengthening, the Owner (Metropolitana Milanese) planned at first the use only of a fluidified fine grained cement grout without colloidal additives.

This procedure, combining permeation to significant hydrofracturing, proved sufficient in predominantly gravelly formations above the water table.

But the gaps left in sandy layers needed to be filled in critical zones (such as in the vicinity of building foundations) and anywhere beneath the water table for effective waterproofing.

Taking into account the above restrictions about chemicals, the problem has been solved by introducing a new type of grout based on activated silica liquor with a calcium reagent.

Differently from classical silicate solutions, the reaction produces no more a gel but a stable crystalline structure as that of cement grouts, allowing an effective uniform consolidation of medium to fine sands with full safety against pollution.

Later on, another research trend has led to a remarkable improvement of particulate suspensions in order to enhance permeation, limiting hydrofracturing effects in sandy-gravelly formations. The most outstanding feature of the new type of grout, composed of fine grained cement and special additives, is a very low filtration rate under pressure, allowing fair permeation of coarse to medium sands.

The good results of an exhaustive laboratory investigation have been confirmed by a large scale trial involving the treatment of 80 m of line tunnel, that has been selected as main topic within the case histories outlined in this paper.

SOIL CONDITIONS

The Milan subsoil is mainly recent alluvium with widely variable mixtures and alternations of gravel, sand and silt to a quite minor extent (4).

The relative density is fair to high, increasing with depth. The porosity ranges from 40-45% for shallow sands to 20-30% for most sandy-gravelly layers beyond 20 m depth (5).

In conventional drilling the core recovery and quality index of gravelly samples may be poor and involve misleading information on groutability, owing to the small core size (usually around 100 mm) and consequent overestimate of sand and silt contents.

The problem to obtain truly representative samples has been dealt with thoroughly by Rodio Co. for soil improvement design of Line 2.

The best results had been obtained by means of rotary core barrels 200 to 300 mm dia., including a liner and driven without circulation of drilling fluid (4-5-7).

This effective but expensive procedure did not seem practicable for Line 3 owing to the intensive investigation required by several factors, such as: the complexity of design layouts, the erratic distribution of sandy layers and pockets, the design specifications limiting more strictly the use of chemical grouts and therefore demanding more detailed soil information than before.

The problem was faced by means of electronically instrumented rigs with facility to record the main drilling parameters (penetration rate, rotation speed, thrust and torque) and to derive in real time the specific energy (1).

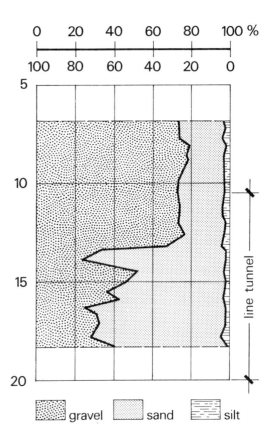

fig. 2 Lot 1PB - Zarotto shaft: mean profile of cumulative grain size distribution

This resultant parameter, expressing the energy required to excavate the unit volume of soil by a non-coring tool, may be statistically correlated with the mean grain size range.

The correlations take into account the influence of depth and hole inclination downwards or upwards.

The calibration has been optimized progressively with reference to grain size analysis of samples taken during the excavation of shafts and tunnels.

Fig. 2 shows the mean grain size profile obtained by manual sampling at Zarotto shaft (Line 3, Lot 1PB), where the soil treatment by means of the new cement grout Mistrà L was started (see last part of the paper).

Fig. 3 shows the two main ranges of grain size distributions in the same Lot with reference to directly checked groutability.

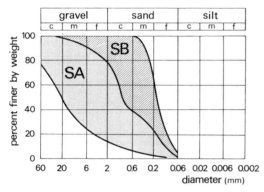

grain size range	permeation effect	
	MISTRA' L suspensions	SILACSOL solutions
SA	very good to fair	very good
SB	fair to poor	very good

fig. 3 Lot 1PB - typical ranges of grain size distributions with reference to groutability

WATER TABLE

The present elevation of water table is fairly uniform in the urban area (approx. between +97 and +100 m).

Since the ground level has a general trend to increase northwards, the depth of water table ranges from about 10-12 m in the southern part of line 3 up to 20-25 m in the central and northern quarters involved by Line 3 and Railway Connecting Line.

GROUTING PROCEDURES AND GROUTS

Basic injection principles

The improvement of soils can be achieved by various injection techniques (4, 9, 10) based on the following main principles and effects:

(a)- permeation, without any essential change of soil volume and structure
(b) - hydrofracturing, when the soil pores cannot be penetrated by the injected grout
(c) - compaction, when a thick mortar-like mix forms bulbs or lenses around the hole, thus displacing and compressing the surrounding soil to some extent
(d) - jet-grouting, when the soil is mixed in place with a grout delivered under a very high nozzle pressure or partly removed by air-water jetting and replaced by the grout

The systematically combined use of particulate suspensions and chemical solutions, adopted for Line 2, ensured a fairly uniform permeation up to fine sands.

As regards the lines under construction, the initial restriction to grouts based on cement involved a combined process with prevailing permeation or hydrofracturing effects, according to local conditions and operating features.

The introduction of a new non-polluting chemical grout (2-3) permitted to fill the gaps in critical zones and particularly below the water table, where uniform permeation must be assured.

As regards the preliminary cement grouting, still required to be as widespread as possible for economic reasons, the new grout proposed by Rodio has proved useful to increase permeation and reduce hydrofracturing effects. The quite different techniques based on jet-grouting have been discussed in a number of recent papers (3-4-9-10) with reference to the applications of Rodinjet procedure in tunnelling problems, including the Milan Metro case records. In this paper we shall emphasize the properties and performance of the most recently developed mixes in order to enhance permeation in conventional grouting by "tube à manchette" downhole equipment.

Rheological classification of grouts

From the rheological point of view the main classes of grouts are, in order of increasing penetrability:
(a) - particulate suspensions (Binghamian fluids)
(b) - colloidal solutions (evolutive Newtonian fluids)
(c) - pure solutions (non-evolutive Newtonian fluids)

A suspension is usually termed "stable" when bleeding is negligible as required in general for the treatment of granular soils.

Stabilized thixotropic grouts have both cohesion (yield strength) and plastic viscosity increasing with time at a rate that may be reduced by fluidifiers and retarders, but more consistently increased by filtration under injection pressure.

Conventional stable grouts tend to produce hydrofracturing when the soil permeability is lower than about 10^{-1} cm/s.

The chemical solutions (b) and (c) exhibit quite different rheological features. The flow properties are only related to the viscosity/time relationship at a given temperature.

The far best known colloidal solutions consist of more or less diluted sodium silicate with inorganic or organic reagents producing soft to hard silica gels; the term evolutive means that viscosity increases before setting at a rate depending on dilution.

The more penetrating and expensive pure solutions based on resins (out of the question in our case history) are nonevolutive since viscosity may be kept constant and low within an adjustable period of time.

Particulate suspensions

The main obstacles to the penetrability of particulate suspensions, though stable with respect to bleeding, are related to:
- the max. actual particle size of the solid components in the injected grout, which must be fairly smaller than the min. void size of the soil
- the filtration rate which may involve a quick clogging even under low injection pressures.

The first problem has been faced introducing finer cements (Blaine specific surface over 5000 cm2/g) and minimizing grain agglomeration by addition of dispersing agents and improvement of mixing plants.

However, the filtration problem remained unsolved, since in conventional so-called stable grouts (type C in fig. 4) the reduction of water loss rate can be obtained only at the cost of increasing viscosity by an additional content of colloids such as bentonite.

Usual chemical additives (fluidifiers, retarders, dispersing agents) reduce viscosity but the filtration rate remains still considerable (grouts type C' in fig. 4).

Recent research on various types of products (cement, bentonite and chemicals) and mixing procedures has led to the development of a new class of grouts named MISTRA' (type B in fig. 4) with the following main properties:
- no bleeding
- filtration rates much lower than those of conventional stable mixes and closer to those of pure bentonite muds, even at very low viscosity
- possibility to keep low the yield strength over an adjustable period of time (up to many hours if required)

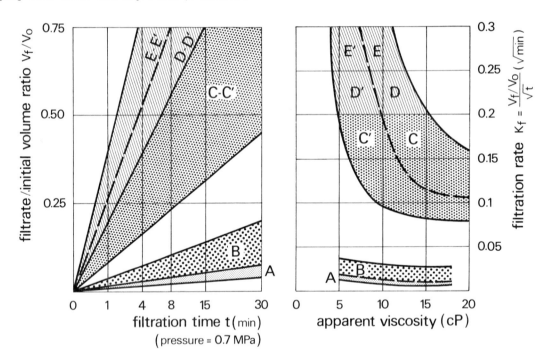

A bentonite muds
B cement grouts with special colloidal additive (MISTRA'-L)
C cement-bentonite grouts
D poorly stabilized cement grouts
E unstable cement grouts
C'·D'·E' types C·D·E with fluidifiers and dispersing agents

fig. 4 Ranges of significant rheological properties for various types of particulate suspensions

- possibility to obtain higher long term strength and reduced permeability in comparison with conventional stable grouts having the same cement content.

As regards composition the cement/water ratio may range between 0,2 and 1; the overall content of additives is generally within 3% and 6% of water, by weight.

The rheological and long-term properties may be therefore widely variable according to specific requirements, but in any case the filtration rate (obtained by conventional filter press tests under 0,7 MPa pressure) is far lower in comparison with all other types of grouts, as emphasized in the graphs of fig. 4.

table **1**

COMPOSITION	CEMENT/WATER	0.35
	ADDITIVES/WATER	0.04 ÷ 0.05
BLEEDING (%)		0 ÷ 2
MARSH VISCOSITY (sec.)		33 ÷ 37
RHEOMETER PARAMETERS	APPARENT VISCOSITY (cP)	8 ÷ 12
	PLASTIC VISCOSITY (cP)	5 ÷ 8
	YIELD STRENGTH (Pa)	1.5 ÷ 5
FILTER PRESS TEST AT 0.7 MPa	FILTRATE (cm^3) AFTER 30'	36 ÷ 72
	FILTRATION RATE (mm$^{-\frac{1}{2}}$)	0.016 ÷ 0.032
U.C. STRENGTH (MPa) OF GROUTED SAND AFTER 28 DAYS		1.2 ÷ 1.8

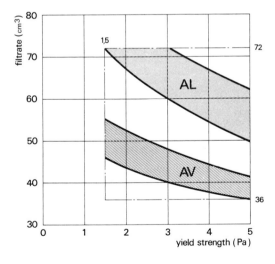

fig. 5 *Mistrà grouts: experimental correlations between filtrate and yield strength for two different combinations of additives*

Considering for instance an apparent viscosity of 10 cP, the mean relative magnitude of filtration rate with reference to good bentonite muds (A) is about: 2,5 for Mistrà grouts (B), 10 to 20 for fluidified cement-bentonite mixes (C'), 20 to 30 for slightly stabilized to unstable cement grouts (D-E).

As regards the Mistrà grouts used in Lot 1PB of the Milan Railway Connecting Line, Table 1 shows the ranges of composition and main characteristics resulting from daily site controls.

Fig. 5 represents the experimental correlations between the most significant rheological parameters, for two different combinations of additives. Within the same range of yield strength, the AV complex involves a filtration decrease of about 50%, exhibiting a rheological behaviour very close to that of bentonite muds, in spite of the remarkable cement content.

Chemical solutions

Chemical solutions based on sodium silicate, used since a long time with inorganic reagents (acyds or polyvalent salts) can produce only soft gels for water stop problems in sands, since a suitable delay of setting requires high dilution.

The introduction of organic reagents in the early sixties allowed to adjust setting time independently from concentration, thus obtaining soft to hard gels according to silicate/ water ratio.

Further improvements have been made in the seventies as regards the quality of reagents used in Italy (ethyl acetate has been replaced by R.P. Hardeners 600) and the trend to increase the hardener/silicate ratio and to limit silicate concentration for a better control of syneresis and creep phenomena.

Permanence of silica gels, mainly related to syneresis is a controversial question widely discussed in geotechnical conferences (4-6-8).

In fact syneresis is important on pure gel samples, as shown in fig. 6 (graph on the left) for a typical hard gel with 50% silicate and a high R.P. Hardener/silicate ratio (0,16).

However the phenomenon tends to fade into the soil pores, becoming negligible in medium fine sands, as shown in the above graph.

Since the larger voids in gravelly-sandy soils can be filled by preliminary injection of particulate suspensions and since hydrofracturing must be strictly avoided when injecting chemical solutions, a properly designed treatment could be fairly safe with respect to potential phenomena leading to gel dissolution and groundwater pollution.

Nevertheless the bad long-term performance in some cases of inadequate design or unskilled execution, the actual difficulty to prevent any risk under the water table in urban areas, and the consequent more and more strict specifications against organic chemicals in particular, have led

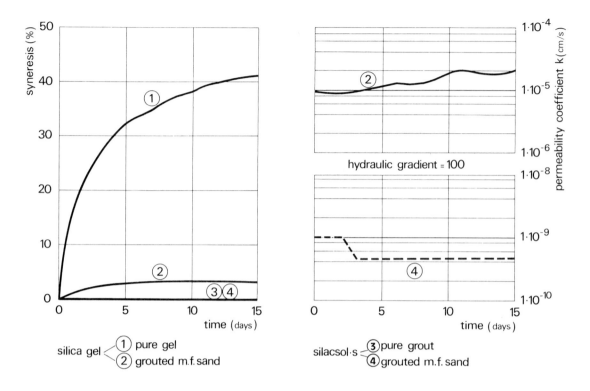

fig. 6 Effect of time on syneresis and permeability of typical chemical grouts

to the research and development of a quite new type of grout (Silacsol) composed of an activated silica liquor with an inorganic reagent based on calcium. Differently from commercial alkalyne sodium silicates, that are aqueous solutions of colloidal silica particles dispersed in soda, the liquor is a true silica solution.

The activated dissolved silica, associated to the mineral reagent, produces calcium hydrosilicates with a crystalline structure quite similar to that obtained by hydration and setting of cement; the resulting product is a complex of permanently stable crystals.

Hence the reaction is no more an evolutive "gelation" involving the formation of macromolecular aggregates and possible loss of silicized water (syneresis); on the contrary it is a direct reaction on molecular scale.

This new class of mixes, developed firstly in France (2-8) then successfully optimized and used in Milan by Rodio Co. (4) has the same groutability range as common silica gels permitting uniform treatment of medium to fine sands.

Fig. 7 presents a typical viscosity/time curve with reference to the most recent formula (Silacsol-S), showing a Newtonian behaviour at fairly low viscosity, up to an effective groutability time of 50 min.; afterwards yield strength appears, increasing with time up to final setting.

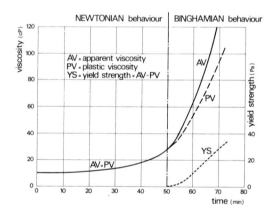

fig. 7 Typical viscosity-time behaviour of Silacsol-S grout

Even in the incidental case of larger voids or fissures created by hydrofracturing, a permanent filling is assured without any syneresis risk (fig. 6 on the left).

In fact the activated silica mix has the stability of cement grouts, thus involving full safety against water pollution.

Other outstanding features are the far lower permeability and the better creep behaviour of treated sands, in comparison with the same soil grouted by means of a silica gel having similar rheological properties and involving the same unconfined compression strength at a quick strain rate (0,65% min): about 2 MPa in the case records of fig. (6-7-8).

The permeability coefficient drops from 10^{-5} cm/s with the silica gel to the order of 10^{-10} with the new mix, remaining quite constant over many days under an hydraulic gradient as high as 100 (fig. 6).

The dead load creep tests (fig. 8) show a much lower longterm deformability at the same stress level and creep rupture at about the double stress level (85% against 45%).

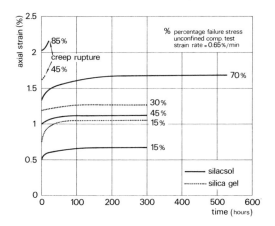

fig. 8 Unconfined creep results for silica gel and Silacsol-S grout (samples of grouted m.f. sand)

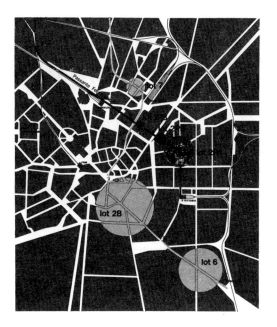

fig. 9 Metro Line 3 and Railway Connecting Line: layout of lots awarded to Rodio Co.

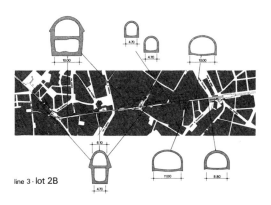

fig. 10 Lot 2B: typical tunnel sections

DESIGN FEATURES AND GROUTING PATTERNS

The following brief review is related to Lots 2B-6-7 of Metro Line 3 and 1PB-2PB-2PA of Railway Connecting Line under construction, awarded to Rodio Co. for soil improvement; the layout of these Lots is shown in fig. 9. More detailed information will be given on Lot 1PB with reference to the experimental treatment with the new type of cement grout (Mistrà).

Lot 2B

This Lot, the longest one of Metro Line 3 (about 2 km) runs southward from Piazza del Duomo, in the very heart of the city, to Porta Romana. Fig. 10 shows the variety of tunnel sections involved by the transition from parallel to superimposed tracks; the latter solution has been adopted also for 2 stations. The bottom of excavation is mostly 2 to 5 m below the water table.

The closeness of buildings, the complexity of public utilities and the necessity to minimize traffic disruptions have required all treatments to be executed underground by means of pilot drifts driven from 4 adit shafts.

The use of shield to drive the first 600 m of drift involved some local overdig and consequent problems of settlements; therefore it was decided a preliminary soil treatment ahead of the bore by successive series of Rodinjet columns as shown in fig. 1 and related in previous papers. (3-4-10).

In the case of two superimposed tunnels (fig. 11) two grouting stages are required: from the drift to allow construction of the upper tunnel and then downward to consent excavation of the lower tunnel partly below the water table.

In all grid patterns the max. hole spacing is between 1,5 and 2 m while the thickness of treated soil around planned bores ranges between 2,0 and 3,5 m according to bore size and local conditions. The overall volume of treated soil between 1985 and 1987 is about 400.000 m3.

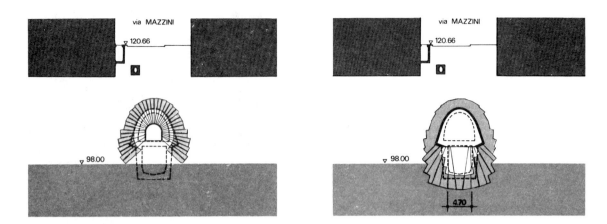

fig. 11 Lot 2B: grouting layout for double tunnel with superimposed railroads.

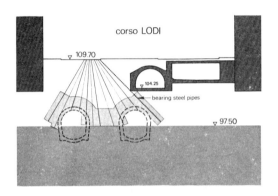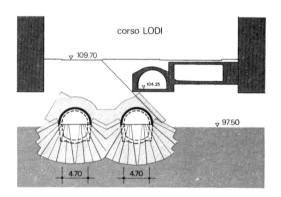

fig. 12 Lot 6: grouting layout for two parallel tunnels

The chemical grout Silacsol has been used in addition to fine grained cement suspensions for some more than one third of the treatment above the water table and systematically in presence of water.

Jetgrouting techniques have been adopted for pilot drifts, as above mentioned (fig. 1) and moreover to form underground earth-retaining structures in order to protect deep shaft excavation (4) (Lamarmora access shaft 12 m dia., 22 m deep) and in critical situations involved by the vicinity of old buildings.

Lot 6

In this Lot, covering the southern part of Metro Line 3 (fig. 9) and about 1200 m long, the structure is formed by two 4,7 m wide parallel tunnels.

The invert section lies about 3 m below the water table. As shown in fig. 12 the treatment is mostly done from the surface for the excavation of the upper part, and subsequently extended to the lower section.

The overall volume of treated soil is 150.000 cu.m, one half of which beneath the water table with the complement of chemical grout.

In critical zones where operations from the surface were impracticable, the upper treatment has been carried out by the subhorizontal Rodinjet technique, supplemented by conventional grouting, in order to support the entire tunnel arch (fig. 13).

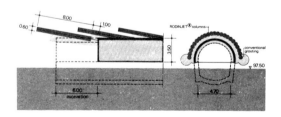

fig. 13 Lot 6: combined treatment by Rodinjet and conventional grouting

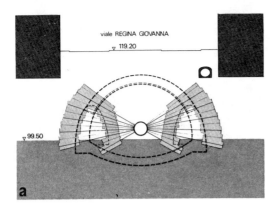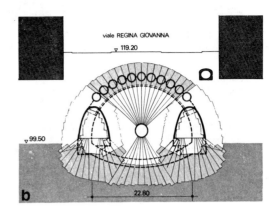

fig. 14 Railway Connecting Line - Lot 2PB - Porta Venezia Station: 2nd stage of treatment from 3 drifts

Lot 7

In the 600 m stretch of Lot 7, at the present northern end of Line 3 (fig. 9) the line structure consists of a dual-track 9,10 m wide gallery.

The treatment is done partly from the surface and partly from a pilot drift. The most complex problems concern the underpass of a railroad and particularly the Sondrio Station (112 m long) where in addition to the central gallery (15 m wide and 60 m long) there are two side 5,60 m tunnels running a few metres below building foundations; the total bore width is over 30 m.

The overall volume of treated soil is about 140.000 cu.m., 30% of which with the complement of chemical grout.

Lot 2PA

This is the longest (about 1 km) and the last of the Railway Connection lots awarded so far to Rodio Co.

The line structure consists of a dual-track gallery 8,80 m wide, underpassing some buildings on a 165 m stretch.

Soil consolidation, 2,5 to 3 m thick around the planned bore will be carried out radially from a shield-driven drift.

The invert will be excavated 1 to 3 m below the water table.

Lot 2PB

Starting from the west end of Lot 2PA (fig. 9) and extending on a 350 m length, this lot consists of variously shaped structures:
- a dual-track gallery 16,40 m wide
- a station (Porta Venezia) covering a great part of the total lot length (207 m); the finished inner structure will be 23 m wide and 16 m high

- a 8,80 m wide gallery flanked by two inclined pedestrian accesses.

The invert section of all structures lies 3 to 6 m beneath the water table.

At the Porta Venezia Station the soil treatment is done at first from a central shield-driven bore, to allow excavation of two larger side drifts (fig. 14-a).

Subsequent treatment stages are summarized in fig. 14-b:
- upward radial grouting from the central drift, for soil consolidation in the crown portion of the tunnel
- downward radial grouting from central and side drifts, in order to obtain an adequate thickness of improved soil consenting safe excavation beneath the water table.

The permanent crown structure will be provided by precast reinforced concrete pipe segments jacked through the grouted soil. The 2 m dia. pipes (fig. 14-b) will then be backfilled with concrete and tied by reinforced concrete arches at 6 m intervals.

In Lot 2PB the overall volume of treated soil would be around 170,000 cu.m.

One of the pedestrian accesses to the Station (7,6 m wide and 70 m long) will be driven full section with ground support provided by sets of 27 subhorizontal Rodinjet columns 9 m long executed ahead of the excavation face.

Lot 1PB

This lot, extending from 1PA to the intersection with Metro Line 3 (fig. 15) has a total length of 333 m including the Repubblica Station 93 m long.

The structural features and grouting patterns are shown in the four cross sections of fig. 16.

The Station (section A-A) involves an excavation 25 m wide under a soil cover of 7-8 m only.

371

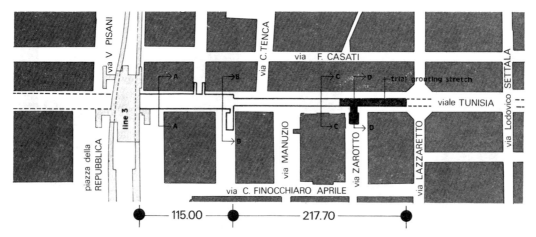

fig. 15 Lot 1PB: general plan

section B·B

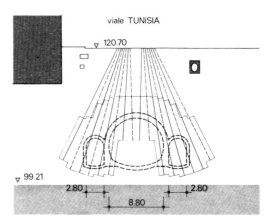

The treatment is carried out from ground surface with a planned thickness ranging from 4,5 m around the arch to 2,4 m beneath the invert. Soil consolidation, mainly based on chemical grouting, would be particularly binding in proximity of a 30 storey building with raft foundations only a few metres distant from the bore perimeter.

Special instrumentation has been installed for accurate and continuous monitoring of strains involved by grouting and tunnelling.

The line gallery is 8,80 m wide (section C-C) and flanked by two access tunnels in the initial stretch beyond the station (section B-B).

Section D-D shows the adit gallery from Zarotto shaft to the shield-driven drift for radial treatment of the line tunnel.

The adit excavation has been protected by subvertical grouting from the surface, extended to the full bore area and thus allowing a more exhaustive analysis on the effectiveness of the new Mistrà grout used at first on a 80 m trial stretch (fig. 15).

This stretch (fig. 17) has been divided in 4 zones (no. 1 to 4) treated by different combinations of grouting parameters; zone 5 corresponds to the adit gallery treated from the surface.

section C·C

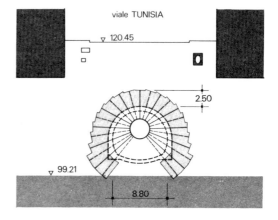

section A·A

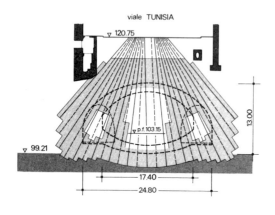

fig. 16 Lot 1PB: cross sections

section D·D

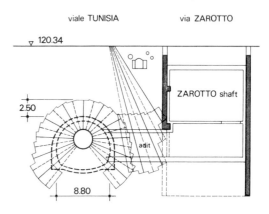

372

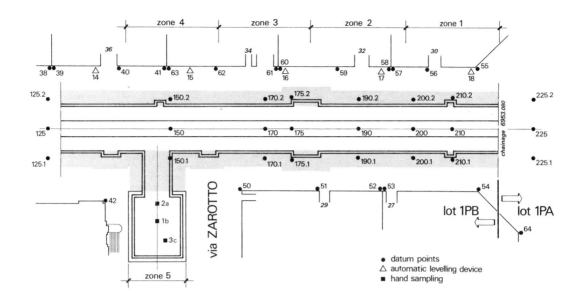

fig. 17 Lot 1PB: plan of trial grouting stretch with layout of datum points and automatic levelling devices

Fig. 17-18 show the layout of instrumentation installed to control vertical movements and consisting of:
- 24 datum points on the road surface (centre and edges)
- 20 datum points on the building facing the road
- 5 automatic levelling hydraulic devices, specially designed for continuous strain monitoring of a cable duct.

The outstanding properties of Mistrà grout, resulting from a wide laboratory investigation, have been already outlined and summarized in fig. 4-5 and Table 1.

The trial treatment along 80 m of line tunnel had the purpose to check the actual performance with an adjustment of operative parameters in order to obtain the best permeation with the least uplifting effects.

As a general rule the injection was based on a "controlled volume" procedure, that means a max. volume per valve and per step according to design geometry and assumptions within a specified limit pressure (2 to 2,5 MPa).

The main variable parameters were the grout discharge (from 400 to 800 l/h), the number of steps (one to three), the volume of grout per step (from 8% to 18% of the theoretical volume of involved soil, in the first step and variable percentages in the following ones according to built up pressure and uplift.

In general the soil uplifting trend was fairly negligible until the grout take reached 16-18% of the involved soil volume.

An average of 20-22% could be injected remaining within the specified limits.

Grouting operations have been carried out from December 1986 to February 1987.

Fig. 19 shows the progress of arch and invert excavation, completed in July.

The vertical movements recorded up to the end of August in 3 datum points above the tunnel crown are plotted versus time in fig. 20 with reference to the significant dates related to beginning and end of grouting and tunnelling.

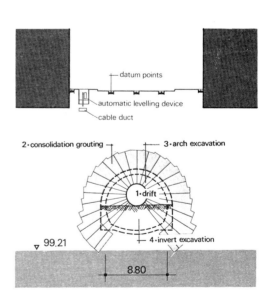

fig. 18 Lot 1PB: typical layout of control instrumentation

373

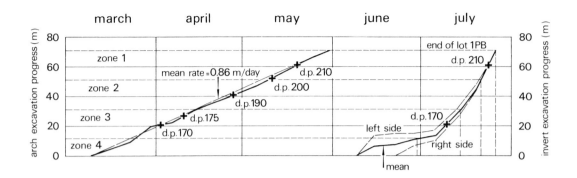

fig. 19 Trial grouting stretch: progress of excavation from adit towards Lot 1PA

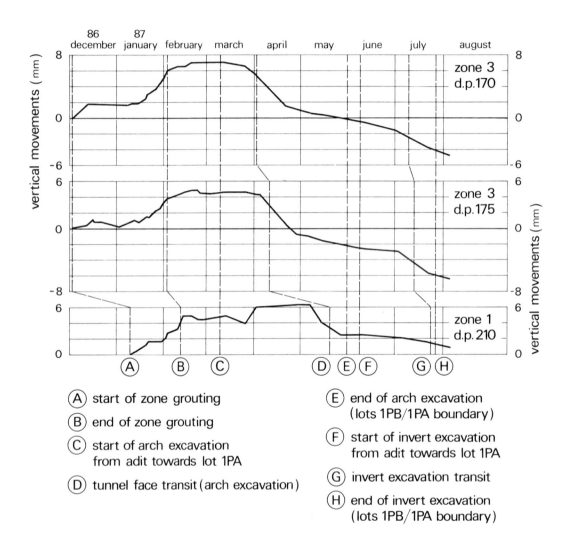

(A) start of zone grouting

(B) end of zone grouting

(C) start of arch excavation
from adit towards lot 1PA

(D) tunnel face transit (arch excavation)

(E) end of arch excavation
(lots 1PB/1PA boundary)

(F) start of invert excavation
from adit towards lot 1PA

(G) invert excavation transit

(H) end of invert excavation
(lots 1PB/1PA boundary)

fig. 20 Trial grouting stretch: vertical movements recorded during soil treatment and excavation stages above the tunnel crown

The max. uplift (7 mm) that has been recorded in datum point 170 can be related to the presence of a thicker sandy layer on the crown, as previously indicated by soil investigation and visually checked afterwards.

The settlements recorded so far from the end of grouting to one month after completion of invert boring range between 6 and 12 mm; the net values (with reference to the original ground level) are within 7 mm.

374

The progress of settlements during arch excavation in all central datum points is shown in fig. 21 as a function of the distance to the corresponding face, when approaching and moving away; the initial uplift of D.P. 210 is due to external factors (grouting in the adjoining Lot 1PA).

The uplifts and subsequent settlements of all buildings have been kept within a few millimetres, with negligible differential values along each building as shown in fig. 22.

Direct observation in the adit tunnel allowed the evaluation of the permeation effect of the new grout in a sequence of different soil layers, as shown in fig. 23.

Permeation was fairly poor, as expected, only in purely sandy layers (type B) where anyway a remarkable compaction effect was produced by a network of thin grout filled fissures.

In terms of overall soil consolidation the results may be considered at the best quality level obtainable by injection of any particulate suspension.

Based on this conclusion, the use of Mistrà grout was extended to a total length of about 250 m including the whole line tunnel and a part of the station.

The overall volume of treated soil in Lot 1PB is around 65.000 cu.m. The supplementary injection of a stable nonpolluting chemical grout (such as Silacsol) would be still necessary for tunnel sections larger than the standard line size of 8,80 m, in critical environmental situations and anyway when a tight water shut off is required.

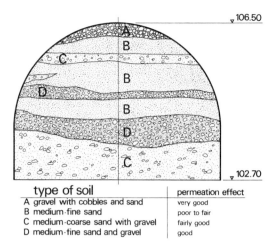

▽106.50

▽102.70

type of soil	permeation effect
A gravel with cobbles and sand	very good
B medium-fine sand	poor to fair
C medium-coarse sand with gravel	fairly good
D medium-fine sand and gravel	good

fig. 23 Adit gallery from Zarotto shaft to line drift: permeation effect of Mistrà grout related to soil profile

REFERENCES

1. De Paoli B., Viola G., Tomiolo A. - The use of drilling energy for soil classification. 2nd International Symposium on Field Measurement in Geomechanics, Kobe, 1987

2. Fenoux G. Y. - Progrès récents dans les techniques spéciales de traitement des fondations de barrage Q. 58 R4, 15th Conference on Large Dams, Lausanne 1985, vol. 3, 49-70.

3. Lunardi P., Mongilardi E., Tornaghi R. - Il preconsolidamento mediante jet-grouting nella realizzazione di opere in sotterraneo. International Congress on Large Underground Openings, Florence, 1986, vol. 2, 601-612.

4. Mongilardi E., Tornaghi R. - Connstruction of large underground openings and use of grouts - International Conference on Deep Foundations, Beijing 1986, vol. 2, 1.58-1.76

5. Tornaghi R. - Experimental criteria for design and control of grouting in sandy-gravelly soils Tunnelling '79, London, 1979, 71-78.

6. Tornaghi R. - Stabilization by injection - Panellist Report and Discussion Session 8 - 7th European Conference on Soil Mechanics and Foundation Engineering, Brighton 1979, vol. 4, 8.3, 8.36

7. Tornaghi R. - Criteri generali di studio e controllo dei trattamenti mediante iniezioni - Atti Istituto Scienza delle Costruzioni, n. 509 - Politecnico di Torino, 1981.

8. Tornaghi R. - Soil grouting - Co-Report and summary of discussion, Specialty Session 2, - 8th European Conference on Soil Mechanics and Foundation Engineering, Helsinki 1983, vol. 3,1089-1094 1099-1101.

9. Tornaghi R. - Soil improvement by hydrofracturing and jet-grouting - Session 5B 11th International Conference on Soil Mechanics and Foundation Engineering, San Francisco, 1985.

10. Tornaghi R., Perelli Cippo A. - Soil improvement by jet grouting for the solution of tunnelling problems - Proc. Tunnelling '85, Brighton 1985 265-275.

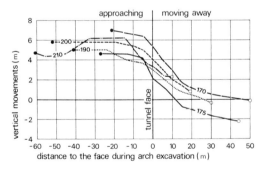

approaching | moving away

• start of arch excavation from adit
○ end of arch excavation at lots 1PB/1PA boundary

fig. 21 Trial grouting stretch: vertical movements as a function of distance to the face during arch excavation

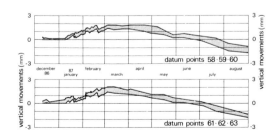

fig. 22 Trial grouting stretch: levelling data of buildings during soil treatment and tunnelling

General philosophy of pipe jacking and caisson sinking lubrication

Jim Washbourne B.Sc.Eng., M.Sc., C.Eng., M.I.C.E.
Oxford Polytechnic, Oxford, United Kingdom

SYNOPSIS

The sliding resistance encountered when structural units are slid through the ground is a fickle phenomenon and may vary widely depending upon depth below the ground surface, ground type, position of water table, and geometry and surface finish of unit. It can also show considerable variation for a given soil type and unit depending upon overcut, efficiency of excavation process, cleanness of bore, time after excavation and the kind of lubrication process which is employed between the sliding surfaces. In some circumstances a so called lubrication process may actually increase sliding resistance; on the other hand very difficult sliding problems can be reduced to insignificant proportions by a well designed and executed lubrication system. The paper examines the mechanics of the generation of sliding resistance for all types of soil and rock and for all types of sliding unit. It also explores the ways in which sliding resistance may be manipulated by lubrication.

INTRODUCTION

When there is a sliding interface between a structural unit and the ground there is a resistance to motion which depends upon adhesion and friction. Where a void fluid is present, instead of ground contact, there is resistance which depends upon the stress required to shear that void fluid. Generally speaking the adhesive resistance depends upon the area of ground contact. It is usually taken as a function of the cohesive strength of the soil which may be modified immediately adjacent to the unit by lubrication. It also depends upon the surface regularity (smoothness) of the unit. The area of contact which generates the adhesive component of sliding resistance is the full outside area of the structural unit only when the ground fully closes around it due to the cohesive strength being low with respect to the ambient pressure. Fig. 1 shows the pattern of scouring on a pipe

Fig. 1. Pattern of scouring on a Pipe Jacking Shield suggesting uneven sliding resistence.

jacking shield used in stiff clay which suggests uneven sliding resistance. In many situations the actual area of contact will be considerably less than the full outside area of the unit and the extent to which contact prevails depends on the ground conditions[1].

SLIDING RESISTANCE

The frictional component of sliding resistance depends upon the coefficient of friction at the sliding interface and the effective pressure. The effective pressure which generates the frictional force is equal to the total ambient pressure less the void fluid pressure. The coefficient of friction is dependent upon the nature of the ground, the material from which the unit is made, the surface regularity of the unit and any lubrication which may be applied. Fig. 2 shows how the friction varies with pressure for a coarse sand in contact with various pipe forming materials. The clayware specimen being both hard and smooth gave the lowest coefficient of friction, the less smooth, though hard, concrete gave an intermediate value and the polyethylene, which became abraded by the sand as it rubbed against it, gave the highest value. Fig. 3 shows how the friction can be reduced for polyethylene with a unpressurised bentonite slurry. From the graph it can be clearly seen how important it is to have a thick slurry to reduce the coefficient of friction. The results used to plot the graphs in Figs. 2 and 3 were obtained, at Oxford Polytechnic, using a standard 60 mm square shear box with a slab of pipe forming material filling the lower half of the box whilst the upper half of the box was filled with well graded sand.

THE BENEFITS OF LUBRICATION

There is considerable evidence that a good lubrication process can impart much benefit to the operation of sliding

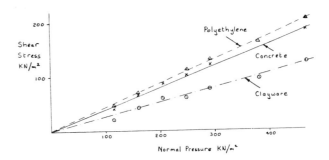

Fig. 2. The Friction Variation for Coarse Sand rubbing on various Pipe Forming Materials.

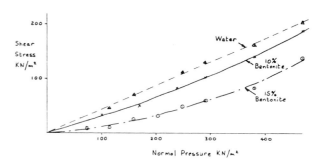

Fig. 3. Friction Reduction using Unpressurised Bentonite Slurry.

structural units through the ground. The best lubrication systems take the form of a layer of thick pressurised slurry in the vicinity of the sliding unit. This lubricating layer reduces the area of contact by pushing the ground away from the unit thereby reducing adhesive resistance. In extreme situations the lubricating fluid virtually eliminates contact altogether. The mixing of the lubricating fluid with the surrounding ground tends to reduce the unit adhesion also. If the lubricating fluid pressure is high it considerably reduces the effective pressure at the sliding interface and thereby considerably reduces friction.

In contrast to the large forces usually required to overcome adhesion and friction the effort required to shear

378

the lubricating fluid or the lubricating fluid soil mixture is relatively small. The art of lubrication depends upon the ability to install a self sustaining layer of lubricating slurry around the structural unit for the period of the sliding operation. The slurry consistency required in civil engineering applications is that which corresponds to a grease and not an oil, because the sliding velocity is very low and there is no continuous dynamic replenishment of the fluid[2]. Many pipe jacking and caisson sinking operations have now been successfully completed using thick slurry lubrication systems. However many projects have suffered severe problems mainly due to a lubricating layer of thin slurry which has escaped or has allowed the ground to collapse. On the other hand, problems may also occur where a lubricating layer of thick slurry has only been partially formed due to the slurry delivery system pressure being too low or the pumping operation being delayed.

THE OBJECTIVE OF LUBRICATION

The objective of lubrication as applied to pipe jacking and caisson sinking is to reduce the sliding resistance to a sufficiently small value so that it can easily be overcome by a movement inducing system. It does this in granular soil by reducing the "intergranular" pressure between the units and the surrounding ground by substituting a slurry pressure. The slurry presence also reduces the coefficient of friction. In the case of cohesive soils the objective should be to maintain a layer of slurry between the structural unit and the surrounding ground. With cohesive soils three things can cause the bore to close. The material surrounding the bore may fail in shear or it may close "elastically" and in either of these instances slurry pressure should maintain the void space

around the unit. On the other hand clays may take up water out of the slurry and swell, thereby closing the bore. Here the answer to the problem is to use a water retaining additive in the slurry; this is common practice in the oil industry to inhibit the swelling. Another way of dealing with this problem, which is used in Germany and which may be used in the U.K. in the near future, is to provide a bore trimming system to counteract closure. At intervals along the pipe run adjustable blades are provided to skim the bore and bring skimmed soil into the pipes for disposal. If the objective of maintaining a slurry layer is achieved it is only necessary to overcome the shear strength of the slurry to slide the pipes or the caisson. Needless to say this objective is only partially attainable in a working situation. The degree to which it is attained depends on the thought and effort applied to the task.

High sliding resistance in pipe jacking may lead to a retreat to conventional tunnelling or damage to equipment. Fig. 4 illustrates a buckled 250 tonnef jack damaged by a high sliding resistance which displaced the jacking wall. The displacement combined with the high load caused the buckling. On the particular

Fig. 4. A Buckled 250 tonnef Pipe Jacking Jack Damaged by the consequences of High Pipe Run Sliding Resistance.

contract where the jack was damaged high
sliding resistance (over 2 tonnef / m²)
was encountered in gravelly sand where
the slurry used for lubrication was
probably too thin to support the bore.
Some surface settlement was observed
associated with the closure of the
overcut and erosion into the face.
Slight damage was caused to adjacent
property and an old cast iron gas main
had to be exposed and supported as the
tunnelling machine passed below. In the
case of caissons, failure in the
lubrication system can necessitate the
expensive use of kentledge as
illustrated in Fig. 5. On one of the
Humber Bridge caissons 7 000 tonnes of
kentledge had to be used to force it
down to its final level[3]. On the Cairo
Waste Water Project, at Ameria, 4,000
tonnes of kentledge was used on a
caisson in an attempt to force it down
through large particle size material.
Here the lubrication system did not
succeed, probably because the material

Fig. 5. Concrete Kentledge Blocks on a
Large Caisson.

in the sides of the excavation was too
coarse to be supported by the
lubricating slurry. The mean sliding
resistance in this instance exceeded 6
tonnef / m² whereas only 3.5 tonnef / m²
was anticipated.

It is often the case that open well
caissons are sunk in waterlogged
granular soil without an effective
lubrication layer. In such situations
material is excavated from below the
cutting edge to such an extent that the
surrounding soil flows downward and
drags the caisson down with it. This
process however may cause settlement in
the surrounding area and this may be
unacceptable. In any case such a sinking
operation is irregular and
unpredictable. The loosening action of
the dredging operation is temporary and
it has to be re-established with each
increment of descent. With such a system
of sinking there is the risk that
violent water upsurges will occur in the
wells caused by the collapse of water
voids. These voids form outside the plan
area of the caisson and are due to the
undermining of the cutting edge and the
consequent erosion of material into the
excavation zone. Sometimes such
catastrophies are alleged to be due to
water under artesian pressure to support
claims for extra payment but such
artesian pressures are usually
detectable during site investigations
and would be anticipated. The use of
effective slurry lubrication eliminates
the need to destabilise closing granular
soil in caisson sinking operations.

METHODS OF LUBRICATION
The introduction of a layer of
lubricating slurry requires the
provision of an overcut space to
accommodate it. Immediately a void is
formed in ground that is not self
supporting, the ground should be
stabilised by the introduction of a

pressurised slurry. However in self supporting ground keeping the overcut open does not present a problem and in this situation lubrication is scarcely necessary. With the River Bollin pipe jack at Manchester Airport, Fairclough, the contractor, was able to jack a run of 693 metres of 1.8 m diameter reinforced concrete pipes without using either intermediate jacking stations or any lubrication. The sliding resistance in this instance was only about 0.25 tonnef / m^2. Fig. 6 shows the Dosco boom cutter machine at the time of breakthrough at the completion of that drive. The Dosco machine proved particularly good at leaving a clean bore for the pipes to slide through; this point will be discussed in more detail later.

Fig. 6. Breakthrough by the Dosco Tunnelling machine on the River Bollin Pipe Jack at Manchester Airport.

With collapsing ground, particularly in water bearing sands and gravels, maintaining the overcut may be very difficult. Fig. 7 shows the surface depression which formed 4 metres above a hand excavated pipe jack face in water bearing ground when the ground collapsed into it and into the overcut. On this particular project, an advanced drainage contract for a bypass scheme in Cornwall, little harm was done and the pipe jacking subcontractors had to introduce an extra jacking pit after only 30 m of a 40 m drive when the sliding resistance exceeded the jacking capacity. The initial slurry lubrication was in the form of bentonite slurry daubed on the pipes and it proved to be ineffective. On the subsequent drives the problem was rectified by the timely injection of lubricating slurry through holes in the pipe wall together with an improved ground water drainage system.

Fig. 7. Surface Depression Formed Over a Pipe Jack in Collapsing Granular Ground.

Bore closure and the consequent loss of oversize space may occur with some of the recently introduced pipeline replacement methods which rely on impactors causing soil displacement to generate underground space. With this method of working the displaced soil normally moves forward and upwards away from the impactor. Compaction may also contribute to the space generating effect. However this is not always the case. Depending upon the length of the compactor, the depth of its operation, the shear strength of the soil it is penetrating and on the amount and kind of displacement exerted by the impact tool, two things can happen. The soil will usually be forced forwards and upwards but it may be forced outwards at the front of the compactor, back along the compactor and then inwards behind the compactor to squeeze on the following pipe as shown in the diagram Fig. 8. This mechanism was recognised on the Cowley Road Foul Sewer Replacement Contract undertaken by Avant P.R.S. for the Oxford City Council. On part of this project squeezing of the pipes by the surrounding soil and the consequent generation of high sliding resistance was attributed to clay in the immediate vicinity of the old sewer being softened by leakage. It had then an insurmountable tendency to flow around the impact tool and cause this problem which the Water Research Council who were advising on the project had not encountered previously.

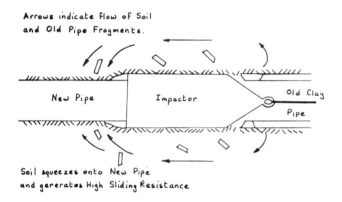

Arrows indicate Flow of Soil and Old Pipe Fragments.

New Pipe   Impactor   Old Clay Pipe

Soil squeezes onto New Pipe and generates High Sliding Resistance

Fig. 8. The Flow of Soil around a Pipe Breaking Impactor which May Occur in Certain Ground Conditions.

If the ground is allowed to collapse freely around the structure it can be difficult to reform the overcut void to accommodate the slurry. The operation, should it become necesary, may require injection pressures of up to twice the overburden pressure in order to force the soil away and there should be sufficient capacity in the pumping system to achieve this objective. However to do this is usually only possible with a very thick slurry injected well away from escape paths which might prevent the high pressure from being contained. Such high slurry pressures are not needed to prevent ground collapse since collapse pressures correspond to active earth pressure and the pressures to reform the overcut correspond to passive ones. On a sewer diversion contract in Poole a closure of the overcut occurred after 300 m of a 520 m pipe jack when the slurry pump located on the surface adjacent to the jacking pit failed to overcome the delivery pipe pressure loss by a sufficient margin. Over about a 20 metre length of the run behind the tunnelling machine the ground, which was gravelly sand, closed tightly around the pipes and generated a sliding resistance locally estimated to be 6 tonnef / m^2 (about 800 tonnef of resistance in total on eight 2.5m pipes). The pipes were freed by injecting through each pipe wall a thick slurry containing special lubricating additives at high pressure, using a pump within the pipe run located close to the injection points. This method of injection was then continued to the end of the drive and at the end of the drive the sliding resistance for the whole of the run was reduced to an average of 0.25 tonnef / m^2.

JAMMING IN HARD BORES

An excavated space does not necessarily have to close in order to grip a sliding unit. There have been many instances of tunnelling machines, jacked pipes and caissons being trapped in quite hard bores. In the rock boring situation the danger is that bore debris will jam in the overcut and apply a wedging action on the sliding unit. This can be one of the most devastating occurrences in underground working. To guard against this problem extreme vigilance must be

382

used to clear the bore of all loose materials prior to any attempt to slide anything into it. Also when the unit has been slid into place a supporting slurry should be used to stabilise the bore if there is any danger of loose material becoming detached.

On a main sewer contract in Halifax extreme difficulty was experienced in a tunnel in rock when the tunnelling machine used in the pipe jacking process was unable to clear the bore. Holes had to be cut in the sides of the machine and jammed pipes had to be broken out to clear the debris that had been left by the boring head[4]. The machine was built with a boring head which could be rotated in either direction, to counteract roll, and back-to-back edge scrapers to recover spoil from the edge of the face. However with this arrangement it did not seem possible to clear the bore of debris. Inevitably with this arrangement one half of the scrapers tended to plough material rather than scoop it up and there was no access to the bore behind the boring head. Another contributory cause was probably that the edge scrapers were not well shaped for a sufficiently efficient scooping action as they are on some other (more expensive) tunnelling machines.

A similar problem was experienced with the pipe jacking on the Bury Interceptor Sewer Contract. There a Lovat soft earth tunnelling machine was modified to bore out rock. The boring head after initial modification (Fig. 9) was similar to the machine used at Halifax. However after experiencing difficulties similar to the ones encountered on the Halifax contract the machine was further modified. It was then converted to operate with a boring head which rotated in only one direction, four of the edge scrapers were removed and the the shape of the

remaining four was improved. A view of the machine in its final form is shown Fig. 10 and in this form its performance was satisfactory.

Fig. 9. The Modified Lovat Tunnelling Machine before its Final Conversion.

Fig. 10. The Modified Lovat Tunnelling Machine after its Final Conversion. Note the Improved Shape of the Edge Scrapers.

FUNCTIONAL REQUIREMENTS FOR LUBRICATING SLURRIES

The requirements for pipe jacking and

caisson sinking lubricating slurries are somewhat different from those for oil well drilling and hydraulic transport in that the former need to be much thicker. Basically the requirements for a lubricating slurry may be listed as follows.

1/ The slurry should be non hazardous and it should be stable for its required functioning period. Here it should be remembered that diesel oil (often used in oil well drilling slurry) is carcinogenic and most biocides which are used to prevent bacteriological decay can cause environmental damage and be unacceptable in certain circumstances; they may also be a hazard to operatives.

2/ The slurry should be capable of being pumped into place without excessive pressure being required. In spite of the fact that a high gel strength is desirable in an insitu slurry it should be sufficiently thixotropic to be capable of being fluidised sufficiently to allow pumping.

3/ The slurry should not leak in excessive quantities. Once in place the slurry should develop sufficiently high gel strength to prevent escape along any potential exit routes.

4/ The slurry should support the ground and form a lubricating layer. For ground support the slurry must have sufficient gel strength to be adequately pressurised so that it is not squeezed out by the surrounding pressure. Also, and this is very important and sometimes overlooked, it should not permit particles from the surrounding ground to settle through it.

5/ The slurry should have sufficient gel strength to resist the flotation tendency of the pipes in the case of a pipe jacking slurry.

SLURRY MIXING

Slurries must be well mixed to a uniform consistency prior to being pumped. The powdered slurry forming materials should be added gradually to the water in a high shear mixer as the mixer is running. They should be mixed in whole batches and, if the constituents are added separately to the mixer, the void blocking additive should be added first followed by the bentonite followed by the polymer once the bentonite is fully dispersed. Polymers can cause difficulties if they are added alone to a slurry as they tend to coagulate; also, when they are added first to the water they prevent bentonite from being dispersed. When cellulose polymers prove to be difficult to disperse in a slurry the problem may be overcome by mixing them in a small quantity of oil prior to introducing them into the mixer. However, it is preferable to use preblended slurry powder formed from bentonite and polymers together with void blocking additives rather than try to blend slurry on site because of difficulties in controlling the operation. It is very much easier to form a slurry with a preblended powder than it is to form one with portions of the individual constituents.

SLURRY PUMPING

Slurries should be pumped into place using a pump with an adequate working pressure. On the outlet of the pump there should be a pressure gauge. Mono pumps with rubber stators, which double as slurry mixers, tend to become worn and the delivery pressure fades as the job progresses and as the pumping distances get longer. A ram pump is suitable for handling lubricating slurry. The pump should be capable of generating a gauge delivery pressure when added to the pressure head in the slurry delivery pipe, sufficient to overcome the gel strength resistance of the slurry in the pipeline when the pipeline has been extended to its final length. In addition, it should provide a pressure of about twice the overburden pressure at the injection points. Further the pump should inject steadily as the overcut void is formed at a rate of delivery sufficient to fill the void and counteract losses wich occur into the surrounding ground and through any leakage paths.

As the gel strength and viscosity of slurry increases, the pressure required to deliver the slurry to the extreme ends of the slurry layer is increased. Usually slurry viscosity is not critical when lubricating slurries have to be pumped. The critical consideration is gel strength. Gel strength increases with time in the manner indicated by the graph in Fig. 11. The pressure P required to initiate

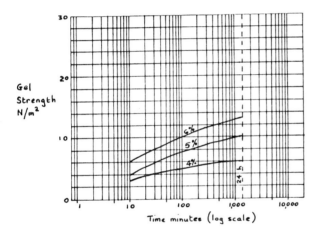

Fig. 11. The Increase of Gel Strength of Bentonite Slurry with Time.

flow in a horizontal pipe length L, diameter D, filled with a slurry with a gel strength G is given by the following equation:-

$$P = \frac{4.G.L}{D}$$

Thus it can be seen that if a slurry filled pipe is left for a long time there may be a problem initiating flow. Fig. 12 has been compiled to give a rapid indication for site work of degelling pressure requirements for standard pipe diameters for various values of gel strength. Gelled slurry is

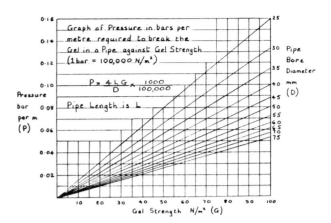

Fig. 12. The Degelling Pressure Requirements for Pipes of Various Diameter.

by no means the only cause of slurry delivery pipe blockage; void blocking additives can cause blockages if they separate out from the slurry and form mats across the slurry path. Slurry weighting agents may also be the cause of delivery pipe blockage if they settle out of slurry especially in vertical runs of pipework. These two things cannot happen if the slurry is thick but both of these phenomena have been observed on projects by the author recently when slurries with a low gel strength were the cause. Sometimes blockages in lubricating slurry pipes may be caused by inadequate mixing. Here thin slurry may contain pockets of thick material and it is of course the latter which can cause the problem.

ESCAPE OF SLURRY

In certain situations lubricating slurries may not have sufficient gel strength to resist substantial migration into the soil voids, into the face or through gaps in the pipe run. The extent to which such migration can take place is indicated by the graph of Fig. 13. In such cases instability can occur and in order to counteract this it is prudent to use a void blocking additive. A suitably efficient material which is widely used in the oil industry for this

385

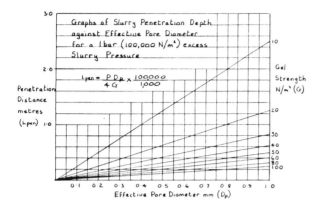

Fig. 13. A Graph giving Distance of Slurry Penetration against Mean Soil Void Size.

purpose consists of fine muscovite mica flakes. However care must be taken in their use to prevent them being inspired by operatives as they can do harm to the lungs. Care should be taken in the selection of void blocking additives since particles that are too large may tend to block the path of the slurry to its required location. There are many particle, flake and fibre void blocking materials available for incorporation into lubricating slurries. Any void blocking additive should effectively seal the voids in the surrounding soil. Using Terzaghi's filter rule this means that the d_{85} of the void blocking additive must be at least 1/4 of the d_{15} of the surrounding soil. If a seal is not achieved in the vicinity of the inside of the bore slurry will be lost, slurry pressure will drop and bore support will not be effectively obtained.

Slurry may tend to escape into the excavation zone past the cutting edge of the tunnelling shield or machine in the case of pipe jacking and past the cutting edge in the case of caissons. It may also tend to escape from the annulus at the point of entry of the structure into the ground. If either of these two things is a problem then the high pressure needed should be introduced as far as possible from the escape points using a slurry with a sufficiently high gel strength to contain the required pressure. In the case of jacked pipe runs this involves the high pressure slurry injection being carried out at intermediate injection points. With caissons the injection is normally above a step located about a metre above the cutting edge (see Fig. 14). Often the only way in which the slurry can be prevented from finding its way from above the step down past the cutting edge is by maintaining a high gel strength. When the lower portion of the large Ameria Caisson in Cairo passed into coarse material, significant quantities of slurry escaped from the overcut annulus, even though the injection points were located 3.5 metres above the cutting edge[5].

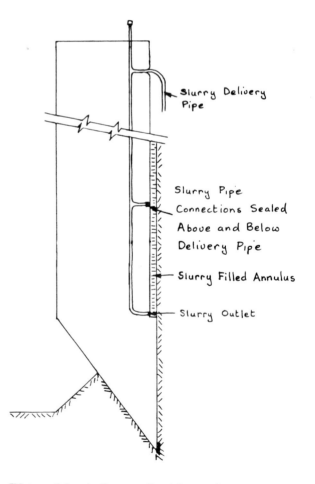

Fig. 14. A Cross Section of the Cutting Edge and Step of a Large Caisson.

GROUND SUPPORT

An important requirement for a lubricating slurry is the ability to support the surrounding ground. In order to support the bulk of the ground it must impart enough pressure to counteract the earth pressure sufficiently to maintain clearance. In the case of jacking pipes the pressure is built up mainly by the pump and the slurry is prevented by its gel strength from escaping along the annulus into the face or jacking pit. The pressure required for such support for a pipe jack bore is discussed. In the case of caissons the cutting edge should contain the slurry at the bottom of the annulus and the support pressure is generated mainly by the hydrostatic head of slurry. For a flat vertical interface between the slurry and the soil the stability is partly derived from arching of the soil provided that the span that the soil has to arch is not excessive[6].

In the case of circular caissons the arching is more pronounced because of the geometry of the interface. Generally speaking active earth pressure in granular soils is generated by a strain movement of the material of the order of 1% (this can taken as the 1% of the depth of the soil interface for a long shallow interface). However in the case of a caisson interface arching is usually quite a dominant factor and active pressure probably generated is only a small proportion of that corresponding to 1% strain. The small (50 mm) step on the outside of most standard commercial segmental caissons (Fig. 15) can therefore be regarded as adequate provided a full slurry layer is incorporated. The danger with granular soils is that if the interface should be allowed to collapse around the caisson above the step then large lateral pressures are usually generated. Half the passive pressure can be generated at

Fig. 15. The 50 mm wide Step on the Outside Face of a Precast Concrete Caisson Segment used to provide Overcut to accommodate Lubricating Slurry.

an interface with a strain of 1% on a long shallow interface and considerably more on an interface with a large depth to length ratio.

The support of individual soil particles in the sides of an excavation is an important functional requirement of an earth support and lubricating slurry. If the soil particles descend through the slurry the annulus will be filled and frictional resistance will ensue. This is particularly important in the situation where loose particles may become detached in hard bores and jam the sliding units. Fig. 16 shows the

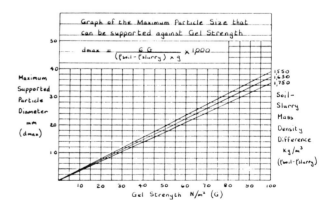

Fig. 16. The Relationship between Gel Strength and Size of Particle that can be supported.

387

relationship between the particle sizes that can be supported and the gel strength of the slurry for various values of mass density difference.

JACKING OF CURVED PIPE RUNS

The jacking of curved pipe runs has become standard practice now in the U.K; it has been included in contracts in Halifax, Bury and the London Docklands. The essential features of this operation are low jacking loads whilst going round the curves, necessitating the use of intermediate jacking stations and the packing out of the joints on the outside of the curve. Adjustments to the joint packing are straight forward if the pipe run is wholly within the curved profile. However this has not always been the case. Where the curve is entered after a length of straight pipe run a joint packing arrangement seems to be necessary somewhere between that required for the curve and that required for the preliminary straight. A method of changing the joint packing whilst the pipes are in the ground has yet to be devised. As far as lubrication is concerned it would be prudent to concentrate the injection points on the outside of the curve to counteract the radial forces induced by the jacking reactions at the joints.

CONCLUSION

A good lubrication system is not an expensive item on a pipe jacking or caisson sinking operation; it is only a small percentage of the total cost. On the other hand failed lubrication systems have involved an enormous level of extra expenditure of time and money. It is therefore worthwhile for civil engineers involved in this kind of work to apply some of their efforts to understanding the basic philosophy of lubrication as have their mechanical engineering colleagues.

ACKNOWLEDGEMENTS

The author wishes to thank the following for providing information used for this paper: Fairclough Civil Engineering Ltd., C.V. Buchan (Concrete) Ltd., Steetley Berk. Ltd., Christiani and Nielsen Ltd., Surveyor (Journal), Avant P.R.S. Ltd., Oxford City Council, The Robbins Co. (UK) Ltd., J.F.Donelon and Co. Ltd.

REFERENCES

1. Washbourne J. Sliding Resistance of Jacking Tunnel Lining. Tunnels and Tunnelling, 14, No.10, 1982, 17-18.
2. Shell International Petroleum Co. Ltd. The Application of Lubricants. 1965. 11-12.
3. Hayward D. New Civil Engineer Supplement May 1981. 9.
4. N.C.E. News. Problems increase for Halifax Pipe Jack. New Civil Engineer 5 December 1985. 9.
5. N.C.E. News. Trench Treatment for Ameria Caisson. New Civil Engineer 28 May 1987. 4.
6. Washbourne J. The Three Dimensional Analysis of Diaphragm Wall Excavations. Ground Engineering May 1984. 17 No.4. 24-29.
7. Lambe T.W. and Witman R.V. Soil Mechanics. S.I. Version 1979. 329.

The A55 North Wales Trunk Road Penmaenbach Tunnel: use of NONEL blasting techniques

Richard Watts B.Sc., C.Eng., F.I.C.E., M.B.I.M.
Balfour Beatty Construction, Ltd., Croydon, Surrey, United Kingdom

SYNOPSIS

A brief description is given of the tunnel and its location in relation to the two existing tunnels in the headland, followed by a description of the need for careful blasting and the search for suitable techniques to be used.

The Paper describes the advantages of the selected NONEL system and goes on to show how it was put to good use at Penmaenbach.

Work was carried out safely and satisfactorily, within the vibration levels specified by the Consultants in agreement with the Railways Authority.

THE SITE

The Penmaenbach headland is situated 3km west of Conwy in the County of Gwynedd on the North Wales coast.

It is an intrusive Rhyolite rock of Ordovician age, and represents a significant natural barrier to communications along the narrow coastal strip. Glacial deposits cover its eastern slopes, while its western flank is overlain with loose, angular rock scree.

The first road to be successfully completed around the headland was constructed by Thomas Telford, and involved cutting into the rock of the headland nose to form a narrow ledge. This road was to become the A55 Trunk Road.

Some 140 years ago, a railway was constructed at a lower level than the road, and passed through the headland itself in a predominantly unlined tunnel.

In 1932 the original Telford road was realigned, and driven through the headland point in a short fully lined tunnel.

THE NEW ROAD TUNNEL

The current scheme at Penmaenbach forms part of a project to upgrade to dual carriageway status the whole of the A55 trunk road. It requires a new tunnel, which will carry the new westbound carriageway to be driven some 60m to the landward side of the rail tunnel. Eastbound traffic will remain on the existing route, although provision has been made for the construction of a further parallel tunnel at a later date.

The length of the new tunnel is 660m, of which some 570m is constructed in hard rock, with the remaining 90m of the East Portal being formed in soft glacial material. The tunnel has a cross section area of $98m^2$. The layout and cross section are indicated in Figure 1 and Figure 2.

The scheme is being constructed for the Welsh Office to the design and specification of Consulting Engineers, Travers Morgan & Partners, in conjunction with Howard Humphreys & Partners.

RESTRICTIONS ON BLASTING

The Consulting Engineers, on behalf of the Client, identified that the specific circumstances of the site would require stringent restrictions and monitoring to alleviate the effects of blasting.

There exists no practical local diversion for the busy road and rail routes that serve North West Wales and the Port of Holyhead. Both routes are vulnerable to rock disturbance on the steep slopes of the headland and the railway is also sensitive to rock fall in the unlined tunnel.

After extensive discussions between the Engineers and the various Transport Authorities, a series of restrictions, designed to protect both the public and the existing structures, was incorporated into the Contract Documents.

Blasts would be allowed only once a day during a 35 minute time window between trains. This window was anticipated to be between 20:00 hrs and 21:30 hrs. During the window a road closure limited to 20 minutes was required, during which time the blast was completed, and then both road and railway had to be inspected and cleared.

To reduce any possible blast effects, vibrations were limited by imposing a maximum peak particle velocity of 50mm/s for work in most of the tunnel and West Portal. However, for the eastern 155m including the portal area within soft material, this velocity was reduced to 25mm/s. Monitoring was undertaken from within the rail tunnel.

The requirements for vibration monitoring were fully specified. Geophone vibration detectors with a natural period of 4.5 Hz had to be set in groups of three, with mutually perpendicular axes. Twenty-two monitoring points were designated on the railway tunnel wall, but no more than 3 points, closest to the round, had to be monitored at each blast.

The geophones were to be connected by a 6-core screened cable to a Cambridge Electronics Design (CED 1401) Laboratory Interface, which was controlled by a BBC B-Plus microcomputer with ancillary printer and disc drive.

This monitoring equipment, when activated, continuously samples and retains for a short time information received from the geophones. A full record over a set period is only taken once the vibrations exceed a pre-set trigger level. The record can begin from a point in time prior to the trigger level being reached so that the onset of the vibrations is available for inspection.

Once an incident is recorded the equipment prints out a summary showing the component and the resultant PPV's for each set of geophones, together with the elapsed time associated with each peak. A more detailed report is available after about two hours. This gives full details of the equipment set-up, a further printout of the peak values, and a detailed trace showing the vibration amplitude plotted against time for each geophone.

SELECTION OF WORKING METHODS

The Contractor, in selecting his working methods, was conscious of the need to maximise the advance obtained from each of the limited number of blasts that the programme duration would allow. This had to be achieved within both the imposed blasting restraints and the requirements to maintain rock stability. The design called for the installation of various rock bolt patterns supplemented with shotcrete as conditions required. It was clear that the choice of explosives and detonating system was of great importance to the successful completion of the contract.

At planning stage various pilot and multiheading options for forming the tunnel cross section were considered. Schemes involving the progressive enlargement of a pilot heading could not be completed within the programme restraints, but larger faces that could be worked more efficiently could involve unacceptable vibrations. The compromise solution adopted was to take the face in three sections, a $52m^2$ full width top heading, a bench, and the pair of service trenches. These sections were each separated by 100m and were to be fired simultaneously, see Figure 3.

This solution still imposed great difficulties on designing the blasting to comply with the vibration limitations whilst maintaining the need for reliability and operational flexibility. It was essential to the progress of the works that blast windows were not missed, irrespective of the need to use electrical equipment for rock bolting adjacent to the face. Additional considerations were the possibility of electrical storms, and although no radio transmitters were in the area, the likelihood of electromagnetic emissions from very low flying military aircraft.

A detonating system was required which could be safely left in a charged face in the circumstances described. Two systems were investigated as being potentially suitable, namely MAGNADET and NONEL. After careful comparison and consideration the NONEL system was chosen, and the blasts designed accordingly.

THE NONEL DETONATING SYSTEM

The NONEL detonator consists of a delay detonator crimped onto a length of NONEL tubing. This narrow bore plastic tube, which is fully sealed, against dampness or contamination, has a small amount of explosive material deposited on the inside face, so that a detonating shock wave can be transmitted along it at the rate of 2000m/s. Initiation may be by either electrical or mechanical means.

The detonators have the advantage of being entirely non-electrical, and are not affected by any stray induced electrical currents. The face can be safely charged irrespective of atmospheric conditions or the use of electrical equipment nearby. Once the face has been charged rock bolting may be carried out to ensure completion prior to the firing time.

The GT/T system specially designed for tunnel work also has a large number of different delays, 25 No being available. The delay interval in the short delay range is 100ms, but intervals of 200ms in the medium range and 500ms in the long delay range are provided, see Figure 4. By using the characteristics of the system, blasts can be designed to ensure the orderly sequential disintegration of the rock, whilst minimising the maximum instantaneous charge

and hence limiting vibrations.

A third advantage claimed by the system was its ease of use. Connection blocks are available which only require a loop of tube to be locked behind a retaining wing on one of the four faces of the block. Thus a simple, but positive, connection can be made rapidly.

IMPLEMENTATION AT PENMAENBACH

The blast patterns at Penmaenbach were designed to give a total advance of approximately 4.0m per day. The tunnel perimeter had to be formed by smooth blasting techniques, this being a requirement of the Contract.

The drill pattern and explosive usage for the top heading is shown in Figure 5. The round was initiated by Gelemex, a highly water resistant gelatinous nitroglycerine based explosive. The bulk of the round was fired with Quarrex A, a low density nitroglycerine based powder explosive. Trimming was achieved by using Gurit, a very low density explosive, in the perimeter holes.

American and Swedish research suggests that to achieve the efficient and orderly removal of the cut, a delay of 25ms per metre depth is required for each hole. In applying this at Penmaenbach the 8 No 4.0m deep cut holes were each given a 100ms delay between successive detonations.

Following removal of the cut, a further sequence of 15 No delays with up to 14 No holes per delay were used to complete the round. Details of the detonator delays are shown in Figure 5.

The NONEL detonator tubes were collected and taped together in bunches of 14 No-20 No. The bunches were each tied around and looped together with a detonating cord called Hericord. This material, which is manufactured by Nitro-Bickford, has a charge weight of 6.5 g/m and detonation speed of 7000-7500 m/s.

The bench and service trench charges were each connected in a similar manner. Electric detonators were connected to each of the Hericord loops, and the three patterns fired simultaneously from the tunnel portal.

PERFORMANCE ACHIEVED

During the main tunnel drive, the system was found to be easy to use and reliable. Average pulls of 3.9m were achieved with only 3 No blasts lost over a 7 month period.

Vibration monitoring was carried out on every blast. The equipment when commissioned was set at a trigger level of 10mm/s, but during the initial blasts vibrations were so small that triggering did not occur, and the level had to be progressively reduced to 1mm/s to ensure that a record was produced. However, at this level of sensitivity the machine could not be set up until after closure of the road and railway immediately prior to the blast.

The results showed that it was possible to keep the peak particle velocities to below 25mm/s for most of the drive. A set of initial summary vibration information from a blast is shown in Figure 6 and a full blast report is shown in Figure 7a, 7b, and 7c.

On one occasion, when nearing the eastern section of tunnel where the more stringent restrictions applied, vibrations were nearing the limiting value. It was considered that the simultaneous detonation of the top heading, the bench and the service trenches was producing enhanced vibration values. It was possible using the NONEL system to separate the three blasts by a few milliseconds, so that the individual peaks did not overlap, and the resultant peak values were reduced. The three sections were offset by using electric delay detonators to fire the Hericord loops. The top heading, bench and service trenches were given delays of 30ms, 55ms and 80ms respectively.

When blasting at more than one location on the same site, and detonating from the same exploder, it is necessary to ensure that all detonators are initiated before any of the charges fire. Since the minimum delay available in the NONEL system is 25ms, detonators of this value could not be used in the rounds. A minimum delay value of 100ms was therefore incorporated into the blast patterns.

The effects of the simultaneous and sequenced blasts on the resultant vibration signature are illustrated diagrammatically in Figures 8 and 9. The results as recorded by the vibration sensors are indicated in Figure 7c.

RECOMMENDATIONS FOR FUTURE USE

The NONEL detonating system should be considered:

- where there is a danger of stray electrical currents being generated by radio or radar emissions, or by high voltage electrical power cables and equipment.
- where electrically operated plant may be required near the face.
- where there is a possibility of electrical storms disrupting and delaying the planned sequence of the work.
- where advantage can be gained from the wide range of detonating times available.

ACKNOWLEDGEMENTS

The Author wishes to thank:
The Client, The Welsh Office, for giving permission for the Paper to be presented.

Travers Morgan and Partners, the Consulting Engineers, for their help and comments.

Explosive and Chemical Products Ltd, supplier of the NONEL detonators, for their advice and assistance.

Soil Mechanics Ltd, for the supply of vibration monitoring and recording instruments.

The Site Staff of Balfour Beatty Construction Ltd, the Main Contractor, who undertook the tunnel construction.

LIST OF FIGURES

Figure 1   Plan of Site

Figure 2   Cross Section of Tunnel

Figure 3   East-West Section - showing blasting

Figure 4   NONEL GT/T Detonator Details

Figure 5   Top Heading - blast pattern and usage of detonators and explosives

Figure 6   Details of Immediate Vibration Record

Figure 7a Vibration Monitoring Equipment
           - Set-up Detaila
Figure 7b Details of Vibration Record
Figure 7c Record of Vibration Trace
Figure 8   Diagrammatic Representation of
           a Simultaneous Blast
Figure 9   Diagrammatic Representation of
           a Sequenced Blast

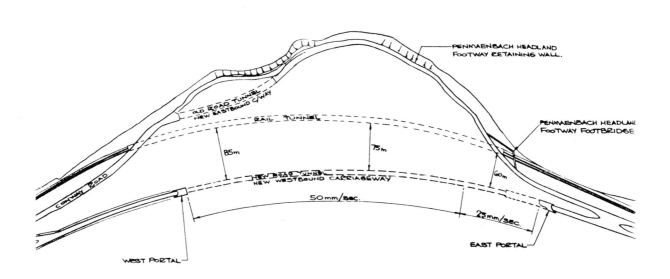

PENMAENBACH TUNNELS LAYOUT

FIGURE 1

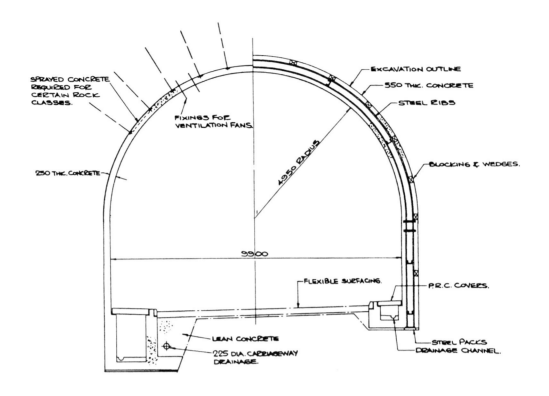

SPRAYED CONCRETE
REQUIRED FOR
CERTAIN ROCK
CLASSES.

FIXINGS FOR
VENTILATION FANS.

EXCAVATION OUTLINE

550 THK. CONCRETE

STEEL RIBS

250 THK. CONCRETE

4950 RADIUS

BLOCKING & WEDGES.

9900

FLEXIBLE SURFACING.

P.R.C. COVERS.

LEAN CONCRETE

225 DIA. CARRIAGEWAY
DRAINAGE.

STEEL PACKS
DRAINAGE CHANNEL.

SECTION OF CENTRAL SECTION.

FIGURE 2

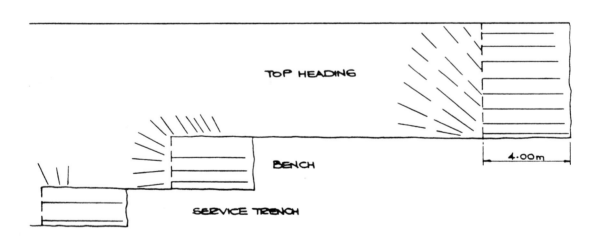

TOP HEADING

BENCH

SERVICE TRENCH

4·00 m

SECTION WEST-EAST SHOWING BLASTING

FIGURE 3

394

Figure 4

NONEL GT/T DETONATOR DETAILS

Period Number	Delay Time ms	Interval ms	Standard Tube Lengths m
0	25	-	}
1-12	100-1200	100	}
14,16,18,20	1400-2000	200	}6.0,7.8
			)
25,30,35,40,45}			)
50,55,60 }	2500-6000	500	}

TOP HEADING BLAST PATTERN
AND EXPLOSIVE USAGE

FIGURE 5

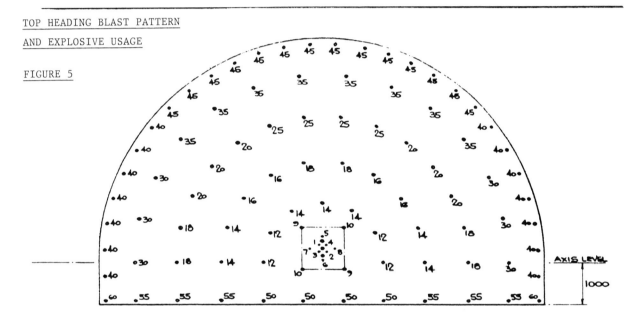

TOP HEADING BLAST SCHEME

	No. OF HOLES	GELEMEX kg.	QUARREX kg.	GURIT kg.
SIZE		32×200	32×600	17×725
PERIMETER HOLES	28	7 (1-STICK/HOLE)	—	24 (5-STICKS/HOLE)
BULK HOLES	49	11	147 (6-STICKS/HOLE)	—
LIFTER HOLES	12	3	36 (6-STICKS/HOLE)	—
CUT HOLES	8	2	26 (6-STICKS/HOLE)	—
TOTAL	97	23	209	24

Figure 6

DETAILS OF IMMEDIATE VIBRATION RECORD

Date of Blast: 28/Nov/86   T ime of Blast: 20:10

Distance from Blast to Geophones - 75m

Maximum Instantaneous Charge - 3.5Kg

Tunnel Location Number	MAXIMUM PEAK LEVELS	
	Component mm/s	Vector mm/s
	(Time in seconds)	
10	19.7 (0.123)	
10	12.9 (0.120)	19.9 (0.123)
10	9.9 (0.108)	
9	2.4 (0.103)	
9	2.1 (0.101)	2.7 (0.103)
9	1.4 (1.602)	
8	1.4 (1.1619)	
8	1.2 (0.147)	1.4 (1.619)
8	0.9 (0.245)	
11	7.7 (0.139)	
11	6.8 (0.110)	9.3 (0.139)
11	5.0 (0.139)	

Figure 7a

VIBRATION MONITORING EQUIPMENT - SET-UP DETAILS

Date	01/Nov/86
Geophone Sensitivity	28.8mV/mm/s
Sampling Rate	3214Hz
Total Record Time	7s
Total Plot Duration	7s
Pre-trigger Time	0.1s
Trigger Level	1mm/s

CED Channels 0-2 at Tunnel Location 10

CED Channels 3-5 at Tunnel Location 11

CED Channels 6-8 at Tunnel Location 12

CED Channels 9-11 at Tunnel Location 13

<u>Figure 7b</u>

DETAILS OF VIBRATION RECORDED

Date of Blast: 03/Nov/86   Time of Blast: 20:16

CED Channel No	Tunnel Location No	MAXIMUM PEAK LEVELS Component mm/s	Vector mm/s
		(Time in seconds)	
0	10	15.2 (2.283)	
1	10	9.7 (2.601)	16.7 (2.283)
2	10	11.2 (2.227)	
3	11	7.7 (4.289)	
4	11	9.2 (0.089)	10.3 (1.994)
5	11	6.6 (0.075)	
6	12	6.2 (0.089)	
7	12	7.2 (0.093)	8.4 (0.116)
8	12	2.9 (0.094)	
9	13	4.6 (0.091)	
10	13	3.6 (0.072)	5.8 (0.072)
11	13	3.0 (0.072)	

397

DATE OF BLAST:- 03/Nov/86   TIME OF BLAST:- 20:16

FIG. 7c   RECORD OF VIBRATION TRACE

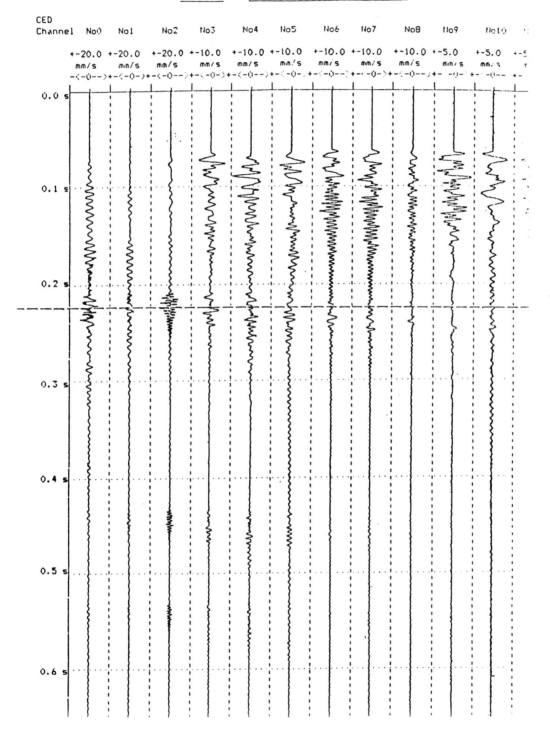

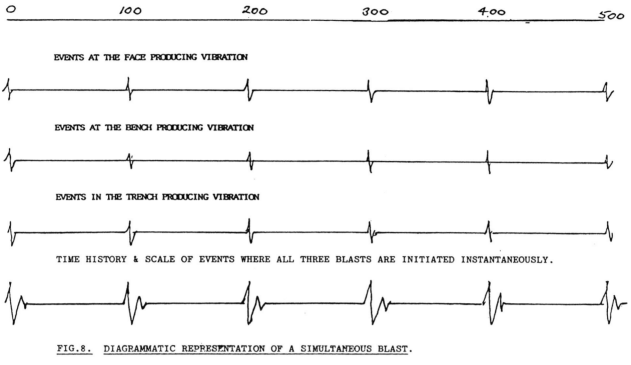

TIME FROM INITIATION (MILLISECONDS)

0   100   200   300   400   500

EVENTS AT THE FACE PRODUCING VIBRATION

EVENTS AT THE BENCH PRODUCING VIBRATION

EVENTS IN THE TRENCH PRODUCING VIBRATION

TIME HISTORY & SCALE OF EVENTS WHERE ALL THREE BLASTS ARE INITIATED INSTANTANEOUSLY.

FIG.8. DIAGRAMMATIC REPRESENTATION OF A SIMULTANEOUS BLAST.

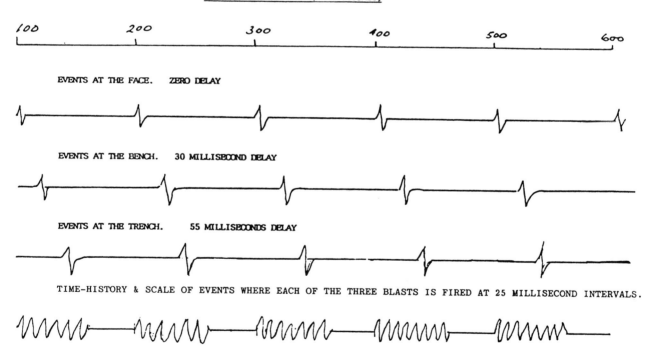

TIME FROM INITIATION (MILLISECONDS)

100   200   300   400   500   600

EVENTS AT THE FACE.   ZERO DELAY

EVENTS AT THE BENCH.   30 MILLISECOND DELAY

EVENTS AT THE TRENCH.   55 MILLISECONDS DELAY

TIME-HISTORY & SCALE OF EVENTS WHERE EACH OF THE THREE BLASTS IS FIRED AT 25 MILLISECOND INTERVALS.

FIG.9. DIAGRAMMATIC REPRESENTATION OF A SEQUENCED BLAST.

399

Undersea cable tunnel between Singapore Mainland and Pulau Seraya—design and construction by the immersed tube method

C. R. Weeks B.Sc., C.Eng., M.I.C.E.
Mott, Hay & Anderson, Croydon, Surrey, United Kingdom
N. S. Rasmussen M.Sc., M.Ing.F.
Christiani & Nielsen A/S, Copenhagen, Denmark

SYNOPSIS

An undersea cable tunnel was completed in 1987 to a very tight schedule for the Public Utilities Board, Singapore, to service their new thermal power station on the island of Pulau Seraya. The tunnel is 2.6 km in length and was constructed in up to 25m depth of water by the immersed tube method. The tunnel is 6.5m wide by 3.7m high and is designed to accommodate 230 kV 500 MVA power transmission cables, potable water mains and special maintenance vehicles.

This tunnel is the first immersed tube to be built in Singapore. It proved very successful in the mixed geology along the tunnel route, which ranged from soft marine clays to hard sedimentary rocks.

The tunnel was fabricated from precast concrete units, 3.5m long, which were joined and post-tensioned longitudinally into 100m long elements. The elements were launched from a platform supported by heavy lift jacks and floated to their sinking location with the aid of special buoyancy tanks.

One of the world's most powerful cutter suction dredgers was used for the majority of the dredging, with the exception of some very hard rock which required underwater blasting.

This paper describes all stages of the project from conception to completion of construction.

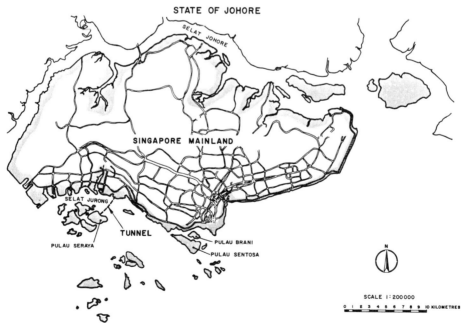

Fig. 1 General Location Plan

PROJECT DESCRIPTION

The Project

As part of a comprehensive policy for the development of electricity generation in Singapore, the Public Utilities Board is currently engaged on the construction of a new 750 MW offshore power station located, for environmental reasons, on the island of Pulau Seraya. The first 250 MW generator came on stream in 1987. When complete the station will be one of the major sources of electricity for Singapore.

Pulau Seraya lies approximately 2.6km south of the Jurong area of mainland Singapore (Fig 1). In order to connect the new power station to the mainland transmission grid, it is necessary to lay very large power cables across the intervening stretch of water, namely the East Jurong Fairway, (Selat Jurong).

Preliminary Concepts

At the conceptual stage of the power station project, the Public Utilities Board ruled out overhead structures for practical, safety and aesthetic reasons. Other alternatives, including undersea tunnel options, were considered and the conclusions reached at that time favoured armoured submarine cables.

In 1983 tenders were called for the laying of six power circuits buried directly in trenches in the seabed. The tenders proved to be very expensive, for two principal reasons. Firstly, the cables themselves are considerably more expensive than their land-laid counterparts. Secondly, the East Jurong Fairway is a very busy waterway, being the main sea route to Jurong Port, thus the Port of Singapore Authority required the cables to be buried in deep trenches in the seabed to provide an allowance for future dredging of the channel. This was exacerbated by the need to lay each circuit in a separate trench for future maintenance and as a safety precaution against accidental snagging by ships anchors.

Following receipt of the tenders for submarine cables, the Public Utilities Board immediately reviewed the alternatives and, in August 1984, appointed Mott, Hay & Anderson Asia Pte to carry out a Feasibility Study for a cable tunnel.

FEASIBILITY STUDY

Objectives

The main objectives of the Feasibility Study were to provide essential data and recommendations in sufficient detail to enable a decision to be made by the Public Utilities Board on the implementation of an undersea tunnel. To this end the study undertook the comparison of several different landfall locations, both on the island and mainland, and various tunnel routes. The corresponding land routes for the cables to link to the main grid were also considered.

A fundamental aspect of the study was to determine the optimum type of tunnel construction, i.e. bored tunnel or immersed tube.

Geology and Site Investigations

The bedrock of the area is the Jurong Formation, of Upper Triassic age, which comprises a variable sedimentary sequence of mudstones, siltstones and sandstones with occasional conglomerate bands.

Intense folding has affected the formation giving rise to a structural strike orientated NW – SE and a set of conjugate faults aligned parallel to and perpendicular to the strike direction. Bedding dips of approximately 70° were observed.

In the fresh condition, the rock is competent. It is characteristic of the Jurong Formation for deep weathering to have taken place, thus reducing the rock to firm clays and sands.

The more recent Kallang Formation overlies the Jurong Formation for most of the relevant area, and consists of marine, estuarine, alluvial and reef deposits.

Both on the island and mainland extensive land

reclamation has taken place, resulting in layers of highly variable fill material at the tunnel landfall locations.

As an integral part of the Feasibility Study a further soils investigation and marine survey was commissioned. A decision on the tunnel route corridor was made in sufficient time to concentrate the site investigation within the chosen area, thus maximising the usefulness of the relatively expensive marine boreholes. Six such boreholes were undertaken together with a bathymetric survey, and a geophysical survey to determine the depth of weathering and superficial deposits. Boreholes were also sunk at the chosen landfall locations.

The site investigation confirmed the anticipated variable nature of the geology, revealing fresh rock outcropping on the seabed on both sides of the channel, soft marine clay close inshore and zones of deep weathering towards the centre of the Fairway.

Outline Planning and Programme

It was recognised from the outset of the Feasibility Study that the actual amount of time available for the Project was exceedingly limited. Therefore the success of any tunnel proposal would depend upon a short construction period with a minimum risk of serious delays. The overall Project Programme is indicated in Fig 3.

The conclusion reached during the study was that construction of a bored tunnel was unlikely to be achieved within the available period. The principle factors in this conclusion were the variability of the Jurong Formation and the equipping of the tunnel, the majority of which could only take place after completion of excavation.

Conversely it was concluded that an immersed tube tunnel would be feasible, using the basic well-proven techniques combined with some innovative

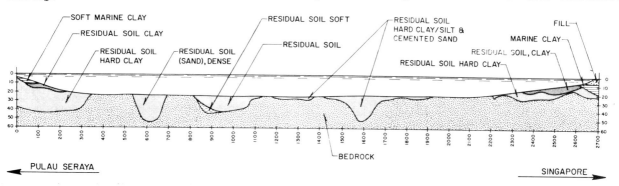

Fig. 2 Longitudinal section showing geology

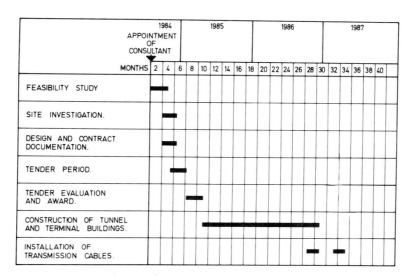

Fig. 3 Overall Project Programme

engineering. This method of construction was felt to be less vulnerable than a bored tunnel to delays caused by unforeseen ground conditions.

The outline planning also included the necessary tunnel services and in particular addressed the problems of tunnel ventilation, the cooling requirements of the power transmission circuits and the protection and safety aspects.

IMMERSED TUBE TUNNELLING

The Fundamental Concepts

The immersed tunnel technique can be suitable for tunnels under waterways, such as rivers, estuaries, canals, harbours, sea inlets and straits, where the waterway provides the mode of transportation of the structural elements of the tunnel.

An immersed tube tunnel is constructed of discrete elements of the tunnel structure which are pre-fabricated on dry land or in a dry dock or on a launching structure. The ends of each tunnel element are sealed with temporary bulkheads and the elements are launched, or the dry dock flooded, and the elements are towed, with or without buoyancy aids as necessary, either to a holding and fitting out area or direct to their sinking location, depending upon the detailed planning of the particular project.

Once at their sinking location each element, or the buoyancy aid, is ballasted and, under guidance from a purpose made sinking rig or lay barge, the element is lowered into a previously dredged and prepared trench in the seabed. After sinking, each element is joined to the previous element, the water remaining between the bulkheads of adjoining elements is pumped out. The foundation can either be a screeded gravel bed or a jetted sand. The trench is backfilled around the tunnel using selected material and the whole is normally protected by a layer of rock armour. The bulkheads are removed and the interior fitting out of the tunnel is then completed.

At each end of the immersed tunnel section the elements abut a length of tunnel constructed in situ, normally within a cofferdam which extends into the water.

Principal Types of Immersed Tunnel

There are two principal types of immersed tunnel construction. Broadly, they are the circular steel shell developed mainly in North America and the rectangular reinforced concrete structures developed in Europe.

Circular Steel Construction

The steel shell tunnels are often constructed by the double skin principal. The inner, structural, shell is prefabricated in short lengths which are then welded together at a slipway location to form the required length of element. Secondary steel stiffening is then added and the external steel skin, which may be ultimately sacrificial, is fitted and welded into place. Holes through which concrete can be placed would be provided in the roof skin. A certain amount of concrete would be placed in the base of the element to ballast and stabilise it for launching. This type of tunnel element would normally be launched sideways and then more concrete would be cast and final preparation made for sinking. Normally this type of tunnel element is lowered directly onto a fully prepared and screeded mattress of gravel. Variants of this arrangement employ a single structural steel shell with internal and/or external concrete linings.

Rectangular Concrete Construction

This form of construction differs radically from the steel construction.

With the exception of tunnels having a very small cross-sectional area, the concrete tunnels are too heavy to be built on slipways or for other forms of launching in the true sense. They are thus built in a dry dock, which can be either an existing facility, or purpose built for the particular project. The dry dock is flooded to enable the tunnel elements to be floated out.

This form of tunnel has been placed sucessfully on a screeded gravel mattress, but the more usual method of founding is to place the element on temporary bearing pads and to inject hydraulically placed sand beneath the element to create a tailor-made foundation.

The concrete tunnels are jointed by means of a flexible rubber gasket mounted on one end of each element which bears against a flat plate mounted at the end of the previously placed element. The rubber gasket has a soft tip to provide an initial seal and a harder body to accommodate the full hydrostatic forces. This gasket is known as the 'Gina' profile. The element being sunk is moved longitudinally until the soft nose of the gasket is compressed. Water is then pumped out of the space between the temporary bulkheads and the hydrostatic force at the exposed end of the new element acts to fully compress the gasket,

Choice of Tunnel Type

Both methods of construction were reviewed and it was concluded that the more economically viable method would be the reinforced concrete rectangular section. The perceived disadvantages of the steel circular shell were the cost of the steel and fabrication, and the shape of the cross section is less favourable for the accommodation of the power circuits and maintenance vehicle. The circular cross section would inevitably be considerably higher than the rectangular section, adding significantly to the cost of dredging.

OUTLINE DESIGN AND CONTRACT DOCUMENTATION

Outline Design Concepts

The route chosen for the tunnel was only marginally longer than the shortest possible undersea crossing and had the advantage of good working site areas at both landfalls.

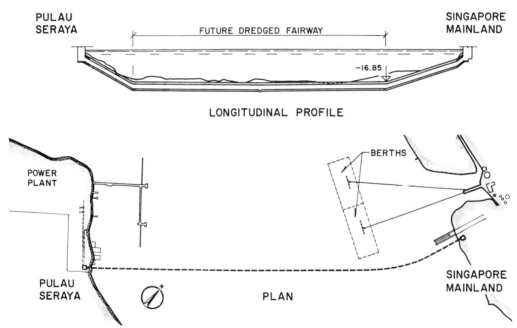

Fig. 4 Plan and longitudinal profile of tunnel

thus creating a fully watertight seal. When the temporary bulkheads have been removed the joint is further sealed internally by means of another rubber seal, shaped as the Greek letter Omega and clamped across the joint between the elements using heavy steel plates on the Omega seal flanges.

To satisfy the Port of Singapore requirements, the tunnel structure, including rock armour had to be set to a depth of 16m below chart datum, over the full width of the Fairway channel. This resulted in having to dredge the tunnel trench to depths of 11 metres below seabed in places. On either side of the buoyed channel the tunnel was located below the level of the existing seabed

(Fig 4). Particular attention was given to minimising the overall height of the tunnel structure. The section was designed to have negative buoyancy when launched, thus saving the height which would have been needed for additional ballast concrete. Because of the quantity of elements to be placed, the use of large buoyancy tanks was considered economically feasible.

Terminal buildings form the entrances to the tunnel at each end and house all the mechanical and electrical equipment necessary for the function of the tunnel and the cooling of the power circuits. The terminal buildings also include a cable jointing basement where the power circuits laid through the tunnel are jointed to the landward cables; Fig. 6 shows the transition structure for the power circuits between tunnel level and the jointing basement.

Fig. 5 Terminal Building at Pulau Seraya.

Fig. 6 Power circuit supports at basement level.

Type of Contract

The basic choice was between a fully detailed Engineer's design or a design and construct package based on an outline performance specification.

Even before the Feasibility Study was commenced, it was appreciated that the overall programme restraints precluded the possibility of preparing a fully detailed Engineer's design prior to calling tenders. On the other hand, the nature of the Project and the particular requirements of the Public Utilities Board in regard to the power circuits meant that a fully design/construct package was not desirable.

A two stage approach was therefore adopted. The first stage was to prepare general conditions of contract, general specifications and a comprehensive set of design criteria and performance specifications. Tenders were then called with this initial documentation, meanwhile a preliminary design for the Engineer's Preferred Scheme was completed by the Consultants during the early part of the tender period. The additional information thus prepared was issued to tenderers and gave more specific details as to the Board's requirements. The advantages of this approach were that the tenderers were given additional time to prepare their tenders based upon their own special expertise and evaluation of the problems, whilst enabling the particular requirements of the Board to be made known to them in sufficient detail to ensure that the tenders would be suitable in respect of the engineering details. It also enabled the Consultants to pursue outline planning consent with the Singapore planning authorities in parallel with tendering procedures.

On award of contract, the Contractor was able to complete the detailed design concurrently with mobilisation and construction of temporary works on site, thus saving valuable time.

The Contract documents also allowed the flexibility for the tenderers to propose minor or more radical alternative tunnelling solutions, including a bored tunnel. In the event, a number of minor modifications to the Engineer's Preferred Scheme were received but no radical changes and no bored tunnel options were offered.

Engineer's Preferred Scheme

Civil Works

The immersed tunnel is the most significant part of the works, being 2.6 km in length. It is made up of 26 no. elements each 100m long. The tunnel is rectangular in cross section, of approximate dimensions 6.5 m wide by 3.7 m high. The tunnel is divided longitudinally into two separate bores as a fire safety precaution. Access between bores is provided at 100 m intervals via fire doors. Fire doors are also provided at each end of each tunnel bore, where the tunnel joins the terminal buildings.

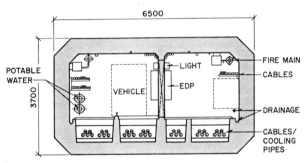

Fig.7 Cross-section of cable tunnel

Seraya Power Station is to be developed in two stages. For Stage I, 4 no. 230 kV 500 MVA oil filled power circuits have been installed in the tunnel. Ultimately 7 no. such circuits will be provided.

The bores are slightly unequal in width; the larger bore accommodates 4 no. power circuits, with a further 3 no. circuits in the smaller bore. In addition, the larger bore contains two 200 mm diameter potable water mains and space for the battery driven, rail-guided maintenance vehicles. Both bores contain lighting, fire detection and protection and ancilliary cables and services. Some additional space is provided in the smaller bore for future services (Fig 7).

The in situ lengths of tunnel, each approximately 25 m long, form a transition between the immersed tunnel and the terminal buildings. They were constructed conventionally by the cut and cover method within steel sheet piled cofferdams. The seaward end was bulkheaded and flooded for the floating in of the adjacent immersed tunnel element.

The design of the immersed tunnel was carried out in accordance with British Standards. For the concrete work the most severe of BS 5400 and CP 110 was used. For major steelwork, such a shear keys, BS 5400 was used, whereas for minor steelwork, such as temporary bulkheads, BS 449 was adhered to.

The longitudinal prestressing of the tunnel elements complies with the stress requirements outlined in the following conditions (negative signs represent compression):

(i)   Normal operation condition:
      Stress requirement - 2.0 to -16.0 MPa
(ii) Extreme operation condition:
      Stress requirement 0.0 to -16.0 MPa
(iii) Accidental condition:
      Stress requirement 2.3 to -16.0 MPa

The condition (ii) is a combination of (i) and a load from a sunken ship of 50 kN/m^2 over a length of 20 m anywhere along the tunnel, or a dragging anchor load of 4000 kN acting perpendicular to the tunnel at roof level. The condition (iii) consists of (ii) and flooding of the tunnel.

The vertical and lateral restraint between adjacent tunnel elements was provided by steel shear keys and pockets.

Electrical and Mechanical Works

The tunnel is fully equipped with its own support services as follows:-

-   Fresh air mechanical ventilation system
-   Normal lighting and battery invertor emergency lighting.
-   Pumped drainage system
-   Fire detection system
-   Medium density total foam flooding fire protection system, additional portable fire extinguishers and breathing apparatus.

- Telephone system and leaky feeder cables for portable radio communication
- LV power supplies and socket outlets.
- Closed circuit cooling water system for the 230 KV power circuit cables.
- Battery driven rail-guided maintenance vehicles

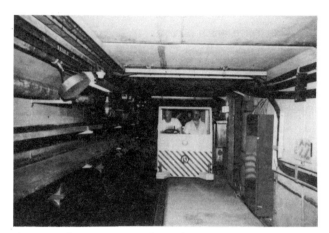

Fig. 8 Maintenance vehicle in larger tunnel bore.

The fresh air mechanical ventilation system consists of six axial flow fans, three for each bore located at the Seraya Terminal Building. The fans are all 2 - stage, 2 - speed and are arranged as 2 duty/1 standby.

In the normal, unmanned condition the fans will be run at a low setting, sufficient air movement being created to keep the tunnel from becoming stale. Some of the heat generated by the 230 kV power cables will be removed by the ventilation flow.

When full tunnel lighting is required during inspection or maintenance work the air speed in the tunnel will be increased accordingly. On the highest setting the air flow is 5 m/s, for use in emergency smoke clearance, and the fans are reversible.

The power transmission cables were laid directly onto the invert of the tunnel in preformed troughs, with two 90mm diameter HDPE cooling water pipes per circuit laid immediately on top of the cables. The whole was protected by cement stabilised thermal sand (Fig.7).

The cable cooling is by a closed circuit system with cooling towers at each terminal building.

Temperature and flow are computer monitored.

The whole of the tunnel services are fully automatic and are designed for minimum maintenance, with comprehensive remote monitoring facilities.

DETAILED DESIGN AND CONSTRUCTION

Award of contract

In late April 1985, after international tendering, the Public Utilities Board of Singapore awarded to Christiani & Nielsen A/S the contract for the design and construction of the tunnel, including the two terminal buildings and the mechanical and electrical installations in the tunnel.

The contract value was of the order of 80 million Singapore Dollars, with the electrical and mechanical installations representing approximately 25% thereof.

Christiani & Nielsen's proposal adhered closely to the Engineer's Preferred Scheme.

The contract stipulated that it should be possible to pull the first high-voltage power cable through the tunnel by mid September 1986, only 16.5 months after award of contract.

Detailed Design

In order to meet this time schedule, close coordination of the design and the construction methods was required, in particular for the immersed tube tunnel section. The detailed design of this section and the planning of the construction methods were consequently done within the Christiani & Nielsen organization, while Ove Arup & Partners, London were engaged for the design of the terminal buildings and of the mechanical and electrical installations.

In the design of the immersed tunnel, the bending moments and shear forces in the longitudinal direction were calculated by use of a soil-structure interaction model, from which the

408

number of tendons was determined for each tunnel element.

The number of tendons per element varied from 19 to 37 depending on the sub-soil conditions along the tunnel. As reports on these conditions became available, from observations during dredging and from supplementary geotechnical investigations carried out during the construction period, the required minimum number of tendons for each element was determined.

CONSTRUCTION OF TUNNEL

General

As shown in Fig.9, the terminal buildings represented a relatively minor part of the works. These buildings are conventional reinforced concrete structures, having up to two storeys above ground and two levels of basement.

For the construction it was necessary to run five worksites simultaneously, as shown in Fig.10.

- a worksite for the Terminal Building on Mainland Singapore
- a casting yard for the fabrication of tunnel segments.
- two marine lifts for assembling and launching of tunnel elements.
- a marine tunnel sinking and founding section
- a worksite for the Terminal Building on Pulau Seraya

In addition, major temporary works were constructed off site in local steel fabrication yards. The buoyancy tank units were fabricated in a dry dock in Jurong shipyard.

SECTION	EXCAVATION CU.M.	REINFORCED CONCRETE CU.M.	SAND FOUNDATION CU.M.	BACKFILLING CU.M.	ARMOUR ROCK CU.M.
TERMINAL BUILDING MAINLAND SINGAPORE	18,000	6,400	—	—	—
UNDERSEA TUNNEL	463,000	27,500	50,000	90,000	75,000
TERMINAL BUILDING PULAU SERAYA	19,000	6,900	—	—	—
TOTAL	500,000	40,800	50,000	90,000	75,000

Fig. 9 Main quantities - civil works

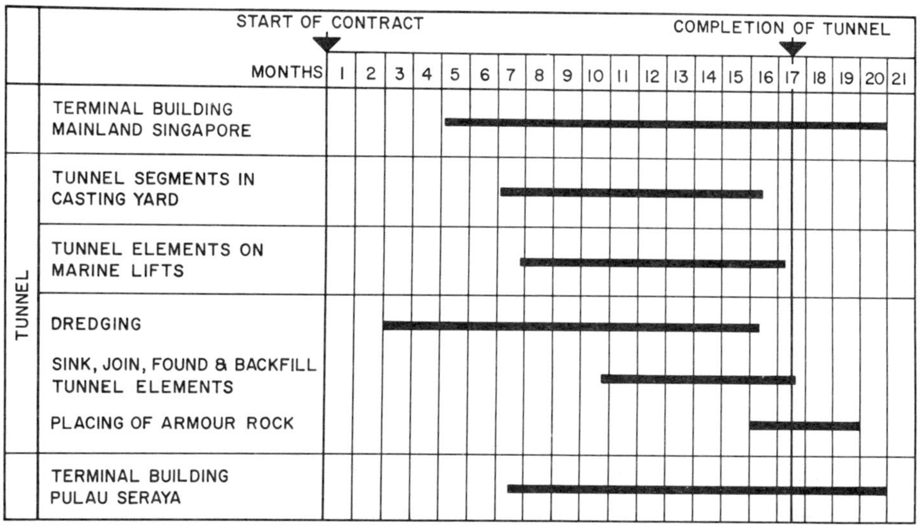

Fig. 10 Construction programme

409

Tunnel Element Prefabrication

Precast Segments

The Public Utilities Board were particularly concerned to achieve a dry tunnel which would require minimal structural maintenance during a design life of at least 25 years.

The relatively small cross-section of the tunnel made it possible to use a special method of ensuring a watertight structure without the need for a complete waterproof membrane. The tunnel was formed of precast segments. Each segment was 3.5 m long, consisting of the whole tunnel cross section, and was cast in the vertical position (Fig.11) without any construction joints between floor, walls and roof. This made for ease of placing the concrete, minimised differential shrinkage stresses and associated cracking and resulted in reinforced concrete of high quality and complete watertightness. Concrete mix design concentrated on achieving a dense impermeable concrete, whilst satisfying the high early strength required for early stripping of formwork. Using cements readily available in Singapore, a blend of OPC and sulphate-resisting cement gave a C_3A content of approximately 6%, considered suitable for immersion in seawater, a strength in the order of 12 MPa at the stripping time of 16 hours and enabled the heat of hydration temperature, in the maximum 520 mm thick sections, to be kept below 60°C. To achieve the temperature requirement, the mixing water was chilled to 4°C. A plasticiser was used to aid placing of the concrete.

The tunnel segments, which weighed between 92 and 98 tons, were cast in rigidly held steel forms.

The reinforcing cages with the required number of ducts for the prestressing cables were fully preassembled on steel jigs.

The concrete was batched on site and pumped into the forms using mobile concrete pumps.

Fig. 11 Casting yard

The forms were stripped after minimum 12 hours and the segments were cured under tailor-made plasticised covers for another 4 days before they were transported to a storage area and transposed into a horizontal position.

Marine Lifts

Two marine lifts were constructed in front of the casting yard and two 50 t gantry cranes, working in tandem, brought the tunnel segments out on the marine lift platforms. These platforms were 120 m long and 10 m wide and each marine lift was suspended on 12 steel cables and hydraulic jacks, each of a capacity of 3500 kN. The platforms could be lowered and raised 8 m at a speed of 2 m per hour. Access to the marine lifts and supplementary working area was provided by two 150 m long, 8 m wide, jetties. (Fig.12).

Jointing of Segments

After having been grit blasted on their end faces, 27 no. normal and two end tunnel segments were lined up on the marine lifts, to form the 100m long elements, leaving a 20 mm wide space between each segment. These spaces were grouted by means of an expanding cementitious grout. The grouted joints were covered, at the external faces, by a narrow double waterproof membrane protected by a band of 20 mm plywood. (Fig.13)

410

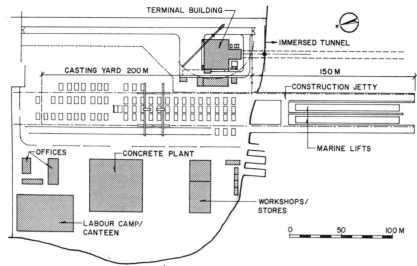

Fig.12 Layout of work site

In order to prevent ingress of grout into the cable ducts, inflatable Ductubes were used in the ducts. An injecting tube system to enable epoxy resin injection at a later stage, if required, was installed along the joint perimeter. All joints have, however, proved watertight without injection.

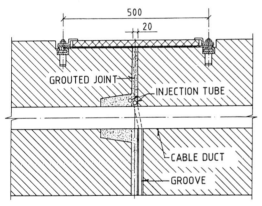

Fig. 13 Joint between segments

Post-tensioning and completion of Elements

Prefabricated tendons were pulled through the cable ducts as soon as the joints had been completed, and stressing of these tendons was started 12 hours after the last joint had been grouted. Each individual tendon was stressed simultaneously from both ends using 2500 kN jacks.

Each element end segment was provided with a permanent steel shroud, with shear dowels or pockets, cast integrally with the end of the segment. A temporary steel bulkhead and watertight door were also provided.

Steel plates were welded onto the steel shrouds at the element ends and a rubber gasket was mounted at one end of each tunnel element, (Fig. 14).

Fig. 14   Gina gasket and temporary bulkhead.

Finally, most of the mechanical and electrical installations were mounted in each tunnel element on a modular basis, thus minimizing the work to be done within the tunnel after the elements were in place. A notable exception being the main tunnel services feeder cables, to avoid an excessive number of joints.

Buoyancy Tanks

The optimum utilization of the tunnel cross-section for permanent use, and the degree to

411

which the tunnel elements were prefabricated, resulted in the tunnel elements at launch having practically their full permanent weight, i.e. a buoyancy aid was needed in order to make the tunnel elements float temporarily during their transport from the marine lift area to the final place in the tunnel trench. This buoyancy aid consisted of a steel buoyancy tank unit weighing 350 tons, which was floated in on top of the tunnel element while this was temporarily lowered by means of the marine lift.

Fig. 15   Tunnel Element being lowered on marine lift

Marine Works

The bulk of the tunnel trench had been dredged prior to the start of sinking, but hard rock was encountered over a length of approximately 850 m. Drilling and blasting of this rock was required prior to completion of the dredging.

Whilst each tunnel element/buoyancy tank assembly was interconnected and the last preparation of the element was being done, the relevant tunnel trench section was cleaned of any accumulated silt, and the lay-barge (Fig. 17) was warped 100 m forward along the tunnel line.

The tunnel element/buoyancy tank assemblies were towed from the marine lift area to the lay-barge at the turn of the tide and, after ballasting with water, lowered into the tunnel trench by means of two standard cranes.

The assemblies were landed on temporary steel supports, joined to the previously placed tunnel

element, and brought into specified line and elevation by operation of hydraulic jacks mounted in the temporary steel supports.

The permanent support of the tunnel was provided by a sand foundation hydraulically placed by the Christiani & Nielsen Method. The sand/water mixing took place on the lay-barge.

The sand backfilling around and over the tunnel was also placed by means of equipment on the lay-barge. The 1m thick layer of rock armour was placed from a separate barge.

Fig. 16   Towing of tunnel element

Fig. 17 Lay-barge

SUMMARY

This cable tunnel is remarkable for a number of reasons:

- the speed with which the whole project was undertaken from conception to completion of construction.

- the length of the tunnel, 2,600 m,
  of which 1,800 m have a floor level
  23 m or more below Mean Sea Level,
  beneath a very busy waterway

- the extent to which assembly line
  methods were used for fabrication
  of the tunnel elements, and the
  high quality, 100% watertight
  concrete works achieved thereby

- the extent to which the permanent
  civil works and the mechanical and
  electrical installations were
  completed prior to launching. In
  consequence the first high voltage
  cable could be pulled through the
  tunnel only 3 weeks after sinking
  of the last tunnel element

- the speed with which the launching,
  floating out, sinking, founding and
  backfilling took place. 26 tunnel
  elements were placed and backfilled
  in 27 weeks from March to September
  1986.

- the extent to which the tunnel
  services are controlled
  automatically and remotely
  monitored to reduce on-site
  inspections.

The Pre-metro link to the left bank of the River Scheldt by means of a bentonite shield

A. Wittemans
E. Hemeryckx
Premetro M.I.V.A., Antwerp, Belgium

Synopsis.

The decision to use a bentonite shield for the driving of the tunnels under the River Scheldt was a result of eight years of successful experience with the shield method in Antwerp. However, for the present project preliminary soil investigations, carried out in 1978, showed a geological profile different from that previously encountered.

In addition to the sandy subsoil, the shield used for the construction of the Scheldt tunnels had to cope with the Boom clay layers and the presence of large loafshaped carbonate concretions, called septaria. This was the main reason for the consideration of a new concept and the adaptation of the shield.

The cutting head was substantially modified in order to reduce the clay adhesion and to facilitate the crushing of the septaria. In addition five breast plates can support the face when driving is at a standstill.

Shield equipment is provided with an installation which allows automatic recording at regular intervals of the most important data during the tunnelling works.

After a 16 week initial tunnelling period at low progress with a prototype shield most of the difficulties were overcome. Subsequently progress was considerably increased.

Shield passage under the quay wall section and under historically valuable buildings was carried out without substantial settlement.

The improved working techniques and the increased slurry injection pressures have contributed to excellent results.

1. THE PRE METRO NETWORK.

Fig. 1 shows the layout of the premetro network.

The present premetro network has 2 lines with a total length of 15km double track, including 21 stations.

Only 2.5km double track is operative. The main construction of the remainder of the network is nearly finished with exception of the 1.7km "Leien" section, together with its 2 stations, which are being designed at present.

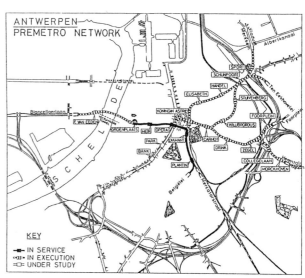

2. DESCRIPTION OF THE PREMETRO SECTION TO THE LEFT BANK OF THE RIVER SCHELDT.

The entire project has been divided into three sections relative to the location of the works, the construction methods envisaged and the available budget : the Left Bank section with a station, a tunnel and open ramp, the section under the river Scheldt and the Groenplaats section.

Fig. 2 shows the horizontal Alignment.

Photo 1 shows an aerial view of the city of Antwerp.

2.1. The Left Bank section.

The Left Bank section comprises a 60m long and 28m wide station consisting of a ticket hall at the upper level and the platforms at the lower level situated at 18m below street level.

2.2. The Tunnel under the river Scheldt.

The tunnel under the river Scheldt is bounded by the Frederik van Eeden station at the Left Bank and by the Groenplaats station at the Right Bank.
Construction started on March 4, 1985. The contractor for this section is the Joint Venture R.O.L.O., represented by 3 Belgian and 1 German firm. The initial works comprised the installation and erection of the shield and the associated preparatory works.

The Scheldt tunnel consists of two adjacent shafts, each having an internal diameter of 5.70m. Both shafts are constructed using the shield method.

The horizontal alignment of the tunnel is mostly straight or has a 1,250m radius, except in the Frederik van Eeden area, where the tunnel has two 400m radius curves and in the Groenplaats area, where the tunnel describes a 600m radius curve.

The total length of the single track is 2,010m of which 2 x 375m is situated under the river bed. The superelevation is a maximum of 5 %.

The horizontal tunnel section under the surface of the river is about 32m beneath average high water level. The effective protective soil cover above this tunnel section is about 7 m.

Vertical security shafts are built behind the river embankment.

2.3. The Groenplaats - Oude Koornmarkt section.

Extension of the east-west axis of the Premetro towards the Left Bank includes complete modification of the Groenplaats station. Works started on this section on February 16, 1987.

3. GEOLOGY AND SOIL INVESTIGATION.

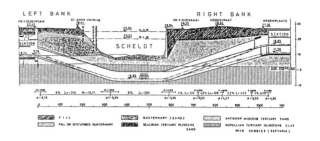

Fig. 3 shows the vertical alignment and longitudinal geological section.

An extensive soil investigation with boreholes and seismic soundings has been undertaken as the shield excavation had to be carried out in different ground layers, including the stiff clay with septaria.

From the preliminary explorations, it appeared that the substrata had the following geological characteristics :

- Fill.

  On both river banks a top layer of fill and disturbed soil with a thickness of about 7m is present. Immediately behind the quay wall on the Right Bank, fill is also found, down to the foundation level of the quay wall.

  On the Left Bank, the underground remains of an old fortress, built in the 18th century, were found.

- Quaternary.

  On the Left River Bank, Quaternary layers consisting of peat, clay, silt and sand are situated from a depth of about 7m down to a depth of about 20m.

  On the Left Bank, two ground water bearing strata were found. In the upper stratum, the groundwater table is situated at 1.5m under the surface and varies with rainfall. Due to the existence of an impervious clay layer under the peat in the lower stratum the ground water is under pressure. This pressure fluctuates with the tides in the river.

  Relieving the water pressure would cause consolidation of the peat layers with consequent serious settlements at street level. Therefore relieving the ground water pressure was not feasible.

- Tertiary.

  Scaldian pliocene tertiary.

  Under the Right River Bank pliocene glauconitic sand with shells was encountered from a depth of about 7m down to a depth of about 9m.

  Antwerp miocene tertiary.

  This dense layer of alluvial sand, containing hard shells and shell pieces, is found both on the Left and Right Bank, up to a depth of 25 m.

  Rupellian oligocene tertiary (Boom type clay.

  From a depth of about 25m down to a depth of more than 50m under the river bank level, the Boom clay is found.

  Calcareous horizons with septaria occur at different levels within the clay. The septaria found in layers are large loaf-shaped concretions with a diameter up to 2 m.

Photo 2 shows a septaria.

Compression tests performed on septaria indicate that the compressive strength of this material may be as high as 100 MN/m^2.

4. TUNNEL UNDER THE RIVER SCHELDT.

4.1. Launching conditions.

a) The shield launching shaft is incorporated into the Frederik van Eeden station.

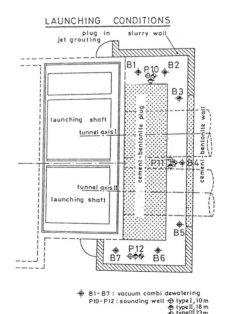

Fig. 4 : Launching conditions

Outside the station a concrete-bentonite plug is formed reaching down to the clay layer.

The plug is constructed in separate panels. Absolute watertightness cannot be guarenteed because of minor movements at the joints. In order to provide watertightness a slurry wall screen was constructed at about 3m distance.

The connection of the slurry walls of the screen and the walls of the station was ensured by means of overlapping jet-grout piles.

The soil between the plug and the screen, was dewatered in order to remove the water pressure from the launching plug.

The lowering of the ground water inside the screen area involved a simultaneous artificial ground water recharge outside the screen.

b) Shield launching.

Before the shield launching, a number of preparatory operations were carried out :

- demolition of the lm slurry wall over the shield passage surface to a depth of 80cm.

- Concreting of the steel cylinder launching eye in the demolished slurry wall and the formation of a ground- and watertight connection around it.
  At the inside of the launching eye, a special eye seal ensures the watertight seal between the steel cylinder and the shield skin.
  An additional joint can be inflated should the eye seal fail.

- Demolition of the remaining 20cm of the slurry wall.
- Shield pushing in the launching eye.
- Assembly of the temporary thrust frame and thrust ring.
- Filling of the bulkhead with bentonite under pressure.
- Shield excavation through the cement-bentonite plug and construction of temporary tunnel lining in the launching shaft.(The temporary shove rings will be removed later.)
  The shield passes through the cement-bentonite plug and the cementbentonite wall of the screen.

Photo 3 shows the shield departure area.

4.2. General description of the shield machine.

The hydroshield outer diameter is 6,800mm. The skin thickness is 80mm at the front (L = 2,400mm), 35mm at the middle (L = 4,140mm) and 16mm at the rear (L = 520mm). The hydroshield weighs 325T when fully equipped.

SHIELD INSTALLATION

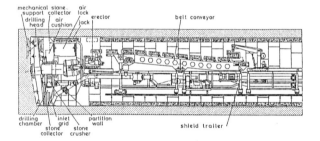

Fig. 5 shows the shield installation.

The drilling chamber is divided into two compartments by means of a partition extending slightly below the tunnel axis and is filled with a bentonite suspension. An air-cushion located in the upper section maintains a constant pressure exerted on the bentonite suspension.

Consequently, the bentonite suspension entirely supports the working face, ensuring proper balance of earth and water pressure, while improving the ground structure, i.e. increasing its cohesiveness.

The cutting head comprises a series of arms in the form of a star arrangement and is

mounted with 42 cutters and 23 wheels. The central part is equipped with a total of 13 disccutters. The cutting head can rotate at speeds, varying from 0 to 2.5 revolutions per minute. The cutting head ensures the uniform mixing of sand and clay.
The 23 wheels can crush the large size stones.

Photo 4 shows the cutting head in assembly phase.

Photo 5 shows the cutting head entirely assembled.

The crushed stones which cannot be evacuated along the pipework, are caught by a stone collector and hoisted up in the drilling chamber to a double crusher.
Excavated material mixed with the bentonite suspension is pumped to a sand removal unit on the surface with an output of about 900m^3/h. Part of the bentonite is recovered by means of a hydrocyclonic process.

4.3. Sand removal unit.

The sand removal unit is composed of 2 curved vibrating screens, 2 primary cyclones with pumps, 2 secondary cyclones with pumps and 2 horizontal vibrating screens.
The excavated material is transported to the vibrating screens where the material > 1.5mm is removed. The remainder is pumped to the 2 primary cyclones.
The coarse material leaves the cyclone at the bottom, passes through the horizontal vibrating screen and is drained.
The finer material that leaves the cyclone at the top, is passed to the storage tank of the secondary pump, which removes the material and passes it to the 2 secondary cyclones, which enables removal of the sand. Leaving only the bentonite or clay. This suspension is returned again to the shield drilling chamber. Once the recycled bentonite slurry reaches a density of 1.14 to 1.15kg/1 it may not be used any longer.
The shield separation plant efficiency with regard to the fraction > 80 μ is 94 %.

4.4. Automatic measurings on the R.O.L.O. – T.B.M.

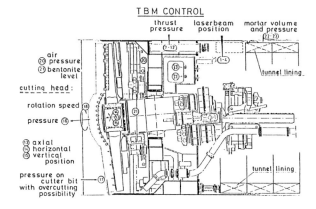

Fig. 6 shows the T.B.M. Control
The shield is provided with monitoring equipment which allows automatic recording of the most important data at regular intervals. The results are transmitted to a memory bank and printer.
The contractor has designed a data-transmission system for this equipment.
The physical constants are measured with analog meters and transferred to a datalogger. This converts the data into a

419

digital signal which is sent to the control centre.

The control centre, placed in a room at the end of the upper shield platform, in turn processes the data converting the position data to absolute coordinates and deviations from the theoretical alignment.

All the data and results can be read locally on the computer screen and using a modem connection, the results and data are sent to a computer installed in the construction management offices.

The installed hardware comprises a Commodore PC 10 computer with a 256K RAM capacity, provided with two floppy-disks with a memory of 360 kbytes each, a screen, a keyboard and a RX-80 EPSONprinter.

Every ten minutes, the transmitted data is updated automatically on the screen and stored on the floppy-disk.

During the entire tunnelling work the data is continually stored on disc and can be recovered at any time.

Numerous items of data are monitored and stored by the software system. The most important are :

- the thrust pressures;
- the liquid pressure or the air pressure at the front and the liquid level;
- the rotation speed and cutter head torque, when operating;
- the exact position of the cutting head and cutters (with regard to possible overcutting);
- progress in terms of rings built (with indication of placing time);
- pressure and injected volume of grout used behind the lining;
- laserbeam position and shield position in relation to laserbeam;
- density and flow readings on the feed and discharge of the bentonitelines.

4.5. Tunnel ring assembly.

The tunnel is built using precast concrete rings composed of 6 segments and a key. Each segment is 1.20m wide, 0.45m thick and weighs 4,500kg.

The wedge-shaped key is installed last and creates a compressive stress within the ring so that the seals are compressed and

the tunnel is made virtually watertight.

The lining segments are provided with a double watertight gasket along the entire contact surface in order to withstand the high water pressures under the Scheldt River and cope with the risk of movement caused by differential settlement.

The outer gasket ensures the watertightness. The inner gasket serves as a rim to lead seepage water into the draining system. The use of a double gasket also results in a better distribution of the contact pressure during the tunnel lining assembly.

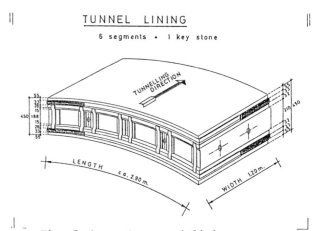

Fig. 7 shows the tunnel lining

Each segment is provided with 4 coupling sleeves and 4 bolt entries for connection during the assembly.

The assembly of the segments starts after completion of a shove. The erector is mechanically operated, segment building starting at the bottom and then alternately to the left and to the right.

The key segments at the top are staggered. Tapered rings (now fairly standard for this type of lining) are used and alignment corrections are made by rotating the whole ring tot place the taper in the correct position. This means that the key may end up at any location around the circumference of the tunnel.

4.6. Shield experiences.

Two kinds of difficulties had to be coped with, namely :

- the initial tunnelling difficulties.

  Personnel had to be trained to operate a

prototype shield;

- the difficulties due to geological conditions.

First, the initial tunnelling difficulties.

- Transport of the lining and mortar on a 5 1/2 % gradient was not easy.
The internal brake system on the train was not adequate and pneumatic brakes had to be installed.

- Shield progress is achieved by means of 24 hydraulic jacks which were coupled in groups of four, the four adjacent jacks being at the same pressure.
The separation between these 6 groups allowes a difference of pressure on the same tunnel lining segment, between two adjacent jacks which caused cracks in the tunnel lining.
A change to 12 steering groups of steering rams was necessary.

- During the tunnel ring "n" assembly, the jacks had to be partially withdrawn over the ring circumference.   This caused an expansion of ring "n-1" with a tendency to push out the wedge-shaped key.
During ring segment building, the problem was solved by anchoring the key to a ring already built.

Second, the difficulties due to ground conditions.

- Problems as clay adhesion and the presence of septaria were expected. In practice the transition (from 100 % sand to 100 % clay and vice versa) presented the most difficulty.
The upper clay layer had a higher water content than expected as a result of which the clay became more adhesive after cutting and choked up the suction system at the front of the shield.   This made ground evacuation impossible.
To prevent long working times under compressed air for the shield cleaning, an intensive investigation was carried out. Based on this study it was decided
  - to change the mud jets direction;
  - to change the suction inlet both in direction and shape, and also to shorten the distance between the shield front and the suction inlet.

In the initial design the shield front was provided with two built-in mud jets. Investigations on a shield scale model suggested that their position was not efficient as a number of "dead areas" existed where the loamy sands could collect.
By using some more mud jets mixing at the shield front was sufficiently increasing to obtain an easy evacuation.
In addition the initial output in the pipework was increased to about $1100m^3/h$. Extra booster pumps had to be used for this.
The distance between the shield front and the sucking mouth was shortened.

- The septaria in the clay layer were fragile enough to be crushed by the wheels and cutters and as a result the stone crushing installation was rarely used.

- In the transition area, between the sand and clay it was necessary to regularly clean the drilling chamber by hand under a 2.6 bar air compression.
A training program and careful operation with strict adherence to the decompression tables prevented any compressed air illness.

- A high concrete quality was required, with a characteristic strength of 55 $N//mm^2$. The prescribed tolerance of $\pm$ 0.5mm was achieved during segment manufacture.
The 1st tunnel was practically 100 % watertight, without any additional measures needing to be taken.

- Particular care was taken during the passage under the historical buildings on the Right River Bank to avoid any risk of differential settlements.

4.7. Tunnelling performance.

In the initial tunnelling area, an important number of difficulties (such as a defective stone reamer, sand removal problems, steering difficulties) had to be coped with.
When the shield was in the first transition area between sand and clay, it was not operative during the frost period.

In this period, the opportunity was taken to adjust the shield thoroughly. After these necessary adjustments, progress increased.

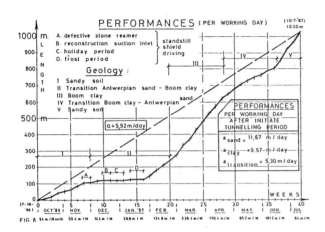

PERFORMANCES (PER WORKING DAY)

Fig. 8 shows the tunnelling progress in five different areas.

An average rate of 9,57m per day in the clay was reached. Progress in the second transition area (IV) was far better than in the first one (II).

The average rate of both transition areas was 5,30m per day. An average rate of 11,67m day was even reached in the sand.

The average progress rate of the entire first tunnel was 5,92m per day.

5. QUAY WALL ANCHORING AND RESTORATION ON THE RIGHT RIVER BANK.

In 1881, the existing quay wall on the Right Bank was constructed in 25m sections, using the compressed air caisson method.

Recent calculations have suggested that the factors of safety against the bearing capacity, overturning and especially sliding, were inadequate. This was a concern as the tunnels are situated at about 5m beneath the quay wall.

5.1. Reinforcement.

In order to ensure the stability of the quay wall, it was decided to install 26 prestressed ground anchors at 0.75m above mean low water level. The total length of this tie rod is 43m with the end being grouted.

Fig. 9 shows the quay wall protection.

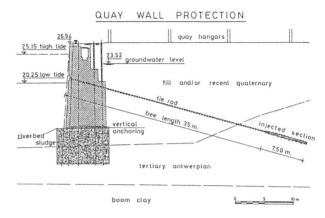

These anchors were succesfully installed from a submersible drilling chamber mounted under a self-propelled jack-up platform.

Photo 6 : Submersible drilling chamber

5.2. Additional difficulties and restoration.

Preliminary investigations showed that the masonry and concrete were highly eroded. Moreover the quay had cavities and contained sludge layers. As a result a complete restoration of the quay wall had to be undertaken.

In a first stage the deteriorated concrete within the working chamber of the caisson was treated by drilling and very high pressure grouting, at 60 points.

Next the masonry was injected with cement-grout and reinforced with ϕ 50mm bars with sleeve joints.

In the last stage the joints between the quay sections were treated by similar very high pressure grouting techniques.

422

5.3. Results.

Shield passage under the first quay wall section was carried out without substantial settlement.

6. SETTLEMENT.

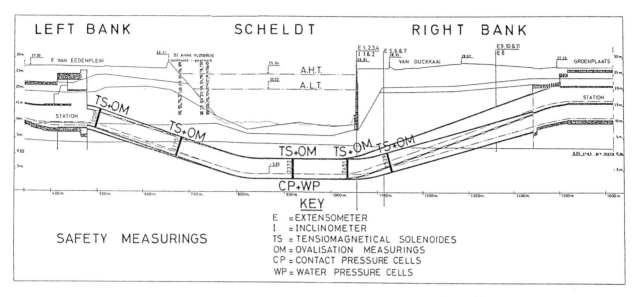

Fig. 10 shows the safety measurings.

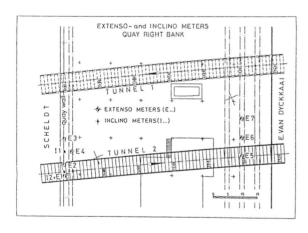

Fig. 11 shows the extenso- and inclinometers.

6.1. Quay.

Seven extensometers and 2 inclinometers were installed in the quay and the quay wall vicinity.

The four extensometers in the quay made it possible to measure the relative movements of a number of typical points with an accuracy of 0.01mm.

Measuring points are provided in the side of the quay foundation, the sand and the Boom clay.

QUAY WALL
SETTLEMENTS IN mm

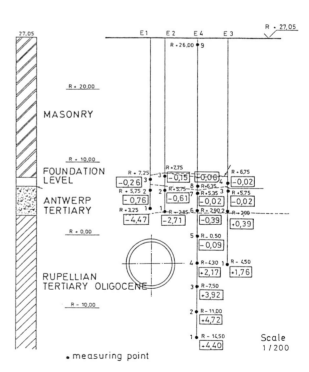

Fig. 12 shows the measured quay wall settlements.

A maximum settlement of about 4mm has been observed at approximately 4m above the tunnel axis.

The ± 5mm clay expansion is also typical.

423

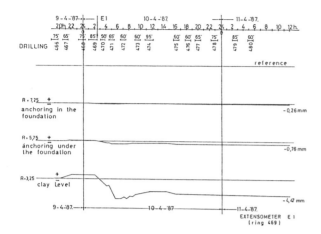

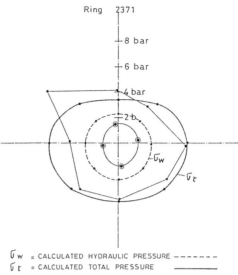

Ring 2371

σ_w = CALCULATED HYDRAULIC PRESSURE ------
σ_t = CALCULATED TOTAL PRESSURE _____
⊚ = MEASURED HYDRAULIC PRESSURE _____
• = MEASURED TOTAL PRESSURE _____

Fig. 13 : Time versus quay wall settlements

At quay level + 7.25, settlements are negligible. At quay level + 5.75, settlements are stabilizing to - 0.76mm.

In the area beneath quay wall foundation, swellings due to clay expansion with a later transition to settlement can be seen. Local gradient changes in the quay can be measured with the inclinometers.

6.2. Tunnel.

An extensive measuring program was developed for determining the loading of the clay on the tunnel.

The reinforcement stresses in about five rings were measured by means of 14 tensio-magnetical solenoïdes. Ovalisation was also measured.

Total stresses on the tunnel lining were measured by installing eight contact pressure cells in a ring in clay. Four hydraulic pressure cells were placed after excavation.

Fig. 15 shows the pressure cells - measuring results.

The influence of the preconsolidation and an approximate correlation with the calculated values were noticed.

6.3. Settlement readings.

Maximum settlements of 3mm and maximum expansions of 2mm in the clay-sand transition area were measured.

Nevertheless the average and maximum settlements in the sand area of the higher tunnel were reaching 2mm and 7mm respectively.

PRESSURE CELL - 2371

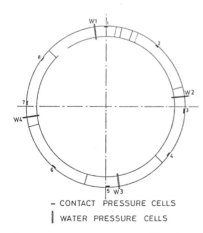

- CONTACT PRESSURE CELLS
| WATER PRESSURE CELLS

Fig. 14 shows a pressure cell ring.

The differential settlements are well below
the criterion of 1/500 for the angular distortion at which damage to the classified
houses could start.

The improved working techniques, the
increased pressure at the face, the injection tubes around the shield skin and the
increased injection pressures undoubtedly
contributed to these remarkable results.

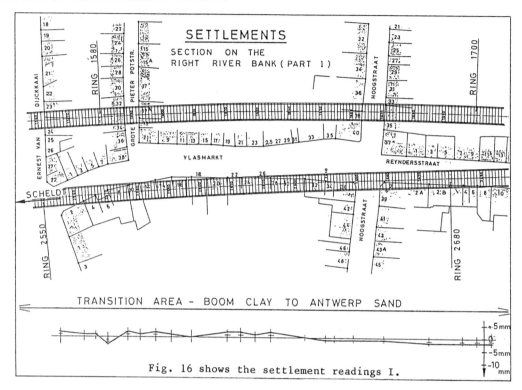

Fig. 16 shows the settlement readings I.

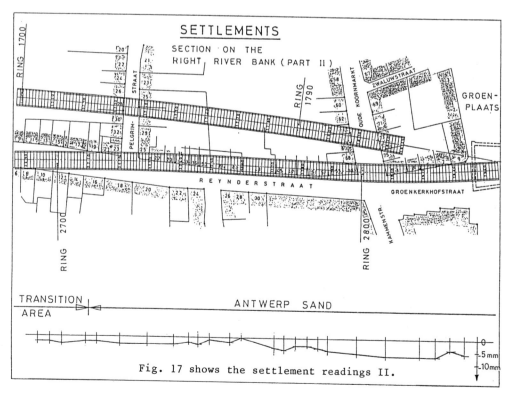

Fig. 17 shows the settlement readings II.

Railroad tunnel modification and rehabilitation in North America

Duncan C. Wyllie P.Eng., B.Sc., B.S., M.S.
Golder Associates, Vancouver, British Columbia, Canada

SYNOPSIS

The majority of railway tunnels in use today in North America were constructed between 50 and 100 years ago; many of them are in excellent condition and have required minimal maintenance in this time. Where work has been carried out, it has been either for safety reasons, or for modifications required as a result of changes in usage or equipment.

This paper describes the inspection and construction methods for the modification and rehabilitation of existing railway tunnels. Modification work has included the conversion of a single track railway freight tunnel into a double-track transit tunnel, and stripping of existing tunnels for improved clearance. Stabilization work has involved replacement of timber sets with steel sets, or rock bolts and shotcrete, and in one case, the "daylighting" of a tunnel after the collapse of one portal. Successful completion of this work requires understanding of the original construction methods and then planning the remedial program to suit the particular conditions of the site. In the case of operational tunnels, the most important consideration is the need to cause minimal disruptions to traffic by using mobile, off-track equipment and carrying out small units of work.

ORIGINAL EXCAVATION AND SUPPORT METHODS

In evaluating the stability conditions of existing tunnels and designing stabilizing measures, information on the original methods of construction will give an indication of the rock quality and the support provided by the existing lining (if any). It has been found that these methods differ considerably from those used today, so review of the original records will reduce the risk of surprises during rehabilitation. The following is a brief description of some excavation and support methods used in the early part of the century.

Excavation Methods

Blasting was the usual excavation method, even in very weak rock which today would be excavated with road headers. Steam shovels could only be used in the weakest rock. The drilling equipment, consisting of light pneumatic drills mounted on posts set between the roof and the floor, was best suited to drilling rings of holes from a pilot drift as illustrated in Figure 1. The advantages of this method were that many holes could be drilled from a single set-up and a number of drills could operate simultaneously so a considerable advance was possible with each blast. In one long tunnel, a second pilot drift was driven to the side of the main tunnel and by putting in a number of cross cuts, several faces were driven simultaneously[1].

The disadvantages of this method were the overbreak and degree of blast damage caused to the rock in the walls and roof. It is likely that the holes in each ring, and possibly several rings, were detonated instantaneously because milli second delays were not available. Slow burning fuses would not be sufficiently accurate for proper sequencing. Detonation of a ring of holes would have produced a tremendous concussion, which together with a high confinement of the explosive at the end of the holes, would result in damage to the surrounding rock and considerable overbreak. The resulting tunnel would experience a much more severe rock fall problems than a tunnel excavated by modern pre-shear blasting methods.

The area where blast damage was most severe was at the portals, and particularly in very steep mountainous terrain where the rib pillar on the outside of the tunnel was narrow. The rock in this pillar is highly stressed in the direction parallel to the slope, with the stress in the perpendicular direction being very low or even tensile. Under these stress conditions, the rock is highly susceptible to blast damage which can result in severe stability problems.

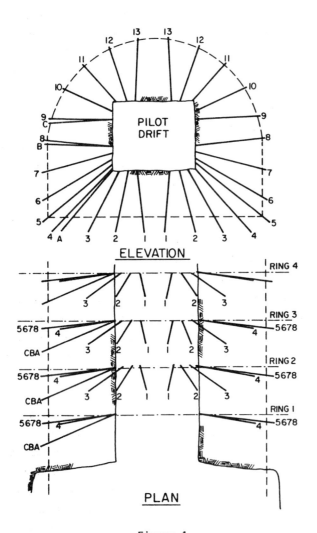

Figure 1

Blast Hole Pattern
from Pilot Drift

Remedial measures are discussed later in this paper.

Support Methods

The methods of support were limited to full brick or concrete linings or timber arch sets, with no support in good quality, strong rock. An important feature of these support methods was that they were not installed in close contact with the roof and walls which allowed movement and loosening of the rock around the tunnel. In some cases, this has resulted in considerable loads being developed on the lining which can be non-uniform as a result of movement of blocks of rock on inclined fractures.

Figure 2a shows a typical full concrete lining; such linings were used in soil, till and very weak rock as well as faulted and highly fractured rock. The tunnelling procedure was to use a heading and bench, with a full timber lining being installed as the excavation proceeded – the wall plates and arch first, followed by the legs and lagging. The roof was supported with timber blocking and the walls with tunnel muck shovelled behind the lagging. At the completion of the excavation, the full, 600 mm thick unreinforced concrete lining was placed with the outside face against the timber lining. In time, the timber rotted to leave a void behind the lining which permitted gradual weathering and loosening of the rock.

Timber arch sets constructed from 300 mm square timber have been used in blocky ground and where narrow fault zones intersect the tunnel. The sets were spaced at about 1 m intervals and were blocked with rough lumber. The disadvantages of the sets were their tendency to rot in wet conditions and to be a fire hazard in dry conditions. Furthermore, there is the difficulty of keeping the arch tightly blocked and the joints between the sections of the arch, which are secured with 5 mm thick steel plates are very weak and have little capacity to withstand non-uniform loads.

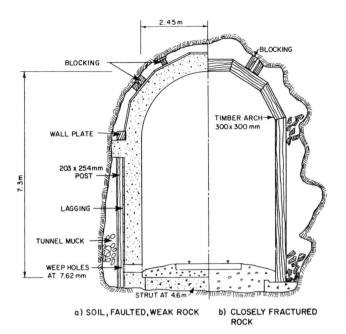

Figure 2

Support Methods in
Poor Ground

INVESTIGATION METHODS

The following is a brief discussion of methods
that have been used to investigate the condition
of tunnels.

A. Historical records - Most railroads
    keep excellent records of original
    contract drawings, and reports on
    construction methods may also be avail-
    able. In some cases, it may be
    possible to obtain additional informa-
    tion from local libraries or historical
    societies.

B. Visual inspections - Because the rock
    surfaces are often covered with exhaust
    deposits, visual inspections will only
    provide reliable data if carried out
    from the level of the tunnel roof.
    This requires the use of a platform,
    which can be raised and lowered, and a
    powerful lighting system.

C. Drilling - Diamond drilling using
    triple tube core barrels to maximize
    core recovery will provide data on the
    thickness and condition of the concrete
    lining (if any), the dimensions of a
    void behind the lining and rock condi-
    tions. Of particular importance is the

extent of weathering and degradation
that has taken place around the tunnel
as the result of ground water flow and
loosening of the rock.

D. Ground Water Studies - Seepage points
    should be mapped and quantities
    measured and the results correlated
    with geological data. Also, pressure
    transducers sealed into boreholes will
    measure ground water pressure in the
    rock surrounding the tunnel.

E. Strength Testing - Drill core samples
    of rock and concrete can be tested for
    such properties as strength, slake
    durability and swelling clay contact.
    In the absence of drilling, in-situ
    testing can be carried out with a
    Schmidt hammer.

F. Void Investigations - In lined tunnels,
    it is sometimes necessary to obtain
    information on the extent and width of
    voids behind the lining. Drilling
    gives reliable data, but only at point
    locations. In order to obtain continu-
    ous measurements, radar equipment has
    been used. On one project in 1979, the
    equipment available at that time could
    not penetrate the reinforcing bars in
    the concrete and obtained no useful
    information; modern equipment may give
    better results. One requirement of the
    radar unit is the need to hold the
    scanning sled at a fixed distance from
    the concrete as it moves along the
    tunnel which requires a rigid support
    frame. Another tool that has been used
    to visually examine voids is the fibre-
    optic boroscope, which is a flexible
    borehole periscope. It has a control-
    lable viewing direction and focus,
    however, it appears to be only of value
    in clean, dry holes where the viewing
    distance is short.

G. Clearance Studies - The most reliable
    clearance measurements are made from
    the analyses of stereo photographs
    accurately referenced to the centre of
    the track (see Figure 3). The photo-
    graphs also provide a useful record of

429

rock conditions for future reference. Clearance measurements with a rail car equipped with a frame and feelers have proved to be unreliable and only accurate to about plus or minus 10 cm.

Figure 3

Stereo Photography Equipment for Clearance Studies

FREIGHT TUNNEL CONVERSION TO RAPID TRANSIT
Between 1982 and 1985 in Vancouver, Canada, the first 21 km long section of light rail transit system was constructed. Special features of this system include propulsion with linear induction motors and a fully automatic operation with driverless trains which operate on headways down to 90 seconds. The downtown section of the route is located in a 1.1 km long tunnel with 20 m of cover which was converted from its original use as a railway freight tunnel originally constructed in 1931 to 1932[2]. The conversion involved lowering the invert to allow two tracks to be stacked vertically, and the construction of two stations with connecting tunnels and ventilation shafts. The rock throughout the project is a very weak, interbedded sequence of sandstones and claystones which weather on

exposure to the atmosphere. The sandstone is massive, while the claystone contains curved, slickensided joints.

The geological conditions were analyzed according to the NGI system for determining rock mass quality with respect to tunnel stability[3]. The rock mass quality number for the claystone and sandstone respectively were 1 to 10 and 10 to 100, with the range of values taking into account the decrease in weathering with the distance from the existng tunnel. Actual support methods corresponded with those proposed by NGI.

The rock mass strengths were defined by curved Mohr envelopes[4] which take into account the rock type, the uniaxial compressive strength and the degree of fracturing. The equation for the Mohr envelope is:

$$\tau = (\mathrm{Cot}\,\phi_i' - \mathrm{Cos}\,\phi_i')\frac{m\sigma_c}{8}$$

where τ is the shear stress at failure, ϕ_i' is the instantaneous friction angle at the given values of τ and σ' - i.e. the inclination of the tangent to the Mohr failure envelope at the point (σ', τ).

The value of the instantaneous friction angle ϕ_i', is given by:

$$\phi_i' = \mathrm{Arctan}\,(4h\,\mathrm{Cos}^2\,(30 + \tfrac{1}{3}\mathrm{Arcsin}\,h^{-3/2}) - 1)^{-1/2}$$

where

$$h = 1 + \frac{16(m\sigma' + s\sigma_c)}{3m^2\,\sigma_c}$$

and σ' is the effective normal stress.

The values of the constants m and s for the two different rock types are:

	m	s
Claystone	0.2 to 1	10^{-4} to 4×10^{-3}
Sandstone	1.5 to 7.5	4×10^{-3} to 10^{-1}

Earthquake Resistance
The original unreinforced concrete lining (see Figures 2 and 4) was essentially free-standing and there was concern that, in the event of a design 0.2 g earthquake, damage consisting of extensive cracking to the concrete lining would

430

occur. It has been found that well constructed underground structures are rarely damaged by earthquakes except when they intersect active faults[5,6]. It was decided that the earthquake resistance of the tunnel could be adequately improved by grouting the void.

The grouting procedure for the walls was to limit grouting to large cavities only, so as to maintain the existing drainage system and avoid build-up of water pressures on the unreinforced concrete. Grouting of the arch was done in two stages with the hole arrangement shown in Figure 4, the rings of holes were on 6 m centres. The ground pressure was limited to 100 kPa to avoid overstressing the lining and the grout was a fluid, low strength mix with the following components:

Type 10 cement - 175 kg
Flyash   - 265 kg
Fine sand   - 1320 kg
Water   - 300 kg

The total volume of grout pumped was 2180 cu.m at an average cost of $220 per cu.m.

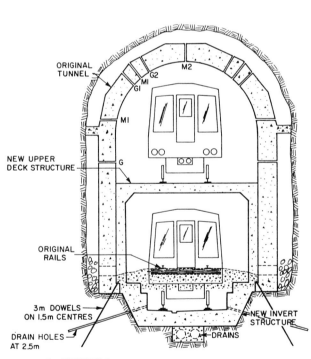

ORIGINAL TUNNEL
NEW UPPER DECK STRUCTURE
ORIGINAL RAILS
3m DOWELS ON 1.5m CENTRES
DRAIN HOLES AT 2.5m
NEW INVERT STRUCTURE
DRAINS

G - GROUT HOLE
M - MONITORING / BREATHER HOLE

Figure 4

Railway Tunnel Conversion to Double Deck Transit Tunnel

Invert Lowering

In the running tunnel, modifications to the existing structure were limited to lowering of the invert and installing an improved underdrain system. This involved first installing 3 m long, fully cement grouted dowels on 1.5 m centres to reinforce the footings of the lining, and then excavating a 2 m deep trench in the invert (Figure 4). In one area, a number of buildings straddling the tunnel were supported on drilled caissons with tip elevations at about the existing tunnel invert level, and loads as high as 1.2 MN (Figure 5). For skin friction type caissons, it has been shown that the majority of the load is carried in the upper two-thirds of the caisson and there is little load at the tip (see graph, Figure 5)[7]. However, because there was concern that excavation of the invert would change stress conditions in the tip area and lead to possible reduction in load capacity, it was decided, in the case of the most heavily loaded caissons, to excavate the invert in two stages. This consisted of excavating a series of trenches across the tunnel leaving rock "struts" adjacent to the caissons. The new concrete invert was then poured in the trench, and when this had set, the rock strut was excavated and the remainder of the invert slab poured.

Stations

The station tunnels were constructed by removing the existing lining and then stripping the rock to a width of 8.5 m (Figure 6). The construction procedure was first to install rings of 8 m long resin grouted bolts through the existing lining with the purpose of reinforcing the weathered rock in the arch. The concrete lining was then removed by blasting and a roadheader used to excavate the rock to the full cross-section. The excavation advance was limited to 3 m before installing a second set of fully grouted, untensioned bolts which were 4 m long on 1 m centres in the closely fractured and weathered claystone, and 2 m long on 2 m centres in the more massive sandstone. All the faces were covered with a 50 mm thick layer of steel fibre reinforced shotcrete[8].

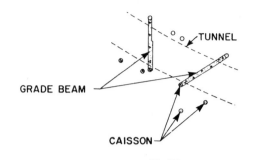

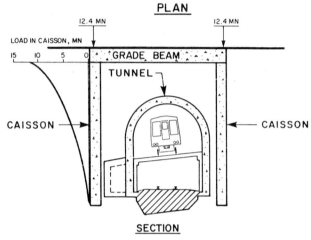

Figure 5
Invert Excavation
Adjacent to Caissons

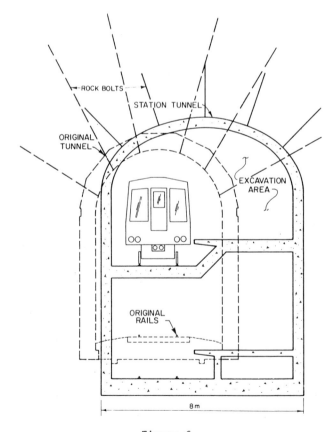

Figure 6
Excavation and Support
of Station Tunnels

The access tunnels into the stations formed a series of tall, thin pillars with width to height ratios as low as 0.79. The pillars were reinforced by installing fully grouted, untensioned bolts in the longitudinal and transverse directions. The rockbolts had the functions of both preventing slip along continuous fractures intersecting the pillar, and increasing the confining pressure. Figure 7 shows a curved strength envelope for claystone and the relationship between the applied confining pressure and the vertical load capacity of the pillar, and how this is used to calculate the factor of safety. For the pillars with the lowest width to height ratios, steel sets were also installed in both the station tunnel and the access tunnels to provide additional support and ensure a minimum factor of safety of 1.5.

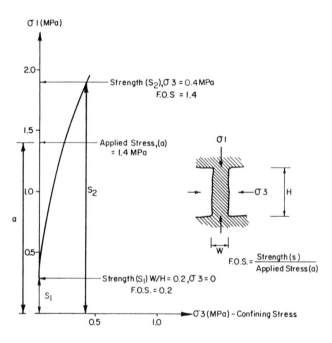

Figure 7
Design of Pillars using
Hoek Brown Rock Strength
Criterea

The access tunnels were 6 m wide and were supported with 2 m long rock bolts on rings on 2 m centres, and shotcrete. In one intersection area between the three tunnels, the width of the opening was 10 m, and since it was not practical to support the span with steel sets, fully cement grouted, untensioned bolts were installed from street level prior to excavation to create an arch of reinforced rock. Additional support was provided with two horizontal steel beams installed during the excavation of the top heading and supported on temporary steel columns (Figure 8).

The principle of primary support design was to maintain the existing strength of the rock mass by installing, wherever possible, fully grouted, untensioned bolts before the excavation was made. This system, known as pre-reinforcement, restricts the loosening of the rock and thus minimizes loss of rock mass strength. There are also considerable cost savings realized by not tensioning the bolts. The rock bolts provided temporary support until the final concrete linings were constructed. The concrete was poured directly against the rock face to save on both the excavation volume and the need to form the back of the structure. Drainage behind the linings was provided by holes drilled through the shotcrete on 2 m centres and strips of Enkadrain drainage fabric placed between the rock face and the concrete on 10 m centres.

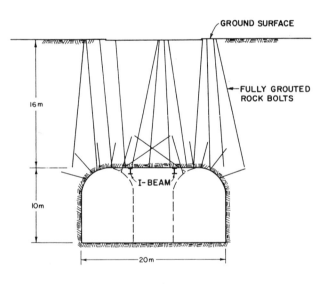

Figure 8

Pre-reinforcement of Station Concourse Roof

REPLACEMENT OF TIMBER SETS

A tunnel excavated in the 1930's in a very strong granitic rock, was supported in several zones of faulted and fractured rock with timber

sets on 0.9 m centres (Figure 2b). Accumulation of seepage water in the invert had resulted in the base of some of the legs rotting out with a consequent loss of support. Replacement of the sets was a slow and costly operation, and as an alternative, longer term support could be provided with steel sets, or rock bolts and shotcrete.

In areas where the rock contained continuous, planar, clay coated fractures on about 0.3 m centres, unstable wedges were formed in both arch and walls and rock bolts and shotcrete could be used for support. The construction procedure was to remove three sets and then spend 10-15 man-hours scaling loose rock before installing 2.5 m long rock bolts on a 1.5 m pattern in the arch with selective bolting in the walls. Because of the loose nature of the rock, Williams expansion shell, tensioned bolts were used, with full length grouting for corrosion protection. Finally, a 70 mm thick layer of steel fibre reinforced shotcrete was placed on the roof and walls.

At one portal, the rock was closely fractured and faulted, and in addition there was an accumulation on the surface of loose talus supported by a thin layer of cemented gravel and deteriorated timber sets (Figure 9). It was decided that the portion of the tunnel in the poorest rock and at the talus location would be supported with steel sets (W200x52) on 1.2 m centres and timber lagging with sand backfill. Upon removal of the first timber sets, there were considerable falls of rock from both the roof and the walls with the result that the span increased at some locations to 10 m and the height to 9 m. These new faces were stabilized with fibre reinforced shotcrete and selective bolting before installing the sets. The sets were backfilled with sand to the height of the top of the sets, but further backfilling to the level of the roof would have overloaded the sets and it would have not been possible to produce a tight support against the roof. As an alternative to sand, rigid urethane with a density of 0.3 kN/m^3 and compressive strength of 200 kPa, was pumped into the void above the sand to produce a lightweight but rigid support exerting uniform pressure distribution on the arch. In order to protect the highly flammable urethane from fire, all exposed surfaces were covered with a 50 mm thick layer of shotcrete.

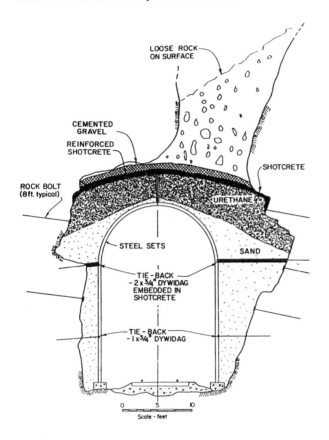

Figure 9

Support with Steel Sets, Sand and Urethane

TUNNEL STRIPPING

Introduction of extra height freight cars such as tri-level automobile carriers and double stacked containers has required an increase in clearance in some tunnels[10,11]. All lined tunnels had been constructed to American Railway Engineering Association (AREA) specifications and needed no modification, but many of the unlined tunnels had areas where rock stripping was required to meet the new clearance standards. After identifying these areas with clearance measuring equipment (Figure 3), trim blasting was carried out at the required locations, followed by bolting and shotcreting as necessary to stabilize the new roof.

Two different construction methods have been used for this work. In single track tunnels with heavy traffic, the drilling, blasting, mucking and scaling cycle had to be carried out between trains because no disruption to traffic was permitted. This required the use of mobile equipment such as a forklift carrying a large platform from which 3 or 4 drillers could drill a 2.5 m long round in about 1 hour. The holes were carefully aligned on a spacing of 0.5 m and every alternate hole was loaded with 19 mm diameter, low velocity dynamite explosive. The holes were detonated on a single delay to produce a uniform, stable arch. After scaling, selective bolting using 2.5 m long, resin anchored bolts, and shotcreting of faulted zones was carried out.

An alternative construction method that has been used where ample track time is available, is to make up a work train from which drilling, scaling, rock bolting and shotcreting can be carried out simultaneously. The cost of setting up such a system is only justified where substantial quantities of work are planned.

PORTAL RECONSTRUCTION AND TUNNEL "DAYLIGHTING"

As discussed earlier on excavation methods, a common cause of instability of portals of tunnels constructed close to the face of a steep mountain slopes is the failure of the narrow, outer pillar. The following is a description of the stabilization carried out following major rock failures of two portals.

The west portal of a tunnel constructed in the 1880's was excavated at the toe of a near-vertical, 80 m high cliff. The rock was a very strong, massive granitic rock of the Canadian shield which contained a number of planar fractures with continuous lengths of several tens of metres. The portal excavation allowed gradual movement of wedges of rock bounded by these joints, and eventually a series of rockfalls occurred that formed an overhang about 8 m wide above the portal. Stabilization work was carried out to both prevent further movement of the rock wedges, and to support the overhang.

The rock bolting program involved installing tensioned and fully grouted rock bolts mainly in the two sides of the portal to reinforce the rock in these two areas. By preventing further loosening of this rock which was supporting the two sides of the overhang, the risk of additional falls was reduced. A practical consideration was that bolts installed in the walls of the tunnel could be readily anchored in sound rock below track level and drilling and grouting of down holes in the walls was easier and more effective than in vertical holes under the overhang.

Support of the overhang itself was provided by a reinforced concrete structure. The most important decision in the design of this structure was the determination of the vertical rock load that it should carry. It was obviously impractical that it should carry the full 80 m vertical cover, so it was decided that it should have the capacity to support the dead load of the next major block in the overhang which had a vertical thickness of about 10 m. It was assumed that the rock bolts and the portal structure would together prevent further loosening of the rock mass so that it would only be necessary for the structure to support this lower part of the overhang. The construction process involved pouring two vertical walls after carrying out trim blasting to provide necessary clearance, and then forming a roof from scrap rails (Figure 10). Mass concrete was then poured to entirely fill the space between the roof of the structure and the underside of the overhang. The total volume of materials used were about 11 tonnes of reinforcing steel and 260 cu.m of concrete.

Tunnel "Daylighting"

On another project, crushing of fractured rock in a thin rib pillar resulted in collapse of a portal below a vertical, 20 m high cut[12]. The volume of broken rock was sufficient to completely block the tunnel. When this material was excavated, tension cracks were discovered above the portal indicating that the next section of the outer pillar was crushing, and the rock above the portal was toppling into the river (Figure 11). The rock at this site was a

Figure 10

Reinforced Concrete Portal to Support Overhang

moderately strong schist which was susceptible to weathering and blast damage. The major geological structure was the foliation planes which were vertical and aligned at right angles to the tunnel axis, so they formed release surfaces for slabs of rock above the portal.

It was decided that it was not practical to stabilize the portal because the outer pillar was too thin and fractured to be reinforced with rockbolts. Also, construction of a reinforced concrete portal would have required extensive blasting to obtain the required clearance, and this work would have lead to further rock falls. Consequently, it was decided that the tunnel would be daylighted to form a steep rock slope about 30 m high. Because of the poor condition of the portal, it was not possible to carry out a traditional bench blasting excavation, and it was decided to daylight the entire 50 m long tunnel in a single blast.

Figure 11 shows the layout of the blastholes which consisted of four groups of holes:
- Shear line holes - 0.7 m centres loaded with Atlas KleenKut Type F, 35 mm diameter powder at 0.27 kg/m.

435

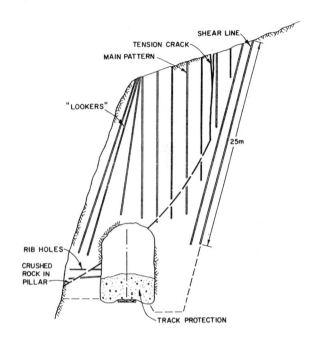

Figure 11

Blast Hole Arrangement
for Tunnel "Daylight-
ing"

- Production holes - 100 mm diameter holes on a
  1.4 m burden by 2.7 m spacing pattern and
  loaded with Atlas Gelmax explosive with an
  average powder factor of 0.72 kg/m^3.

- "Looker" holes - 100 mm diameter holes are on
  the approximate 2 m x 2 m square pattern
  drilled into the upper portion of the outer
  pillar and loaded with Atlas Gelmax explosive.

- Rib holes - 75 mm diameter holes on 0.7 m
  centres loaded with Gelmax explosive.

  In total, there were approximately 600 holes
  drilled and the total explosive load was
  about 15,000 kg. The length of the shear
  holes at 26 m was far in excess of the maximum length recommended for good alignment
  control (usually about 10 m). Because of
  wander in the hole direction, the final face
  was somewhat ragged, but blast damage to the
  rock behind the face was minimal.

  In order to ensure that the holes were
  detonated in the correct sequence, a combination
  of 25 ms electric delay detonators and an electronic sequencer were used to detonate each hole
  on a separate delay. The detonation sequence
  started at a free-face above one portal and

progressed along the length of the tunnel with
the rib holes being last in the sequence at a
time of 4 seconds. The shear line was detonated
in a series of 9 holes per delay detonated with
the main blast. A pre-shear was not carried out
because of the danger of displacing the entire
volume of rock and cutting off the main blast.

Drilling was conducted on a single 12-hour
shift per day using up to six air-track drills;
the total drilling time was 24 days. The railway limited the track closure time for loading,
shooting and mucking the rock to 48 hours which
was achieved in the following manner. Loading
of the holes started at 8:00 on a Saturday
morning and was completed at 4:00 pm on Sunday
afternoon (total time - about 20 hours). The
shot was detonated at 5:00 pm and the track was
open by 9:00 am on Monday after the equipment
had worked throughout Sunday night to clear the
blasted rock.

The final face was stable and scaling was
limited to cleaning of the face with the excavation equipment as the muckpile was removed. The
only stability problem encountered was a wedge
which failed on the bench beside the track.
Fortunately, there was sufficient shoulder width
to permit train operations.

REFERENCES

1. Sullivan. Methods Adopted in Construction of Rogers Pass Tunnel. Canadian Society of Civil Engineers, 1916.

2. Winter, J.B. CP Rail Tunnel; Report on Progress and Completion of Work. Letter to City Engineer, Vancouver City Hall, August 23, 1932.

3. Barton, N., Lien, R. and Lund, J. Engineering Classification of Rock Masses for the Design of Tunnel Support. Rock Mechanics, Volume 6, No. 4, Pages 189-236, 1974.

4. Hoek, E., Strength of Jointed Rock Masses. Geotechnique 33, No. 3, Pages 187-223, 1983.

5. U.S. Department of Transportation. Federal Highway Administration. Earthquake Engineering of Large Underground Structures, Report No. FHWA/RD-80/195, January, 1981.

6. Department of Transportation. Urban Mass Transportation Administration. Behaviour of the Bay Area Rapid Transit Tunnels Through the Hayward Fault. Report No. UMTA-CA-06-0120-81-1, June, 1981.

5. Mattes, N.S. and Poulos, H.G. Settlement of Single Compression Piles. American Society of Civil Engineers, Soil and Foundations Division, Vol. 95, No. SM1, January, 1969, pp. 189.

8. Jones, M.B. Testing Sprayed Concrete Fibre, Tunnels and Tunnelling, July 1987.

9. Hoek, E. and Brown, E.T. Underground Excavations in Rock, Institute of Mining and Metallurgy, London, 1980.

10. Emerson, M.W.C. and Mukholkar, V.V. Rehabilitation of Belden Tunnel, American Railway Engineering Association, Bulletin No. 706 Volume 87, May, 1986.

11. Millar, G. Tunnel Rehabilitation. Presentation at American Railroad Engineering Association Annual Conference, March 1985.

12. Weeks, F.C., Trueblood, T.B., Krause A., Wyllie, D.C. Tunnel "Daylighting" on the Alaska Railroad. Tunnels and Tunnelling, October, 1985.